Ex Libris

David C. Ricketts

Understanding Fiction

Understanding Fiction

By CLEANTH BROOKS, Jr.
LOUISIANA STATE UNIVERSITY

and ROBERT PENN WARREN
UNIVERSITY OF MINNESOTA

1946

F. S. CROFTS & Company NEW YORK

TO DONALD DAVIDSON

LETTER TO THE TEACHER

MOST STUDENTS read some kind of fiction of their own free will and for pleasure. Most students do not, except under academic pressure, read essays or poetry. This contrast may lull a teacher into a false sense of security when he gives a course in fiction. He does not have to "make" the student read fiction, he feels, as he has to "make" the student read poetry, any kind of poetry. He simply sets himself the easier problem of persuading the student that some stories or novels which are called "good" from the literary point of view, or which are important in the history of literature, are also interesting in themselves. Frequently the student does discover that the "good" story or novel is interesting to him. Then the teacher says, in substance: "Look, you did like that story, and that story is literature. Therefore, you like literature, after all. You see, literature is not so bad." And having reached this conclusion, the teacher may feel that the objective of the course in fiction has been achieved.

But let us suppose that the student should read any number of stories which are called literature. No doubt, if he is somewhat more intelligent and sensitive than most, he will begin to ask questions of himself and to make comparisons, and his general taste will, as a result, be improved. But, unless he does attempt to read analytically, it is doubtful whether any beneficial result can be had, no matter how many stories he reads or how many details of plot he can remember or how many characters he can name. The editors of this book believe that before extensive reading can be profitable, the student must have some practice in intensive reading. Otherwise, the interests which he originally brings to his reading will remain unchanged.

It is probably true, however, that a teacher must always build upon the interests which the student already possesses. But it is one thing to build upon those interests and quite another to take them as the standard of values by which the course is to be conducted. If the criti-

vii

cal standards which the student possesses when he begins the course
are adequate, then the course is superfluous and merely flatters him in
his convictions. If the course merely encourages the student to systema-
tize his views somewhat—to try to say why he likes or dislikes a story
—some gain has certainly been made, for this process is essential to
the development of taste. But if the views remain substantially unchanged, if the interests which he brings to fiction in the first place are
not broadened and refined, the course has scarcely fulfilled its purpose: the student has merely grown more glib and complacent in his
limitations.

Let us take a particular case. A student likes Kipling's "The Man
Who Would Be King" because it is a story of romantic adventure, because he wants to know how it "comes out," but does not like Chekhov's "The Kiss" because "nothing happens in it." One immediately
realizes that the student is not giving a clear account of either story
or even of his own reactions; that, in fact, he has not really "read"
either story. In the first place, it is improbable that he likes "The Man
Who Would Be King" simply because of the suspense concerning the
external action. Matters of character, psychological development, and
moral decision are inextricably involved with the action. It is true that
the student may have a perfectly usual bias toward fiction of romantic
setting and violent action, but it is only through a failure of introspec-
tion that he bases his case for the story merely on those elements. A
little reflection should bring him to the conclusion that, even in the
crudest story of violent action, he demands a certain modicum of characterization, a certain concern with the psychological basis of action,
a certain interest in moral content and general meaning. And a little
further reflection should lead him to the conclusion that his liking for
the story may depend upon the organic relation existing among these
elements—that his interest did not depend upon the element of violent
plot, or the element of romantic setting, taken in isolation. If he has
once faced this question, he may realize that his liking for a story does
not depend finally upon his threshold interests, but rather depends, in
one sense at least, upon the total structure, upon the logic of the whole,
the relationships existing among elements of character and psychology,
action, social situation, ideas and attitudes, style, and so on.

There are innumerable types of threshold interest which bring read ers to fiction. Some of these types are clearly defined and well recognized in the field of magazine fiction. There are "sport" stories, "young love" stories, "marriage problem" stories, "moral" stories, "child" stories, "sea" stories, "Wild West" stories, "farm" stories, "business" stories, "crime" stories, and the like. Such threshold interests as are appealed to by these types may derive from a variety of factors. A man who knows the world of baseball may come to fiction that deals with that subject expecting the pleasure of recognition, of dwelling on what he knows and likes in real life. Such a reader demands a high degree of fidelity to the external facts of the world in which he is interested. But another reader may come, let us say, to baseball stories or to Wild West stories, expecting the pleasure of escape from a life which does not afford him sport or adventure. He is scarcely concerned with incidental realism, with recognizing a world which he already knows, but with extending his experience into a world which he does not know.

Both of these impulses, the impulse to dwell on the known world in fiction and to judge the fictional rendering by the facts of observation, and the impulse to enlarge experience through fiction, are perfectly normal and admirable; they are, in rudimentary form, the impulse toward contemplation and the impulse toward fulfillment, the demand for logic and the demand for imagination. They are pernicious only when they operate in isolation from each other and when they stop at the level of the threshold interest. For instance, if the baseball player or fan who reads only baseball stories should apply his criteria of realism, his tests of recognition and logic, to matters of characterization and psychology and theme as well as to the technical questions concerning the world of baseball, he would probably find unsatisfactory many of the stories which ordinarily satisfy his threshold interest. Or, if the reader who goes to adventure stories for escape from a humdrum existence could realize that his experience could be extended more fully by reading fiction which does not merely emphasize the elements of violent action and romantic setting but which also leads to some understanding of the inner lives of other people, or to some understanding of his own life, he might be less content with the escape based on merely external differences from the circumstances of his own experience.

The hypothetical student may object that he has lost, and not gained, by such a process, for his area of potential enjoyment has been limited by the process. But actually the process which leads him past the mere threshold interest to the fuller interests implicit in fiction causes an enlargement of the area of his potential enjoyment. As a human being, he has interests wider than baseball or Western adventure, and he may come to realize that, even in the shoddiest story dealing with baseball or the Wild West, his other more fundamental interests have been covertly engaged. And he may realize, further, that without the appeal to those other interests there would be no story at all. The Wild West and baseball, finally, interest him in terms of certain persons, with certain motivations and with certain characteristics, who have certain experiences; and these experiences themselves are of little interest to him except in so far as they involve certain meanings—success and failure, courage and cowardice, generosity and cruelty, and the like—which are dramatized in character and action. This returns us to the notion that the liking for a piece of fiction does not depend upon the satisfaction of the threshold interest, whatever it may be, football or moral message-hunting or sociological documentation, but upon the total structure, upon a set of organic relationships, upon the logic of the whole.

This book is based on the belief that the student can best be brought to an appreciation of the more broadly human values implicit in fiction by a course of study which aims at the close analytical and interpretative reading of concrete examples. It seems to us that the student may best come to understand an author's basic intention in a given piece of fiction by understanding the functions of the various elements which go to make up fiction and by understanding their relationships to each other in the whole construct. The editors believe that such an end may best be achieved by the use of an inductive method, by the use of concrete cases which can be investigated and interpreted and compared with each other. The organization of the book is based on that principle.

The problem of the nature and structure of fiction is first approached (pp. 1–28) through the investigation of three negative examples: one, which is almost pure action, an anecdote from Parkman's *The Oregon*

Trail; one, which is almost pure description of character, the portrait of Henry Hastings; one, which is narrative developed almost as pure symbol, the account of the sinking of the *Titanic*. Each of these examples, although interesting in itself, lacks some element which is vital to fiction. In other words, the attempt is here made to illustrate by particular examples the difference between the interest which specifically attaches to fiction and the interests which may merely be involved in the materials of fiction. Further, the fact that all of the examples used are drawn from history raises a second question, that of the kind of truth aimed at by fiction. It is not pretended that these complicated questions are answered in these first pages, but the editors believe that an awareness of their importance is an absolutely necessary preliminary to the proper reading of fiction.

The method is now reversed, and the rest of Section I is devoted to the presentation of three fully developed stories: one which emphasizes action, one which emphasizes character, and one which emphasizes theme in terms of allegory and symbol. The purpose here is to illustrate, by the analysis and interpretation of the various stories, the fact that the particular emphases in the individual stories—on plot, on character, on theme—are merely superficial, that the element which is emphasized in each case is inextricably involved with other elements in the fictional construct.

Sections II, III, and IV are closely related to each other and really represent an extension and development of the principles touched on in Section I. Section II deals primarily with problems of plot. This is not to say that the stories involved are stories in which the plot interest obtrudes itself—that they are examples of what is called "the plot story." As a matter of fact, some of the stories in this section, such as "War," by Pirandello, and "A Piece of News," by Eudora Welty, scarcely involve overt action at all. Rather, the stories chosen for this section, along with their interpretations and exercises, are intended to illustrate a variety of types and functions of plot with a constant emphasis on the relationship of the plot to other factors. In Section III the same method is used in regard to certain problems of character in fiction; and in Section IV, in regard to certain problems of realizing theme in fiction. But in all of these sections other questions have been raised in the course of the discussions and in the exercises, questions of style and tone, for example, as related to the basic intentions of the stories.

Section V raises a number of special problems, and re-emphasizes certain problems already discussed: irony, tragic and comic and humorous effects, indirection, fantasy, allegory and symbolism, style and tone, scale, pace, and focus. The stories used in Section V are not intended, and could not well be expected, to exhaust the special problems which appear in fiction. And certainly it cannot be expected that an exhaustive treatment of these questions could be given in the accompanying discussions. The editors simply hope to raise these questions in concrete terms for the student and to increase his awareness of the various subtle means by which an author of fiction may achieve his total communication.

The Appendix will have, it is hoped, a double function, a function for the student reader of fiction and for the student writer of fiction. It has no doubt been observed that the discussions of stories in this book have not frequently touched on the questions which are usually called "technical" in the narrow sense of the word: questions of exposition, complication, climax, proportion, focus of interest, focus of narration, and the like. The editors feel, rather, that it is usually fruitless to raise such superficially technical questions until the student has some grasp of the more fundamental considerations,* some notion of the relationships among the elements which go to make up the fictional structure.

Therefore, it is suggested that, for classes in which the reading of fiction is the sole objective, the study of the Appendix may well be undertaken after the completion of Section V. At that time certain of the stories already studied may be investigated anew in the light of the technical questions discussed in the Appendix. To facilitate this process, the Appendix draws all of its examples from the stories in this collection.

For classes in which the students are expected to write stories, it is suggested that a similar program may be followed, though such

---

* But these "more fundamental considerations" are just as positively the concern of technical study in the broader sense of the word, for only in terms of their interrelationships does the fictional structure exist at all.

classes may find it profitable to undertake the study of the Appendix after the completion of Section IV. The editors would justify this delay in the study of the Appendix on the following grounds. First, the early concern with questions of exposition, complication, climax, and so on, tends to encourage the student in the all too ordinary view that the composition of fiction is primarily a mechanical activity, that to write fiction he has only to get the hang of a bag of tricks. It tends to distract him from the more fundamental considerations which, it is hoped, are the subject matter of the discussions and exercises up through Section IV. Further, this book does not pretend to be a collection of "models" for short-story writers. The editors believe, in fact, that the tendency to emphasize certain stories as models encourages imitation at the wrong level. It encourages imitation of particular effects found in the model and not imitation in terms of principles by which effects are rendered. The imitation of particular effects distracts the student from the candid exploration of his own feelings and attitudes; the imitation in terms of principles should give him the instruments by which he can explore his own feelings and attitudes and realize them in form. This is only one way of saying that the only way to teach something about writing may be through a discipline in critical reading.

The selection of stories has been undertaken with the hope of providing as wide a range of examples in terms of fictional method as could be reasonably expected in a book of this size. There has been no attempt at great novelty in selection. Rather, the editors have, in large part, chosen stories which are popular and widely anthologized. Nor has there been any attempt at making this book a representative collection or a collection of masterpieces. Many authors of great importance, and many stories for which the editors feel the keenest admiration, are omitted. Furthermore, certain stories which are definitely inferior are included in order to give the student exercise in destructive analysis and criticism. Again, there has been no attempt to present key examples in the history of the short story. In fact, the history of the short story, except at the narrowest technical level, can scarcely be discussed at all in isolation from the history of fiction in general and of poetry. But the editors have undertaken to give materials for some historical investigation of the influences and methods found in the modern short story. For instance, exercises might be framed on the comparisons or contrasts between Katherine Mansfield and Chekhov; between Hawthorne and Kafka or Eudora Welty; between Bret Harte or Kipling and Hemingway; between Poe and Faulkner; and between other pairs. The selection is necessarily smaller than the editors would have wished, for the number of stories which can be admitted to a single volume is limited.

It will no doubt be observed, and by some readers objected to, that for the most part the interpretations in this book are descriptive and analytical rather than evaluative. But the editors feel that, in general, the matter of the relative grading of stories, except for broad distinctions, should arise late rather than early in the critical process. The first problem is to understand the nature of fictional structure, to become acquainted with the idiom in terms of which the art operates, and to broaden the imaginative sympathies so that the student can transcend stock responses and threshold interests. But this process necessarily will lead to evaluation in a broad sense. A student does not have to go very far in the investigation of fictional structure before he understands that O. Henry's "The Furnished Room" depends for its effect not on a functional relationship among its elements but on arbitrary manipulation by the author, or before he understands that the irony here is accidental as compared with the irony in Pirandello's "War," or in Chekhov's "The Kiss." Such a discrimination as this should come early and naturally, but an attempt to discriminate between the value of "The Kiss" and that of "Two Little Soldiers," by Maupassant ought probably to come rather late. It is very important, to be sure, to be able to discriminate between the methods and effects of "The Kiss" and those of "Two Little Soldiers," for such discrimination should lead to a fuller appreciation of both pieces; but an early effort to grade two such successful stories on their relative merits may encourage critical vindictiveness and literary priggishness. It has been aptly said that a literary dictator has no place in the republic of letters.

Another and more specific objection which may be raised concerns the apparent emphasis on formal considerations in the evaluation of fiction—what may be thought the editors' failure to give adequate heed to the importance, on ethical, religious, philosophical, or sociological grounds, of the "idea" in a piece of fiction. In attempting to reply to such an objection the editors would first say that idea or theme is one of the elements in the fictional structure, but that the structure is not to be set over against the idea in any mechanical fashion. Rather, it is their first article of faith that the structure of a piece of fiction, in so far as that piece of fiction is successful, must involve a vital and functional relationship between the idea and the other elements in that structure—plot, style, character, and the like. In the second place, they would agree that to be good, a piece of fiction must involve an idea of some real significance for mature and thoughtful human beings. This does not mean that to appreciate a piece of fiction such a mature and thoughtful reader must *agree* with the idea realized in it; but it does mean that the question raised by the piece of fiction must seem to him worthy of serious exploration. For instance, the mature and thoughtful reader whom we have posited might not accept the view of the world which underlies Hemingway's fiction, but he might very well realize the difficulty of transcending such a view of the world. That is, he might admit that the question implicit in Hemingway's fiction is a real question, even though he might feel that he himself had transcended Hemingway's solution. If, on the other hand, he is of such an unrelentingly dogmatic disposition that he restricts his approbation to works which involve ideas with which he is in precise accord, he will probably find himself subsisting on very poverty-stricken literary diet. Worse still, he will not even be able to receive nourishment from the diet which he accepts, for he will be reading merely in terms of his threshold interest and will not be submitting his beliefs to the test of imaginative experience. In literature, ideas leave their cloisters and descend into the dust and heat to prove their virtue anew.

But the editors would wish to make a further remark on this general point, a remark concerning the level at which an idea in fiction becomes important. The mere presence in a piece of fiction of an idea which is held to be important in itself on ethical, religious, philosophical, sociological, or other grounds, does not necessarily indicate anything about the importance of the piece of fiction. One might almost as well commend a piece of fiction for exemplifying good grammatical usage. The mere presence of the "good" idea or the "good" grammar tells us nothing about the final success of the item in question. The idea is important in a story in so far as it is incorporated into the total structure—in so far as the story lives out the idea and, in the process of living, modifies the idea. The idea as an abstraction is absolute; but the idea in a story forfeits that privilege of absoluteness and must accept the dangers of qualification and modification. Everyone is familiar with stories in which "good" ideas emerge as cruel parodies of themselves, brutally debased by insensitive style and crude characterization and arbitrary psychology, for instance, or else sentimentalized by defects in logic and mechanical plot management. In fact, most popular fiction aims at flattering the ethical sense of the public. That such fiction is often, in the last analysis, corrupt derives from the fact that the author does not recognize the necessity of attempting to realize the idea fully in the experience of his characters and in the structure of his story. The villain bites the dust; the good heart triumphs over all. The author does not recognize the difficulty, let us say, in making a moral decision, and simply follows the idea as blueprint, as dogma. Situations which qualify an idea of virtue and emphasize the difficulty of moral decision—such as the situation which confronts Cordelia in the first scene of *King Lear* or that which confronts Isabella in her condemned brother's cell in *Measure for Measure* —do not flourish in the fiction of our best family magazines. Such fiction is deficient in *irony*.

With the mention of this term, we come to a further objection which may be raised by readers of this book, as it has been raised by certain readers of the companion book *Understanding Poetry,* concerning the subject of irony. The editors have, perhaps, been guilty of wrenching the word from its usual context—of at once specializing and broadening it. But one does not have a fixed and generally acceptable critical vocabulary except for certain rare and on the whole elementary instances. One faces the problem of creating a critical vocabulary as one goes along, and, unless one coins words, one must face the embarrassing necessity of wrenching words—of adding to or subtracting from the burden they bear in their function as common carriers. This is not to deny, however, that the critic should be scrupulous in his effort to indicate the precise nature of such wrenching, and in so far as the editors have been deficient in such scrupulousness, they now endeavor to make some slight amends: at least, in connection with the one word.

A piece of fiction is a unity, in so far as the piece of fiction is successful. Its elements are so related that we feel an expressive interpenetration among them, a set of vital relationships. But the unity which the fictional structure possesses is of a very special kind. It is not the result of a purely genial conspiracy among the constituent elements. There is conflict and tension present, and the structure involves almost as much of vindictive opposition as of genial conspiracy. One says "almost" because some sort of resolution, however provisional and marginal, must be implicit in the tensions of the fictional structure, if the unity is to be achieved—if the revelation is to be had. The fact of conflict as an essential aspect of fiction is clearly stated in every handbook. In its most obvious form it concerns a collision of interests in the external world. In a somewhat more subtle and sophisticated form conflict concerns a division of interests or obligations in the self. In an even more subtle and sophisticated form, it concerns the alignment of judgments and sympathies on the part of the author—the problem of his own self-division.

The dogmatist who is author paints a world of black and white, a world in which right and wrong, truth and falsehood, are clear with statutory distinctness, a world of villain and hero. The artist who is author paints a world in which there is, in the beginning, neither black nor white, neither right nor wrong which can be defined with absolute certainty. The certainty can only come in terms of the process, and must be *earned,* as it were, through the process. In other words, the artist is sporting enough to put the best case possible for the opposition. But this is not mere sportsmanship. The artist realizes that, if the opponent—"villain" or "idea"—is a straw man, the conflict will lack interest. In a simple example such as *Richard III,* we observe that Shakespeare makes the traditional and historical Tudor villain the vessel of certain virtues which the Tudor age seems to have admired inordinately. Without this ironical ambivalence, the play would be a tedious recital of butcheries to prove that you can't kill all of the people all of the time. It would have had no psychological center for tension, either in terms of the main character or in terms of the audience. Or, to glance at other simple cases, we may recall that in *Uncle Tom's Cabin* Simon Legree is a Yankee, and that in Hemingway's *For Whom the Bell Tolls* the scene of greatest brutality is that of the massacre of Fascists by Loyalists, or that the book closes with the distant figure of the young Fascist lieutenant (whom Hemingway has previously presented as a sympathetic character) caught in the gunsights of the hero. In all of these cases, the irony is intended, on the one hand, to intensify the implications of the conflict, and on the other, to raise the issue above the level of merely dogmatic and partisan vilification. But these two functions are closely interrelated and only by an act of abstraction can one, in many cases, separate them out.

Another function, also closely related, is to indicate an awareness of the multiplicity of options in conduct, idea, or attitude—an awareness of the full context. This suggests one of the objections which may be brought against the emphasis on irony; the objection that such an emphasis ends in the celebration of a smug and futile skepticism which is at variance with the actual effect which most successful literary compositions leave upon the reader. The editors would hope that, by this time, the grounds upon which they would answer this particular objection are clear. They would not endorse an irony which precluded resolution but they would endorse an irony which forced the resolution to take stock of as full a context as possible. The reader wants the resolution, but he does not want it too easy or too soon. He wants to see the knockout, but he does not want to see it until the fifteenth round. And, if he feels that the fight has been fixed, he will want to stop at the box office on the way out and demand his money back.

There is still another question concerning the use of the term *irony*. Why have the editors lighted upon this particular term? The terms one uses in attempting criticism probably represent, in most cases, the result of a long process of trial and error in the analysis of literary productions, and when the process is complete, it is often difficult to recapitulate the stages in the argument which led to the adopting of a particular term. But the editors would present their case somewhat like this: they felt the need of a term which would have significance, in relation both to the completed literary structure and to the process of exploration which led to the creation of the structure. They wanted a term which would accommodate reference to details of style, definition of character, symbolic force of action, and the like, as well as to the ordering of ideas and attitudes involved in the work. And the ordinary distinction between irony as device and irony as mode seemed to make possible the use of the term in this connection without too much wantonness.

The editors perhaps should crave the indulgence of the teacher for intruding this discussion of their general views into what should be a mere description of the aims and methods of this textbook. But they hope that the utility of this book for the individual teacher will not stand or fall by the teacher's assent to those views, just as they hope that it will not stand or fall by the teacher's assent to the editors' interpretation of particular stories. Certainly they do not wish to be dogmatic, for they realize too acutely the pitfalls in the way of even the most elementary critical analysis. They merely hope that this book raises certain profitable questions in a relatively systematic form for the student, and that by so doing it may render the task of the teacher a little easier. For the editors feel that no book, however much better than this, can do more than be of some slight assistance to the teacher in the classroom, upon whom the final responsibility must rest.

Contents

SECTION III

What Character Reveals

SECTION IV

What Theme Reveals

SECTION V

Special Problems

Chronological Chart

* Signifies first publication in a volume; other dates refer to first publication.

ACKNOWLEDGMENT

The editors wish to thank the various authors and publishers who have given their kind permission to reprint certain materials used in this collection. More specific acknowledgment is made in the text in connection with each item.

Understanding Fiction

SECTION I

The Intentions of Fiction

THIS IS a book about the reading of fiction, and it might seem desirable to begin with a definition of the subject. But in one sense a definition is unnecessary, because everyone feels that he knows what fiction is. It is a story, a made-up story, about characters. (Even when the "characters" are animals, it is the human trait read into the animal which makes it a character at all.) But the trouble with this definition is that it is too easy, too simple, and throws little light on the stories which one encounters. It would be possible to construct a much more elaborate definition, but such a definition would necessarily be complicated and abstract. At this point, therefore, it may be more fruitful to work toward an understanding of our subject through an investigation of particular instances. Furthermore it may be helpful to treat first of some pieces of writing which do not pretend to be fiction, but which, because they exhibit some of the qualities of fiction, may throw some light on fiction itself.

Consider first, for example, the following paragraphs taken from Francis Parkman's *The Oregon Trail,* a work in which Parkman, who actually went West in the early days, tells what life on the Great Plains was like.

The Attack on the Fort
FRANCIS PARKMAN

Six years ago, a fellow named Jim Beckworth, a mongrel of French, American, and Negro blood, was trading for the Fur Company, in a large village of the Crows. Jim Beckworth was last summer at St. Louis. He is a ruffian of the worst stamp, bloody and treacherous, without honor or honesty; such at least is the character he bears upon the prairie. Yet in his case the standard rules of character fail, for though he will stab a man in his sleep, he will also perform most desperate acts of daring; such, for instance, as the following: While he was in the Crow village, a Blackfoot war-party, between thirty and forty in number, came stealing through the country, killing stragglers and carrying off horses. The Crow warriors got upon their trail and pressed them so closely that they could not escape, at which the Blackfeet, throwing up a semi-circular breastwork of logs at the foot of a precipice, coolly awaited their approach. The logs and sticks, piled four or five feet high, protected them in front. The Crows might have swept over the breastwork and exterminated their enemies; but though outnumbering them tenfold, they did not dream of storming the little fortification. Such a proceeding would be altogether repugnant to their notions of warfare. Whooping and yelling, and jumping from side to side like devils incarnate, they showered bullets and arrows upon the logs; not a Blackfoot was hurt, but several Crows, in spite of their leaping and dodging, were shot down. In this childish manner, the fight went on for an hour or two. Now and then a Crow warrior, in an ecstasy of valor and vainglory, would scream forth his war song, boast himself the bravest and greatest of mankind, grasp his hatchet, rush up, strike it upon the breastwork, and then, as he retreated to his companions, fall dead under a shower of arrows; yet no combined attack was made. The Blackfeet remained secure in their intrenchment. At last Jim Beckworth lost patience.

"You are all fools and old women," he said to the Crows; "come with me, if any of you are brave enough, and I will show you how to fight."

He threw off his trapper's frock of buckskin and stripped himself naked, like the Indians themselves. He left his rifle on the ground, took in his hand a small light hatchet, and ran over the prairie to the right, concealed by a hollow from the eyes of the Blackfeet. Then climbing up the rocks, he gained the top of the precipice behind them. Forty or fifty young Crow warriors followed him. By the cries and whoops that rose from below he knew that the Blackfeet were just beneath him; and running forward, he leaped down the rock into the midst of them. As he fell he caught one by the long loose hair, and dragging him down, tomahawked him; then grasping another by the belt at his waist, he struck him also a stunning blow, and, gaining his feet, shouted the Crow war cry. He swung his hatchet so fiercely around him that the astonished Blackfeet bore back and gave him room. He might, had he chosen, have leaped over the breastwork and escaped; but this was not necessary, for with devilish yells the Crow warriors came dropping in quick succession over the rock among their enemies. The main body of the Crows, too, answered the cry from the front, and rushed up simultaneously. The convulsive struggle within the breastwork was frightful; for an instant the Blackfeet fought and yelled like pent-up tigers; but the butchery was soon complete, and the mangled bodies lay piled together under the precipice. Not a Blackfoot made his escape.*

There are two preliminary observations which one may make on this anecdote. First, it really happened, it is not made up. Second, Parkman wrote it, not primarily because it was spirited and interesting in itself, but because it illustrated one aspect of the life which he wanted to describe to the people back at home. These observations raise two questions. First, would this anecdote be fiction if Parkman had simply made it up out of his head? Second, would it be fiction if Parkman had written it, not to instruct his readers, but because it was interesting in itself? The answer to both of these questions is "no."

We must answer "no" to the first question because, though fiction is not tied to fact, it may use fact. Many pieces of fiction make as much use of historical fact as does this. We must answer "no" to the second question because, though many pieces of fiction are written with a desire to instruct the reader, they are not written with the purpose to instruct the reader merely about matters of fact.

If we are not debarred from calling this anecdote fiction because it is true and not because the author's purpose was to instruct the reader, why, then, is it not to be considered fiction? To answer this question, we must look at the nature of the anecdote itself.

The anecdote proper is simply a spirited piece of action which, as a piece of action, is unified. That is, we have the situation precipitating the fight, the cunning defense by the Blackfeet Indians which creates a problem for the attackers, the failure of the attackers to solve their problem, then the daring solution by Beckworth. The anecdote, as action, is unified because it presents problem and solution, because it has a beginning, middle, and end. Our curiosity about the outcome is satisfied. But does this outcome satisfy fully the interest which we bring to fiction?

* From *The Oregon Trail*.

Certainly, our curiosity about the outcome of an action, as action, is one of the elements of our interest in fiction. A great deal of fiction is written with the appeal to this curiosity in the foreground, as for instance, detective stories and adventure stories. But even in these types of fiction, there are other important interests involved. In a detective story, one wants to know not only who did "it," but why "it" was done. The author of even the crudest detective or adventure story always feels obligated to satisfy this interest: he attributes *motive* to his characters. But does Parkman's anecdote satisfy this interest? Why did Jim Beckworth undertake the daring feat? It is a question which is raised in the mind of anyone who reads the episode, but it is a question for which the author gives no answer. We can guess at a number of answers, but the author takes no responsibility for any of our guesses; he simply gives us the *external* action, what was said and done, and does not give us any real inkling as to the *internal* action, as to what went on inside Jim Beckworth's head. We must confess, however, that Parkman does raise a general question about Beckworth's character: "in his case the standard rules of character fail, for though he will stab a man in his sleep, he will also perform most desperate acts of daring." But this remark is merely preliminary to the anecdote, which illustrates the author's statement, and does not do anything to answer the question as to why Beckworth behaves in this fashion, and does not help us to understand more clearly the process by which Beckworth arrives at his decision.

Why, then, do we not call this anecdote fiction? Certainly one reason is that its action is purely *external;* it does not sufficiently involve character and motive; it does not answer fully enough our basic interest about human action.

Let us look at another example, the description of a man by one of his acquaintances:

Portrait of Henry Hastings

ANTHONY COOPER, FIRST EARL OF SHAFTESBURY

Mr. Hastings, by his quality, being the son, brother and uncle to the Earls of Huntingdon, and his way of living, had the first place amongst us. He was peradventure an original in our age, or rather the copy of our nobility in ancient days in hunting and not warlike times: he was low, very strong and very active, of a reddish flaxen hair, his clothes always green cloth, and never all worth when new five pounds.

His house was perfectly of the old fashion, in the midst of a large park well stocked with deer, and near the house rabbits to serve his kitchen, many fish ponds, and great store of wood and timber; a bowling-green in it, long but narrow, full of high ridges, it being never leveled since it was plowed; they used round sand bowls, and it had a banqueting house like a stand, a large one built in a tree. He kept all manner of sport hounds that ran buck, fox, hare, otter, and badger, and hawks long and short winged; he had all sorts of nets for fishing; he had a walk in the New Forest and the manor of Christ Church. This last supplied him with red deer, sea and river fish; and indeed all his neighbors' grounds and royalties were free to him, who bestowed all his time in such sports, but what he borrowed to caress his neighbors' wives and daughters, there being not a woman in all his walks of the degree of a yeoman's wife or under, and under the age of forty, but it was extremely her fault if he were not intimately acquainted with her. This made him very popular, always speaking kindly to the husband, brother, or father, who was to boot very welcome to his house whenever he came; there he found beef pudding and small beer in great plenty, a house not so neatly kept as to shame him or his dirty shoes, the great hall strewed with marrow bones, full of hawks' perches, hounds, spaniels, and terriers, the upper sides of the hall hung with the fox skins of this and the last year's skinning, here and there a polecat intermixed, guns and keepers' and huntsmen's poles in abundance. The parlor was a large long room, as properly furnished; in a great hearth paved with brick lay some terriers and the choicest hounds and spaniels; seldom but two of the great chairs had litters of young cats in them, which were not to be disturbed, he having always three or four attending him at dinner, and a little white round stick of fourteen inches long lying by his trencher that he might defend such meat as he had no mind to part with to them. The windows, which were very large, served for places to lay his arrows, crossbows, stonebows, and other such like accouterments; the corners of the room full of the best chose hunting and hawking poles; an oyster table at the lower end, which was of constant use twice a day all the year round, for he never failed to eat oysters before dinner and supper through all seasons: the neighboring town of Poole supplied him with them. The upper part of this room had two small tables and a desk,

on the one side of which was a church Bible, on the other the Book
of Martyrs; on the tables were hawks' hoods, bells, and such like, two
or three old green hats with the crowns thrust in so as to hold ten
or a dozen eggs, which were of a pheasant kind of poultry he took
much care of and fed himself; tables, dice, cards, and boxes were not
wanting. In the hole of the desk were store of tobacco pipes that had
been used. On one side of this end of the room was the door of a
closet, wherein stood the strong beer and the wine, which never came
thence but in single glasses, that being the rule of the house exactly
observed, for he never exceeded in drink or permitted it. On the other
side was a door into an old chapel not used for devotion; the pulpit,
as the safest place, was never wanting of a cold chine of beef, pasty
of venison, gammon of bacon, or great apple pie with thick crust extremely baked. His table cost him not much, though it was very good
to eat at, his sports supplying all but beef and mutton, except Friday,
when he had the best sea fish he could get, and was the day that his
neighbors of best quality most visited him. He never wanted a London
pudding, and always sung it in with "my part lies therein-a." He drank
a glass of wine or two at meals, very often syrup of gilliflower in his
sack, and had always a tun glass without feet stood by him holding a
pint of small beer, which he often stirred with a great sprig of rose-
mary. He was well natured, but soon angry, calling his servants bastard
and cuckoldy knaves, in one of which he often spoke truth to his own
knowledge, and sometimes in both, though of the same man. He lived
to a hundred, never lost his eyesight, but always writ and read without
spectacles, and got to horse without help. Until past fourscore he rode
to the death of a stag as well as any.*

Obviously this is not a piece of fiction. It is irrelevant that this is a
portrait of a real person who lived in the seventeenth century. Even
if this were the portrait of an imaginary person, it still would not be
fiction. It is a character sketch. Even though it does not give much
analysis of the subject's character, it gives a great many details of the
way the subject lives; and these details serve to suggest to us the man's
nature. In this connection, we must remember that ordinarily fiction
does not give us a great deal of character analysis in general and abstract terms; rather, it gives us just such concrete and suggestive de-

* Quoted by Mark Van Doren in *The Poetry of John Dryden*.

tails as are found here. But fiction gives us character by other, and more important means, as well: *it gives us character through action.*

How overt the action in a piece of fiction should be is not a matter easily determined. Frequently the action may be very slight in the physical sense, but may involve very important psychological changes, as for example in the story "Old Red," p. 64, or "The Lament," p. 242. But no matter how slight the action may appear to be in a piece of fiction, it always provides us with a "line," a progression of events which may be either external or internal in emphasis, and comes to some definite conclusion. The conclusion may result in very positive external changes or merely in a new awareness on the part of a character, but things are not as they were before. A story involves change.

The basic reason for regarding this piece of writing as a character sketch and not as fiction is that it has no "line" and shows no change. It is static. But though this sketch is not a story, yet it uses, as we have pointed out above, a number of the methods which fiction uses; and indeed it is full of incipient stories. For instance, there are suggestions of stories about hunting and hawking, stories about Hastings' attitude toward religious practices, stories about his illicit love-making in the neighborhood. Indeed, we have, from the standpoint of fiction, *too many* suggested stories here. We can see that all of these suggested stories belong logically to such a man, but the trouble is that no one of them is developed. They are all presented at the same level of importance. Had Shaftesbury cared to develop this sketch as a piece of fiction, he would have been compelled to choose what story he wanted to tell and to scale down the other "stories" into subordinate position.

But to consider the sketch a moment longer as potential fiction: One other point ought to be perfectly evident. If there are many incipient stories here, there are many other stories ruled out completely. For instance, we cannot imagine this man's becoming a martyr to a great idea. Let us consider a situation in which a writer of fiction conceivably might place Hastings. Hastings lived in the seventeenth century, and in his later life witnessed, and perhaps took sides in, the Civil War in England, the war between the Royalists and the Puritans. On what side would the fiction writer logically place such a character? Temperamentally, he would seem to be a Royalist. But suppose the writer wanted to put him on the Puritan side. Then the writer would have the problem of squaring Hastings' temperament with his politics; that is, the writer would have to use the motivation of blood ties or economic advantage or love of adventure to account for his Puritan alignment. In such a case, we would find Hastings careless of the total issue at stake in the war or involved in a psychological conflict between his personal temperament and his public affiliations. In other words, when a character does get into action, he must do so in accordance with a logic inherent in his character.

But assuming that fiction involves character in action, and that the action involves a real change, is any other difference involved in distinguishing between fiction and nonfiction? In this connection, let us look at the following account of the sinking of the *Titanic*.

R.M.S. *Titanic*
HANSON BALDWIN

The White Star liner *Titanic,* largest ship the world had ever known, sailed from Southampton on her maiden voyage to New York on April 10, 1912. The paint on her strakes was fair and bright; she was fresh from Harland and Wolff's Belfast yards, strong in the strength of her forty-six thousand tons of steel, bent, hammered, shaped and riveted through the three years of her slow birth.

There was little fuss and fanfare at her sailing; her sister ship, the *Olympic*—slightly smaller than the *Titanic*—had been in service for some months and to her had gone the thunder of the cheers.

But the *Titanic* needed no whistling steamers or shouting crowds to call attention to her superlative qualities. Her bulk dwarfed the ships near her as longshoremen singled up her mooring lines and cast off the turns of heavy rope from the dock bollards. She was not only the largest ship afloat, but was believed to be the safest. Carlisle, her builder, had given her double bottoms and had divided her hull into sixteen watertight compartments, which made her, men thought, unsinkable. She had been built to be and had been described as a gigantic lifeboat. Her designers' dreams of a triple-screw giant, a luxurious, floating hotel, which could speed to New York at twenty-three knots, had been carefully translated from blue prints and mold-loft lines at the Belfast yards into a living reality.

The *Titanic's* sailing from Southampton, though quiet, was not wholly uneventful. As the liner moved slowly toward the end of her dock that April day, the surge of her passing sucked away from the quay the steamer *New York*, moored just to seaward of the *Titanic's* berth. There were sharp cracks as the manila mooring lines of the *New York* parted under the strain. The frayed ropes writhed and whistled through the air and snapped down among the waving crowd on the pier; the *New York* swung toward the *Titanic's* bow, was checked and dragged back to the dock barely in time to avert a collision. Seamen muttered, thought it an ominous start.

Past Spithead and the Isle of Wight the *Titanic* steamed. She called at Cherbourg at dusk and then laid her course for Queenstown. At 1:30 P.M. on Thursday, April 11, she stood out of Queenstown harbor, screaming gulls soaring in her wake, with 2,201 persons—men, women, and children—aboard.

Occupying the Empire bedrooms and Georgian suites of the first-class accommodations were many well-known men and women—Colonel John Jacob Astor and his young bride; Major Archibald Butt, military aide to President Taft, and his friend, Frank D. Millet, the painter; John B. Thayer, vice-president of the Pennsylvania Railroad, and Charles M. Hays, president of the Grand Trunk Railway of Canada; W. T. Stead, the English journalist; Jacques Futrelle, French novelist; H. B. Harris, theatrical manager, and Mrs. Harris; Mr. and Mrs. Isidor Straus; and J. Bruce Ismay, chairman and managing director of the White Star line.

Down in the plain wooden cabins of the steerage class were 706 immigrants to the land of promise, and trimly stowed in the great holds was a cargo valued at $420,000: oak beams, sponges, wine, calabashes, and an odd miscellany of the common and the rare.

The *Titanic* took her departure on Fastnet Light and, heading into the night, laid her course for New York. She was due at Quarantine the following Wednesday morning.

Sunday dawned fair and clear. The *Titanic* steamed smoothly toward the west, faint streamers of brownish smoke trailing from her funnels. The purser held services in the saloon in the morning; on the steerage deck aft the immigrants were playing games and a Scotsman was puffing "The Campbells Are Coming" on his bagpipes in the midst of the uproar.

At 9 A.M. a message from the steamer *Caronia* sputtered into the wireless shack:

CAPTAIN, TITANIC—WESTBOUND STEAMERS REPORT BERGS
GROWLERS AND FIELD ICE IN 42 DEGREES N. FROM 49 DEGREES
TO 51 DEGREES W. 12TH APRIL.

COMPLIMENTS—

BARR.

It was cold in the afternoon; the sun was brilliant, but the *Titanic,* her screws turning over at 75 revolutions per minute, was approaching the Banks.

In the Marconi cabin Second Operator Harold Bride, earphones clamped on his head, was figuring accounts; he did not stop to answer when he heard MWL, Continental Morse for the nearby Leyland liner, *Californian,* calling the *Titanic.* The *Californian* had some message about three icebergs; he didn't bother then to take it down. About 1:42 P. M. the rasping spark of those days spoke again across the water. It was the *Baltic,* calling the *Titanic,* warning her of ice on the steamer track. Bride took the message down and sent it up to the bridge. The officer-of-the-deck glanced at it; sent it to the bearded master of the *Titanic,* Captain E. C. Smith, a veteran of the White Star service. It was lunch time then; the Captain, walking along the promenade deck, saw Mr. Ismay, stopped, and handed him the message without comment. Ismay read it, stuffed it in his pocket, told two ladies about the icebergs, and resumed his walk. Later, about 7:15 P. M., the Captain requested the return of the message in order to post it in the chart room for the information of officers.

Dinner that night in the Jacobean dining room was gay. It was bitter on deck, but the night was calm and fine; the sky was moonless but studded with stars twinkling coldly in the clear air.

After dinner some of the second-class passengers gathered in the saloon, where the Reverend Mr. Carter conducted a "hymn singsong." It was almost ten o'clock and the stewards were waiting with biscuits and coffee as the group sang:

> *O, hear us when we cry to Thee*
> *For those in peril on the sea.*

On the bridge Second Officer Lightoller—short, stocky, efficient—was relieved at ten o'clock by First Officer Murdock. Lightoller had talked with other officers about the proximity of ice; at least five wireless ice warnings had reached the ship; lookouts had been cautioned to be alert; captains and officers expected to reach the field at any time after 9:30 P. M. At twenty-two knots, its speed unslackened, the *Titanic* plowed on through the night.

Lightoller left the darkened bridge to his relief and turned in. Captain Smith went to his cabin. The steerage was long since quiet; in the first and second cabins lights were going out; voices were growing still, people were asleep. Murdock paced back and forth on the bridge, peering out over the dark water, glancing now and then at the compass in front of Quartermaster Hichens at the wheel.

In the crow's-nest, Lookout Frederick Fleet and his partner, Leigh, gazed down at the water, still and unruffled in the dim, starlit darkness. Behind and below them the ship, a white shadow with here and there a last winking light; ahead of them a dark and silent and cold ocean.

There was a sudden clang. "Dong-dong. Dong-dong. Dong-dong. Dong!" The metal clapper of the great ship's bell struck out 11:30. Mindful of the warnings, Fleet strained his eyes, searching the darkness for the dreaded ice. But there were only the stars and the sea.

In the wireless room, where Phillips, first operator, had relieved Bride, the buzz of the *Californian*'s set again crackled into the earphones:

Californian: "Say, old man, we are stuck here, surrounded by ice."
Titanic: "Shut up, shut up; keep out. I am talking to Cape Race; you are jamming my signals."

Then, a few minutes later—about 11:40 . . .

Out of the dark she came, a vast, dim, white, monstrous shape, directly in the *Titanic's* path. For a moment Fleet doubted his eyes. But she was a deadly reality, this ghastly *thing*. Frantically, Fleet struck three bells—*something dead ahead*. He snatched the telephone and called the bridge:

"Iceberg! Right ahead!"

The First Officer heard but did not stop to acknowledge the message.

"Hard astarboard!"

Hichens strained at the wheel; the bow swung slowly to port. The monster was almost upon them now.

Murdock leaped to the engine-room telegraph. Bells clanged. Far below in the engine room those bells struck the first warning. Danger! The indicators on the dial faces swung round to "Stop!" Then "Full speed astern!" Frantically the engineers turned great valve wheels; answered the bridge bells. . . .

There was a slight shock, a brief scraping, a small list to port. Shell ice—slabs and chunks of it—fell on the foredeck. Slowly the *Titanic* stopped.

Captain Smith hurried out of his cabin.

"What has the ship struck?"

Murdock answered, "An iceberg, sir. I hard-astarboarded and reversed the engines, and I was going to hard-aport around it, but she was too close. I could not do any more. I have closed the watertight doors."

Fourth Officer Boxhall, other officers, the carpenter, came to the bridge. The Captain sent Boxhall and the carpenter below to ascertain the damage.

A few lights switched on in the first and second cabins; sleepy passengers peered through porthole glass; some casually asked the stewards:

"Why have we stopped?"

"I don't know, sir, but I don't suppose it is anything much."

In the smoking room a quorum of gamblers and their prey were still sitting round a poker table; the usual crowd of kibitzers looked on. They had felt the slight jar of the collision and had seen an eighty-foot ice mountain glide by the smoking-room windows, but the night was calm and clear, the *Titanic* was "unsinkable"; they hadn't bothered to go on deck.

But far below, in the warren of passages on the starboard side forward, in the forward holds and boiler rooms, men could see that the *Titanic*'s hurt was mortal. In No. 6 boiler room, where the red glow from the furnaces lighted up the naked, sweaty chests of coal-blackened firemen, water was pouring through a great gash about two feet above the floor plates. This was no slow leak; the ship was open to the sea;

in ten minutes there were eight feet of water in No. 6. Long before
then the stokers had raked the flaming fires out of the furnaces and
had scrambled through the watertight doors into No. 5 or had climbed
up the long steel ladders to safety. When Boxhall looked at the mail
room in No. 3 hold, twenty-four feet above the keel, the mailbags were
already floating about in the slushing water. In No. 5 boiler room a
stream of water spurted into an empty bunker. All six compartments
forward of No. 4 were open to the sea; in ten seconds the iceberg's
jagged claw had ripped a three-hundred-foot slash in the bottom of
the great *Titanic*.

Reports came to the bridge; Ismay in dressing gown ran out on deck
in the cold, still, starlit night, climbed up the bridge ladder.

"What has happened?"

Captain Smith: "We have struck ice."

"Do you think she is seriously damaged?"

Captain: "I'm afraid she is."

Ismay went below and passed Chief Engineer William Bell fresh
from an inspection of the damaged compartments. Bell corroborated
the Captain's statement; hurried back down the glistening steel ladders to his duty. Man after man followed him—Thomas Andrews, one
of the ship's designers, Archie Frost, the builder's chief engineer, and
his twenty assistants—men who had no posts of duty in the engine
room but whose traditions·called them there.

On deck, in corridor and stateroom, life flowed again. Men, women,
and children awoke and questioned; orders were given to uncover the
lifeboats; water rose into the firemen's quarters; half-dressed stokers
streamed up on deck. But the passengers—most of them—did not
know that the *Titanic* was sinking. The shock of the collision had
been so slight that some were not awakened by it; the *Titanic* was so
huge that she must be unsinkable; the night was too calm, too beautiful, to think of death at sea.

Captain Smith half ran to the door of the radio shack. Bride, partly
dressed, eyes dulled with sleep, was standing behind Phillips, waiting.

"Send the call for assistance."

The blue spark danced: "CQD—CQD—CQD—CQ—"

Miles away Marconi men heard. Cape Race heard it, and the steam-
ships *La Provence* and *Mt. Temple*.

The sea was surging into the *Titanic*'s hold. At 12:20 the water burst into the seamen's quarters through a collapsed fore-and-aft wooden bulkhead. Pumps strained in the engine rooms—men and machinery making a futile fight against the sea. Steadily the water rose.

The boats were swung out—slowly; for the deckhands were late in reaching their stations, there had been no boat drill, and many of the crew did not know to what boats they were assigned. Orders were shouted; the safety valves had lifted, and steam was blowing off in a great rushing roar. In the chart house Fourth Officer Boxhall bent above a chart, working rapidly with pencil and dividers.

12:15 A. M.   Boxhall's position is sent out to a fleet of vessels: "Come at once; we have struck a berg."

To the Cunarder *Carpathia* (Arthur Henry Rostron, Master, New York to Liverpool, fifty-eight miles away): "It's a CQD, old man. Position 41–46 N.; 50–14 W."

The blue spark dancing: "Sinking; cannot hear for noise of steam."

12:30 A. M.   The word is passed: "Women and children in the boats." Stewards finish waking their passengers below; life preservers are tied on; some men smile at the precaution. "The *Titanic* is unsinkable." The *Mt. Temple* starts for the *Titanic;* the *Carpathia,* with a double watch in her stokeholds, radios, "Coming hard." The CQD changes the course of many ships—but not of one; the operator of the *Californian,* near by, has just put down his earphones and turned in.

The CQD flashes over land and sea from Cape Race to New York; newspaper city rooms leap to life and presses whir.

On the *Titanic,* water creeps over the bulkhead between Nos. 5 and 6 firerooms. She is going down by the head; the engineers—fighting a losing battle—are forced back foot by foot by the rising water. Down the promenade deck, Happy Jock Hume, the bandsman, runs with his instrument.

12:45 A. M.   Murdock, in charge on the starboard side, eyes tragic, but calm and cool, orders boat No. 7 lowered. The women hang back; they want no boat ride on an ice-strewn sea; the *Titanic* is unsinkable. The men encourage them, explain that this is just a precautionary measure: "We'll see you again at breakfast." There is little confusion; passengers stream slowly to the boat deck. In the steerage the immigrants chatter excitedly.

A sudden sharp hiss—a streaked flare against the night; Boxhall sends a rocket toward the sky. It explodes, and a parachute of white stars lights up the icy sea. "God! Rockets!" The band plays ragtime.

No. 8 is lowered, and No. 5. Ismay, still in dressing gown, calls for women and children, handles lines, stumbles in the way of an officer, is told to "get the hell out of here." Third Officer Pitman takes charge of No. 5; as he swings into the boat Murdock grasps his hand. "Good-by and good luck, old man."

No. 6 goes over the side. There are only twenty-eight people in a lifeboat with a capacity of sixty-five.

A light stabs from the bridge; Boxhall is calling in Morse flashes, again and again, to a strange ship stopped in the ice jam five to ten miles away. Another rocket drops its shower of sparks above the ice-strewn sea and the dying ship.

1:00 A.M. Slowly the water creeps higher; the fore ports of the *Titanic* are dipping into the sea. Rope squeaks through blocks; lifeboats drop jerkily seaward. Through the shouting on the decks comes the sound of the band playing ragtime.

The "Millionaires' Special" leaves the ship—boat No. 1, with a capacity of forty people, carries only Sir Cosmo and Lady Duff Gordon and ten others. Aft, the frightened immigrants mill and jostle and rush for a boat. An officer's fist flies out; three shots are fired into the air, and the panic is quelled. . . . Four Chinese sneak unseen into a boat and hide in its bottom.

1:20 A.M. Water is coming into No. 4 boiler room. Stokers slice and shovel as water laps about their ankles—steam for the dynamos, steam for the dancing spark! As the water rises, great ash hoes rake the flaming coals from the furnaces. Safety valves pop; the stokers retreat aft, and the watertight doors clang shut behind them.

The rockets fling their splendor toward the stars. The boats are more heavily loaded now, for the passengers know the *Titanic* is sinking. Women cling and sob. The great screws aft are rising clear of the sea. Half-filled boats are ordered to come alongside the cargo ports and take on more passengers, but the ports are never opened—and the boats are never filled. Others pull for the steamer's light miles away but never reach it; the light disappears, the unknown ship steams off.

The water rises and the band plays ragtime.

1:30 A. M. Lightoller is getting the port boats off; Murdock the starboard. As one boat is lowered into the sea a boat officer fires his gun along the ship's side to stop a rush from the lower decks. A woman tries to take her great Dane into a boat with her; she is refused and steps out of the boat to die with her dog. Millet's "little smile which played on his lips all through the voyage" plays no more; his lips are grim, but he waves good-by and brings wraps for the women.

Benjamin Guggenheim, in evening clothes, smiles and says, "We've dressed up in our best and are prepared to go down like gentlemen."

1:40 A. M. Boat 14 is clear, and then 13, 16, 15, and C. The lights still shine, but the *Baltic* hears the blue spark say, "Engine room getting flooded."

The *Olympic* signals, "Am lighting up all possible boilers as fast as can."

Major Butt helps women into the last boats and waves good-by to them. Mrs. Straus puts her foot on the gunwale of a lifeboat, then she draws back and goes to her husband: "We have been together many years; where you go I will go." Colonel John Jacob Astor puts his young wife in a lifeboat, steps back, taps cigarette on fingernail: "Good-by, dearie; I'll join you later."

1:45 A. M. The foredeck is under water, the fo'c'sle head almost awash; the great stern is lifted high toward the bright stars; and still the band plays. Mr. and Mrs. Harris approach a lifeboat arm in arm.

Officer: "Ladies first, please."

Harris bows, smiles, steps back: "Of course, certainly; ladies first."

Boxhall fires the last rocket, then leaves in charge of boat No. 2.

2:00 A. M. She is dying now; her bow goes deeper, her stern higher. But there must be steam. Below in the stokeholds the sweaty firemen keep steam up for the flaring lights and the dancing spark. The glowing coals slide and tumble over the slanted grate bars; the sea pounds behind that yielding bulkhead. But the spark dances on.

The *Asian* hears Phillips try the new signal—SOS.

Boat No. 4 has left now; boat D leaves ten minutes later. Jacques Futrelle clasps his wife: "For God's sake, go! It's your last chance; go!" Madame Futrelle is half forced into the boat. It clears the side.

There are about 660 people in the boats, and 1,500 still on the sinking *Titanic*.

On top of the officers' quarters men work frantically to get the two collapsibles stowed there over the side. Water is over the forward part of A deck now; it surges up the companionways toward the boat deck. In the radio shack, Bride has slipped a coat and lifejacket about Phillips as the first operator sits hunched over his key, sending—still sending—"41-46 N.; 50-14 W. CQD—CQD—SOS—SOS—"

The Captain's tired white face appears at the radio-room door: "Men, you have done your full duty. You can do no more. Now, it's every man for himself." The Captain disappears—back to his sinking bridge, where Painter, his personal steward, stands quietly waiting for orders. The spark dances on. Bride turns his back and goes into the inner cabin. As he does so, a stoker, grimed with coal, mad with fear, steals into the shack and reaches for the lifejacket on Phillips' back. Bride wheels about and brains him with a wrench.

2:10 A.M.   Below decks the steam is still holding, though the pressure is falling—rapidly. In the gymnasium on the boat deck the athletic instructor watches quietly as two gentlemen ride the bicycles and another swings casually at the punching bag. Mail clerks stagger up the boat-deck stairways, dragging soaked mail sacks. The spark still dances. The band still plays—but not ragtime:

Nearer my God to Thee,
Nearer to Thee . . .

A few men take up the refrain; others kneel on the slanting decks to pray. Many run and scramble aft, where hundreds are clinging above the silent screws on the great uptilted stern. The spark still dances and the lights still flare; the engineers are on the job. The hymn comes to its close. Bandmaster Hartley, Yorkshireman violinist, taps his bow against a bulkhead, calls for "Autumn" as the water curls about his feet, and the eight musicians brace themselves against the ship's slant. People are leaping from the decks into the near by water —the icy water. A woman cries, "Oh, save me, save me!" A man answers, "Good lady, save yourself. Only God can save you now." The band plays "Autumn":

God of Mercy and Compassion!
Look with pity on my pain . . .

The water creeps over the bridge where the *Titanic*'s master stands; heavily he steps out to meet it.

2:17 A. M. "CQ—" The *Virginian* hears a ragged, blurred CQ, then an abrupt stop. The blue spark dances no more. The lights flicker out; the engineers have lost their battle.

2:18 A. M. Men run about blackened decks; leap into the night; are swept into the sea by the curling wave which licks up the *Titanic*'s length. Lightoller does not leave the ship; the ship leaves him; there are hundreds like him, but only a few who live to tell of it. The funnels still swim above the water, but the ship is climbing to the perpendicular; the bridge is under and most of the foremast; the great stern rises like a squat leviathan. Men swim away from the sinking ship; others drop from the stern.

The band plays in the darkness, the water lapping upwards:

> *Hold me up in mighty waters,*
> *Keep my eyes on things above,*
> *Righteousness, divine atonement,*
> *Peace and everlas . . .*

The forward funnel snaps and crashes into the sea; its steel tons hammer out of existence swimmers struggling in the freezing water. Streams of sparks, of smoke and steam, burst from the after funnels. The ship upends to fifty—to sixty degrees.

Down in the black abyss of the stokeholds, of the engine rooms, where the dynamos have whirred at long last to a stop, the stokers and the engineers are reeling against hot metal, the rising water clutching at their knees. The boilers, the engine cylinders, rip from their bed plates; crash through bulkheads; rumble—steel against steel.

The *Titanic* stands on end, poised briefly for the plunge. Slowly she slides to her grave—slowly at first, and then more quickly—quickly—quickly.

2:20 A. M. The greatest ship in the world has sunk. From the calm, dark waters, where the floating lifeboats move, there goes up, in the white wake of her passing, "one long continuous moan."

The boats that the *Titanic* had launched pulled safely away from the slight suction of the sinking ship, pulled away from the screams that came from the lips of the freezing men and women in the water. The boats were poorly manned and badly equipped, and they had been unevenly loaded. Some carried so few seamen that women bent to the oars. Mrs. Astor tugged at an oar handle; the Countess of Rothes took a tiller. Shivering stokers in sweaty, coal-blackened singlets and light trousers steered in some boats; stewards in white coats rowed in others. Ismay was in the last boat that left the ship from the starboard side; with Mr. Carter of Philadelphia and two seamen he tugged at the oars. In one of the lifeboats an Italian with a broken wrist—disguised in a woman's shawl and hat—huddled on the floor boards, ashamed now that fear had left him. In another rode the only baggage saved from the *Titanic*—the carry-all of Samuel L. Goldenberg, one of the rescued passengers.

There were only a few boats that were heavily loaded; most of those that were half empty made but perfunctory efforts to pick up the moaning swimmers, their officers and crew fearing that they would endanger the living if they pulled back into the midst of the dying. Some boats beat off the freezing victims; fear-crazed men and women struck with oars at the heads of swimmers. One woman drove her fist into the face of a half-dead man as he tried feebly to climb over the gunwale. Two other women helped him in and stanched the flow of blood from the ring cuts on his face.

One of the collapsible boats, which had floated off the top of the officers' quarters when the *Titanic* sank, was an icy haven for thirty or forty men. The boat had capsized as the ship sank; men swam to it, clung to it, climbed upon its slippery bottom, stood knee-deep in water in the freezing air. Chunks of ice swirled about their legs; their soaked clothing clutched their bodies in icy folds. Colonel Archibald Gracie was cast up there, Gracie who had leaped from the stern as the *Titanic* sank; young Thayer who had seen his father die; Lightoller who had twice been sucked down with the ship and twice blown to the surface by a belch of air; Bride, the second operator, and Phillips, the first. There were many stokers, half-naked; it was a shivering company. They stood there in the icy sea, under the far stars, and sang and prayed—the Lord's Prayer. After a while a lifeboat came and picked them off, but Phillips was dead then or died soon afterward in the boat.

Only a few of the boats had lights; only one—No. 2—had a light that was of any use to the *Carpathia*, twisting through the ice field to the rescue. Other ships were "coming hard" too; one, the *Californian*, was still dead to opportunity.

The blue sparks still danced, but not the *Titanic*'s. *La Provence* to *Celtic:* "Nobody has heard the *Titanic* for about two hours."

It was 2:40 when the *Carpathia* first sighted the green light from No. 2 boat; it was 4:10 when she picked up the first boat and learned that the *Titanic* had foundered. The last of the moaning cries had just died away then.

Captain Rostron took the survivors aboard, boatload by boatload. He was ready for them, but only a small minority of them required much medical attention. Bride's feet were twisted and frozen; others were suffering from exposure; one died, and seven were dead when taken from the boats, and were buried at sea.

It was then that the fleet of racing ships learned they were too late; the *Parisian* heard the weak signals of MPA, the *Carpathia*, report the death of the *Titanic*. It was then—or soon afterward, when her radio operator put on his earphones—that the *Californian*, the ship that had been within sight as the *Titanic* was sinking, first learned of the disaster.

And it was then, in all its white-green majesty, that the *Titanic*'s survivors saw the iceberg, tinted with the sunrise, floating idly, pack ice jammed about its base, other bergs heaving slowly near by on the blue breast of the sea.*

This selection, like our previous selections, does not pretend to be fiction, but it has one important aspect of fiction which is lacking in the first two selections. It has "point," or "idea," or "meaning." We may, perhaps, arrive at an understanding of this "point" or "meaning" by asking ourselves why the sinking of the *Titanic* is memorable, while the loss, since that time, of many other fine ships with thousands of lives has been forgotten. The sinking of the *Lusitania* has much more importance historically, but the sinking of the *Titanic* has, somehow, appealed much more to the general imagination. It is not merely the size of the ship or the number of lives lost or the acts of heroism or the acts of cowardice which account for this appeal to the

* From *Harper's Magazine;* copyright 1934 by Hanson W. Baldwin.

imagination, for large ships have been sunk since that time and acts just as heroic and just as cowardly have been performed. If one agrees that the incident is memorable, one must find some other way to account for the fact.

Mr. Baldwin, in his account of the disaster, does not, to be sure, give any explicit statement of the meaning, but he does emphasize certain aspects of the event, aspects which do imply a meaning. If we consider what these aspects are, we may have our definition of the meaning.

We notice in the first sentence that the *Titanic* was the "largest ship the world had ever known." Another thing, it was her maiden voyage, and her paint was "fair and bright." Most of all, "she was believed to be the safest." Baldwin goes on to point out how the designers planned to make her "unsinkable," a "luxurious floating hotel." It is true, there was a slight accident at her start, but this was taken to be an ill omen only by common seamen, known by nature to be superstitious. The event was without meaning for the great and famous people who had chosen to be passengers on this maiden voyage and who trusted in the skill of designers and officers.

With this introduction, Baldwin skips over to the day of the disaster, which dawned "fair and clear." Messages began to come in from other ships that ice had been sighted, but one of the messages was not even taken down, and the others did not cause the ship to slacken speed. In the evening, the second-class passengers gathered for a "hymn sing-song." While coffee and sandwiches were being passed, they sang:

> *O, hear us when we cry to Thee*
> *For those in peril on the sea.*

At eleven-thirty that night the ship was still rushing ahead, without diminished speed, when the *Californian* reported that it had hove to, surrounded by ice. But the operator on the *Titanic* asked the *Californian* to "shut up . . . you are jamming my signals." This was less than ten minutes before the great ship crashed into the iceberg.

We can find running through all of these details a basic contrast between what people expected to happen and what actually happened; between the assumption by the passengers that the designers and the ship's officers had conquered the perils of nature, and the actual disaster to the ship; between the scene in which the passengers, almost in a festive mood (as the word "sing-song" indicates), sing a hymn praying for the safety of others at sea, and the scene, a few minutes later, in which they will sing in bitter earnest,

Hold me up in mighty waters,
Keep my eyes on things above.

These contrasts are *ironical* (see Glossary). That is, they involve, as any instance of *irony* involves, a disparity. In this case, the irony is simply inherent in a situation: the passengers assume one meaning in the situation while its true meaning is quite different. Men feel that the maiden voyage of the great ship marks the conquest by man of the perils of the sea; in fact, they take it to be another milestone toward man's total conquest of nature. In other words, we have here the irony of pride going before destruction.

We can see that on this basis Baldwin has chosen the details which he emphasizes. He never states this general "point," but his selection of events, great and trivial, leads us inevitably to this conclusion. For instance, he quotes from the hymns the lines which bear most positively on the actual situation; he might have referred to other hymns sung on the same occasion. This is not to say that Baldwin puts this general meaning into the situation; he merely sharpens meanings which were actually inherent in the situation. That they were inherent in the situation probably accounts for the fact that the sinking of the *Titanic* has held such a grip on man's imagination for a number of years.

In the description of the actual collision and the reaction of the passengers in the hours which follow, Baldwin develops further the irony of the situation. For instance, in the smoking room the gamblers see the great shape glide by the windows, but they do not even go on deck. When the first boats are lowered the men encourage the women by saying, "We'll see you again at breakfast." But the lifeboats are not filled to capacity and there is great confusion because boat drill had not been thought necessary on such a ship. The *Californian* radio operator, who had been told to "shut up," has "shut up," and consequently that ship, which is almost within sight of the *Titanic,* cannot be reached to come to the rescue. In this connection, we might even examine the author's intention in the last paragraph:

> And it was then, in all its white-green majesty, that the *Titanic*'s survivors saw the iceberg, tinted with the sunrise, floating idly, pack ice jammed about its base, other bergs heaving slowly near by on the blue breast of the sea.

The instrument of terror is observed here in its majestic placidity, and appears not horrible, but delicately tinted and beautiful. Nature, in other words, is both terrible and beautiful, and it acts with a bland unawareness of humanity.

Thus far we have been dealing with the general irony underlying the situation. But there are many types of response among the passengers. Some behave with shameful cowardice, some with hysterical irrationality, some with fortitude, some with heroism. Some of the passengers speak their feelings with direct earnestness. Others cover their feelings, or even their courageous actions, with jokes and banter.

In the behavior of the passengers, there emerges another level of irony, different from the general underlying irony of "pride before the fall." If the general situation reflects on the folly of man's overweening pride in his confidence that he has, actually, conquered nature, there remains, after all, a sense in which man can rise superior to nature. Those men who meet the circumstance heroically do, actually, conquer nature: though dying, they keep their dignity as men and do not behave like trapped animals. This irony hinges on two contrasts: First, the men, though dying, are victorious. Second, these men, who had been confident of conquering nature by the machine, finally conquer it by means of something within themselves.

One may sum up the meaning of this account by saying that here we are dealing with a kind of *metaphor* (see Glossary). As we have said before, the thing which makes the story of the *Titanic* interesting and ultimately meaningful is not the tonnage of the ship, nor the particular individuals who perished heroically or shamefully, nor any of the other "facts" as such connected with the disaster. What makes the story meaningful is what the event represents in our minds: it is a metaphor for certain elements which are constantly inherent in our experience. In one form or another, man is constantly engaged in the attempt to conquer nature, and sooner or later he must confront a situation in which the only victory possible is a victory over himself. In its baldest terms, the matter may be stated thus: every man must die, but there are many ways in which man can confront this fact.

Every *tragedy* (see Glossary) is concerned with this question, and the sinking of the *Titanic* as given here involves some of the elements of the tragic experience. This is no place to undertake a definition of tragedy, but surely this much is true: the tragic hero is always defeated— his sin, by the way, is usually an overweening pride—but he always manages to wrest something from the defeat and from death.

The account of the sinking of the *Titanic,* then, has in it certain elements of the tragic experience, but it is not a tragedy in the formal sense. In fact, it is not even a piece of fiction. The reason why Baldwin's account is not to be so regarded we shall consider in a moment, but first it is only fair to indicate that it exhibits one important aspect of fiction which is lacking in either of the other two examples which we have considered. It is built to convey a definite "point," a definite idea or meaning, which, though it is never expressed explicitly—and fiction itself rarely expresses its idea explicitly—nevertheless is felt by almost any reader.

In this connection, we might profitably glance again at the first two examples. It is true that a fiction writer, in using the story of Jim Beckworth, could give the episode a "point." Parkman himself indicates something of this when he says: in Beckworth's case "the standard rules of character fail, for though he will stab a man in his sleep, he will also perform the most desperate acts of daring." Parkman's intention in using the episode is simply to show that the characters of the plainsmen do not fit the "standard rules of character" which are accepted in more civilized societies. He is merely using the episode as a sociological example. But if a fiction writer should undertake to employ the episode, he might, by developing the character of Beckworth (which is exactly what Parkman does not do) arrive at some such point as this: individuals cannot be judged by rule of thumb; every individual character is unique and has mixtures of good and evil within it. Of course, it is not to be thought that this would be the only possible point in this episode for a fiction writer, but it is the one hinted at but not developed by Parkman.

In the portrait of Hastings, the author does indicate a point, but again it is a sociological and not a fictional point. He simply says that Hastings is an example of the life of a former time. But just as a fiction writer would find many potential stories suggested by the character of Hastings, so he would find many potential points appropriate to fiction.

To return to our question concerning the account of the loss of the *Titanic:* why is it not fiction? The primary objection, although there may be other objections, is fairly obvious. It lacks a character or characters.* We have only fleeting glimpses of the individuals. Moreover, it cannot be argued that the ship itself will serve as a character; it stands merely as a *symbol* (see Glossary) for certain human attitudes—

---

* This matter is raised because it might be objected that there are stories in which animals are characters. But the animal only serves this function in so far as the animal is given traits which are recognizably human.

pride, confidence, and the like. Even if the account were extended to give fairly full portraits of some of the individuals, of some of the passengers and officers, this added characterization would not, in itself, remove the objection. The characterizations would have to be *functional* (see Glossary), would have to have some bearing on the total situation, would have to be tied into the total account in terms of both action and meaning. For example, a fiction writer might develop the character of the captain to show why, under the special circumstances, he neglected ordinary precautions; or develop the character of the wireless operator to show why he ordered the operator on the *Californian* off the air; or develop the character of some passenger or seaman to show why he behaved courageously or shamefully. Such a process would do much to convert the account into fiction, but it would raise the whole problem of *unity* (see Glossary). That is, the following questions would arise for the fiction writer: Whose story is this? Is there a central character? As a rule, in most pieces of fiction, there is a central character, but there are instances in which this is not true. In such cases, however, the fiction writer is not freed from the obligation to maintain a unity, that is, to build his story so that the characters in action are related to each other and to a dominating idea or theme.*

The reader will observe that in none of the three instances we have examined has the matter of the historical truth or falsity been taken as the basis for distinguishing fiction from nonfiction. At first glance this may seem strange, for ordinarily people think of "fiction" as being opposed to "fact." Instead, we have considered the decisive matter to be the *structure* (see Glossary) of the particular example under consideration; that is, the way in which the elements (character, events, meanings) are related to each other. To make the structure the important matter, not the question of historical truth or untruth, is not mere perversity. Certainly, fiction may make use of facts. Most fiction writers get their suggestions for stories from real life. But real life, either present or past, never fully gives the fiction writer the kind of facts in which he, and the reader, are most interested. For those facts concern psychological processes and human motives. It is easy enough, for instance, to check the tonnage of the *Titanic,* or get the names of the passenger list, but it is very hard to know what passed in the captain's

---

* In such cases, although there is no single dominating character, all characters must be related to the governing idea. It is conceivable that a fiction writer might make such a story out of the *Titanic* disaster, but this type of story is always more difficult to handle successfully than the type in which the action is strongly centralized.

mind in the moment when he stepped forward from the slanting bridge to meet the rising waters. Indeed, the historian and the biographer are up against the same sort of problem when they attempt to interpret a historical character. The biographer finds certain recorded facts about his subject and certain recorded opinions expressed by his subject or expressed by other people concerning his subject; but the biographer must, on the basis of this recorded evidence, try, by an act of his own imagination, to tell us what his subject was like as a man. The proof of this may be found in the fact that no two biographers present us with exactly the same interpretation of any historical personage. Of course, the interpretation presented by a biographer should never violate the facts, but the same facts can sometimes bear different interpretations; what the biographer is trying to do is to see the logic behind the facts. Certainly, the logic by which a biographer must interpret his subject involves consistency of character, a logic of motivation, and the cause-and-effect relationship of one action to another.

To turn once more to the fiction writer, it is perfectly true that he may make use of facts. Indeed, many pieces of fiction find their germ in some actual happening which stirred the writer's imagination, and a writer may even stay very close to the facts. If the biographer, as we have said, is interested, not in the mere assemblage of facts, but in the interpretation of facts, the fiction writer, who is not bound by facts as such, has an even more obvious concern with the matter of interpretation. We can summarize in this way: the biographer or historian is concerned to discover the pattern implied by the facts; the fiction writer may choose or create "facts" in accordance with the pattern of human conduct which he wishes to present. In saying this, we do not mean to imply that the writer of fiction is bound by no laws whatsoever. Obviously, he must convince the reader that his story does not violate the known probabilities of human action.*

This distinction between the problem which the biographer must face and that which the fiction writer must face is sharply illustrated by Baldwin's account of the sinking of the *Titanic*. In the actual circumstances of the event the ironical coincidences are so numerous and so obvious that a fiction writer might well have feared to make such full use of them as Baldwin does. For a fiction writer to make so full

---

* The whole matter of probability in fiction is a difficult one. Each piece has to be judged on its own merits and in the light of the author's intentions. Some special cases will be discussed later in this book. It is enough to say here that probability is not to be determined by considering any mere average of conduct or event.

a use might seem to strain the reader's sense of probability. If this account were pure fiction, the reader would have to be convinced simply in terms of probability, but Baldwin is merely presenting certain facts which are matters of history. We have in Baldwin's account, then, an example of the old saying that truth is stranger than fiction. A fiction writer would probably feel constrained to "play down" the ironical coincidences and suggest his ironical theme more subtly. To approach this matter in another way: one often thinks of "fiction" as being opposed to "fact." But in one real sense, this is a false opposition. It is simply a matter of what kind of facts fiction can use and of the way in which it can use them.

For this reason, one should not conceive of fiction as being a "make-believe." It is make-believe only in so far as it does not claim that the *particular* persons or events of which it treats are historically real. Instead of being primarily concerned with make-believe, fiction is primarily concerned with "truth." In discussing the stories which appear in this book we shall frequently deal with the kind of "truth" which is involved in fiction. But for the present it can be said that the truth of fiction involves such matters as the following: (1) the consistency and comprehensibility of character; (2) the motivation and credibility of action; and (3) the acceptability of the total meaning. As for the method of fiction, it should also be evident, even at this point, that these three matters, character, action, and theme, are intimately bound up together. For instance, many stories never state their themes at all; in such cases the theme is simply presented in terms of the characters and the action. In the same way, character is usually defined by action, and action is to be understood in terms of its effect on character or as a result of character.

We have said that these three matters are intimately bound up together; in fact, they may be said to be simply aspects of one thing— the particular work of fiction. How these matters are related to each other in a given work of fiction will be studied in the course of this book. For reasons of convenience, we shall group our stories according to an emphasis on problems of "plot," "character," or "theme." But it is to be understood that this grouping is based merely on a matter of emphasis in individual stories, and that the study of one aspect, say character, will always, in the end, involve the study of other aspects.

Since these aspects are involved in any story, the student will do well, in reading any story, to ask himself such questions as the following:

1. What are the characters like?
2. Are they "real"?
3. What do they want? (motivation)
4. Why do they do what they do? (motivation)
5. Do their actions logically follow from their natures? (consistency of character)
6. What do their actions tell about their characters?
7. How are the individual pieces of action—the special incidents—related to each other? (plot organization)
8. How are the characters related to each other? (subordination and emphasis among characters; conflict among characters)
9. What is the theme?
10. How are the characters and incidents related to the theme?

The Man Who Would Be King
RUDYARD KIPLING

"Brother to a Prince and fellow to a beggar if he be found worthy."

THE LAW, as quoted, lays down a fair conduct of life, and one not easy to follow. I have been fellow to a beggar again and again under circumstances which prevented either of us finding out whether the other was worthy. I have still to be brother to a Prince, though I once came near to kinship with what might have been a veritable King and was promised the reversion of a Kingdom—army, law courts, revenue and policy all complete. But, today, I greatly fear that my King is dead, and if I want a crown I must go and hunt it for myself.

The beginning of everything was in a railway train upon the road to Mhow from Ajmir. There had been a Deficit in the Budget, which necessitated traveling, not Second-class, which is only half as dear as First-class, but by Intermediate, which is very awful indeed. There are no cushions in the Intermediate class, and the population are either Intermediate, which is Eurasian, or native, which for a long night journey is nasty, or Loafer, which is amusing though intoxicated. Intermediates do not patronize refreshment rooms. They carry their food in bundles and pots, and buy sweets from the native sweatmeat-sellers, and drink the roadside water. That is why in the hot weather Intermediates are taken out of the carriages dead, and in all weathers are most properly looked down upon.

My particular Intermediate happened to be empty till I reached Nasirabad, when a huge gentleman in shirt sleeves entered, and, following the custom of Intermediates, passed the time of day. He was a wanderer and a vagabond like myself, but with an educated taste for whisky. He told tales of things he had seen and done, of out-of-the-way corners of the Empire into which he had penetrated, and of adventures in which he risked his life for a few days' food. "If India was filled with men like you and me, not knowing more than the crows where they'd get their next day's rations, it isn't seventy millions of revenue the land would be paying—it's seven hundred millions," said he; and as I looked at his mouth and chin I was disposed to agree with him. We talked politics—the politics of Loaferdom that sees things from the underside where the lath and plaster is not smoothed off—and we talked postal arrangements because my friend wanted to send a telegram back from the next station to Ajmir, which is the turning-off place from the Bombay to the Mhow line as you travel westward. My friend had no money beyond eight annas which he wanted for dinner, and I had no money at all, owing to the hitch in the Budget before-mentioned. Further, I was going into a wilderness where, though I should resume touch with the Treasury, there were no telegraph offices. I was, therefore, unable to help him in any way.

"We might threaten a Stationmaster, and make him send a wire on tick," said my friend, "but that'd mean inquiries for you and for me, and I've got my hands full these days. Did you say you are traveling back along this line within any days?"

"Within ten," I said.

"Can't you make it eight?" said he. "Mine is rather urgent business."

"I can send your telegram within ten days if that will serve you," I said.

"I couldn't trust the wire to fetch him now I think of it. It's this way. He leaves Delhi on the twenty-third for Bombay. That means he'll be running through Ajmir about the night of the twenty-third."

"But I'm going into the Indian Desert," I explained.

"Well *and* good," said he. "You'll be changing at Marwar Junction to get into Jodhpore territory—you must do that—and he'll be coming through Marwar Junction in the early morning of the twenty-fourth by the Bombay Mail. Can you be at Marwar Junction on that time? 'Twon't be inconveniencing you because I know that there's precious few pickings to be got out of these Central India States—even though you pretend to be correspondent of the *Backwoodsman.*"

"Have you ever tried that trick?" I asked.

"Again and again, but the Residents find you out, and then you get escorted to the Border before you've time to get your knife into them. But about my friend here. I *must* give him a word o' mouth to tell him what's come to me or else he won't know where to go. I would take it more than kind of you if you was to come out of Central India in time to catch him at Marwar Junction, and say to him, 'He has gone South for the week.' He'll know what that means. He's a big man with a red beard, and a great swell he is. You'll find him sleeping like a gentleman with all his luggage round him in a Second-class compartment. But don't you be afraid. Slip down the window, and say, 'He has gone South for the week,' and he'll tumble. It's only cutting your time of stay in those parts by two days. I ask you as a stranger—going to the West," he said, with emphasis.

"Where have *you* come from?" said I.

"From the East," said he, "and I am hoping that you will give him the message on the Square—for the sake of my Mother as well as your own."

Englishmen are not usually softened by appeals to the memory of their mothers, but for certain reasons, which will be fully apparent, I saw fit to agree.

"It's more than a little matter," said he, "and that's why I ask you to do it—and now I know that I can depend on you doing it. A Second-class carriage at Marwar Junction, and a red-haired man asleep in it. You'll be sure to remember. I get out at the next station, and I must hold on there till he comes or sends me what I want."

"I'll give the message if I catch him," I said, "and for the sake of your Mother as well as mine I'll give you a word of advice. Don't try to run the Central India States just now as the correspondent of the

Backwoodsman. There's a real one knocking about here, and it might lead to trouble."

"Thank you," said he, simply, "and when will the swine be gone? I can't starve because he's ruining my work. I wanted to get hold of the Degumber Rajah down here about his father's widow, and give him a jump."

"What did he do to his father's widow, then?"

"Filled her up with red pepper and slippered her to death as she hung from a beam. I found that out myself, and I'm the only man that would dare going into the State to get hush money for it. They'll try to poison me, same as they did in Chortumna when I went on the loot there. But you'll give the man at Marwar Junction my message?"

He got out at a little roadside station, and I reflected. I had heard, more than once, of men personating correspondents of newspapers and bleeding small Native States with threats of exposure, but I had never met any of the caste before. They lead a hard life, and generally die with great suddenness. The Native States have a wholesome horror of English newspapers, which may throw light on their peculiar methods of government, and do their best to choke correspondents with champagne, or drive them out of their mind with four-in-hand barouches. They do not understand that nobody cares a straw for the internal administration of Native States so long as oppression and crime are kept within decent limits, and the ruler is not drugged, drunk, or diseased from one end of the year to the other. Native States were created by Providence in order to supply picturesque scenery, tigers, and tall writing. They are the dark places of the earth, full of unimaginable cruelty, touching the Railway and the Telegraph on one side, and, on the other, the days of Harun-al-Raschid. When I left the train I did business with divers Kings, and in eight days passed through many changes of life. Sometimes I wore dress clothes and consorted with Princes and Politicals, drinking from crystal and eating from silver. Sometimes I lay out upon the ground and devoured what I could get, from a plate made of a flapjack, and drank the running water, and slept under the same rug as my servant. It was all in the day's work.

Then I headed for the Great Indian Desert upon the proper date, as I had promised, and the night Mail set me down at Marwar Junction, where a funny little, happy-go-lucky, native-managed railway runs to Jodhpore. The Bombay Mail from Delhi makes a short halt at Marwar. She arrived as I got in, and I had just time to hurry to her platform and go down the carriages. There was only one Second-class on the train. I slipped the window, and looked down upon a flaming red beard, half covered by a railway rug. That was my man, fast asleep, and I dug him gently in the ribs. He woke with a grunt, and I saw his face in the light of the lamps. It was a great and shining face.

"Tickets again?" said he.

"No," said I. "I am to tell you that he is gone South for the week. He is gone South for the week!"

The train had begun to move out. The red man rubbed his eyes. "He has gone South for the week," he repeated. "Now that's just like his impidence. Did he say that I was to give you anything?—'Cause I won't."

"He didn't," I said, and dropped away, and watched the red lights die out in the dark. It was horribly cold, because the wind was blowing off the sands. I climbed into my own train—not an Intermediate Carriage this time—and went to sleep.

If the man with the beard had given me a rupee I should have kept it as a memento of a rather curious affair. But the consciousness of having done my duty was my only reward.

Later on I reflected that two gentlemen like my friends could not do any good if they foregathered and personated correspondents of newspapers, and might, if they "stuck up" one of the little rat-trap states of Central India or Southern Rajputana, get themselves into serious difficulties. I therefore took some trouble to describe them as accurately as I could remember to people who would be interested in deporting them; and succeeded, so I was later informed, in having them headed back from Degumber borders.

Then I became respectable, and returned to an Office where there were no Kings and no incidents except the daily manufacture of a newspaper. A newspaper office seems to attract every conceivable sort of person, to the prejudice of discipline. Zenana-mission ladies arrive,

and beg that the Editor will instantly abandon all his duties to describe
a Christian prize-giving in a back-slum of a perfectly inaccessible village; Colonels who have been overpassed for commands sit down and
sketch the outline of a series of ten, twelve, or twenty-four leading
articles on Seniority *versus* Selection; missionaries wish to know why
they have not been permitted to escape from their regular vehicles of
abuse and swear at a brother missionary under special patronage of
the editorial We; stranded theatrical companies troop up to explain
that they cannot pay for their advertisements, but on their return from
New Zealand or Tahiti will do so with interest; inventors of patent
punkah-pulling machines, carriage couplings, and unbreakable swords
and axletrees call with specifications in their pockets and hours at their
disposal; tea companies enter and elaborate their prospectuses with the
office pens; secretaries of ball committees clamor to have the glories of
their last dance more fully expounded; strange ladies rustle in and
say, "I want a hundred lady's cards printed *at once,* please," which is
manifestly part of an Editor's duty; and every dissolute ruffian that
ever tramped the Grand Trunk Road makes it his business to ask for
employment as a proofreader. And, all the time, the telephone bell is
ringing madly, and Kings are being killed on the Continent, and
Empires are saying—"You're another," and Mister Gladstone is calling down brimstone upon the British Dominions, and the little black
copy boys are whining, "*ḳaa-pi chay-ha-yeh*" (copy wanted) like tired
bees, and most of the paper is as blank as Modred's shield.

But that is the amusing part of the year. There are other six months
wherein none ever come to call, and the thermometer walks inch by
inch up to the top of the glass, and the office is darkened to just above
reading light, and the press machines are red-hot of touch, and nobody
writes anything but accounts of amusements in the Hill stations or
obituary notices. Then the telephone becomes a tinkling terror, because it tells you of the sudden deaths of men and women that you
knew intimately, and the prickly heat covers you as with a garment,
and you sit down and write: "A slight increase of sickness is reported
from the Khuda Janta Khan District. The outbreak is purely sporadic
in its nature, and, thanks to the energetic efforts of the District authorities, is now almost at an end. It is, however, with deep regret we
record the death, etc."

Then the sickness really breaks out, and the less recording and reporting the better for the peace of the subscribers. But the Empires and the Kings continue to divert themselves as selfishly as before, and the Foreman thinks that a daily paper really ought to come out once in twenty-four hours, and all the people at the Hill stations in the middle of their amusements say, "Good gracious! Why can't the paper be sparkling? I'm sure there's plenty going on up here."

That is the dark half of the moon, and, as the advertisements say, "must be experienced to be appreciated."

It was in that season, and a remarkably evil season, that the paper began running the last issue of the week on Saturday night, which is to say, Sunday morning, after the custom of a London paper. This was a great convenience, for immediately after the paper was put to bed, the dawn would lower the thermometer from 96° to almost 84° for half an hour, and in that chill—you have no idea how cold is 84° on the grass until you begin to pray for it—a very tired man could set off to sleep ere the heat roused him.

One Saturday night it was my pleasant duty to put the paper to bed alone. A King or courtier or a courtesan or a community was going to die or get a new Constitution, or do something that was important on the other side of the world, and the paper was to be held open till the latest possible minute in order to catch the telegram. It was a pitchy black night, as stifling as a June night can be, and the *loo,* the red-hot wind from the westward, was booming among the tinder-dry trees and pretending that the rain was on its heels. Now and again a spot of almost boiling water would fall on the dust with the flop of a frog, but all our weary world knew that was only pretense. It was a shade cooler in the press room than the office, so I sat there, while the type clicked and clicked and the nightjars hooted at the windows, and the all but naked compositors wiped the sweat from their foreheads and called for water. The thing that was keeping us back, whatever it was, would not come off, though the *loo* dropped and the last type was set, and the whole round earth stood still in the choking heat, with its finger on its lip, to wait the event. I drowsed, and wondered whether the telegraph was a blessing, and whether this dying man, or struggling people, was aware of the inconvenience the delay was causing. There was no special reason beyond the heat and worry to make tension, but, as the clock hands crept up to three o'clock and the machines spun their flywheels two or three times to see that all was in order, before I said the word that would set them off, I could have shrieked aloud.

Then the roar and rattle of the wheels shivered the quiet into little bits. I rose to go away, but two men in white clothes stood in front of me. The first one said, "It's him!" The second said, "So it is!" And they both laughed almost as loudly as the machinery roared, and mopped their foreheads. "We see there was a light burning across the road and we were sleeping in that ditch there for coolness, and I said to my friend here, 'The office is open. Let's come along and speak to him as turned us back from the Degumber State,'" said the smaller of the two. He was the man I had met in the Mhow train, and his fellow was the red-bearded man of Marwar Junction. There was no mistaking the eyebrows of the one or the beard of the other.

I was not pleased, because I wished to go to sleep, not to squabble with loafers. "What do you want?" I asked.

"Half an hour's talk with you cool and comfortable, in the office," said the red-bearded man. "We'd *like* some drink—the Contrack doesn't begin yet, Peachey, so you needn't look—but what we really want is advice. We don't want money. We ask you as a favor, because you did us a bad turn about Degumber."

I led from the press room to the stifling office with the maps on the walls, and the red-haired man rubbed his hands. "That's something like," said he. "This was the proper shop to come to. Now, Sir, let me introduce to you Brother Peachey Carnehan, that's him, and Brother Daniel Dravot, that is *me,* and the less said about our professions the better, for we have been most things in our time. Soldier, sailor, compositor, photographer, proofreader, street preacher, and correspondents of the *Backwoodsman* when we thought the paper wanted one. Carnehan is sober, and so am I. Look at us first and see that's sure. It will save you cutting into my talk. We'll take one of your cigars apiece, and you shall see us light."

I watched the test. The men were absolutely sober, so I gave them each a tepid peg.

"Well *and* good," said Carnehan of the eyebrows, wiping the froth from his mustache. "Let me talk now, Dan. We have been all over

India, mostly on foot. We have been boiler-fitters, engine-drivers, petty contractors, and all that, and we have decided that India isn't big enough for such as us."

They certainly were too big for the office. Dravot's beard seemed to fill half the room and Carnehan's shoulders the other half, as they sat on the big table. Carnehan continued: "The country isn't half worked out because they that governs it won't let you touch it. They spend all their blessed time in governing it, and you can't lift a spade, nor chip a rock, nor look for oil, nor anything like that without all the Government saying, 'Leave it alone and let us govern.' Therefore, such as it is, we will let it alone, and go away to some other place where a man isn't crowded and can come to his own. We are not little men, and there is nothing that we are afraid of except Drink, and we have signed a Contrack on that. *Therefore,* we are going away to be Kings."

"Kings in our own right," muttered Dravot.

"Yes, of course," I said. "You've been tramping in the sun, and it's a very warm night, and hadn't you better sleep over the notion? Come tomorrow."

"Neither drunk nor sunstruck," said Dravot. "We have slept over the notion half a year, and require to see Books and Atlases, and we have decided that there is only one place now in the world that two strong men can Sar-a-*whack*. They call it Kafiristan. By my reckoning it's the top right-hand corner of Afghanistan, not more than three hundred miles from Peshawur. They have two and thirty heathen idols there, and we'll be the thirty-third. It's a mountainous country, and the women of those parts are very beautiful."

"But that is provided against in the Contrack," said Carnehan. "Neither Women nor Liqu-or, Daniel."

"And that's all we know, except that no one has gone there, and they fight, and in any place where they fight, a man who knows how to drill men can always be a King. We shall go to those parts and say to any King we find, 'D'you want to vanquish your foes?' and we will show him how to drill men; for that we know better than anything else. Then we will subvert that King and seize his Throne and establish a Dy-nasty."

"You'll be cut to pieces before you're fifty miles across the Border," I said. "You have to travel through Afghanistan to get to that country. It's one mass of mountains and peaks and glaciers, and no Englishman has been through it. The people are utter brutes, and even if you reached them you couldn't do anything."

"That's more like," said Carnehan. "If you could think us a little more mad we would be more pleased. We have come to you to know about this country, to read a book about it, and to be shown maps. We want you to tell us that we are fools and to show us your books." He turned to the bookcases.

"Are you at all in earnest?" I said.

"A little," said Dravot, sweetly. "As big a map as you have got, even if it's all blank where Kafiristan is, and any books you've got. We can read, though we aren't very educated."

I uncased the big thirty-two-miles-to-the-inch map of India, and two smaller Frontier maps, hauled down volume INF-KAN of the *Encyclopaedia Britannica,* and the men consulted them.

"See here!" said Dravot, his thumb on the map. "Up to Jagdallak, Peachey and me know the road. We was there with Roberts's Army. We'll have to turn off to the right at Jagdallak through Laghmann territory. Then we get among the hills—fourteen thousand feet—fifteen thousand—it will be cold work there, but it don't look very far on the map."

I handed him Wood on the *Sources of the Oxus.* Carnehan was deep in the *Encyclopaedia.*

"They're a mixed lot," said Dravot, reflectively; "and it won't help us to know the names of their tribes. The more tribes the more they'll fight, and the better for us. From Jagdallak to Ashang. H'mm!"

"But all the information about the country is as sketchy and inaccurate as can be," I protested. "No one knows anything about it really. Here's the file of the *United Services' Institute.* Read what Bellew says."

"Blow Bellew!" said Carnehan. "Dan, they're an all-fired lot of heathens, but this book here says they think they're related to us English."

I smoked while the men pored over *Raverty, Wood,* the maps, and the *Encyclopaedia.*

"There is no use your waiting," said Dravot, politely. "It's about four o'clock now. We'll go before six o'clock if you want to sleep, and we won't steal any of the papers. Don't you sit up. We're two harmless lunatics and if you come, tomorrow evening, down to the Serai we'll say good-by to you."

"You *are* two fools," I answered. "You'll be turned back at the Frontier or cut up the minute you set foot in Afghanistan. Do you want any money or a recommendation down-country? I can help you to the chance of work next week."

"Next week we shall be hard at work ourselves, thank you," said Dravot. "It isn't so easy being a King as it looks. When we've got our Kingdom in going order we'll let you know, and you can come up and help us to govern it."

"Would two lunatics make a Contrack like that?" said Carnehan, with subdued pride, showing me a greasy half sheet of note paper on which was written the following. I copied it, then and there, as a curiosity:

This Contract between me and you persuing witnesseth in the name of God—Amen and so forth.

(ONE) *That me and you will settle this matter together: i. e., to be Kings of Kafiristan.*

(TWO) *That you and me will not, while this matter is being settled, look at any Liquor, nor any Woman, black, white or brown, so as to get mixed up with one or the other harmful.*

(THREE) *That we conduct ourselves with dignity and discretion and if one of us gets into trouble the other will stay by him.*

Signed by you and me this day.

PEACHEY TALIAFERRO CARNEHAN.

DANIEL DRAVOT.

Both Gentlemen at Large.

"There was no need for the last article," said Carnehan, blushing modestly; "but it looks regular. Now you know the sort of men that Loafers are—we *are* Loafers, Dan, until we get out of India—and *do* you think that we would sign a Contrack like that unless we was in earnest? We have kept away from the two things that make life worth having."

"You won't enjoy your lives much longer if you are going to try this idiotic adventure. Don't set the office on fire," I said, "and go away before nine o'clock."

I left them still poring over the maps and making notes on the back of the "Contrack." "Be sure to come down to the Serai tomorrow," were their parting words.

The Kumharsen Serai is the great four-square sink of humanity where the strings of camels and horses from the North load and unload. All the nationalities of Central Asia may be found there, and most of the folk of India proper. Balkh and Bokhara there meet Bengal and Bombay, and try to draw eyeteeth. You can buy ponies, turquoises, Persian pussy cats, saddlebags, fat-tailed sheep, and musk in the Kumharsen Serai, and get many strange things for nothing. In the afternoon I went down there to see whether my friends intended to keep their word or were lying about drunk.

A priest attired in fragments of ribbons and rags stalked up to me, gravely twisting a child's paper whirligig. Behind was his servant bending under the load of a crate of mud toys. The two were loading up two camels, and the inhabitants of the Serai watched them with shrieks of laughter.

"The priest is mad," said a horse-dealer to me. "He is going up to Kabul to sell toys to the Amir. He will either be raised to honor or have his head cut off. He came in here this morning and has been behaving madly ever since."

"The witless are under the protection of God," stammered a flat-cheeked Usbeg in broken Hindi. "They foretell future events."

"Would they could have foretold that my caravan would have been cut up by the Shinwaris almost within shadow of the Pass!" grunted the Eusufzai agent of a Rajputana trading house whose goods had been feloniously diverted into the hands of other robbers just across the Border, and whose misfortunes were the laughingstock of the bazaar. "Ohé, priest, whence come you and whither do you go?"

"From Roum have I come," shouted the priest, waving his whirligig; "from Roum, blown by the breath of a hundred devils across the sea! O thieves, robbers, liars, the blessing of Pir Khan on pigs, dogs, and perjurers! Who will take the Protected of God to the North to sell charms that are never still to the Amir? The camels shall not gall, the sons shall not fall sick, and the wives shall remain faithful while they are away, of the men who give me place in their caravan. Who will assist me to slipper the King of the Roos with a golden slipper with a silver heel? The protection of Pir Khan be upon his labors!" He spread out the skirts of his gaberdine and pirouetted between the lines of tethered horses.

"There starts a caravan from Peshawur to Kabul in twenty days, *Huzrut,*" said the Eusufzai trader. "My camels go therewith. Do thou also go and bring us good luck."

"I will go even now!" shouted the priest. "I will depart upon my winged camels, and be at Peshawur in a day! Ho! Hazar Mir Khan," he yelled to his servant, "drive out the camels, but let me first mount my own."

He leaped on the back of his beast as it knelt, and, turning round to me, cried, "Come thou also, Sahib, a little along the road, and I will sell thee a charm—an amulet that shall make thee King of Kafiristan."

Then the light broke upon me, and I followed the two camels out of the Serai till we reached open road and the priest halted.

"What d'you think o' that?" said he in English. "Carnehan can't talk their patter, so I've made him my servant. He makes a handsome servant. 'Tisn't for nothing that I've been knocking about the country for fourteen years. Didn't I do that talk neat? We'll hitch on to a caravan at Peshawur till we get to Jagdallak, and then we'll see if we can get donkeys for our camels, and strike into Kafiristan. Whirligigs for the Amir, O Lor'! Put your hand under the camel bags and tell me what you feel."

I felt the butt of a Martini, and another and another.

"Twenty of 'em," said Dravot, placidly. "Twenty of 'em, and ammunition to correspond, under the whirligigs and the mud dolls."

"Heaven help you if you are caught with those things!" I said. "A Martini is worth her weight in silver among the Pathans."

"Fifteen hundred rupees of capital—every rupee we could beg, borrow, or steal—are invested on these two camels," said Dravot. "We won't get caught. We're going through the Khyber with a regular caravan. Who'd touch a poor mad priest?"

"Have you got everything you want?" I asked, overcome with astonishment.

"Not yet, but we shall soon. Give us a memento of your kindness, *Brother*. You did me a service yesterday, and that time in Marwar. Half my Kingdom shall you have, as the saying is." I slipped a small charm compass from my watch chain and handed it up to the priest.

"Good-by," said Dravot, giving me hand cautiously. "It's the last time we'll shake hands with an Englishman these many days. Shake hands with him, Carnehan," he cried, as the second camel passed me.

Carnehan leaned down and shook hands. Then the camels passed away along the dusty road, and I was left alone to wonder. My eye could detect no failure in the disguises. The scene in Serai attested that they were complete to the native mind. There was just the chance, therefore, that Carnehan and Dravot would be able to wander through Afghanistan without detection. But, beyond, they would find death, certain and awful death.

Ten days later a native friend of mine, giving me the news of the day from Peshawur, wound up his letter with:—"There has been much laughter here on account of a certain mad priest who is going in his estimation to sell petty gauds and insignificant trinkets which he ascribes as great charms to H. H. the Amir of Bokhara. He passed through Peshawur and associated himself to the Second Summer caravan that goes to Kabul. The merchants are pleased, because through superstition they imagine that such mad fellows bring good fortune."

The two, then, were beyond the Border. I would have prayed for them, but, that night, a real King died in Europe, and demanded an obituary notice.

*   *   *   *

The wheel of the world swings through the same phases again and again. Summer passed and winter thereafter, and came and passed again. The daily paper continued and I with it, and upon the third summer there fell a hot night, a night issue, and a strained waiting for something to be telegraphed from the other side of the world, exactly as had happened before. A few great men had died in the past two years, the machines worked with more clatter, and some of the trees in the Office garden were a few feet taller. But that was all the difference.

I passed over to the press room, and went through just such a scene as I have already described. The nervous tension was stronger than it had been two years before, and I felt the heat more acutely. At three o'clock I cried, "Print off," and turned to go, when there crept to my chair what was left of a man. He was bent into a circle, his head was sunk between his shoulders, and he moved his feet one over the other like a bear. I could hardly see whether he walked or crawled— this rag-wrapped, whining cripple who addressed me by name, crying that he was come back. "Can you give me a drink?" he whimpered. "For the Lord's sake, give me a drink!"

I went back to the office, the man following with groans of pain, and I turned up the lamp.

"Don't you know me?" he gasped, dropping into a chair, and he turned his drawn face, surmounted by a shock of gray hair, to the light.

I looked at him intently. Once before had I seen eyebrows that met over the nose in an inch-broad black band, but for the life of me I could not tell where.

"I don't know you," I said, handing him the whisky. "What can I do for you?"

He took a gulp of the spirit raw, and shivered in spite of the suffo- cating heat.

"I've come back," he repeated; "and I was the King of Kafiristan— me and Dravot—crowned Kings we was! In this office we settled it— you setting there and giving us the books. I am Peachey—Peachey Taliaferro Carnehan, and you've been setting here ever since—O Lord!"

I was more than a little astonished, and expressed my feelings ac- cordingly.

"It's true," said Carnehan, with a dry cackle, nursing his feet, which were wrapped in rags. "True as gospel. Kings we were, with crowns upon our heads—me and Dravot—poor Dan—oh, poor, poor Dan, that would never take advice, not though I begged of him!"

"Take the whisky," I said, "and take your own time. Tell me all you can recollect of everything from beginning to end. You got across the border on your camels, Dravot dressed as a mad priest and you his servant. Do you remember that?"

"I ain't mad—yet, but I shall be that way soon. Of course I remember. Keep looking at me, or maybe my words will go all to pieces. Keep looking at me in my eyes and don't say anything."

I leaned forward and looked into his face as steadily as I could. He dropped one hand upon the table and I grasped it by the wrist. It was twisted like a bird's claw, and upon the back was a ragged, red, diamond-shaped scar.

"No, don't look there. Look at *me*," said Carnehan.

"That comes afterward, but for the Lord's sake don't distrack me. We left with that caravan, me and Dravot playing all sorts of antics to amuse the people we were with. Dravot used to make us laugh in the evenings when all the people was cooking their dinners—cooking their dinners, and . . . what did they do then? They lit little fires with sparks that went into Dravot's beard, and we all laughed—fit to die. Little red fires they was, going into Dravot's big red beard—so funny." His eyes left mine and he smiled foolishly.

"You went as far as Jagdallak with that caravan," I said, at a venture, "after you had lit those fires. To Jagdallak, where you turned off to try to get into Kafiristan."

"No, we didn't neither. What are you talking about? We turned off before Jagdallak, because we heard the roads was good. But they wasn't good enough for our two camels—mine and Dravot's. When we left the caravan, Dravot took off all his clothes and mine too, and said we would be heathen, because the Kafirs didn't allow Mohammedans to talk to them. So we dressed betwixt and between, and such a sight as Daniel Dravot I never saw yet nor expect to see again. He burned half his beard, and slung a sheepskin over his shoulder, and shaved his head into patterns. He shaved mine, too, and made me wear outrageous things to look like a heathen. That was in a most mountaineous country, and our camels couldn't go along any more because of the mountains. They were tall and black, and coming home I saw them fight like wild goats—there are lots of goats in Kafiristan. And these mountains, they never keep still, no more than goats. Always fighting they are, and don't let you sleep at night."

"Take some more whisky," I said, very slowly. "What did you and Daniel Dravot do when the camels could go no further because of the rough roads that led into Kafiristan?"

"What did which do? There was a party called Peachey Taliaferro

Carnehan that was with Dravot. Shall I tell you about him? He died out there in the cold. Slap from the bridge fell old Peachey, turning and twisting in the air like a penny whirligig that you can sell to the Amir— No; they was two for three ha'pence, those whirligigs, or I am much mistaken and woful sore. And then these camels were no use, and Peachey said to Dravot—'For the Lord's sake, let's get out of this before our heads are chopped off,' and with that they killed the camels all among the mountains, not having anything in particular to eat, but first they took off the boxes with the guns and the ammunition, till two men came along driving four mules. Dravot up and dances in front of them, singing,—'Sell me four mules.' Says the first man,— 'If you are rich enough to buy, you are rich enough to rob'; but before ever he could put his hand to his knife, Dravot breaks his neck over his knee, and the other party runs away. So Carnehan loaded the mules with the rifles that was taken off the camels, and together we starts forward into those bitter cold mountaineous parts, and never a road broader than the back of your hand."

He paused for a moment, while I asked him if he could remember the nature of the country through which he had journeyed.

"I am telling you as straight as I can, but my head isn't as good as it might be. They drove nails through it to make me hear better how Dravot died. The country was mountaineous and the mules were most contrary, and the inhabitants was dispersed and solitary. They went up and up, and down and down, and that other party, Carnehan, was imploring of Dravot not to sing and whistle so loud, for fear of bringing down the tremenjus avalanches. But Dravot says that if a King couldn't sing it wasn't worth being King, and whacked the mules over the rump, and never took no heed for ten cold days. We came to a big level valley all among the mountains, and the mules were near dead, so we killed them, not having anything in special for them or us to eat. We sat upon the boxes, and played odd and even with the cartridges that was jolted out.

"Then ten men with bows and arrows ran down that valley, chasing twenty men with bows and arrows, and the row was tremenjus. They was fair men—fairer than you or me—with yellow hair and remarkable well built. Says Dravot, unpacking the guns—'This is the beginning of the business. We'll fight for the ten men,' and with that he fires two rifles at the twenty men, and drops one of them at two hundred yards from the rock where we was sitting. The other men began to run, but Carnehan and Dravot sits on the boxes picking them off at all ranges, up and down the valley. Then we goes up to the ten men that had run across the snow too, and they fires a footy little arrow at us. Dravot he shoots above their heads and they all falls down flat. Then he walks over and kicks them, and then he lifts them up and shakes hands all around to make them friendly like. He calls them and gives them the boxes to carry, and waves his hand for all the world as though he was King already. They takes the boxes and him across the valley and up the hill into a pine wood on the top, where there was half a dozen big stone idols. Dravot he goes to the biggest—a fellow they call Imbra—and lays a rifle and a cartridge at his feet, rubbing his nose respectful with his own nose, patting him on the head, and saluting in front of it. He turns round to the men and nods his head, and says, 'That's all right. I'm in the know too, and all these old jim-jams are my friends.' Then he opens his mouth and points down it, and when the first man brings him food, he says 'No'; and when the second man brings him food, he says 'No'; but when one of the old priests and the boss of the village brings him food, he says 'Yes'; very haughty, and eats it slow. That was how we came to our first village, without any trouble, just as though we had tumbled from the skies. But we tumbled from one of those damned rope bridges, you see, and you couldn't expect a man to laugh much after that."

"Take some more whisky and go on," I said. "That was the first village you came into. How did you get to be King?"

"I wasn't King," said Carnehan. "Dravot he was the King, and a handsome man he looked with the gold crown on his head and all. Him and the other party stayed in that village, and every morning Dravot sat by the side of old Imbra, and the people came and worshiped. That was Dravot's order. Then a lot of men came into the valley, and Carnehan and Dravot picks them off with the rifles before they knew where they was, and runs down into the valley and up again the other side, and finds another village, same as the first one, and the people all falls down flat on their faces, and Dravot says, 'Now what is the trouble between you two villages?' and the people points to a woman, as fair as you or me, that was carried off, and Dravot takes her back to the first village and counts up the dead—eight there was. For each dead man Dravot pours a little milk on the ground and waves his arms like a whirligig and 'That's all right,' says he. Then he and Carnehan takes the big boss of each village by the arm and walks them down into the valley, and shows them how to scratch a line with a spear right down the valley, and gives each a sod of turf from both sides o' the line. Then all the people comes down and shouts like the devil and all, and Dravot says, 'Go and dig the land, and be fruitful and multiply,' which they did, though they didn't understand. Then we asks the names of things in their lingo—bread and water and fire and idols and such, and Dravot leads the priest of each village up to the idol, and says he must sit there and judge the people, and if anything goes wrong he is to be shot.

"Next week they was all turning up the land in the valley as quiet as bees and much prettier, and the priests heard all the complaints and told Dravot in dumb show what it was about. 'That's just the beginning,' says Dravot. 'They think we're Gods.' He and Carnehan picks out twenty good men and shows them how to click off a rifle, and form fours, and advance in line, and they was very pleased to do so, and clever to see the hang of it. Then he takes out his pipe and his 'baccy pouch and leaves one at one village and one at the other, and off we two goes to see what was to be done in the next valley. That was all rock, and there was a little village there, and Carnehan says, 'Send 'em to the old valley to plant,' and takes 'em there and gives 'em some land that wasn't took before. They were a poor lot, and we blooded 'em with a kid before letting 'em into the new Kingdom. That was to impress the people, and then they settled down quiet, and Carnehan went back to Dravot, who had got into another valley, all snow and ice and most mountaineous. There was no people there, and the Army got afraid, so Dravot shoots one of them, and goes on till he finds some people in a village, and the Army explains that unless the people wants to be killed they had better not shoot their little matchlocks; for they had matchlocks. We makes friends with the priest and I stays there alone with two of the Army, teaching the men how to drill, and a thundering big Chief comes across the snow with kettledrums and horns twanging, because he heard there was a new God kicking about.

Carnehan sights for the brown of the men half a mile across the snow and wings one of them. Then he sends a message to the Chief that, unless he wished to be killed, he must come and shake hands with me and leave his arms behind. The Chief comes alone first, and Carnehan shakes hands with him and whirls his arms about, same as Dravot used, and very much surprised that Chief was, and strokes my eyebrows. Then Carnehan goes alone to the Chief, and asks him in dumb show if he had an enemy he hated. 'I have,' says the Chief. So Carnehan weeds out the pick of his men, and sets the two of the Army to show them drill, and at the end of two weeks the men can maneuver about as well as Volunteers. So he marches with the Chief to a great big plain on the top of a mountain, and the Chief's men rushes into a village and takes it; we three Martinis firing into the brown of the enemy. So we took that village too, and I gives the Chief a rag from my coat and says, 'Occupy till I come'; which was scriptural. By way of a reminder, when me and the Army was eighteen hundred yards away, I drops a bullet near him standing on the snow, and all the people falls flat on their faces. Then I sends a letter to Dravot, wherever he be by land or by sea."

At the risk of throwing the creature out of train I interrupted, "How could you write a letter up yonder?"

"The letter?—Oh!—The letter! Keep looking at me between the eyes, please. It was a string-talk letter, that we'd learned the way of it from a blind beggar in the Punjab."

I remember that there had once come to the office a blind man with a knotted twig and a piece of string which he wound round the twig according to some cipher of his own. He could, after the lapse of days or hours, repeat the sentence which he had reeled up. He had reduced the alphabet to eleven primitive sounds; and tried to teach me his method, but failed.

"I sent that letter to Dravot," said Carnehan; "and told him to come back because this Kingdom was growing too big for me to handle, and then I struck for the first valley, to see how the priests were working. They called the village we took along with the Chief, Bashkai, and the first village we took, Er-Heb. The priests at Er-Heb was doing all right, but they had a lot of pending cases about land to show me, and some men from another village had been firing arrows at night. I went out and looked for that village and fired four rounds at it from a thousand yards. That used all the cartridges I cared to spend, and I waited for Dravot, who had been away two or three months, and I kept my people quiet.

"One morning I heard the devil's own noise of drums and horns, and Dan Dravot marches down the hill with his Army and a tail of hundreds of men, and, which was the most amazing--a great gold crown on his head. 'My Gord, Carnehan,' says Daniel, 'this is a tremenjus business, and we've got the whole country as far as it's worth having. I am the son of Alexander by Queen Semiramis, and you're my younger brother and a God too! It's the biggest thing we've ever seen. I've been marching and fighting for six weeks with the Army, and every footy little village for fifty miles has come in rejoiceful; and more than that, I've got the key of the whole show, as you'll see, and I've got a crown for you! I told 'em to make two of 'em at a place called Shu, where the gold lies in the rock like suet in mutton. Gold I've seen, and turquoise I've kicked out of the cliffs, and there's garnets in the sands of the river, and here's a chunk of amber that a man brought me. Call up all the priests and, here, take your crown.'

"One of the men opens a black hair bag and I slips the crown on. It was too small and too heavy, but I wore it for the glory. Hammered gold it was—five pound weight, like a hoop of a barrel.

" 'Peachey,' says Dravot, 'we don't want to fight no more. The Craft's the trick, so help me!' and he brings forward that same Chief that I left at Bashkai—Billy Fish we called him afterward, because he was so like Billy Fish that drove the big tank engine at Mach on the Bolan in the old days. 'Shake hands with him,' says Dravot, and I shook hands and nearly dropped, for Billy Fish gave me the Grip. I said nothing, but tried him with the Fellow Craft Grip. He answers, all right, and I tried the Master's Grip, but that was a slip. 'A Fellow Craft he is!' I says to Dan. 'Does he know the word?' 'He does,' says Dan, 'and all the priests know. It's a miracle! The Chiefs and the priests can work a Fellow Craft Lodge in a way that's very like ours, and they've cut the marks on the rocks, but they don't know the Third Degree, and they've come to find out. It's Gord's Truth. I've known these long years that the Afghans knew up to the Fellow Craft Degree, but this is a miracle. A God and a Grand Master of the Craft am I, and a Lodge in the Third Degree I will open, and we'll raise the head priests and the Chiefs of the villages.'

"'It's against all the law,' I says, 'holding a Lodge without warrant from anyone; and we never held office in any Lodge.'

"'It's a master stroke of policy,' says Dravot. 'It means running the country as easy as a four-wheeled bogy on a down grade. We can't stop to inquire now, or they'll turn against us. I've forty Chiefs at my heel, and passed and raised according to their merit they shall be. Billet these men on the villages and see that we run up a Lodge of some kind. The temple of Imbra will do for the Lodge room. The women must make aprons as you show them. I'll hold a levee of Chiefs tonight and Lodge tomorrow.'

"I was fair run off my legs, but I wasn't such a fool as not to see what a pull this Craft business gave us. I showed the priests' families how to make aprons of the degrees, but for Dravot's apron the blue border and marks was made of turquoise lumps on white hide, not cloth. We took a great square stone in the temple for the Master's chair, and little stones for the officers' chairs, and painted the black pavement with white squares, and did what we could to make things regular.

"At the levee which was held that night on the hillside with big bonfires, Dravot gives out that him and me were Gods and sons of Alexander, and Past Grand Masters in the Craft, and was come to make Kafiristan a country where every man should eat in peace and drink in quiet, and specially obey us. Then the Chiefs come round to shake hands, and they was so hairy and white and fair it was just shaking hands with old friends. We gave them names according as they was like men we had known in India—Billy Fish, Holly Wilworth, Pikky Kergan that was Bazaar-master when I was at Mhow, and so on and so on.

"*The* most amazing miracle was at Lodge next night. One of the old priests was watching us continuous, and I felt uneasy, for I knew we'd have to fudge the Ritual, and I didn't know what the men knew. The old priest was a stranger come in from beyond the village of Bashkai. The minute Dravot puts on the Master's apron that the girls had made for him, the priest fetches a whoop and a howl, and tried to overturn the stone that Dravot was sitting on. 'It's all up now,' I says. 'That comes of meddling with the Craft without warrant!' Dravot never winked an eye, not when ten priests took and tilted over the Grand Master's chair—which was to say the stone of Imbra. The priest begins rubbing the bottom end of it to clear away the black dirt, and presently he shows all the other priests the Master's Mark, same as was on Dravot's apron, cut into the stone. Not even the priests of the temple of Imbra knew it was there. The old chap falls flat on his face at Dravot's feet and kisses 'em. 'Luck again,' says Dravot, across the Lodge to me, 'they say it's the missing Mark that no one could understand the why of. We're more than safe now.' Then he bangs the butt of his gun for a gavel and says, 'By virtue of the authority vested in me by my own right hand and the help of Peachey, I declare myself Grand Master of all Freemasonry in Kafiristan in this the Mother Lodge o' the country, and King of Kafiristan equally with Peachey!' At that he puts on his crown and I puts on mine—I was doing Senior Warden—and we opens the Lodge in most ample form. It was a amazing miracle! The priests moved in Lodge through the first two degrees almost without telling, as if the memory was coming back to them. After that, Peachey and Dravot raised such as was worthy—high priests and Chiefs of far-off villages. Billy Fish was the first, and I can tell you we scared the soul out of him. It was not in any way according to Ritual, but it served our turn. We didn't raise more than ten of the biggest men, because we didn't want to make the Degree common. And they was clamoring to be raised.

"'In another six months,' says Dravot, 'we'll hold another Communication and see how you are working.' Then he asks them about their villages, and learns that they was fighting one against the other and were fair sick and tired of it. And when they wasn't doing that they was fighting with the Mohammedans. 'You can fight those when they come into our country,' says Dravot. 'Tell off every tenth man of your tribes for a Frontier guard, and send two hundred at a time to this valley to be drilled. Nobody is going to be shot or speared any more so long as he does well, and I know that you won't cheat me because you're white people—sons of Alexander—and not like common, black Mohammedans. You are *my* people and by God,' says he, running off into English at the end—'I'll make a damned fine Nation of you, or I'll die in the making!'

"I can't tell all we did for the next six months because Dravot did a lot I couldn't see the hang of, and he learned their lingo in a way I never could. My work was to help the people plow, and now and again go out with some of the Army and see what the other villages were doing, and make 'em throw rope bridges across the ravines which cut up the country horrid. Dravot was very kind to me, but when he walked up and down in the pine wood pulling that bloody red beard of his with both fists I knew he was thinking plans I could not advise him about, and I just waited for orders.

"But Dravot never showed me disrespect before the people. They were afraid of me and the Army, but they loved Dan. He was the best of friends with the priests and the Chiefs; but anyone could come across the hills with a complaint and Dravot would hear him out fair, and call four priests together and say what was to be done. He used to call in Billy Fish from Bashkai, and Pikky Kergan from Shu, and an old Chief we called Kafuzelum—it was like enough to his real name—and hold councils with 'em when there was any fighting to be done in small villages. That was his Council of War, and the four priests of Bashkai, Shu, Khawak, and Madora was his Privy Council. Between the lot of 'em they sent me, with forty men and twenty rifles, and sixty men carrying turquoises, into the Ghorband country to buy those hand-made Martini rifles, that come out of the Amir's workshops at Kabul, from one of the Amir's Herati regiments that would have sold the very teeth out of their mouths for turquoises.

"I stayed in Ghorband a month, and gave the Governor there the pick of my baskets for hush money, and bribed the Colonel of the regiment some more, and, between the two and the tribespeople, we got more than a hundred hand-made Martinis, a hundred good Kohat Jezails that'll throw to six hundred yards, and forty manloads of very bad ammunition for the rifles. I came back with what I had, and distributed 'em among the men that the Chiefs sent to me to drill. Dravot was too busy to attend to those things, but the old Army that we first made helped me, and we turned out five hundred men that could drill, and two hundred that knew how to hold arms pretty straight. Even those corkscrewed, hand-made guns was a miracle to them. Dravot talked big about powder shops and factories, walking up and down in the pine wood when the winter was coming on.

" 'I won't make a Nation,' says he. 'I'll make an Empire! These men aren't niggers; they're English! Look at their eyes—look at their mouths. Look at the way they stand up. They sit on chairs in their own houses. They're the Lost Tribes, or something like it, and they've grown to be English. I'll take a census in the spring if the priests don't get frightened. There must be a fair two million of 'em in these hills. The villages are full o' little children. Two million people—two hundred and fifty thousand fighting men—and all English! They only want the rifles and a little drilling. Two hundred and fifty thousand men, ready to cut in on Russia's right flank when she tries for India! Peachey, man,' he says, chewing his beard in great hunks, 'we shall be Emperors—Emperors of the Earth! Rajah Brooke will be a suckling to us. I'll treat with the Vice-roy on equal terms. I'll ask him to send me twelve picked English—twelve that I know of—to help us govern a bit. There's Mackray, Sergeant-pensioner at Segowli—many's the good dinner he's given me, and his wife a pair of trousers. There's Donkin, the Warder of Tounghoo Jail; there's hundreds that I could lay my hand on if I was in India. The Vice-roy shall do it for me. I'll send a man through in the spring for those men, and I'll write for a dispensation from the Grand Lodge for what I've done as Grand Master. That—and all the Sniders that'll be thrown out when the native troops in India take up the Martini. They'll be worn smooth, but they'll do for fighting in these hills. Twelve English, a hundred thousand Sniders run through the Amir's country in driblets—I'd be content with twenty thousand in one year—and we'd be an Empire. When everything was shipshape, I'd hand over the crown—this crown I'm wearing now—to Queen Victoria on my knees, and she'd say: "Rise up, Sir Daniel Dravot." Oh, it's big! It's big, I tell you! But there's so much to be done in every place—Bashkai, Khawak, Shu, and everywhere else.'

" 'What is it?' I says. 'There are no more men coming in to be drilled this autumn. Look at those fat, black clouds. They're bringing the snow.'

" 'It isn't that,' says Daniel, putting his hand very hard on my shoulder; 'and I don't wish to say anything that's against you, for no other living man would have followed me and made me what I am as you have done. You're a first-class Commander-in-Chief, and the people know you; but—it's a big country, and somehow you can't help me, Peachey, in the way I want to be helped.'

" 'Go to your blasted priests, then!' I said, and I was sorry when I made that remark, but it did hurt me sore to find Daniel talking so superior when I'd drilled all the men, and done all he told me.

" 'Don't let's quarrel, Peachey,' says Daniel, without cursing. 'You're a King, too, and the half of this Kingdom is yours; but can't you see, Peachey, we want cleverer men than us now—three or four of 'em, that we can scatter about for our Deputies. It's a hugeous great State, and I can't always tell the right thing to do, and I haven't time for all I want to do, and here's the winter coming on and all.' He put half his beard into his mouth, and it was as red as the gold of his crown.

" 'I'm sorry, Daniel,' says I. 'I've done all I could. I've drilled the men and shown the people how to stack their oats better; and I've brought in those tinware rifles from Ghorband—but I know what you're driving at. I take it Kings always feel oppressed that way.'

" 'There's another thing too,' says Dravot, walking up and down. 'The winter's coming and these people won't be giving much trouble and if they do we can't move about. I want a wife.'

" 'For Gord's sake leave the women alone!' I says. 'We've both got all the work we can, though I *am* a fool. Remember the Contrack, and keep clear o' women.'

" 'The Contrack only lasted till such time as we was Kings; and Kings we have been these months past,' says Dravot, weighing his crown in his hand. 'You go get a wife too, Peachey—a nice, strappin', plump girl that'll keep you warm in the winter. They're prettier than English girls, and we can take the pick of 'em. Boil 'em once or twice in hot water, and they'll come as fair as chicken and ham.'

" 'Don't tempt me!' I says. 'I will not have any dealings with a woman not till we are a dam' side more settled than we are now. I've been doing the work o' two men, and you've been doing the work o' three. Let's lie off a bit, and see if we can get some better tobacco from Afghan country and run in some good liquor; but no women.'

" 'Who's talking o' *women?*' says Dravot. 'I said *wife*—a Queen to breed a King's son for the King. A Queen out of the strongest tribe, that'll make them your blood brothers, and that'll lie by your side and tell you all the people thinks about your you and their own affairs. That's what I want.'

" 'Do you remember that Bengali woman I kept at Mogul Serai when I was a plate layer?' says I. 'A fat lot o' good she was to me. She taught me the lingo and one or two other things; but what happened? She ran away with the Stationmaster's servant and half my month's pay. Then she turned up at Dadur Junction in tow of a half-caste, and had the impidence to say I was her husband—all among the drivers in the running shed!'

" 'We've done with that,' says Dravot. 'These women are whiter than you or me, and a Queen I will have for the winter months.'

" 'For the last time o' asking, Dan, do *not*,' I says. 'It'll only bring us harm. The Bible says that Kings ain't to waste their strength on women, 'specially when they've got a new raw Kingdom to work over.'

" 'For the last time of answering, I will,' said Dravot, and he went away through the pine trees looking like a big red devil. The low sun hit his crown and beard on one side and the two blazed like hot coals.

"But getting a wife was not as easy as Dan thought. He put it before the Council, and there was no answer till Billy Fish said that he'd better ask the girls. Dravot damned them all round. 'What's wrong with me?' he shouts, standing by the idol Imbra. 'Am I a dog or am I not enough of a man for your wenches? Haven't I put the shadow of my hand over this country? Who stopped the last Afghan raid?' It was me really, but Dravot was too angry to remember. 'Who brought your guns? Who repaired the bridges? Who's the Grand Master of the sign cut in the stone?' and he thumped his hand on the blo:k that he used to sit on in Lodge, and at Council, which opened like Lodge always. Billy Fish said nothing, and no more did the others. 'Keep your hair on, Dan,' said I; 'and ask the girls. That's how it's done at Home, and these people are quite English.'

" 'The marriage of the King is a matter of State,' says Dan, in a white-hot rage, for he could feel, I hope, that he was going against his better mind. He walked out of the Council room, and the others sat still, looking at the ground.

" 'Billy Fish,' says I to the Chief of Bashkai, 'what's the difficulty here? A straight answer to a true friend.' 'You know,' says Billy Fish. 'How should a man tell you who know everything? How can daughters of men marry Gods or Devils? It's not proper.'

"I remembered something like that in the Bible; but if, after seeing us as long as they had, they still believed we were Gods, it wasn't for me to undeceive them.

"'A God can do anything,' says I. 'If the King is fond of a girl he'll not let her die.' 'She'll have to,' said Billy Fish. 'There are all sorts of Gods and Devils in these mountains, and now and again a girl marries one of them and isn't seen any more. Besides, you two know the Mark cut in the stone. Only the Gods know that. We thought you were men till you showed the sign of the Master.'

"I wished then that we had explained about the loss of the genuine secrets of a Master Mason at the first go-off; but I said nothing. All that night there was a blowing of horns in a little dark temple half-way down the hill, and I heard a girl crying fit to die. One of the priests told us that she was being prepared to marry the King.

"'I'll have no nonsense of that kind,' says Dan. 'I don't want to interfere with your customs, but I'll take my own wife.' 'The girl's a little bit afraid,' says the priest. 'She thinks she's going to die, and they are a-heartening of her up down in the temple.'

"'Hearten her very tender, then,' says Dravot, 'or I'll hearten you with the butt of a gun so that you'll never want to be heartened again.' He licked his lips, did Dan, and stayed up walking about more than half the night, thinking of the wife that he was going to get in the morning. I wasn't any means comfortable, for I knew that dealings with a woman in foreign parts, though you was a crowned King twenty times over, could not but be risky. I got up very early in the morning while Dravot was asleep, and I saw the priests talking together in whispers, and the Chiefs talking together too, and they looked at me out of the corners of their eyes.

"'What is up, Fish?' I says to the Bashkai man, who was wrapped up in his furs and looking splendid to behold.

"'I can't rightly say,' says he; 'but if you can induce the King to drop all this nonsense about marriage, you'll be doing him and me and yourself a great service.'

"'That I do believe,' says I. 'But sure, you know, Billy, as well as me, having fought against and for us, that the King and me are nothing more than two of the finest men that God Almighty ever made. Nothing more, I do assure you.'

" 'That may be,' says Billy Fish, 'and yet I should be sorry if it was.' He sinks his head upon his great fur cloak for a minute and thinks. 'King,' says he, 'be you man or God or Devil, I'll stick by you today. I have twenty of my men with me, and they will follow me. We'll go to Bashkai until the storm blows over.'

"A little snow had fallen in the night, and everything was white except the greasy fat clouds that blew down and down from the north. Dravot came out with his crown on his head, swinging his arms and stamping his feet, and looking more pleased than Punch.

" 'For the last time, drop it, Dan,' says I, in a whisper. 'Billy Fish here says that there will be a row.'

" 'A row among my people!' says Dravot. 'Not much. Peachey, you're a fool not to get a wife too. Where's the girl?' says he, with a voice as loud as the braying of a jackass. 'Call up all the Chiefs and priests, and let the Emperor see if his wife suits him.'

"There was no need to call anyone. They were all there leaning on their guns and spears round the clearing in the center of the pine wood. A deputation of priests went down to the little temple to bring up the girl, and the horns blew up fit to wake the dead. Billy Fish saunters round and gets as close to Daniel as he could, and behind him stood his twenty men with matchlocks. Not a man of them under six feet. I was next to Dravot, and behind me was twenty men of the regular Army. Up comes the girl, and a strapping wench she was, covered with silver and turquoises, but white as death, and looking back every minute at the priests.

" 'She'll do,' said Dan, looking her over. 'What's to be afraid of, lass? Come and kiss me.' He puts his arm round her. She shuts her eyes, gives a bit of a squeak, and down goes her face in the side of Dan's flaming red beard.

" 'The slut's bitten me!' says he, clapping his hand to his neck, and, sure enough, his hand was red with blood. Billy Fish and two of his matchlock men catches hold of Dan by the shoulders and drags him into the Bashkai lot, while the priests howl in their lingo, 'Neither God nor Devil, but a man!' I was all taken aback, for a priest cut at me in front, and the Army behind began firing into the Bashkai men.

" 'God A-mighty!' says Dan. 'What is the meaning o' this?'

" 'Come back! Come away!' says Billy Fish. 'Ruin and Mutiny is the matter. We'll break for Bashkai if we can.'

"I tried to give some sort of orders to my men—the men o' the regular Army—but it was no use, so I fired into the brown of 'em with an English Martini and drilled three beggars in a line. The valley was full of shouting, howling creatures, and every soul was shrieking, 'Not a God nor a Devil, but only a man!' The Bashkai troops stuck to Billy Fish all they were worth, but their matchlocks wasn't half as good as the Kabul breechloaders, and four of them dropped. Dan was bellowing like a bull, for he was very wrathy; and Billy Fish had a hard job to prevent him running out at the crowd.

" 'We can't stand,' says Billy Fish. 'Make a run for it down the valley! The whole place is against us.' The matchlock men ran, and we went down the valley in spite of Dravot's protestations. He was swearing horribly and crying out that he was a King. The priests rolled great stones on us, and the regular Army fired hard, and there wasn't more than six men, not counting Dan, Billy Fish, and Me, that came down to the bottom of the valley alive.

"Then they stopped firing and the horns in the temple blew again. 'Come away—for Gord's sake come away!' says Billy Fish. 'They'll send runners out to all the villages before ever we get to Bashkai. I can protect you there, but I can't do anything now.'

"My own notion is that Dan began to go mad in his head from that hour. He stared up and down like a stuck pig. Then he was all for walking back alone and killing the priests with his bare hands; which he could have done. 'An Emperor am I,' says Daniel, 'and next year I shall be a Knight of the Queen.'

" 'All right, Dan,' says I; 'but come along now while there's time.'

" 'It's your fault,' says he, 'for not looking after your Army better. There was mutiny in the midst and you didn't know—you damned engine-driving, plate-laying, missionary's-pass-hunting hound!' He sat upon a rock and called me every foul name he could lay tongue to. I was too heartsick to care, though it was all his foolishness that brought the smash.

" 'I'm sorry, Dan,' says I, 'but there's no accounting for natives.

This business is our Fifty-Seven. Maybe we'll make something out of it yet, when we've got to Bashkai.'

" 'Let's get to Bashkai, then,' says Dan, 'and, by God, when I come back here again I'll sweep the valley so there isn't a bug in a blanket left!'

"We walked all that day, and all that night Dan was stumping up and down on the snow, chewing his beard and muttering to himself.

" 'There's no hope o' getting clear,' said Billy Fish. 'The priests will have sent runners to the villages to say that you are only men. Why didn't you stick on as Gods till things was more settled? I'm a dead man,' says Billy Fish, and he throws himself down on the snow and begins to pray to his Gods.

"Next morning we was in a cruel bad country—all up and down, no level ground at all, and no food either. The six Bashkai men looked at Billy Fish hungrywise as if they wanted to ask something, but they said never a word. At noon we came to the top of a flat mountain all covered with snow, and when we climbed up into it, behold, there was an Army in position waiting in the middle!

" 'The runners have been very quick,' says Billy Fish, with a little bit of a laugh. 'They are waiting for us.'

"Three or four men began to fire from the enemy's side, and a chance shot took Daniel in the calf of the leg. That brought him to his senses. He looks across the snow at the Army, and sees the rifles that we had brought into the country.

" 'We're done for,' says he. 'They are Englishmen, these people— and it's my blasted nonsense that has brought you to this. Get back, Billy Fish, and take your men away; you've done what you could, and now cut for it. Carnehan,' says he, 'shake hands with me and go along with Billy. Maybe they won't kill you. I'll go and meet 'em alone. It's me that did it. Me, the King!'

" 'Go!' says I. 'Go to Hell, Dan. I'm with you here. Billy Fish, you clear out, and we two will meet those folk.'

" 'I'm a Chief,' says Billy Fish, quite quiet. 'I stay with you. My men can go.'

"The Bashkai fellows didn't wait for a second word, but ran off, and Dan and Me and Billy Fish walked across to where the drums were drumming and the horns were horning. It was cold—awful cold. I've got that cold in the back of my head now. There's a lump of it there."

The punkah coolies had gone to sleep. Two kerosene lamps were blazing in the office, and the perspiration poured down my face and splashed on the blotter as I leaned forward. Carnehan was shivering, and I feared that his mind might go. I wiped my face, took a fresh grip of the piteously mangled hands, and said, "What happened after that?"

The momentary shift of my eyes had broken the clear current.

"What was you pleased to say?" whined Carnehan. "They took them without any sound. Not a little whisper all along the snow, not though the King knocked down the first man that set hand on him— not though old Peachey fired his last cartridge into the brown of 'em. Not a single solitary sound did those swines make. They just closed up tight, and I tell you their furs stunk. There was a man called Billy Fish, a good friend of us all, and they cut his throat, Sir, then and there, like a pig; and the King kicks up the bloody snow and says, 'We've had a dashed fine run for our money. What's coming next?' But Peachey, Peachey Taliaferro, I tell you, Sir, in confidence as be-twixt two friends, he lost his head, Sir. No, he didn't neither. The King lost his head, so he did, all along o' one of those cunning rope bridges. Kindly let me have the paper cutter, Sir. It tilted this way. They marched him a mile across that snow to a rope bridge over a ravine with a river at the bottom. You may have seen such. They prodded him behind like an ox. 'Damn your eyes!' says the King. 'D'you suppose I can't die like a gentleman?' He turns to Peachey— Peachey that was crying like a child. 'I've brought you to this, Peachey,' says he. 'Brought you out of your happy life to be killed in Kafiristan, where you was late Commander-in-Chief of the Emperor's forces. Say you forgive me, Peachey.' 'I do,' says Peachey. 'Fully and freely do I forgive you, Dan.' 'Shake hands, Peachey,' says he. 'I'm going now.' Out he goes, looking neither right nor left, and when he was plumb in the middle of those dizzy dancing ropes, 'Cut, you beggars,' he shouts; and they cut, and old Dan fell, turning round and round and round twenty thousand miles, for he took half an hour to fall till he struck the water, and I could see his body caught on a rock with the gold crown close beside.

"But do you know what they did to Peachey between two pine

trees? They crucified him, Sir, as Peachey's hand will show. They used wooden pegs for his hands and his feet; and he didn't die. He hung there and screamed, and they took him down next day, and said it was a miracle that he wasn't dead. They took him down—poor old Peachey that hadn't done them any harm—that hadn't done them any . . ."

He rocked to and fro and wept bitterly, wiping his eyes with the back of his scarred hands and moaning like a child for some ten minutes.

"They was cruel enough to feed him up in the temple, because they said he was more of a God than old Daniel that was a man. Then they turned him out on the snow, and told him to go home, and Peachey came home in about a year, begging along the roads quite safe; for Daniel Dravot he walked before and said, 'Come along, Peachey. It's a big thing we're doing.' The mountains they danced at night, and the mountains they tried to fall on Peachey's head, but Dan he held up his hand, and Peachey came along bent double. He never let go of Dan's hand, and he never let go of Dan's head. They gave it to him as a present in the temple, to remind him not to come again, and though the crown was pure gold, and Peachey was starving, never would Peachey sell the same. You knew Dravot, Sir! You knew Right Worshipful Brother Dravot! Look at him now!"

He fumbled in the mass of rags round his bent waist; brought out a black horsehair bag embroidered with silver thread; and shook therefrom on to my table—the dried, withered head of Daniel Dravot! The morning sun that had long been paling the lamps struck the red beard and blind sunken eyes; struck, too, a heavy circlet of gold studded with raw turquoises, that Carnehan placed tenderly on the battered temples.

"You behold now," said Carnehan, "the Emperor in his habit as he lived—the King of Kafiristan with his crown upon his head. Poor old Daniel that was a monarch once!"

I shuddered, for, in spite of defacements manifold, I recognized the head of the man of Marwar Junction. Carnehan rose to go. I attempted to stop him. He was not fit to walk abroad. "Let me take away the whisky, and give me a little money," he gasped. "I was a King once. I'll go to the Deputy Commissioner and ask to set in the Poorhouse till I get my health. No, thank you, I can't wait till you get a carriage for me. I've urgent private affairs—in the South—at Marwar."

He shambled out of the office and departed in the direction of the Deputy Commissioner's house. That day at noon I had occasion to go down the blinding hot Mall, and I saw a crooked man crawling along the white dust of the roadside, his hat in his hand, quavering dolorously after the fashion of street-singers at Home. There was not a soul in sight, and he was out of all possible earshot of the houses. And he sang through his nose, turning his head from right to left:

> *The Son of Man goes forth to war,*
> *A golden crown to gain;*
> *His blood-red banner streams afar—*
> *Who follows in his train?*

I waited to hear no more, but put the poor wretch into my carriage and drove him off to the nearest missionary for eventual transfer to the Asylum. He repeated the hymn twice while he was with me, whom he did not in the least recognize, and I left him singing it to the missionary.

Two days later I inquired after his welfare of the Superintendent of the Asylum.

"He was admitted suffering from sunstroke. He died early yesterday morning," said the Superintendent. "Is it true that he was half an hour bareheaded in the sun at midday?"

"Yes," said I, "but do you happen to know if he had anything upon him by any chance when he died?"

"Not to my knowledge," said the Superintendent.

And there the matter rests.

INTERPRETATION

At first glance, this seems to be merely a good story of adventure in a far-off and exotic place. There are difficult journeys, mysterious strangers, battles, pagan temples, madness, a crucifixion. The reader's curiosity about the turn of events is whetted by many cunning devices for provoking suspense. (For instance, the first stranger's mysterious message leads to the red-bearded man in the second-class carriage. The trader and his servant in the bazaar turn out to be the adventurers ready for their journey. Or, to go further into the story, in the episode concerning the mark on the stone, everything hangs for a moment in the balance until the mark is disclosed. Kipling, in other words, not only plays on the reader's curiosity about the final outcome, but plays up our suspense as to the outcome of the individual steps in the story's development.)

Furthermore, we can see how, in this story in which *plot* (see Glossary) seems to be so dominant in interest, one incident is caused by another. For instance, the marriage causes the discovery which brings on the ruin of the kings. But though we can link up the various episodes into a chain of cause and effect, we can see that this chain really depends upon the characters themselves.

Again, considered superficially, the matter of *motivation* (see Glossary) seems to present little difficulty. Many men desire riches and power, as do Peachey and Dravot; and it may seem that we need go no further into the matter in our discussion of motivation and character. (Indeed, this is as far as most adventure stories do go in presenting motivation.) But we can see that in this story, despite its apparent emphasis on action, the motivation is more complicated. For example, as the kings acquire their power, the simple desire for riches and power begins to change. There is a growing sense of responsibility for, and pride in, the people that they rule. Dravot begins to talk about bringing in skilled administrators, recognizing with an unexpected kind of humility that the business of kingship is more complicated than he had thought. He even begins to dream of turning over his kingdom to Queen Victoria—of taking his place in history as one of the Empire Builders. Actually, it is this development of character that proves to be one of the factors leading to his downfall, for the desire for marriage is not merely his simple human desire for companionship— though this is present—but it is also a desire to found a royal line, to leave someone to carry on the kingdom after his death. The wedding, therefore, must be public, and it must be carried out with due ceremony and ritual.

The course of the adventure itself has gone hand in hand with a development of character. That is, the men whom we meet at the beginning of the story are loafers—even if rather unusual loafers—yet men who are outcasts and who see "things from the underside where the lath and plaster is not smoothed off." But Dravot does not die like the loafer: "They prodded him behind like an ox. 'Damn your eyes!' says the King. 'D'you suppose I can't die like a gentleman?'"

He dies like a king, "like a gentleman," not like the trapped animal, the ox. And even Peachey, whose position is subordinate to Dravot's throughout the story, participates in this new dignity. Peachey comes back through the wild mountains, through terrors and hardships, but he never relinquishes the bag in which are the head of the King, and the crown, the symbol of kingship. So, as a *paradox* (see Glossary), the two loafers become most truly kings in the moment when their false kingship is taken from them. That is, when external kingship is lost, internal kingship is achieved.

This idea may prompt us to look back again at the meaning of the situation which brings about the ruin of the adventurers. The natives have thought of them as gods—not as human kings. The power of Peachey and Dravot is, thus, that of the king-as-god, not that of the king-as-man. But Dravot, the king-as-god, wants to be a man— he has human instincts which the mere exercise of godlike power cannot satisfy. He wants to have power, to be a god (for, to have power over the natives, he must be a god, as we discover), and he longs to be a man. This is the dilemma in which he is caught, and the dilemma which ruins him. The story at this point shows itself to be in a sense, then, a study of kingship; and there is a continuation of this study of kingship as the story goes on to recount Dravot's death, where, as we have seen, Dravot achieves another kind of kingship, and the nature of kingship is redefined.

Perhaps the general point may be summarized as follows: The loafers are impelled by a dream of kingship, but not a kingship hedged about by constitutional limitations, not a kingship which depends upon a mere social arrangement, not a kingship which is a mere figurehead or symbol for the real power of the state, but a "real" kingship, a kingship of absolute power. Such power depends upon their remaining aloof from humanity as gods; yet they are men, and man, not even for power, will forfeit his humanity. It is ironical that Dravot finally exercises his godlike power only in order to become a man—to satisfy his basic human desires. This step brings ruin, but there is a further irony in the fact that Dravot becomes most truly kingly at the moment of his ruin. Especially is this true for the reader who sees simply a kind of tawdry showmanship and deception in the parade of godlike power over the ignorant tribesmen, but who admires the way in which Dravot meets his death. Thus the story involves a contrast between kinds of kingship, between kinds of power, external and internal, power over others and power over oneself.

At this point, it may have occurred to the student that the theme of this story is closely related to the basic idea that seems involved in and implied by "R.M.S. *Titanic*." In "The Man Who Would Be King," true kingship is found to lie in the exercise of power over the self; in "R.M.S. *Titanic*" the attempt to conquer nature fails except in so far as men conquer their own human nature.

To recur to the list of questions suggested earlier on page 28: it ought to be apparent that the account of "The Man Who Would Be King" just given represents what may be regarded as at least a beginning to an answer to those questions. But the account also makes it very plain that the questions are all interrelated, and that a full answer to one of them tends to involve the answers to the others. It should also be plain that such questions as are suggested at the beginning of this story actually go on to raise many further questions. The account of the story given above does not pretend to provide a full interpretation of the story. For instance, the following are some of the questions which would be involved in a full analysis of the story:

1. Why is it appropriate that Peachey should be heard singing the particular hymn which he sings? Is it in his character to sing this particular hymn? How is the hymn related to the "meaning" of the story? Define the ironies involved in this incident.

2. Is Billy Fish loyal to Dravot as "god" or as "man"? What light does the fact of his loyalty shed on the rest of the story?

3. Is the contract signed by Dravot and Peachey humorous, pathetic, or heroic?

4. How does the fact that this story is told by a first-person narrator help us to define the characters?

5. What is the significance of the crucifixion of Peachey?

These are only a few of the possible questions which might be raised about the story. The student should choose several of these topics as exercises and write a full discussion of them.

Old Red

CAROLINE GORDON

I

WHEN THE door had closed behind his daughter, Mister Maury went to the window and stood a few moments looking out. The roses that had grown in a riot all along that side of the fence had died or been cleared away, but the sun lay across the garden in the same level lances of light that he remembered. He turned back into the room. The shadows had gathered until it was nearly all in gloom. The top of his minnow bucket just emerging from the duffel bag glinted in the last rays of the sun. He stood looking down at his traps all gathered neatly in a heap at the foot of the bed. He would leave them like that. Even if they came in here sweeping and cleaning up—it was only in hotels that a man was master of his own room—even if they came in here cleaning up, he would tell them to leave all his things exactly as they were. It was reassuring to see them all there together, ready to be taken up in the hand, to be carried down and put into a car, to be driven off to some railroad station at a moment's notice.

As he moved toward the door, he spoke aloud, a habit that was growing on him:

"Anyhow, I won't stay but a week. . . . I ain't going to stay but a week, no matter what they say. . . ."

Downstairs in the dining room they were already gathered at the supper table, his white-haired, shrunken mother-in-law, his tall sister-in-law who had the proud carriage of the head, the aquiline nose, but not the spirit of his dead wife, his lean, blond new son-in-law, his black-eyed daughter who, but that she was thin, looked so much like him, all of them gathered there waiting for him, Alexander Maury. It occurred to him that this was the first time he had sat down in the bosom of the family for some years. They were always writing saying that he must make a visit this summer or certainly next fall. ". . . all had a happy Christmas together but missed you. . . ." They had even made the pretext that he ought to come up to inspect his new son-in-law. As if he hadn't always known exactly the kind of young man Sarah would marry! What was the boy's name? Stephen, yes, Stephen. He must be sure and remember that.

He sat down, and shaking out his napkin spread it over his capacious paunch and tucked it well up under his chin in the way his wife had never allowed him to do. He let his eyes rove over the table and released a long sigh.

"Hot batter bread," he said, "and ham. Merry Point ham. I sure am glad to taste them one more time before I die."

The old lady was sending the little Negro girl scurrying back to the kitchen for a hot plate of batter bread. He pushed aside the cold plate and waited. She had bridled when he spoke of the batter bread and a faint flush had dawned on her withered cheeks. Vain she had always been as a peacock, of her housekeeping, her children, the animals on her place, anything that belonged to her. And she went on, even at her advanced age, making her batter bread, smoking her hams according to that old recipe she was so proud of; but who came here now to this old house to eat or to praise?

He helped himself to a generous slice of batter bread, buttered it, took the first mouthful and chewed it slowly. He shook his head.

"There ain't anything like it," he said. "There ain't anything else like it in this world."

His dark eye roving the table fell on his son-in-law. "You like batter bread?" he inquired.

Stephen nodded, smiling. Mister Maury, still masticating slowly, regarded his face, measured the space between the eyes—his favorite test for man, horse, or dog. Yes, there was room enough for sense between the eyes. But how young the boy looked! And infected already with the fatal germ, the *cacoëthes scribendi*. Well, their children would probably escape. It was like certain diseases of the eye, skipped every other generation. His own father had had it badly all his life. He could see him now sitting at the head of the table spouting his own poetry—or Shakespeare's—while the children watched the preserve dish to see if it was going around. He, Aleck Maury, had been lucky to be born in the generation he had. He had escaped that at least. A few translations from Heine in his courting days, a few fragments from the Greek, but no, he had kept clear of that on the whole. . . .

The eyes of his sister-in-law were fixed on him. She was smiling faintly. "You don't look much like dying, Aleck. Florida must agree with you."

The old lady spoke from the head of the table. "I can't see what you do with yourself all winter long. Doesn't time hang heavy on your hands?"

Time, he thought, time! They were always mouthing the word and what did they know about it? Nothing in God's world! He saw time suddenly, a dull, leaden-colored fabric depending from the old lady's hands, from the hands of all of them, a blanket that they pulled about, now this way, now that, trying to cover up their nakedness. Or they would cast it on the ground and creep in among the folds, finding one day a little more tightly rolled than another, but all of it everywhere the same dull gray substance. But time was a banner that whipped before him always in the wind. He stood on tiptoe to catch at the bright folds, to strain them to his bosom. They were bright and glittering. But they whipped by so fast and were whipping always ever faster. The tears came into his eyes. Where, for instance, had this year gone? He could swear he had not wasted a minute of it, for no man living, he thought, knew better how to make each day a pleasure to him. Not a minute wasted and yet here it was already May! If he lived to the Biblical three score and ten, which was all he ever allowed himself in his calculations, he had before him only nine more Mays. Only nine more Mays out of all eternity, and they wanted him to waste one of them sitting on the front porch at Merry Point!

The butter plate which had seemed to swim in a glittering mist was coming solidly to rest upon the white tablecloth. He winked his eyes rapidly and laying down his knife and fork squared himself about in his chair to address his mother-in-law:

"Well, ma'am, you know I'm a man that always likes to be learning something. Now this year I learned how to smell out fish." He glanced around the table, holding his head high and allowing his well-cut nostrils to flutter slightly with his indrawn breaths. "Yes, sir," he said, "I'm probably the only white man in this country knows how to smell out feesh."

There was a discreet smile on the faces of the others. Sarah was laughing outright. "Did you have to learn how or did it just come to you?" she asked.

"I learned it from an old nigger woman," her father said. He shook his head reminiscently. "It's wonderful how much you can learn from niggers. But you have to know how to handle them. I was half the winter wooing that old Fanny. . . ."

He waited until their laughter had died down. "We used to start off every morning from the same little cove and we'd drift in there together at night. I noticed how she always brought in a good string, so

I says to her, 'Fanny, you just lemme go 'long with you.' But she wouldn't have nothing to do with me. I saw she was going to be a hard nut to crack, but I kept right on. Finally I began giving her presents. . . ."

Laura was regarding him fixedly, a queer look on her face.

"What sort of presents did you give her, Aleck?"

He made his tones hearty in answer. "I give her a fine string of fish one day and I gave her fifty cents. And finally I made her a present of a Barlow knife. That was when she broke down. She took me with her that morning. . . ."

"Could she really smell fish?" the old lady asked curiously.

"You ought to 'a' seen her," Mister Maury said. "She'd sail over that lake like a hound on the scent. She'd row right along and then all of a sudden she'd stop rowing." He bent over, wrinkling his nose and peering into the depths of imaginary water. " 'Thar they are, White Folks, thar they are. Cain't you smell 'em?' "

Stephen was leaning forward, eyeing his father-in-law intently. "Could you?" he asked.

"I got so I could smell feesh," Mister Maury told him. "I could smell out the feesh, but I couldn't tell which kind they were. Now Fanny could row over a bed and tell just by the smell whether it was bass or bream. But she'd been at it all her life." He paused, sighing. "You can't just pick these things up. You have to give yourself to them. Who was it said 'Genius is an infinite capacity for taking pains'?"

Sarah was rising briskly. Her eyes sought her husband's across the table. She was still laughing. "Sir Izaak Walton," she said, "we'd better go in the other room. Mandy wants to clear the table."

The two older ladies remained in the dining room. Mister Maury walked across the hall to the sitting room, accompanied by Steve and Sarah. He lowered himself cautiously into the most solid-looking of the rocking chairs that were drawn up around the fire. Steve was standing on the hearthrug, back to the fire, gazing abstractedly off across the room.

Mister Maury glanced up at him curiously. "What are you thinking about, feller?" he asked.

Steve looked down. He smiled, but his gaze was still contemplative. "I was thinking about the sonnet," he said, "in the form in which it first came to England."

Mister Maury shook his head. "Wyatt and Surrey," he said. "Hey, nonny, nonny. . . . You'll have hardening of the liver long before you're my age." He looked past Steve's shoulder at the picture that hung over the mantel shelf: Cupid and Psyche holding between them a fluttering veil and running along a rocky path toward the beholder. "Old Merry Point," he said; "it don't change much, does it?"

He settled himself more solidly in his chair. His mind veered from the old house to his own wanderings in brighter places. He regarded his daughter and son-in-law affably.

"Yes, sir," he said, "this winter in Florida was valuable to me just for the acquaintances I made. Take my friend, Jim Barbee. Just to live in the same hotel with that man is an education." He paused, smiling reminiscently into the fire. "I'll never forget the first time I saw him. He came up to me there in the lobby of the hotel. 'Professor Maury!' he says, 'You been hearin' about me for twenty years and I been hearin' about you for twenty years. And now we've done met!'"

Sarah had sat down in the little rocking chair by the fire. She leaned toward him now, laughing. "They ought to have put down a cloth of gold for the meeting," she said.

Mister Maury shook his head. "Nature does that in Florida," he said. "I knew right off the reel it was him. There were half a dozen men standing around. I made 'em witness. 'Jim Barbee,' I says, 'Jim Barbee of Maysville or I'll eat my hat!'"

"Why is he so famous?" Sarah asked.

Mister Maury took out his knife and cut a slice from a plug of tobacco. When he had offered a slice to his son-in-law and it had been refused, he put the plug back in his pocket. "He's a man of imagination," he said slowly. "There ain't many in this world."

He took a small tin box out of his pocket and set it on the little table that held the lamp. Removing the top he tilted the box so that they could see its contents: an artificial lure, a bug with a dark body and a red, bulbous head, a hook protruding from what might be considered its vitals.

"Look at her," he said, "ain't she a killer?"

Sarah leaned forward to look and Steve, still standing on the hearth-rug, bent above them. The three heads ringed the light.

Mister Maury disregarded Sarah and addressed himself to Steve. "She takes nine strips of rind," he said, "nine strips just thick enough." He marked off the width of the strips with his two fingers on the table, then picking up the lure and cupping it in his palm he moved it back and forth quickly so that the painted eyes caught the light.

"Look at her," he said, "look at the wicked way she sets forward."

Sarah was poking at the lure with the tip of her finger.

"Wanton," she said, "simply wanton. What does he call her?"

"This is his Devil Bug," Mister Maury said. "He's the only man in this country makes it. I myself had the idea thirty years ago and let it slip by me the way I do with so many of my ideas." He sighed, then elevating his tremendous bulk slightly above the table level and continuing to hold Steve with his gaze he produced from his coat pocket the oilskin book that held his flies. He spread it open on the table and began to turn the pages. His eyes sought his son-in-law's as his hand paused before a gray, rather draggled-looking lure.

"Old Speck," he said. "I've had that fly for twenty years. I reckon she's taken five hundred pounds of fish in her day. . . ."

The fire burned lower. A fiery coal rolled from the grate and fell onto the hearthrug. Sarah scooped it up with a shovel and threw it among the ashes. In the circle of the lamplight the two men still bent over the table looking at the flies. Steve was absorbed in them but he spoke seldom. It was her father's voice that rising and falling filled the room. He talked a great deal, but he had a beautiful speaking voice. He was telling Steve now about Little West Fork, the first stream ever he put a fly in. "My first love," he kept calling it. It sounded rather pretty, she thought, in his mellow voice. "My first love . . ."

II

When Mister Maury came downstairs the next morning the dining room was empty except for his daughter, Sarah, who sat dawdling over a cup of coffee and a cigarette. Mister Maury sat down opposite her. To the little Negro girl who presented herself at his elbow he outlined his wants briefly. "A cup of coffee and some hot batter bread just like we had last night." He turned to his daughter. "Where's Steve?"

"He's working," she said, "he was up at eight and he's been working ever since."

Mister Maury accepted the cup of coffee from the little girl, poured half of it into his saucer, set it aside to cool. "Ain't it wonderful," he said, "the way a man can sit down and work day after day? When I think of all the work I've done in my time. . . . Can he work *every* morning?"

"He sits down at his desk every morning," she said, "but of course he gets more done some mornings than others."

Mister Maury picked up his saucer, found the coffee cool enough for his taste. He sipped it slowly, looking out of the window. His mind was already busy with his day's program. No water—no running water —nearer than West Fork three miles away. He couldn't drive a car and Steve was going to be busy writing all morning. There was nothing for it but a pond. The Willow Sink. It was not much but it was better than nothing. He pushed his chair back and rose.

"Well," he said, "I'd better be starting."

When he came downstairs with his rod a few minutes later the hall was still full of the sound of measured typing. Sarah sat in the dining room in the same position in which he had left her, smoking. Mister Maury paused in the doorway while he slung his canvas bag over his shoulders. "How you ever going to get anything done if you don't take advantage of the morning hours?" he asked. He glanced at the door opposite as if it had been the entrance to a sick chamber.

"What's he writing about?" he inquired in a whisper.

"It's an essay on John Skelton."

Mister Maury looked out at the new green leaves framed in the doorway. "John Skelton," he said. "God Almighty!"

He went through the hall and stepped down off the porch onto the ground that was still moist with spring rains. As he crossed the lower yard he looked up into the branches of the maples. Yes, the leaves were full grown already even on the late trees. The year, how swiftly, how steadily it advanced! He had come to the far corner of the yard. Grown up it was in pokeberry shoots and honeysuckle, but there was a place to get through. The top strand of wire had been pulled down and fastened to the others with a ragged piece of rope. He rested his weight on his good leg and swung himself over onto the game one. It gave him a good, sharp twinge when he came down on it. It was getting worse all the time, that leg, but on the other hand he was learning better all the time how to handle it. His mind flew back to a dark, startled moment, that day when the cramp first came on him. He had been sitting still in the boat all day long and that evening when he had stood up to get out his leg had failed him utterly. He had pitched forward among the reeds, had lain there a second, face downwards, before it came to him what had happened. With the realization came a sharp picture of his faraway youth: Uncle Quent lowering himself ponderously out of the saddle after a hard day's hunting had fallen forward in exactly the same way, into a knot of yowling little Negroes. He had got up and cursed them all out of the lot. It had scared the old boy to death, coming down like that. The black dog he had had on his shoulder all that fall. But he himself had never lost one day's fishing on account of his leg. He had known from the start how to handle it. It meant simply that he was slowed down that much. It hadn't really made much difference in fishing. He didn't do as much wading but he got around just about as well on the whole. Hunting, of course, had had to go. You couldn't walk all day shooting birds, dragging a game leg. He had just given it up right off the reel, though it was a shame when a man was as good a shot as he was. That day he was out with Tom Kensington last November, the only day he got out during the season. Nine shots he'd had and he'd bagged nine birds. Yes, it was a shame. But a man couldn't do everything. He had to limit himself. . . .

He was up over the little rise now. The field slanted straight down before him to where the pond lay, silver in the morning sun. A Negro cabin was perched halfway up the opposite slope. A woman was hanging out washing on a line stretched between two trees. From the open doorway little Negroes spilled down the path toward the pond. Mister Maury surveyed the scene, spoke aloud:

"Ain't it funny now? Niggers always live in the good places."

He stopped under a wild cherry tree to light his pipe. It had been hot crossing the field, but the sunlight here was agreeably tempered by the branches. And that pond down there was fringed with willows. His eyes sought the bright disk of the water, then rose to where the smoke from the cabin chimney lay in a soft plume along the crest of the hill.

When he stooped to pick up his rod again it was with a feeling of sudden, keen elation. An image had risen in his memory, an image that was familiar but came to him infrequently of late and that only in moments of elation: the wide field in front of his uncle's old house in

Albemarle, on one side the dark line of undergrowth that marked the Rivanna River, on the other the blue of Peters' Mountain. They would be waiting there in that broad plain when they had the first sight of the fox. On that little rise by the river, loping steadily, not yet alarmed. The sun would glint on his bright coat, on his quick-turning head as he dove into the dark of the woods. There would be hullabaloo after that and shouting and riding. Sometimes there was the tailing of the fox—that time old Whisky was brought home on a mattress! All of that to come afterward, but none of it ever like that first sight of the fox there on the broad plain between the river and the mountain.

There was one fox, they grew to know him in time, to call him affectionately by name. Old Red it was who showed himself always like that there on the crest of the hill. "There he goes, the damn' impudent scoundrel!" . . . Uncle Quent would shout and slap his thigh and yell himself hoarse at Whisky and Mag and the pups, but they would have already settled to their work. They knew his course, every turn of it by heart. Through the woods and then down across the fields again to the river. Their hope was always to cut him off before he could circle back to the mountain. If he got in there among those old field pines it was all up. But he always made it. Lost 'em every time and then dodged through to his hole in Pinnacle Rock. . . . A smart fox, Old Red. . . .

He descended the slope and paused in the shade of a clump of willows. The little Negroes who squatted, dabbling in the water, watched him out of round eyes as he unslung his canvas bag and laid it on a stump. He looked down at them gravely.

"D'you ever see a white man that could conjure?" he asked.

The oldest boy laid the brick he was fashioning out of mud down on a plank. He ran the tip of his tongue over his lower lip to moisten it before he spoke. "Naw suh."

"I'm the man," Mister Maury told him. "You chillun better quit that playin' and dig me some worms."

He drew his rod out of the case, jointed it up and laid it down on a stump. Taking out his book of flies he turned the pages, considering. "Silver Spinner," he said aloud. "They ought to take that . . . in May. Naw, I'll just give Old Speck a chance. It's a long time now since we had her out."

The little Negroes had risen and were stepping quietly off along the path toward the cabin, the two little boys hand in hand, the little girl following, the baby astride her hip. They were pausing now before a dilapidated building that might long ago have been a henhouse. Mister Maury shouted at them. "Look under them old boards. That's the place for worms." The biggest boy was turning around. His treble "Yassuh" quavered over the water. Then their voices died away. There was no sound except the light turning of the willow boughs in the wind.

Mister Maury walked along the bank, rod in hand, humming: "Bangum's gone to the wild boar's den . . . *Bangum's* gone to the wild boar's den . . ." He stopped where a white, peeled log protruded six or seven feet into the water. The pond made a little turn here. Two lines of willows curving in framed the whole surface of the water. He stepped out squarely upon the log, still humming. The line rose smoothly, soared against the blue and curved sweetly back upon the still water. His quick ear caught the little whish that the fly made when it clove the surface, his eye followed the tiny ripples of its flight. He cast again, leaning a little backward as he did sometimes when the mood was on him. Again and again his line soared out over the water. His eye rested now and then on his wrist. He noted with detachment the expert play of the muscles, admired each time the accuracy of his aim. It occurred to him that it was four days now since he had wet a line. Four days. One whole day packing up, parts of two days on the train and yesterday wasted sitting there on that front porch with the family. But the abstinence had done him good. He had never cast better than he was casting this morning.

There was a rustling along the bank, a glimpse of blue through the trees. Mister Maury leaned forward and peered around the clump of willows. A hundred yards away Steve, hatless, in an old blue shirt and khaki pants, stood jointing up a rod.

Mister Maury backed off his log and advanced along the path. He called out cheerfully, "Well, feller, do any good?"

Steve looked up. His face had lightened for a moment, but the abstracted expression stole over it again when he spoke. "Oh, I fiddled with it," he said, "all morning, but I didn't do much good."

Mister Maury nodded sympathetically. *"Minerva invita erat,"* he said; "you can do nothing unless Minerva perches on the rooftree. Why, I been castin' here all morning and not a strike. But there's a boat tied

up over on the other side. What say we get in it and just drift around?"
He paused, looked at the rod Steve had finished jointing up. "I brought
another rod along," he said. "You want to use it?"

Steve shook his head. "I'm used to this one."

An expression of relief came over Mister Maury's face. "That's right,"
he said, "a man always does better with his own rod."

The boat was only a quarter full of water. They heaved her over and
dumped it out, then dragged her down to the bank. The little Negroes
had come up, bringing a can of worms. Mister Maury threw them each
a nickel and set the can in the bottom of the boat. "I always like to have
a few worms handy," he told Steve, "ever since I was a boy." He lowered
himself ponderously into the bow and Steve pushed off and dropped
down behind him.

The little Negroes still stood on the bank staring. When the boat
was a little distance out on the water the boldest of them spoke: "You
reckon 'at ole jawnboat going to hold you up, Cap'm?"

Mister Maury turned his head to call over his shoulder. "Go 'way, boy,
ain't I done tole you I's a conjure?"

The boat dipped ominously. Steve changed his position a little and
she settled to the water. Sitting well forward Mister Maury made graceful casts, now to this side, now to that. Steve, in the stern, made occasional casts, but he laid his rod down every now and then to paddle,
though there was really no use in it. The boat drifted well enough with
the wind. At the end of half an hour seven sizable bass lay on the bottom
of the boat. Mister Maury had caught five of them. He reflected that
perhaps he really ought to change places with Steve. The man in the
bow certainly had the best chance at the fish. "But no," he thought, "it
don't make any difference. He don't hardly know where he is now."

He stole a glance over his shoulder at the young man's serious, abstracted face. It was like that of a person submerged. Steve seemed to
float up to the surface every now and then, his expression would lighten,
he would make some observation that showed he knew where he was,
then he would sink again. If you asked him a question he answered
punctiliously, two minutes later. Poor boy, dead to the world and would
probably be that way the rest of his life! A pang of pity shot through
Mister Maury, and on the heels of it a gust of that black fear that occasionally shook him. It was he, not Steve, that was the queer one! The

world was full of people like this boy, all of them walking around with their heads so full of this and that they hardly knew where they were going. There was hardly anybody—there was *nobody* really in the whole world like him. . . .

Steve, coming out of his abstraction, spoke politely. He had heard that Mister Maury was a fine shot. Did he like to fish better than hunt?

Mister Maury reflected. "Well," he said, "they's something about a covey of birds rising up in front of you . . . they's something. And a good dog. Now they ain't anything in this world that I like better than a good bird dog." He stopped and sighed. "A man has got to come to himself early in life if he's going to amount to anything. Now I was smart, even as a boy. I could look around me and see all the men of my family, Uncle Jeems, Uncle Quent, my father, every one of 'em weighed two hundred by the time he was fifty. You get as heavy on your feet as all that and you can't do any good shooting. But a man can fish as long as he lives. . . . Why, one place I stayed last summer there was an old man ninety years old had himself carried down to the river every morning. . . . Yes, sir, a man can fish as long as he can get down to the water's edge. . . ."

There was a little plop to the right. He turned just in time to see the fish flash out of the water. He watched Steve take it off the hook and drop it on top of the pile in the bottom of the boat. Eight bass that made and two bream. The old lady would be pleased. "Aleck always catches me fish," she'd say.

The boat glided on over the still water. There was no wind at all now. The willows that fringed the bank might have been cut out of paper. The plume of smoke hung perfectly horizontal over the roof of the Negro cabin. Mister Maury watched it stream out in little eddies and disappear into the bright blue.

He spoke softly: "Ain't it wonderful . . . ain't it wonderful now that a man of my gifts can content himself a whole morning on this here little old pond?"

III

Mister Maury woke with a start. He realized that he had been sleeping on his left side again. A bad idea. It always gave him palpitations of the heart. It must be that that had waked him up. He had gone to sleep almost immediately after his head hit the pillow. He rolled over, cautiously, as he always did since that bed in Leesburg had given down with him, and lying flat on his back stared at the opposite wall.

The moon rose late. It must be at its height now. That patch of light was so brilliant he could almost discern the pattern of the wall paper. It hung there, wavering, bitten by the shadows into a semblance of a human figure, a man striding with bent head and swinging arms. All the shadows in the room seemed to be moving toward him. The protruding corner of the washstand was an arrow aimed at his heart, the clumsy old-fashioned dresser was a giant towering above him.

They had put him to sleep in this same room the night after his wife died. In the summer it had been, too, in June, and there must have been a full moon, for the same giant shadows had struggled there with the same towering monsters. It would be like that here on this wall every full moon, for the pieces of furniture would never change their position, had never been changed, probably, since the house was built.

He turned back on his side. The wall before him was dark, but he knew every flower in the pattern of the wall paper, interlacing pink roses with thrusting up between every third cluster the enormous, spreading fronds of ferns. The wall paper in the room across the hall was like that too. The old lady slept there, and in the room next to his own, Laura, his sister-in-law, and in the east bedroom downstairs the young couple. He and Mary had slept there when they were first married, when they were the young couple in the house.

He tried to remember Mary as she must have looked the day he first saw her, the day he arrived from Virginia to open his school in the old office that used to stand there in the corner of the yard. He could see Mister Allard plainly, sitting there under the sugar tree with his chair tilted back, could discern the old lady—young she had been then!—hospitably poised in the doorway, could hear her voice: "Well, here are two of your pupils to start with. . . ." He remembered Laura, a shy child of nine hiding her face in her mother's skirts, but Mary was only a shadow in the dark hall. He could not even remember how her voice had sounded. "Professor Maury," she would have said and her mother would have corrected her with "Cousin Aleck. . . ."

That day a year later when she was getting off her horse at the stile blocks. . . . She had turned as she walked across the lawn to look back at him. Her white sunbonnet had fallen back on her shoulders, her eyes meeting his had been wide and startled. He had gone on and had hitched both the horses before he leaped over the stile to join her. But he had known in that moment that she was the woman he was going to have. He could not remember all the rest of it, only that moment stood out. He had won her. She had become his wife, but the woman he had won was not the woman he had sought. It was as if he had had her only in that moment there on the lawn. As if she had paused there only for that one moment, and was ever after retreating before him down a devious, a dark way that he would never have chosen.

The death of the first baby had been the start of it, of course. It had been a relief when she took so definitely to religion. Before that there had been those sudden, unaccountable forays out of some dark lurking place that she had. Guerrilla warfare and trying to the nerves, but that had been only at the first. For many years they had been two enemies contending in the open. . . . Toward the last she had taken mightily to prayer. He would wake often to find her kneeling by the side of the bed in the dark. It had gone on for years. She had never given up hope. . . .

Ah, a stout-hearted one, Mary! She had never given up hope of changing him, of making him over into the man she thought he ought to be. Time and again she almost had him. And there were long periods, of course, during which he had been worn down by the conflict, one spring when he himself said, when she had told all the neighbors that he was too old now to go fishing any more. . . . But he had made a comeback. She had had to resort to stratagem. His lips curved in a smile, remembering the trick.

It had come over him suddenly, a general lassitude, an odd faintness in the mornings, the time when his spirits ordinarily were always at their highest. He had sat there looking out of the window at the woods glistening with spring rain; he had not even taken his gun down to shoot a squirrel.

Remembering Uncle Quent's last days, he had been alarmed, had decided finally that he must tell her so that they might begin preparations for the future—he had shuddered at the thought of eventual confinement, perhaps in some institution. She had looked up from her sewing, unable to repress a smile.

"You think it's your mind, Aleck. . . . It's coffee. . . . I've been giving you a coffee substitute every morning. . . ."

They had laughed together over her cleverness. He had not gone back to coffee, but the lassitude had worn off. She had gone back to the attack with redoubled vigor. In the afternoons she would stand on the porch calling after him as he slipped down to the creek, "Now, don't stay long enough to get that cramp. You remember how you suffered last time. . . ." He would have forgotten all about the cramp until that moment, but it would hang over him then through the whole afternoon's sport, and it would descend upon him inevitably when he left the river and started for the house.

Yes, he thought with pride. She was wearing him down—he didn't believe there was a man living who could withstand her a lifetime!— she was wearing him down and would have had him in another few months, another year certainly. But she had been struck down just as victory was in her grasp. The paralysis had come on her in the night. It was as if a curtain had descended, dividing their life sharply into two parts. In the bewildered year and a half that followed he had found himself forlornly trying to reconstruct the Mary he had known. The pressure she had so constantly exerted upon him had become for him a part of her personality. This new, calm Mary was not the woman he had loved all these years. She had lain there—heroically they all said—waiting for death. And lying there, waiting, all her faculties engaged now in defensive warfare, she had raised as it were her lifelong siege; she had lost interest in his comings and goings, had once even encouraged him to go out for an afternoon's sport. He felt a rush of warm pity. Poor Mary! She must have realized toward the last that she had wasted herself in conflict; she had spent her arms and her strength against an inglorious foe when all the time the real, the invincible adversary waited. . . .

He turned over on his back again. The moonlight was waning, the contending shadows paler now and retreating toward the door. From across the hall came the sound of long, sibilant breaths, ending each one on a little upward groan. The old lady . . . she would maintain till her dying day that she did not snore. He fancied that he could hear from the next room Laura's light, regular breathing, and downstairs were the young couple asleep in each other's arms. . . .

All of them quiet and relaxed now, but they had been lively enough at dinner time! It had started with the talk about Aunt Sally Crenfew's funeral Tuesday. Living as he had for some years away from women of his family he had forgotten the need to be cautious. He had spoken up before he thought:

"But that's the day Steve and I were going to Barker's Mill. . . ."

Sarah had cried out at the idea. "Barker's Mill!" she had said, "right on the Crenfew land . . . well, if not on the very farm in the very next field." It would be a scandal if he, Professor Maury, known by everybody to be in the neighborhood, could not spare one afternoon, one insignificant summer afternoon from his fishing long enough to attend the funeral of his cousin, the cousin of all of them, the oldest lady in the whole family connection. . . .

She had got him rattled; he had fallen back upon technicalities:

"I'm not a Crenfew. I'm a Maury. Aunt Sally Crenfew is no more kin to me than a catfish. . . ."

An unlucky crack, that about the catfish. Glancing around the table he had caught the same look in every eye. He had felt a gust of the same fright that had shaken him there on the pond. That look! Sooner or later you met it in every human eye. The thing was to be up and ready, ready to run for your life at a moment's notice. Yes, it had always been like that. It always would be. His fear of them was shot through suddenly with contempt. It was as if Mary was there laughing at them with him. *She* knew that none of them could have survived what he had survived, could have paid the price for freedom that he had paid. . . .

Sarah had come to a full stop. He had to say something. He shook his head:

"You think we just go fishing to have a good time. The boy and I hold high converse on that pond. . . . I'm starved for intellectual companionship, I tell you. In Florida I never see anybody but niggers. . . ."

They had all laughed out at that. "As if you didn't *prefer* the society of niggers," Sarah said scornfully.

The old lady had been moved to anecdote:

"I remember when Aleck first came out here from Virginia, Cousin Sophy said: 'Professor Maury is so well educated. Now Cousin Cave Maynor is dead, who is there in this neighborhood for him to associate with?' 'Well,' I said, 'I don't know about that. He seems perfectly satisfied now with Ben Hooser. They're off to the creek together every evening soon as school is out.' "

Ben Hooser. . . . He could see now the wrinkled face, overlaid with that ashy pallor of the aged Negro, the shrewd, smiling eyes, the pendulous lower lip that dropping away showed always some of the rotten teeth. A finer nigger, Ben, and on to a lot of tricks, the only man really that he'd ever cared to take fishing with him. . . .

But the first real friend of his bosom had been old Uncle Teague, back in Virginia. Once a week, or more likely every ten days, he fed the hounds on the carcass of a calf that had had time to get pretty high. They would drive the spring wagon out into the lot, he, a boy of ten, beside Uncle Teague on the driver's seat. The hounds would come in a great rush and rear their slobbering jowls against the wagon wheels. Uncle Teague would wield his whip, chuckling while he threw the first hunk of meat to Old Mag, his favorite.

"Dey goin' run on dis," he'd say, "dey goin' run like a shadow. . . ."

He shifted his position again, cautiously. People, he thought . . . people . . . so bone ignorant, all of them. Not one person in a thousand realized that a fox hound remains at heart a wild beast and must kill and gorge, and then when he is ravenous kill and gorge again. . . . Or that the channel cat is a night feeder. . . . Or . . . his daughter had told him once that he ought to set all his knowledges down in a book. "Why?" he had asked. "So everybody else can know as much as I do?"

If he allowed his mind to get active, really active, he would never get any sleep. He was fighting an inclination now to get up and find a cigarette. He relaxed again upon his pillows, deliberately summoned pictures up before his mind's eye. Landscapes—and streams. He observed their outlines, watched one flow into another. The Black River into West Fork, that in turn into Spring Creek and Spring Creek into the Withlicoochee. Then they were all flowing together, merging into one broad plain. He watched it take form slowly: the wide field in front of Hawkwood, the Rivanna River on one side, on the other Peters' Mountain. They would be waiting there till the fox showed himself on that little rise by the river. The young men would hold back till Uncle Quent had wheeled Old Filly, then they would all be off pell-mell across the plain. He himself would be mounted on Jonesboro. Blind as a bat, but she would take anything you put her at. That first thicket on the edge of the woods. They would break there, one half of them going around, the other half streaking it through the woods. He was always of those going around to try to cut the fox off on the other side. No, he was down off his horse. He was coursing with the fox. He could hear the sharp, pointed feet padding on the dead leaves, see the quick head turned now and then over the shoulder.

The trees kept flashing by, one black trunk after another. And now it was a ragged mountain field and the sage grass running before them in waves to where a narrow stream curved in between the ridges. The fox's feet were light in the water. He ran steadily, head down. The hounds' baying was louder now. Old Mag knew the trick. She had stopped to give tongue by the big rock, and now they had all leaped the gulch and were scrambling up through the pines. But the fox's feet were already hard on the mountain path. He ran slowly now, past the big boulder, past the blasted pine to where the shadow of the Pinnacle Rock was black across the path. He ran on and the shadow rose and swayed to meet him. Its cool touch was on his hot tongue, his heaving flanks. He had slipped in under it. He was sinking down, panting, in black dark, on moist earth while the hounds' baying filled the bowl of the valley and reverberated from the mountainside.*

INTERPRETATION

At first glance, this story may seem to be merely another character sketch somewhat like the "Portrait of Henry Hastings." (This impression may be given additional color by the fact that both Hastings and Mister Maury are men who have a passion for hunting and fishing.) We decided that the "Portrait of Henry Hastings" was not to be regarded as an example of fiction. It may be well to remind ourselves of the basis for our decision: it was not that the portrait was the portrait of a real man rather than that of a "made-up" character; and it was not that the character as portrayed was unconvincing. The decision was based on the fact that nothing "happened"—the fact that there was no development of character—not even the sudden revelation of the character in a new light.

"Old Red" may seem to the casual reader equally devoid of meaningful happenings. Mister Maury comes to his mother-in-law's home

* From *Seribners*, copyright, 1933; by permission of the author.

for a visit. He eats dinner with the family; he exhibits his fishing tackle; next morning he goes fishing; and waking that night in the room in which he had slept on the night of his wife's death, he meditates on his earlier life. It is easy to feel that the author is interested only in finding opportunities and occasions for exhibiting Maury's character, and that such little scenes of action as do occur serve merely as convenient pegs on which to hang further character description.

There is a sense, of course, in which this statement of the matter is true: the whole narrative *is* constructed to reveal the character of the man. The important question we have to answer, if we are to determine whether or not "Old Red" is to be accounted an example of fiction, is this: is the method of character revelation merely expository and descriptive (as in the "Portrait of Henry Hastings"), or does it involve that interplay of character with action—either subjective or objective action—which is peculiar to fiction?

A satisfactory answer to this question will necessarily involve an examination of the whole story. Suppose that we begin by considering certain aspects of Mister Maury's character. We learn that his fishing is his life—the more so now that his crippled leg has forced him to give up hunting. His sport is not merely a passion—it is an art and a philosophy. To it he has given the thought and discipline that other men give to their businesses or their professions. He does not fish merely to kill time or to get away from himself: rather, it is in his sport that he truly finds himself; and, as for wasting time, "Time, he thought, time! They were always mouthing the word and what did they know about it? . . . The tears came into his eyes. Where, for instance, had this year gone? He could swear that he had not wasted a minute of it. . . . Not a minute wasted and yet here it was already May!" He knows the true value of time, he feels, for he enjoys his fishing so much that he covets for it every instant of time allowed to him. Far from being careless of time, he sees with a real poignance the few seasons still left to him slip away. Time, for him, is infinitely precious.

Maury, then, is not the thoughtless man nor the indolent man nor the disappointed man. But it is easy for other people to think him so, and because he is an observant and reflective man, he is acutely aware that they do think him so. His mother-in-law, for example, asks him: "Doesn't time hang heavy on your hands?"—as if he had no vocation! Or, his daughter, who does realize in a sense that his sport is for him an art, suggests that "he ought to set his knowledges down in a book." For her, his sport would be justified if out of it he could publish a book—as if the art had no justification as an end in itself but only as a means to some other end: fame, a reputation for out-of-the-way knowledge, public adulation.

The criticism of Mister Maury by the world and Maury's own counter-criticism of the world become increasingly emphasized as the story develops. We are being given more than an amusing description of a rather picturesque character. We are being given the character's own justification of the way of life which he exemplifies; and, as the story unfolds, we are made aware that the character has had to struggle to hold on to a pattern of living to which the outside world is inimical.

For example, Maury judges his son-in-law with a sort of pity: "If you asked him a question he answered punctiliously, two minutes later. Poor boy, dead to the world and would probably be that way the rest of his life! A pang of pity shot through Mister Maury. . . . ." The judgment springs from his own way of living in which life has a purpose, a meaning, a way of expressing itself concretely, and yet meaningfully through a discipline which involves, not only technical skill of wrist and arm, but learning, self-control, and even a sort of ritual. From this point of view, the young man's life is disordered, abstract, and indeed, hardly life at all. Yet, in this same scene, Mister Maury realizes, perhaps for the first time clearly, that it is the young man's way of living that represents the norm, not his own: "It was he, not Steve, that was the queer one! . . . There was hardly anybody—there was *nobody* really in the whole world like him. . . ."

Mister Maury has not only to justify his way of living. As we have remarked above, he has actually had to struggle to maintain it. That struggle, in its most drastic phase, has been a struggle with his wife who had felt that he was wasting his talents, and who had tried through the years to "change" him. This we learn in the long *cutback* (see Glossary) in the last scene of the story when Maury, waking in the night, revolves in memory his life with her. There is humor, and tenderness, and pity in his memories of their contention. He remembers with a certain pride—pride in her—her stubbornness in her efforts to convert him: "Yes, he thought with pride. She was wearing him down—he didn't believe there was a man living who could withstand her a lifetime!—she was wearing him down and would have had him in a few months, another year certainly. But she had been struck down just as victory was in her grasp."

But he escaped. He has escaped, but the chase is still on. That evening in the conversation he "had felt a gust of the same fright that had shaken him there on the pond. That look! Sooner or later you met it in every human eye. . . . Yes, it had always been like that. It always would be."

What is this freedom which he has tried to preserve? It is difficult to describe. Certainly Mister Maury himself has difficulty in trying to state it, even to his family circle. He had tried to state it to them earlier that evening: "You think that we just go fishing to have a good time. The boy and I hold high converse on that pond. . . . I'm starved for intellectual companionship, I tell you. . . ." The last statement provokes a burst of friendly laughter. Presumably, Mister Maury, too, realizes how inadequate and apparently fantastic his statement sounds.

What is it, then, that he gets from his fishing? Why does he fish, anyway? Mister Maury cannot tell us—would have some difficulty perhaps even in stating the matter to himself. But the author has told us, or at least has suggested it in the story itself. May we not summarize it somewhat as follows?

Man craves an activity in which he can participate as a whole man, not merely as a mind, not merely as a body—an activity in which body and mind participate harmoniously. Man also craves some sort of harmony between means and ends: in other words, it is not enough for a man to give himself to some abstract activity in which there is no interest or pleasure in itself merely in order that he may gain money and time to enjoy himself in some other activity. Under such conditions, the pursuit of pleasure tends to become feverish and hysterical, the pursuit of mere excitement and forgetfulness.

The old man feels himself to be in a hostile world, a world which has nothing but criticism for him. "Sooner or later you met it in every human eye," he thinks. Why do people think that he is indolent? Because they feel that his occupation can only be a time-killer, and do not see that it requires its own knowledge and discipline. They tend to feel that anything which gives so much pleasure must be wrong, because they think of pleasure as separate from "work"—important work can't be pleasurable. Why do they think that he is a failure? Because they think that he has nothing "to show" for his life. Important activity, according to their view, gains something, "makes money," or leaves some mark of influence on the world. They cannot understand that success may be measured in terms of inner happiness and not in terms of a bank account and public esteem. Why do people think that Mister Maury is thoughtless? Because they cannot understand that a man may use his mind, or create his own philosophy, for his own pleasure and not to "put into a book." We have already seen how Mister Maury tries to indicate this when he says that he and the boy "hold high converse on that pond," and then gives up at the burst of friendly laughter.

We have said that Mister Maury does not, and perhaps could not, really state his position; but the objective toward which the story moves is the realization, by the old man, of the meaning of his own life in relation to the world. This realization, however, does not come in terms of statement. It comes in terms of a symbol, the symbol of the fox.

How is this symbol prepared for? We notice that in the earlier part of the story there are various references to his life as a young man in Virginia, and among them, references to his fox-hunting on the plain betwen the Rivanna River and Peters' Mountain. One fox, in particular, he remembers, Old Red, the fox they could never catch, the fox that showed himself as in challenge, and which, because they could never catch him, they came to regard with a certain affection. It is implied that Old Red himself came to regard the chase as a sporting event: the fox staked his life again and again on his knowledge of the course, his cunning, and his speed. "A smart one, Old Red," they said about him.

So, in the last scene, when Mister Maury is lying sleepless in the very bed where he had been put on the night of his wife's death, and when he is thinking back over his past life, he suddenly feels that he himself is like the fox—no, that he *is* the fox, leading the chase to the safety of his lair on Peters' Mountain. But this is not the only preparation which has been given for the final symbol. Incidents in the immediate past have picked up and recapitulated the long struggle which he has had with his wife and with the world: the gentle chiding of the family that evening; memories of his wife's long struggle to "change him"; the attempt that evening to persuade him to go to the funeral; Sarah's remark, "As if you didn't *prefer* the society of niggers"; memories of the Negroes he has liked, of Ben Hooser, and, earlier still, of Uncle Teague and the fox hounds. As he tries to drift off to sleep, the picture of the fox hunt comes before his mind and summarizes the meaning of his whole life. He has always thought of himself as the hunter, but now he finds himself to be the hunted; but, like Old Red, the smart fox, he finds that that, too, may be sport. And he, like Old Red, is safe; he has won his race.

Our first question was: how does this story differ from a mere character sketch, like the "Portrait of Henry Hastings"? The answer seems to lie in the fact that one finds here a definite progression, a definite movement toward a solution, toward the discovery on the part of the old man of the meaning of his life. This is a psychological progression, it is true; but, as we have seen, it is none the less dramatic for that. Furthermore, we have seen, as in the case of "The Man Who Would Be King," that stories which emphasize action and excitement, if they are good ones, have a similar psychological progression.

Has this story a more general meaning than the one which we have discussed? Is not the story, in one sense, a story about a basic conflict in our civilization—the conflict between man's desire for a harmonious development of all his faculties and a set of social conditions which tend to compartmentalize life and to make "work" and "pleasure" viciously antithetical? The question of importance is not whether or not we feel that Mister Maury's solution is ideal; it is rather whether Mister Maury might not have felt, in a more balanced society, that he did not need to take such drastic measures with his life in order to save himself as a human being.

1. Why does Mister Maury prefer the society of Negroes to that of white people?

2. Why is it significant that Mister Maury is an able and educated man?

3. Why is the conclusion with the symbol of the fox more effective here than a mere statement by Mister Maury of his "philosophy" would have been? *A concrete picture.*

The Birthmark
NATHANIEL HAWTHORNE

IN THE latter part of the last century there lived a man of science, an eminent proficient in every branch of natural philosophy, who not long before our story opens had made experience of a spiritual affinity more attractive than any chemical one. He had left his laboratory to the care of an assistant, cleared his fine countenance from the furnace smoke, washed the stain of acids from his fingers, and persuaded a beautiful woman to become his wife. In those days when the comparatively recent discovery of electricity and other kindred mysteries of Nature seemed to open paths into the region of miracle, it was not unusual for the love of science to rival the love of woman in its depth and absorbing energy. The higher intellect, the imagination, the spirit, and even the heart might all find their congenial aliment in pursuits which, as some of their ardent votaries believed, would ascend from one step of powerful intelligence to another, until the philosopher should lay his hand on the secret of creative force and perhaps make new worlds for himself. We know not whether Aylmer possessed this degree of faith in man's ultimate control over Nature. He had devoted himself, however, too unreservedly to scientific studies ever to be weaned from them by any second passion. His love for his young wife might prove the stronger of the two; but it could only be by intertwining itself with his love of science, and uniting the strength of the latter to his own.

Such a union accordingly took place, and was attended with truly remarkable consequences and a deeply impressive moral. One day, very soon after their marriage, Aylmer sat gazing at his wife with a trouble in his countenance that grew stronger as he spoke.

"Georgiana," said he, "has it never occurred to you that the mark upon your cheek might be removed?"

"No, indeed," said she, smiling; but perceiving the seriousness of his manner, she blushed deeply. "To tell you the truth, it has been so often called a charm that I was simple enough to imagine it might be so."

"Ah, upon another face perhaps it might," replied her husband; "but never on yours. No, dearest Georgiana, you came so nearly perfect from the hand of Nature that this slightest possible defect, which we hesitate whether to term a defect or a beauty, shocks me, as being the visible mark of earthly imperfection."

"Shocks you, my husband!" cried Georgiana, deeply hurt; at first reddening with momentary anger, but then bursting into tears. "Then why did you take me from my mother's side? You cannot love what shocks you!"

To explain this conversation it must be mentioned that in the center of Georgiana's left cheek there was a singular mark, deeply interwoven, as it were, with the texture and substance of her face. In the usual state of her complexion—a healthy though delicate bloom—the mark wore a tint of deeper crimson, which imperfectly defined its shape amid the surrounding rosiness. When she blushed it gradually became more indistinct, and finally vanished amid the triumphant rush of blood that bathed the whole cheek with its brilliant glow. But if any shifting motion caused her to turn pale there was the mark again, a crimson stain upon the snow, in what Aylmer sometimes deemed an almost fearful distinctness. Its shape bore not a little similarity to the human hand, though of the smallest pygmy size. Georgiana's lovers were wont to say that some fairy at her birth hour had laid her tiny hand upon the infant's cheek, and left this impress there in token of the magic endowments that were to give her such sway over all hearts. Many a desperate swain would have risked life for the privilege of pressing his lips to the mysterious hand. It must not be concealed, however, that the impression wrought by this fairy sign manual varied exceedingly, according to the difference of temperament in the beholders. Some fastidious persons— but they were exclusively of her own sex—affirmed that the bloody hand, as they chose to call it, quite destroyed the effect of Georgiana's beauty, and rendered her countenance even hideous. But it would be as reasonable to say that one of those small blue stains which sometimes occur in the purest statuary marble would convert the Eve of Powers to a monster. Masculine observers, if the birthmark did not heighten their admiration, contented themselves with wishing it away, that the world might possess one living specimen of ideal loveliness without the semblance of a flaw. After his marriage—for he thought little or nothing of the matter before—Aylmer discovered that this was the case with himself.

Had she been less beautiful—if Envy's self could have found aught else to sneer at—he might have felt his affection heightened by the prettiness of this mimic hand, now vaguely portrayed, now lost, now stealing forth again and glimmering to and fro with every pulse of emotion that throbbed within her heart; but seeing her otherwise so perfect, he found this one defect grow more and more intolerable with every moment of their united lives. It was the fatal flaw of humanity which Nature, in one shape or another, stamps ineffaceably on all her productions, either to imply that they are temporary and finite, or that their perfection must be wrought by toil and pain. The crimson hand expressed the ineludible gripe in which mortality clutches the highest and purest of earthly mold, degrading them into kindred with the lowest, and even with the very brutes, like whom their visible frames return to dust. In this manner, selecting it as the symbol of his wife's liability to sin, sorrow, decay, and death, Aylmer's somber imagination was not long in rendering the birthmark a frightful object, causing him more trouble and horror than ever Georgiana's beauty, whether of soul or sense, had given him delight.

At all the seasons which should have been their happiest, he invariably and without intending it, nay, in spite of a purpose to the contrary, reverted to this one disastrous topic. Trifling as it at first appeared, it so connected itself with innumerable trains of thought and modes of feeling that it became the central point of all. With the morning twilight Aylmer opened his eyes upon his wife's face and recognized the symbol of imperfection; and when they sat together at the evening hearth his eyes wandered stealthily to her cheek, and beheld, flickering with the blaze of the wood fire, the spectral hand that wrote mortality where he would fain have worshiped. Georgiana soon learned to shudder at his gaze. It needed but a glance with the peculiar expression that his face often wore to change the roses of her cheek into a deathlike paleness, amid which the crimson hand was brought strongly out, like a bas-relief of ruby on the whitest marble.

Late one night when the lights were growing dim, so as hardly to betray the stain on the poor wife's cheek, she herself, for the first time, voluntarily took up the subject.

"Do you remember, my dear Aylmer," said she, with a feeble attempt at a smile, "have you any recollection of a dream last night about this odious hand?"

"None! none whatever!" replied Aylmer, starting; but then he added, in a dry, cold tone, affected for the sake of concealing the real depth of his emotion, "I might well dream of it; for before I fell asleep it had taken a pretty firm hold of my fancy."

"And you did dream of it!" continued Georgiana, hastily; for she dreaded lest a gush of tears should interrupt what she had to say. "A terrible dream! I wonder that you can forget it. Is it possible to forget this one expression?—'It is in her heart now; we must have it out!' Reflect, my husband; for by all means I would have you recall that dream."

The mind is in a sad state when Sleep, the all-involving, cannot confine her specters within the dim region of her sway, but suffers them to break forth, affrighting this actual life with secrets that perchance belong to a deeper one. Aylmer now remembered his dream. He had fancied himself with his servant Aminadab, attempting an operation for the removal of the birthmark; but the deeper went the knife, the deeper sank the hand, until at length its tiny grasp appeared to have caught hold of Georgiana's heart; whence, however, her husband was inexorably resolved to cut or wrench it away.

When the dream had shaped itself perfectly in his memory, Aylmer sat in his wife's presence with a guilty feeling. Truth often finds its way to the mind close muffled in robes of sleep, and then speaks with uncompromising directness of matters in regard to which we practice an unconscious self-deception during our waking moments. Until now he had not been aware of the tyrannizing influence acquired by one idea over his mind, and of the lengths which he might find in his heart to go for the sake of giving himself peace.

"Aylmer," resumed Georgiana, solemnly, "I know not what may be the cost to both of us to rid me of this fatal birthmark. Perhaps its removal may cause cureless deformity; or it may be the stain goes as deep as life itself. Again: do we know that there is a possibility, on any terms, of unclasping the firm gripe of this little hand which was laid upon me before I came into the world?"

"Dearest Georgiana, I have spent much thought upon the subject," hastily interrupted Aylmer. "I am convinced of the perfect practicability of its removal."

"If there be the remotest possibility of it," continued Georgiana, "let the attempt be made at whatever risk. Danger is nothing to me; for life, while this hateful mark makes me the object of your horror and disgust—life is a burden which I would fling down with joy. Either remove this dreadful hand, or take my wretched life! You have deep science. All the world bears witness of it. You have achieved great wonders. Cannot you remove this little, little mark, which I cover with the tips of two small fingers? Is this beyond your power, for the sake of your own peace, and to save your poor wife from madness?"

"Noblest, dearest, tenderest wife," cried Aylmer, rapturously, "doubt not my power. I have already given this matter the deepest thought— thought which might almost have enlightened me to create a being less perfect than yourself. Georgiana, you have led me deeper than ever into the heart of science. I feel myself fully competent to render this dear cheek as faultless as its fellow; and then, most beloved, what will be my triumph when I shall have corrected what Nature left imperfect in her fairest work! Even Pygmalion, when his sculptured woman assumed life, felt not greater ecstasy than mine will be."

"It is resolved, then," said Georgiana, faintly smiling. "And, Aylmer, spare me not, though you should find the birthmark take refuge in my heart at last."

Her husband tenderly kissed her cheek—her right cheek—not that which bore the impress of the crimson hand.

The next day Aylmer apprised his wife of a plan that he had formed whereby he might have opportunity for the intense thought and constant watchfulness which the proposed operation would require; while Georgiana, likewise, would enjoy the perfect repose essential to its success. They were to seclude themselves in the extensive apartments occupied by Aylmer as a laboratory, and where, during his toilsome youth, he had made discoveries in the elemental powers of Nature that had roused the admiration of all the learned societies in Europe. Seated calmly in this laboratory, the pale philosopher had investigated the secrets of the highest cloud region and of the profoundest mines; he had satisfied himself of the causes that kindled and kept alive the fires of the volcano; and had explained the mysteries of fountains, and how it is that they gush forth, some so bright and pure, and others with such rich medicinal virtues, from the dark bosom of the earth. Here, too, at an earlier period, he had studied the wonders of the human frame, and attempted to fathom the very process by which Nature assimilates all her precious influences from earth and air, and from the spiritual world, to create and foster man, her masterpiece. The latter pursuit, however, Aylmer had long laid aside in unwilling recognition of the truth— against which all seekers sooner or later stumble—that our great creative Mother, while she amuses us with apparently working in the broadest sunshine, is yet severely careful to keep her own secrets, and, in spite of her pretended openness, shows us nothing but results. She permits us, indeed, to mar, but seldom to mend, and, like a jealous patentee, on no account to make. Now, however, Aylmer resumed these half-forgotten investigations; not, of course, with such hopes or wishes as first suggested them; but because they involved much physiological truth and lay in the path of his proposed scheme for the treatment of Georgiana.

As he led her over the threshold of the laboratory, Georgiana was cold and tremulous. Aylmer looked cheerfully into her face, with intent to reassure her, but was so startled with the intense glow of the birthmark upon the whiteness of her cheek that he could not restrain a strong convulsive shudder. His wife fainted.

"Aminadab! Aminadab!" shouted Aylmer, stamping violently on the floor.

Forthwith there issued from an inner apartment a man of low stature, but bulky frame, with shaggy hair hanging about his visage, which was grimed with the vapors of the furnace. This personage had been Aylmer's underworker during his whole scientific career, and was admirably fitted for that office by his great mechanical readiness, and the skill with which, while incapable of comprehending a single principle, he executed all the details of his master's experiments. With his vast strength, his shaggy hair, his smoky aspect, and the indescribable earthiness that incrusted him, he seemed to represent man's physical nature; while Aylmer's slender figure and pale, intellectual face, were no less apt a type of the spiritual element.

"Throw open the door of the boudoir, Aminadab," said Aylmer, "and burn a pastille."

"Yes, master," answered Aminadab, looking intently at the lifeless form of Georgiana; and then he muttered to himself, "If she were my wife, I'd never part with that birthmark."

When Georgiana recovered consciousness she found herself breathing an atmosphere of penetrating fragrance, the gentle potency of which had recalled her from her deathlike faintness. The scene around her looked like enchantment. Aylmer had converted those smoky, dingy somber rooms, where he had spent his brightest years in recondite pursuits, into a series of beautiful apartments not unfit to be the secluded abode of a lovely woman. The walls were hung with gorgeous curtains, which imparted the combination of grandeur and grace that no other species of adornment can achieve; and as they fell from the ceiling to the floor, their rich and ponderous folds, concealing all angles and straight lines, appeared to shut in the scene from infinite space. For aught Georgiana knew, it might be a pavilion among the clouds. And Aylmer, excluding the sunshine, which would have interfered with his chemical processes, had supplied its place with perfumed lamps, emitting flames of various hue, but all uniting in a soft, impurpled radiance. He now knelt by his wife's side, watching her earnestly, but without alarm; for he was confident in his science, and felt that he could draw a magic circle round her within which no evil might intrude.

"Where am I? Ah, I remember," said Georgiana, faintly; and she placed her hand over her cheek to hide the terrible mark from her husband's eyes.

"Fear not, dearest!" exclaimed he. "Do not shrink from me! Believe me, Georgiana, I even rejoice in this single imperfection, since it will be such a rapture to remove it."

"Oh, spare me!" sadly replied his wife. "Pray do not look at it again. I never can forget that convulsive shudder."

In order to soothe Georgiana, and, as it were, to release her mind from the burden of actual things, Aylmer now put in practice some of the light and playful secrets which science had taught him among its profounder lore. Airy figures, absolutely bodiless ideas, and forms of unsubstantial beauty came and danced before her, imprinting their momentary footsteps on beams of light. Though she had some indistinct idea of the method of these optical phenomena, still the illusion was almost perfect enough to warrant the belief that her husband possessed sway over the spiritual world. Then again, when she felt a wish to look forth from her seclusion, immediately, as if her thoughts were answered, the procession of external existence flitted across a screen. The scenery and the figures of actual life were perfectly represented, but with that bewitching, yet indescribable difference which always makes a picture, an image, or a shadow so much more attractive than the original. When wearied of this, Aylmer bade her cast her eyes upon a vessel containing a quantity of earth. She did so, with little interest at first; but was soon startled to perceive the germ of a plant shooting upward from the soil. Then came the slender stalk; the leaves gradually unfolded themselves; and amid them was a perfect and lovely flower.

"It is magical!" cried Georgiana. "I dare not touch it."

"Nay, pluck it," answered Aylmer—"pluck it, and inhale its brief perfume while you may. The flower will wither in a few moments and leave nothing save its brown seed vessels; but thence may be perpetuated a race as ephemeral as itself."

But Georgiana had no sooner touched the flower than the whole plant suffered a blight, its leaves turning coal-black as if by the agency of fire.

"There was too powerful a stimulus," said Aylmer, thoughtfully.

To make up for this abortive experiment, he proposed to take her portrait by a scientific process of his own invention. It was to be effected by rays of light striking upon a polished plate of metal. Georgiana assented; but, on looking at the result, was affrighted to find the features of the portrait blurred and indefinable; while the minute figure of a hand appeared where the cheek should have been. Aylmer snatched the metallic plate and threw it into a jar of corrosive acid.

Soon, however, he forgot these mortifying failures. In the intervals of study and chemical experiment he came to her flushed and exhausted, but seemed invigorated by her presence, and spoke in glowing language of the resources of his art. He gave a history of the long dynasty of the alchemists, who spent so many ages in quest of the universal solvent by which the golden principle might be elicited from all things vile and base. Aylmer appeared to believe that, by the plainest scientific logic, it was altogether within the limits of possibility to discover this long-sought medium; "but," he added, "a philosopher who should go deep enough to acquire the power would attain too lofty a wisdom to stoop to the exercise of it." Not less singular were his opinions in regard to the *elixir vitae*. He more than intimated that it was at his option to concoct a liquor that should prolong life for years, perhaps interminably; but that it would produce a discord in Nature which all the world, and chiefly the quaffer of the immortal nostrum, would find cause to curse.

"Aylmer, are you in earnest?" asked Georgiana, looking at him with amazement and fear. "It is terrible to possess such power, or even to dream of possessing it."

"Oh, do not tremble, my love," said her husband. "I would not wrong either you or myself by working such inharmonious effects upon our lives; but I would have you consider how trifling, in comparison, is the skill requisite to remove this little hand."

At the mention of the birthmark, Georgiana, as usual, shrank as if a red-hot iron had touched her cheek.

Again Aylmer applied himself to his labors. She could hear his voice in the distant furnace room giving directions to Aminadab, whose harsh, uncouth, misshapen tones were audible in response, more like the grunt or growl of a brute than human speech. After hours of absence, Aylmer reappeared and proposed that she should now examine his cabinet of chemical products and natural treasures of the earth. Among the former he showed her a small vial, in which, he remarked, was contained a gentle yet most powerful fragrance, capable of impregnating all the breezes that blow across a kingdom. They were of inestimable value, the contents of that little vial; and, as he said so, he threw some of the perfume into the air and filled the room with piercing and invigorating delight.

"And what is this?" asked Georgiana, pointing to a small crystal globe containing a gold-colored liquid. "It is so beautiful to the eyes that I could imagine it the elixir of life."

"In one sense it is," replied Aylmer; "or, rather, the elixir of immortality. It is the most precious poison that ever was concocted in this world. By its aid I could apportion the lifetime of any mortal at whom you might point your finger. The strength of the dose would determine whether he were to linger out years, or drop dead in the midst of a breath. No king on his guarded throne could keep his life if I, in my private station, should deem that the welfare of millions justified me in depriving him of it."

"Why do you keep such a terrific drug?" inquired Georgiana in horror.

"Do not mistrust me, dearest," said her husband, smiling; "its virtuous potency is yet greater than its harmful one. But see! here is a powerful cosmetic. With a few drops of this in a vase of water, freckles may be washed away as easily as the hands are cleansed. A stronger infusion would take the blood out of the cheek, and leave the rosiest beauty a pale ghost."

"Is it with this lotion that you intend to bathe my cheek?" asked Georgiana, anxiously.

"Oh, no," hastily replied her husband; "this is merely superficial. Your case demands a remedy that shall go deeper."

In his interviews with Georgiana, Aylmer generally made minute inquiries as to her sensations and whether the confinement of the rooms and the temperature of the atmosphere agreed with her. These questions had such a particular drift that Georgiana began to conjecture that she was already subjected to certain physical influences, either breathed in with the fragrant air or taken with her food. She fancied likewise, but it might be altogether fancy, that there was a stirring up of her system—a strange, indefinite sensation creeping through her veins, and tingling, half painfully, half pleasurably, at her heart. Still, whenever she dared to look into the mirror, there she beheld herself pale as a white rose and with the crimson birthmark stamped upon her cheek. Not even Aylmer now hated it so much as she.

To dispel the tedium of the hours which her husband found it necessary to devote to the processes of combination and analysis, Georgiana turned over the volumes of his scientific library. In many dark old tomes she met with chapters full of romance and poetry. They were works of philosophers of the middle ages, such as Albertus Magnus, Cornelius Agrippa, Paracelsus, and the famous friar who created the prophetic Brazen Head. All these antique naturalists stood in advance of their centuries, yet were imbued with some of their credulity, and therefore were believed, and perhaps imagined themselves to have acquired from the investigation of Nature a power above Nature, and from physics a sway over the spiritual world. Hardly less curious and imaginative were the early volumes of the *Transactions of the Royal Society* in which the members, knowing little of the limits of natural possibility, were continually recording wonders or proposing methods whereby wonders might be wrought.

But to Georgiana the most engrossing volume was a large folio from her husband's own hand, in which he recorded every experiment of his scientific career, its original aim, the methods adopted for its development, and its final success or failure, with the circumstances to which either event was attributable. The book, in truth, was both the history and emblem of his ardent, ambitious, imaginative, yet practical and laborious life. He handled physical details as if there were nothing beyond them; yet spiritualized them all, and redeemed himself from materialism by his strong and eager aspiration towards the infinite. In his grasp the veriest clod of earth assumed a soul. Georgiana, as she read, reverenced Aylmer and loved him more profoundly than ever, but with a less entire dependence on his judgment than heretofore. Much as he had accomplished, she could not but observe that his most splendid successes were almost invariably failures, if compared with the ideal at which he aimed. His brightest diamonds were the merest pebbles, and felt to be so by himself, in comparison with the inestimable gems which lay hidden beyond his reach. The volume, rich with achievements that had won renown for its author, was yet as melancholy a record as ever mortal hand had penned. It was the sad confession and continual exemplification of the shortcomings of the composite man, the spirit burdened with clay and working in matter, and of the despair that assails the higher nature at finding itself so miserably thwarted by the earthly part. Perhaps every man of genius in whatever sphere might recognize the image of his own experience in Aylmer's journal.

So deeply did these reflections affect Georgiana that she laid her face upon the open volume and burst into tears. In this situation she was found by her husband.

"It is dangerous to read in a sorcerer's books," said he with a smile, though his countenance was uneasy and displeased. "Georgiana, there are pages in that volume which I can scarcely glance over and keep my senses. Take heed lest it prove as detrimental to you."

"It has made me worship you more than ever," said she.

"Ah, wait for this one success," rejoined he, "then worship me if you will. I shall deem myself hardly unworthy of it. But come, I have sought you for the luxury of your voice. Sing to me, dearest."

So she poured out the liquid music of her voice to quench the thirst of his spirit. He then took his leave with a boyish exuberance of gayety, assuring her that her seclusion would endure but a little longer, and that the result was already certain. Scarcely had he departed when Georgiana felt irresistibly impelled to follow him. She had forgotten to inform Aylmer of a symptom which for two or three hours past had begun to excite her attention. It was a sensation in the fatal birthmark, not painful, but which induced a restlessness throughout her system. Hastening after her husband, she intruded for the first time into the laboratory.

The first thing that struck her eye was the furnace, that hot and feverish worker, with the intense glow of its fire, which by the quantities of soot clustered above it seemed to have been burning for ages. There was a distilling apparatus in full operation. Around the room were retorts, tubes, cylinders, crucibles, and other apparatus of chemical research. An electrical machine stood ready for immediate use. The atmosphere felt oppressively close, and was tainted with gaseous odors which had been tormented forth by the processes of science. The severe and homely simplicity of the apartment, with its naked walls and brick pavement, looked strange, accustomed as Georgiana had become to the fantastic elegance of her boudoir. But what chiefly, indeed almost solely, drew her attention, was the aspect of Aylmer himself.

He was pale as death, anxious and absorbed, and hung over the furnace as if it depended upon his utmost watchfulness whether the liquid which it was distilling should be the draught of immortal happiness or misery. How different from the sanguine and joyous mien that he had assumed for Georgiana's encouragement!

"Carefully now, Aminadab; carefully, thou human machine; carefully, thou man of clay!" muttered Aylmer, more to himself than his assistant. "Now, if there be a thought too much or too little, it is all over."

"Ho! ho!" mumbled Aminadab. "Look, master! look!"

Aylmer raised his eyes hastily, and at first reddened, then grew paler than ever, on beholding Georgiana. He rushed toward her and seized her arm with a gripe that left the print of his fingers.

"Why do you come hither? Have you no trust in your husband?" cried he, impetuously. "Would you throw the blight of that fatal birthmark over my labors? It is not well done. Go, prying woman, go!"

"Nay, Aylmer," said Georgiana with the firmness of which she possessed no stinted endowment, "it is not you that have a right to complain. You mistrust your wife; you have concealed the anxiety with which you watch the development of this experiment. Think not so unworthily of me, my husband. Tell me all the risk we run, and fear not that I shall shrink; for my share in it is far less than your own."

"No, no, Georgiana!" said Aylmer, impatiently; "it must not be."

"I submit," replied she calmly. "And, Aylmer, I shall quaff whatever draught you bring me; but it will be on the same principle that would induce me to take a dose of poison if offered by your hand."

"My noble wife," said Aylmer, deeply moved, "I knew not the height and depth of your nature until now. Nothing shall be concealed. Know, then, that this crimson hand, superficial as it seems, has clutched its grasp into your being with a strength of which I had no previous conception. I have already administered agents powerful enough to do aught except to change your entire physical system. Only one thing remains to be tried. If that fail us we are ruined."

"Why did you hesitate to tell me this?" asked she.

"Because, Georgiana," said Aylmer, in a low voice, "there is danger."

"Danger? There is but one danger—that this horrible stigma shall be left upon my cheek!" cried Georgiana. "Remove it, remove it, whatever be the cost, or we shall both go mad!"

"Heaven knows your words are too true," said Aylmer, sadly. "And now, dearest, return to your boudoir. In a little while all will be tested."

He conducted her back and took leave of her with a solemn tenderness which spoke far more than his words how much was now at stake. After his departure Georgiana became rapt in musings. She considered the character of Aylmer, and did it completer justice than at any previous moment. Her heart exulted, while it trembled, at his honorable love— so pure and lofty that it would accept nothing less than perfection nor miserably make itself contented with an earthlier nature than he had dreamed of. She felt how much more precious was such a sentiment than that meaner kind which would have borne with the imperfection for her sake, and have been guilty of treason to holy love by degrading its perfect ideal to the level of the actual; and with her whole spirit she prayed that, for a single moment, she might satisfy his highest and deepest conception. Longer than one moment she well knew it could not be; for his spirit was ever on the march, ever ascending, and each instant required something that was beyond the scope of the instant before.

The sound of her husband's footsteps aroused her. He bore a crystal goblet containing a liquor colorless as water, but bright enough to be the draught of immortality. Aylmer was pale; but it seemed rather the consequence of a highly wrought state of mind and tension of spirit than of fear or doubt.

"The concoction of the draught has been perfect," said he, in answer to Georgiana's look. "Unless all my science have deceived me, it cannot fail."

"Save on your account, my dearest Aylmer," observed his wife, "I might wish to put off this birthmark of mortality by relinquishing mortality itself in preference to any other mode. Life is but a sad possession to those who have attained precisely the degree of moral advancement at which I stand. Were I weaker and blinder it might be happiness. Were I stronger, it might be endured hopefully. But, being what I find myself, methinks I am of all mortals the most fit to die."

"You are fit for heaven without tasting death!" replied her husband.

"But why do you speak of dying? The draught cannot fail. Behold its effect upon this plant."

On the window seat there stood a geranium diseased with yellow blotches, which had overspread all its leaves. Aylmer poured a small quantity of the liquid upon the soil in which it grew. In a little time, when the roots of the plant had taken up the moisture, the unsightly blotches began to be extinguished in a living verdure.

"There needed no proof," said Georgiana, quietly. "Give me the goblet. I joyfully stake all upon your word."

"Drink, then, thou lofty creature!" exclaimed Aylmer with fervid admiration. "There is no taint of imperfection on thy spirit. Thy sensible frame, too, shall soon be all perfect."

She quaffed the liquid and returned the goblet to his hand.

"It is grateful," said she with a placid smile. "Methinks it is like water from a heavenly fountain; for it contains I know not what of unobtrusive fragrance and deliciousness. It allays a feverish thirst that had parched me for many days. Now, dearest, let me sleep. My earthly senses are closing over my spirit like the leaves around the heart of a rose at sunset."

She spoke the last words with a gentle reluctance, as if it required almost more energy than she could command to pronounce the faint and lingering syllables. Scarcely had they loitered through her lips ere she was lost in slumber. Aylmer sat by her side, watching her aspect with the emotions proper to a man the whole value of whose existence was involved in the process now to be tested. Mingled with this mood, however, was the philosophic investigation characteristic of the man of science. Not the minutest symptom escaped him. A heightened flush of the cheek, a slight irregularity of breath, a quiver of the eyelid, a hardly perceptible tremor through the frame—such were the details which, as the moments passed, he wrote down in his folio volume. Intense thought had set its stamp upon every previous page of that volume, but the thoughts of years were all concentrated upon the last.

While thus employed, he failed not to gaze often at the fatal hand, and not without a shudder. Yet once, by a strange and unaccountable impulse, he pressed it with his lips. His spirit recoiled, however, in the very act; and Georgiana, out of the midst of her deep sleep, moved uneasily and murmured as if in remonstrance. Again Aylmer resumed his watch. Nor was it without avail. The crimson hand, which at first had been strongly visible upon the marble paleness of Georgiana's cheek, now grew more faintly outlined. She remained not less pale than ever; but the birthmark, with every breath that came and went, lost somewhat of its former distinctness. Its presence had been awful; its departure was more awful still. Watch the stain of the rainbow fading out the sky, and you will know how the mysterious symbol passed away.

"By Heaven! it is well-nigh gone!" said Aylmer to himself, in almost irrepressible ecstasy. "I can scarcely trace it now. Success! success! And now it is like the faintest rose color. The lightest flush of blood across her cheek would overcome it. But she is so pale!"

He drew aside the window curtain and suffered the light of natural day to fall into the room and rest upon her cheek. At the same time he heard a gross, hoarse chuckle, which he had long known as his servant Aminadab's expression of delight.

"Ah, clod! ah, earthly mass!" cried Aylmer, laughing in a sort of frenzy, "you have served me well! Matter and spirit—earth and heaven —have both done their part in this! Laugh, thing of the senses! You have earned the right to laugh."

These exclamations broke Georgiana's sleep. She slowly unclosed her eyes and gazed into the mirror which her husband had arranged for that purpose. A faint smile flitted over her lips when she recognized how barely perceptible was now that crimson hand which had once blazed forth with such disastrous brilliancy as to scare away all their happiness. But then her eyes sought Aylmer's face with a trouble and anxiety that he could by no means account for.

"My poor Aylmer!" murmured she.

"Poor? Nay, richest, happiest, most favored!" exclaimed he. "My peerless bride, it is successful! You are perfect!"

"My poor Aylmer," she repeated with a more than human tenderness, "you have aimed loftily; you have done nobly. Do not repent that with so high and pure a feeling, you have rejected the best the earth could offer. Aylmer, dearest Aylmer, I am dying!"

Alas! it was too true! The fatal hand had grappled with the mystery of life, and was the bond by which an angelic spirit kept itself in union with a mortal frame. As the last crimson tint of the birthmark—that sole token of human imperfection—faded from her cheek, the parting breath of the now perfect woman passed into the atmosphere, and her soul, lingering a moment near her husband, took its heavenward flight. Then a hoarse, chuckling laugh was heard again! [Thus ever does the gross fatality of earth exult in its invariable triumph over the immortal essence which, in this dim sphere of half development, demands the completeness of a higher state. Yet, had Aylmer reached a profounder wisdom, he need not thus have flung away the happiness which would have woven his mortal life of the selfsame texture with the celestial. The momentary circumstance was too strong for him; he failed to look beyond the shadowy scope of time, and, living once for all in eternity, to find the perfect future in the present.]

INTERPRETATION

This story amounts to a sort of *parable* (see Glossary). Indeed, Hawthorne frankly applies the term "parable" to one or two of his other stories of this kind. In the second paragraph of this story, Hawthorne says quite explicitly that the story of Aylmer and Georgiana has a "deeply impressive moral." But if we as readers are deeply impressed with the moral, we will be so because the presentation has been sufficiently concrete and sufficiently dramatic to impress us: the moral will hardly be "deeply impressive" in isolation. Even if we grant that Hawthorne is primarily interested here in the theme and does not hesitate to bring his theme to the fore, we are still compelled to ask the same questions with regard to this story which we have had to ask with regard to other stories. We may well begin with the problem which will probably present itself early to any reader: the problem of motivation.

Why is Aylmer anxious to remove the birthmark from his wife's cheek? She herself is frankly shocked when her husband first suggests removing it. She had not thought of it as a blemish; she had actually been complimented on it as something which was rather charming; and obviously, the birthmark had not prevented Aylmer from thinking her very beautiful, or from marrying her. Indeed, we are told, only a few women, jealous of her surpassing beauty, had ever regarded it as a disfigurement.

It is ironical that even Aylmer would not have come to regard the birthmark as a blemish if Georgiana had been less beautiful. As it is, the birthmark arrests his attention and gradually provokes his desire to remove it from the very fact that it remains the only possible blemish upon otherwise perfect beauty: ". . . his eyes wandered stealthily to her cheek, and beheld, flickering with the blaze of the wood fire, the spectral hand that wrote mortality where he would fain have worshiped."

Even so, had Aylmer not been a scientist, a daring experimenter, the birthmark on his wife's cheek would hardly have come to obsess him; for it was neither so large nor so prominent that it might not have been dismissed from mind, had not the thought that it lay within his power to remove it insinuated itself into Aylmer's imagination. That this is a very prominent part of his motivation is indicated in his remark to Georgiana: "I feel myself fully competent to render this cheek as faultless as its fellow; and then, most beloved, what will be my triumph when I shall have corrected what Nature left imperfect in her fairest work!"

We are not, of course, to conceive of Aylmer as a monster, a man who would experiment on his own wife for his own greater glory. Hawthorne does not mean to suggest that Aylmer *is* depraved and heartless. The triumph of which Aylmer speaks will not be for vulgar display and self-advertisement. It will be a triumph which his wife will share and a triumph to be won for her sake. And he *is* confident that he will be successful. The element of pride is there, but the kind of pride, it is suggested, is that which enters into and colors many of man's nobler purposes. What the story emphasizes is not Aylmer's self-conceit but rather his possession of the questing spirit which will not resign itself to the limitations and imperfections of nature. Nature itself is to be corrected, to be made perfect.

The decision to attempt to remove the birthmark is, of course, not arrived at in a moment, but by stages. Aylmer, before he allows the experiment to become a part of his conscious purpose, finds himself dreaming of it. His wife, who had paid no attention to her birthmark, soon begins to become self-conscious about it, and finally the mark becomes something hateful to her. Moreover, when she finds how much the thought of its removal has come to mean to her husband, she urges him on as a proof of her love for him. Others had counted the blemish charming, and other lovers would have risked life to kiss it; but just before the final experiment is to be made Georgiana can say that she fears only one thing—not death, but "that this horrible stigma shall be left upon my cheek!" As for Aylmer, the enterprise, which at the beginning was little more than a fantastic notion, has become a "rapture."

Aminadab, Aylmer's assistant, provides a sort of measuring stick for the folly and nobility of the husband and wife. He is, as Aylmer calls him, a "man of clay." He lacks the imagination for the noble enterprise of daring to surpass nature. The tiny blemish in a woman so beautiful as Georgiana would cause him no uneasiness at all, and he says, with a shrewd and solid common sense, "If she were my wife, I'd never part with that birthmark."

The birthmark is removed. Aylmer has his "peerless bride" in entire perfection for a moment, but the birthmark, symbol of the earthy, the mortal, can be eradicated only at the price of life itself. Aylmer has not realized that perfection is something never achieved on earth and in terms of mortality.

Here, of course, appears the theme of the story, the "impressive moral" which we have been told the story contains. But if the story is to be merely the vehicle for this moral, why has Hawthorne chosen to use the method of fiction at all? It is true that the story, as he has constructed it, is a rather transparent symbol for the basic idea, and that the characters have a rather obvious symbolic reference: Aminadab stands for the earthy, gross side of man's nature; Aylmer, for the aspiring and imaginative element in man. But, even so, why has Hawthorne written a story at all rather than an essay, say, or a sermon?

An obvious reason in favor of the story, of course, is our basic interest as human beings in a story, even a story which is closely tied to an idea. The story allows the author to develop suspense, to provide a dramatic form for the situation, to engage our interests more intensely. But there are other things which Hawthorne gains from his use of fiction here, matters usually overlooked but perhaps more important ultimately than the added interest and intensity. We shall see what these things are if we consider Hawthorne's attitude toward the situation which he has described. What, for example, is Hawthorne's attitude toward the various characters and toward the decisions which they make? Aminadab, for instance, would seem to support Hawthorne's moral, but does Hawthorne consider him to be a higher type than Aylmer? Hardly. Aminadab is for the author, too, a "man of clay," gross, animal-like, easily satisfied. Aylmer tries to achieve what is impossible and thus commits a folly; but it would be misreading the story to infer that Hawthorne dismisses him as merely a foolish man. The author is sympathetic to him, and obviously sees in his ruinous experiment a certain nobility.

What is the author's attitude toward the moral itself? Is man to give up all his attempts to conquer nature? Would Hawthorne have men settle down into a supine and passive acceptance of what nature gives? A careful reading of the story will suggest that Hawthorne himself does not take his own moral in these terms. There are many qualifications to be made, one would gather—matters of emphasis and matters of application to be taken into account. One cannot range the characters into two absolute categories, the good and the bad, the right and the wrong; and the moral itself is not a rule to be applied absolutely and without qualification.

Most important of all, it should be apparent that Hawthorne is *not interested in having us apply a rule*—he is not interested merely in trying to win our assent to a particular generalization, or in trying to make us adopt a certain course of action. His story, even with its heavy emphasis on a particular theme, is something more than a sermon or a lawyer's brief. His total intention, like that of any writer of fiction, is wider than this.

The whole matter of the relation of fiction to its theme is difficult and complicated. It will be discussed in more detail in Section IV of this book. It may suffice at this time to say no more than this: "The Birthmark," in its full intention, is far closer to a story so unlike it as "The Man Who Would Be King" than it is to any tract.

Science over Nature

1. Compare the theme of this story with that of "R.M.S. *Titanic*."

2. Do the characters become oversimplified in Hawthorne's preoccupation with his theme?

3. How do the various experiments which Aylmer performs in the laboratory for Georgiana's amusement *foreshadow* (see Glossary) the outcome of the story?

4. Is Georgiana's analysis of her husband's character (see pp. 97–98) convincing?

5. Is Hawthorne's explication of the meaning of his story, an explication which occupies the last three sentences, necessary? Or is it a blemish on the story?

Georgiana: the symbol of imperfection.
Aylmer: the perfectionist in the realm of abstract idea.
Aminadab: the grossness of the world

How Plot Reveals

What is the author trying to do?? (Our objective)!

IN THE comments accompanying the preceding stories, we have been concerned simply with describing some of the basic aspects of fiction, —plot, character, theme—and with pointing out how these aspects are related to each other. As a careful student will have observed, the analyses have not only confined themselves to description, but have made no pretension to being exhaustive as description. But any reader has preferences among stories. He values some stories more highly than others. Why does he prefer one story to another? Why does he call one story good and one story bad?

One reason for preference may be found in the reader's own special interests and beliefs. A man strongly interested in baseball tends to be interested in *any* story about baseball. Or a very religious person tends to applaud *any* story which seems to support his religious views. Naturally, any person tends to have a predisposition to follow his interests and convictions. But in appreciating, or judging, a piece of literature, one may well keep in mind that such interests and convictions are preliminary and not final considerations. Even the man who is interested in baseball prefers some baseball stories to other baseball stories. The instant such a man says that he prefers one baseball story to another baseball story, he admits that he has brought into play certain factors of judgment which have nothing to do with his interest in baseball. In maintaining that story A is better than story B, he has admitted that one story is better than the other as *story* and not as a baseball story.* Inevitably, the preference will depend, to a degree at least, on something in the nature of the story as story—on whether the motivation is

---

* But the student may well conclude that he is satisfied to enjoy his preferences in fiction without having to defend them in argument. He reads to enjoy stories and not to become a critic of stories. There is a sense in which the student is perfectly correct. His aim should be enjoyment. The intentions behind this textbook are thoroughly modest. The aim is to develop a closer and more intelligent reading. This involves critical discriminations—for, after all, every reader, whether he knows it or not, is a critic. But the end of criticism, even of the most high-flown and ambitious criticism, is, or should be, the increase of enjoyment.

acceptable, on how characters are related to plot, on the degree of plausibility in incidents, and the like. In other words, the preference depends on the *form* (see Glossary) of the story—the arrangement of characters and incidents in terms of a total meaning.

As we have remarked above, the comments on the preceding stories have been descriptive and not evaluative. As we go on to read more stories, however, we shall observe that some are more successful than others. (Of those already given in this book, some are more successful than others.) Some, we shall also observe, are more difficult than others. But sometimes we shall find that, in the end, we like best the stories which at first seemed difficult. In any case, if we are to examine our preferences and enlarge our enjoyment, we shall need to go further into the study of the forms of the story. Every story, in a sense, will present a new problem in understanding. But by investigating individual stories we may come to an understanding of certain principles which can lead us to a readier enjoyment of other stories.

As a matter of convenience we might very well consider a group of stories with special reference to their handling of the matter of plot. These stories are not selected because they necessarily emphasize the matter of plot. Nor shall we be able to discuss them solely in terms of plot, for, as we have already indicated, plot always involves the other aspects of a story. But these stories will provide us with the opportunity of studying some special ways in which plot may be related to the total meaning of a story.

The Furnished Room

O. HENRY

RESTLESS, shifting, fugacious as time itself is a certain vast bulk of the population of the red brick district of the lower West Side. Homeless, they have a hundred homes. They flit from furnished room to furnished room, transients forever—transients in abode, transients in heart and mind. They sing "Home, Sweet Home" in ragtime; they carry their *lares et penates* in a bandbox; their vine is entwined about a picture hat; a rubber plant is their fig tree.

Hence the houses of this district, having had a thousand dwellers, should have a thousand tales to tell, mostly dull ones, no doubt; but it would be strange if there could not be found a ghost or two in the wake of all these vagrant guests.

One evening after dark a young man prowled among these crumbling red mansions, ringing their bells. At the twelfth he rested his lean hand baggage upon the step and wiped the dust from his hatband and forehead. The bell sounded faint and far away in some remote, hollow depths.

To the door of this, the twelfth house whose bell he had rung, came a housekeeper who made him think of an unwholesome, surfeited worm that had eaten its nut to a hollow shell and now sought to fill the vacancy with edible lodgers.

He asked if there was a room to let.

"Come in," said the housekeeper. Her voice came from her throat; her throat seemed lined with fur. "I have the third floor, back, vacant since a week back. Should you wish to look at it?"

The young man followed her up the stairs. A faint light from no particular source mitigated the shadows of the halls. They trod noiselessly upon a stair carpet that its own loom would have forsworn. It seemed to have become vegetable; to have degenerated in that rank, sunless air to lush lichen or spreading moss that grew in patches to the staircase and was viscid under the foot like organic matter. At each turn of the stairs were vacant niches in the wall. Perhaps plants had once been set within them. If so, they had died in that foul and tainted air. It may be that statues of the saints had stood there, but it was not difficult to conceive that imps and devils had dragged them forth in the darkness and down to the unholy depths of some furnished pit below.

"This is the room," said the housekeeper, from her furry throat. "It's a nice room. It ain't often vacant. I had some most elegant people in it last summer—no trouble at all, and paid in advance to the minute. The water's at the end of the hall. Sprowls and Mooney kept it three months. They done a vaudeville sketch. Miss B'retta Sprowls—you may have heard of her—oh, that was just the stage names—right there over the dresser is where the marriage certificate hung, framed. The gas is here, and you see there is plenty of closet room. It's a room everybody likes. It never stays idle long."

"Do you have many theatrical people rooming here?" asked the young man.

"They comes and goes. A good proportion of my lodgers is connected with the theaters. Yes, sir, this is the theatrical district. Actor people never stays long anywhere. I get my share. Yes, they comes and they goes."

He engaged the room, paying for a week in advance. He was tired, he said, and would take possession at once. He counted out the money. The room had been made ready, she said, even to towels and water. As the housekeeper moved away he put, for the thousandth time, the question that he carried at the end of his tongue.

"A young girl—Miss Vashner—Miss Eloise Vashner—do you remember such a one among your lodgers? She would be singing on the stage, most likely. A fair girl, of medium height and slender, with reddish, gold hair and a dark mole near her left eyebrow."

"No, I don't remember the name. Them stage people has names they change as often as their rooms. They comes and they goes. No, I can't call that one to mind."

No. Always no. Five months of ceaseless interrogation and the inevitable negative. So much time spent by day in questioning managers, agents, schools, and choruses; by night among the audiences of theaters from all-star casts down to music halls so low that he dreaded to find what he most hoped for. He who had loved her best had tried to find her. He was sure that since her disappearance from home this great, water-girt city held her somewhere, but it was like a monstrous quicksand, shifting its particles constantly, with no foundation, its upper granules of today buried tomorrow in ooze and slime.

The furnished room received its latest guest with a first glow of pseudo-hospitality, a hectic, haggard, perfunctory welcome like the specious smile of a demirep. The sophistical comfort came in reflected gleams from the decayed furniture, the ragged brocade upholstery of a couch and two chairs, a foot-wide cheap pier glass between the two windows, from one or two gilt picture frames and a brass bedstead in a corner.

The guest reclined, inert, upon a chair, while the room, confused in speech as though it were an apartment in Babel, tried to discourse to him of its divers tenantry.

A polychromatic rug like some brilliant-flowered rectangular, tropical islet lay surrounded by a billowy sea of soiled matting. Upon the gay-papered wall were those pictures that pursue the homeless one from house to house—The Huguenot Lovers, The First Quarrel, The

Wedding Breakfast, Psyche at the Fountain. The mantel's chastely severe outline was ingloriously veiled behind some pert drapery drawn rakishly askew like the sashes of the Amazonian ballet. Upon it was some desolate flotsam cast aside by the room's marooned when a lucky sail had borne them to a fresh port—a trifling vase or two, pictures of actresses, a medicine bottle, some stray cards out of a deck.

One by one, as the characters of a cryptograph become explicit, the little signs left by the furnished room's procession of guests developed a significance. The threadbare space in the rug in front of the dresser told that lovely woman had marched in the throng. The tiny finger prints on the wall spoke of little prisoners trying to feel their way to sun and air. A splattered stain, raying like the shadow of a bursting bomb, witnessed where a hurled glass or bottle had splintered with its contents against the wall. Across the pier glass had been scrawled with a diamond in staggering letters the name "Marie." It seemed that the succession of dwellers in the furnished room had turned in fury— perhaps tempted beyond forbearance by its garish coldness—and wreaked upon it their passions. The furniture was chipped and bruised; the couch, distorted by bursting springs, seemed a horrible monster that had been slain during the stress of some grotesque con- vulsion. Some more potent upheaval had cloven a great slice from the marble mantel. Each plank in the floor owned its particular cant and shriek as from a separate and individual agony. It seemed incredible that all this malice and injury had been wrought upon the room by those who had called it for a time their home; and yet it may have been the cheated home instinct surviving blindly, the resentful rage at false household gods that had kindled their wrath. A hut that is our own we can sweep and adorn and cherish.

The young tenant in the chair allowed these thoughts to file, soft- shod, through his mind, while there drifted into the room furnished sounds and furnished scents. He heard in one room a tittering and in- continent, slack laughter; in others the monologue of a scold, the rattling of dice, a lullaby, and one crying dully; above him a banjo tinkled with spirit. Doors banged somewhere; the elevated trains roared intermittently; a cat yowled miserably upon a back fence. And he breathed the breath of the house—a dank savor rather than a smell —a cold, musty effluvium as from underground vaults mingled with the reeking exhalations of linoleum and mildewed and rotten wood-work.

Then, suddenly, as he rested there, the room was filled with the strong, sweet odor of mignonette. It came as upon a single buffet of wind with such sureness and fragrance and emphasis that it almost seemed a living visitant. And the man cried aloud: "What, dear?" as if he had been called, and sprang up and faced about. The rich odor clung to him and wrapped him around. He reached out his arms for it, all his senses for the time confused and commingled. How could one be peremptorily called by an odor? Surely it must have been a sound. But, was it not the sound that had touched, that had caressed him?

"She has been in this room," he cried, and he sprang to wrest from it a token, for he knew he would recognize the smallest thing that had belonged to her or that she had touched. This enveloping scent of mignonette, the odor that she had loved and made her own—whence came it?

The room had been but carelessly set in order. Scattered upon the flimsy dresser scarf were half a dozen hairpins—those discreet, in-distinguishable friends of womankind, feminine of gender, infinite of mood and uncommunicative of tense. These he ignored, conscious of their triumphant lack of identity. Ransacking the drawers of the dresser, he came upon a discarded, tiny, ragged handkerchief. He pressed it to his face. It was racy and insolent with heliotrope; he hurled it to the floor. In another drawer he found odd buttons, a theater pro-gram, a pawnbroker's card, two lost marshmallows, a book on the divination of dreams. In the last was a woman's black satin hair bow, which halted him, poised between ice and fire. But the black satin hair bow also is femininity's demure, impersonal, common ornament and tells no tales.

And then he traversed the room like a hound on the scent, skim-ming the walls, considering the corners of the bulging matting on his hands and knees, rummaging mantel and tables, the curtains and hangings, the drunken cabinet in the corner, for a visible sign, unable to perceive that she was there beside, around, against, within, above him, clinging to him, wooing him, calling him so poignantly through the finer senses that even his grosser ones became cognizant of the call. Once again he answered loudly: "Yes, dear!" and turned, wild-eyed, to gaze on vacancy, for he could not yet discern form and color and love and outstretched arms in the odor of mignonette. Oh, God! whence that odor, and since when have odors had a voice to call? Thus he groped.

He burrowed in crevices and corners, and found corks and cigarettes. These he passed in passive contempt. But once he found in a fold of the matting a half-smoked cigar, and this he ground beneath his heel with a green and trenchant oath. He sifted the room from end to end. He found dreary and ignoble small records of many a peripatetic tenant; but of her whom he sought, and who may have lodged there, and whose spirit seemed to hover there, he found no trace.

And then he thought of the housekeeper.

He ran from the haunted room downstairs and to a door that showed a crack of light. She came out to his knock. He smothered his excitement as best he could.

"Will you tell me, madam," he besought her, "who occupied the room I have before I came?"

"Yes, sir. I can tell you again. 'Twas Sprowls and Mooney, as I said. Miss B'retta Sprowls it was in the theaters, but Missis Mooney she was. My house is well known for respectability. The marriage certificate hung, framed, on a nail over—"

"What kind of a lady was Miss Sprowls—in looks, I mean?"

"Why, black-haired, sir, short, and stout, with a comical face. They left a week ago Tuesday."

"And before they occupied it?"

"Why, there was a single gentleman connected with the draying business. He left owing me a week. Before him was Missis Crowder and her two children that stayed four months; and back of them was old Mr. Doyle, whose sons paid for him. He kept the room six months. That goes back a year, sir, and further I do not remember."

He thanked her and crept back to his room. The room was dead. The essence that had vivified it was gone. The perfume of mignonette had departed. In its place was the old, stale odor of moldy house furniture, of atmosphere in storage.

The ebbing of his hope drained his faith. He sat staring at the yellow, singing gaslight. Soon he walked to the bed and began to tear the sheets into strips. With the blade of his knife he drove them tightly into every crevice around windows and door. When all was snug and taut, he turned out the light, turned the gas full on again, and laid himself gratefully upon the bed.

*   *   *   *

It was Mrs. McCool's night to go with the can for beer. So she fetched it and sat with Mrs. Purdy in one of those subterranean retreats where housekeepers foregather and the worm dieth seldom.

"I rented out my third floor, back, this evening," said Mrs. Purdy, across a fine circle of foam. "A young man took it. He went up to bed two hours ago."

"Now, did ye, Mrs. Purdy, ma'am?" said Mrs. McCool, with intense admiration. "You do be a wonder for rentin' rooms of that kind. And did ye tell him, then?" she concluded in a husky whisper laden with mystery.

"Rooms," said Mrs. Purdy, in her furriest tones, "are furnished for to rent. I did not tell him, Mrs. McCool."

" 'Tis right ye are, ma'am; 'tis by rentin' rooms we kape alive. Ye have the rale sense for business, ma'am. There be many people will rayjict the rentin' of a room if they be tould a suicide has been after dyin' in the bed of it."

"As you say, we has our living to be making," remarked Mrs. Purdy.

"Yis, ma'am; 'tis true. 'Tis just one wake ago this day I helped ye lay out the third floor, back. A pretty slip of a colleen she was to be killin' herself wid the gas—a swate little face she had, Mrs. Purdy, ma'am."

"She'd a-been called handsome, as you say," said Mrs. Purdy, assenting but critical, "but for that mole she had a-growin' by her left eyebrow. Do fill up your glass again, Mrs. McCool." *

INTERPRETATION

This story is obviously divided into two parts. The first part, which ends with the death of the lodger, concerns his failure in the search for

* From *The Four Million;* copyright 1905, 1933, by Doubleday, Doran & Company, Inc.

his sweetheart and the motivation of his suicide; the second part concerns the revelation, by the landlady to her crony, that his sweetheart had, a week earlier, committed suicide in the same room. What accounts for the fact that O. Henry felt it necessary to treat the story in this fashion? What holds the two parts of the story together? To discover the answers to these two related questions, let us consider the story itself.

The most interesting question has to do with the young man's motivation. In one sense, O. Henry has deliberately made the problem of his motivation more difficult by withholding the information that the sweetheart is dead. The young man does not know that she is dead; indeed, in the room, he gets, with the scent of mignonette, a renewed hope. Why then, under these circumstances, does he commit suicide? Presumably, the explanation is this: he has been searching fruitlessly for five months; he is, we are told, tired—and, we assume, not only momentarily tired physically, but spiritually weary. Indeed, we are told: "He was sure that since her disappearance from home this great water-girt city held her somewhere, but it was like a monstrous quicksand, shifting its particles constantly, with no foundation, its upper granules of today buried tomorrow in ooze and slime." But we are not supposed to believe, even so, that he would have necessarily turned on the gas this particular evening, except as a despairing reaction from the hope which has been raised by the scent of mignonette. This is the author's account of the motivation of the suicide. But is the motivation, as presented, really convincing? That will depend on the character of the man. What sort of man is he? Actually, O. Henry has told us very little about him except that he is young, has searched for his sweetheart for five months, and is tired. Especially does the question of the man's character, and state of mind, come up in the incident in which he notices the odor of mignonette. Did he really smell it? Did he merely imagine that he smelled it? "And he breathed the breath of the house . . . a cold, musty effluvium . . . mingled with the reeking exhalations of linoleum and mildewed and rotten woodwork. . . . Then, suddenly, as he rested there, the room was filled with the strong, sweet odor of mignonette. It came as upon a single buffet of wind. . . . The rich odor clung to him and wrapped him around."

The suddenness with which he notices the odor, the power of the odor, the fact that he can find no source for the odor, and finally the complete disappearance of the odor, all tend to imply that he merely imagines it. But over against this view, we have the testimony of the landlady that the sweetheart had actually occupied the room. This question is important, for it is crucial for the young man's lapse into acute despair. If the odor is real, the author must convince his reader that it exists; if it is imaginary, the author must convince his reader that the psychological condition of the young man will account for its apparent existence. These are the tests which the reader must apply to the situation. We have already pointed out that there is some evidence on both sides of the question. The reader must, of course, decide for himself which explanation must be taken, and more importantly, whether the explanation is convincing, and renders the action credible. The author, however, seems to weight the evidence toward the presence of the real odor. If this is the case, how are we to account for the fact that the search reveals no source of it, especially since the odor is so overpoweringly strong? Or, perhaps the author has in mind some idea that the odor provokes a mystical communion between the two lovers. But this does not relieve the fiction writer from the necessity for furnishing some sort of specific clue to his meaning. (Moreover, if we are to take the whole experience as an hallucination, the author is certainly not relieved from providing some clear motivation for the event.)

To sum up: it is obvious enough, from the detailed description of the room, that O. Henry is trying to suggest a ground for the man's experience in the nature of the room itself. That is, the room in its disorder, its squalor, its musty smell, its rubbish and debris of nameless lives, reflects the great city, or the world, in which his sweetheart has been lost, and in which all humanity seems to become degraded and brutalized. It is easy enough to see why O. Henry should want to suggest the contrast between what the sordid surroundings mean to the hero and what the odor of mignonette means to him. As the girl is lost somewhere in the great city, so the odor is lost somewhere in the room. After the young man is told that the girl has not been there, and after he has been unable to find the source of the odor, the room itself is supposed to become a sort of overwhelming symbol for the futility of his effort. This intention on the part of the author may be sound enough, but the fact that we see what the intention is does not mean that the intention has been carried out. The whole effect of the story depends on the incident of the odor, and we have seen that the handling of this detail is confused.

Assuming that this objection is valid, the basic remedy suggests itself at once. The author needed to go back and fill in the character of the young man much more fully. The reader might then have been able to follow the processes of his mind as he goes through his crucial experience, and the specific nature of his response to the odor would have been clarified. But O. Henry chooses an easier solution. Resting upon his rather thin and sketchy characterization of the young man, the author chooses to give a turn to the plot by a last-minute surprise. In the second part of the story the landlady tells her crony that she has lied to the young man about the girl.

What is the effect of this revelation? It is intended, obviously, to underline the "irony of fate," to illustrate the hard-heartedness of the city in which the young man finds himself, to justify the young man's overwhelming sense that the girl has been in the room, and, all in all, to pull the story together. For the sympathetic reader this conclusion is supposed to suggest that the bonds of love stretch across the confusion and squalor of the great city, and that, in a sense, the young man has finally succeeded in his search, for the lovers are at last united in death. The young man finds, as it were, the proper room in the great city in which to die.

But is the story really pulled together? The end of the story depends on the lie. But are the lives of the lovers altered by the lie? Does the lie cause the death of the young man? It is conceivable that, had the landlady told the truth, the shock of the information might have saved the young man from suicide, but this is the merest speculation. The character, as given in the story, commits suicide in despair when the landlady tells him that the girl has not been there; the landlady's telling him that the girl is irretrievably lost, is dead, would presumably have had the same effect.

Actually, is there any point in the lie except to trick the reader—to provide the illusion of a meaningful ending? Whatever irony lies in the ending is based on a far-fetched coincidence, and does not depend on the fact that the woman said one thing rather than another. (Readers who are inclined to accept the conclusion of the story as meaningful might try reconstructing the story with the young man's calling at the door, finding with horror that his sweetheart has committed suicide there a week before, renting the room, and turning on the gas. We would then still have the ironical coincidence and a sort of union of the lovers, but the story would seem very tame and flat.) O. Henry, by withholding certain information and thus surprising us with it at the end, has simply tried to give the reader the illusion that the information was meaningful. The irony, in the story as we have it, simply resides in a trick played on the reader rather than in a trick which fate has played on the young man.

Readers who feel that the end of this story is a shabby trick will be able to point out other symptoms of cheapness: the general thinness of characterization, the cluttered and sometimes mawkish description, the wheedling tone taken by the author, and the obvious play for emotional sympathy in such writing as the following: "Oh, God! whence that odor, and since when have odors had a voice to call?" In other words, we can readily surmise that the trickery involved in the surprise ending may be an attempt to compensate for defects within the body of the story itself.

But a trick of plot does not make a story. A surprise ending may appear in a very good story, but only if the surprise has been prepared for so that, upon second thought, the reader realizes that it is, after all, a logical and meaningful development from what has gone before, and not merely a device employed by the author to give him an easy way out of his difficulties. The same principle applies to *coincidence* (see Glossary) in general. Coincidences do occur in real life, sometimes quite startling ones, and in one sense every story is based on a coincidence—namely, that the particular events happen to occur together, that such and such characters happen to meet, for example. But since fiction is concerned with a logic of character and action, coincidence, in so far as it is purely illogical, has little place in fiction. Truth can afford to be stranger than fiction, because truth is "true"—is acceptable on its own merits—but the happenings of fiction, as we have seen, must justify themselves in terms of logical connection with other elements in fiction and in terms of meaningfulness. (See pp. 25–27.)

The Necklace

GUY DE MAUPASSANT

SHE was one of those pretty and charming girls who are sometimes, as if by a mistake of destiny, born in a family of clerks. She had no dowry, no expectations, no means of being known, understood, loved, wedded by any rich and distinguished man; and she let herself be married to a little clerk at the Ministry of Public Instruction.

She dressed plainly because she could not dress well, but she was as unhappy as though she had really fallen from her proper station, since with women there is neither caste nor rank; and beauty, grace, and charm act instead of family and birth. Natural fineness, instinct for what is elegant, suppleness of wit, are the sole hierarchy, and make from women of the people the equals of the very greatest ladies.

She suffered ceaselessly, feeling herself born for all the delicacies and all the luxuries. She suffered from the poverty of her dwelling, from the wretched look of the walls, from the worn-out chairs, from the ugliness of the curtains. All those things, of which another woman of her rank would never even have been conscious, tortured her and made her angry. The sight of the little Breton peasant who did her humble housework aroused in her regrets which were despairing, and distracted dreams. She thought of the silent antechambers hung with Oriental tapestry, lit by tall bronze candelabra, and of the two great footmen in knee breeches who sleep in the big armchairs, made drowsy by the heavy warmth of the hot-air stove. She thought of the long *salons* fitted up with ancient silk, of the delicate furniture carrying priceless curiosities, and of the coquettish perfumed boudoirs made for talks at five o'clock with intimate friends, with men famous and sought after, whom all women envy and whose attention they all desire.

When she sat down to dinner, before the round table covered with a tablecloth three days old, opposite her husband, who uncovered the soup tureen and declared with an enchanted air, "Ah, the good *pot-au-feu!* I don't know anything better than that," she thought of dainty dinners, of shining silverware, of tapestry which peopled the walls with ancient personages and with strange birds flying in the midst of a fairy forest; and she thought of delicious dishes served on marvelous plates, and of the whispered gallantries which you listen to with a sphinxlike smile, while you are eating the pink flesh of a trout or the wings of a quail.

She had no dresses, no jewels, nothing. And she loved nothing but that; she felt made for that. She would so have liked to please, to be envied, to be charming, to be sought after.

She had a friend, a former schoolmate at the convent, who was rich, and whom she did not like to go and see any more, because she suffered so much when she came back.

But one evening, her husband returned home with a triumphant air, and holding a large envelope in his hand.

"There," said he. "Here is something for you."

She tore the paper sharply, and drew out a printed card which bore these words:

"The Minister of Public Instruction and Mme. Georges Ramponneau request the honor of M. and Mme. Loisel's company at the palace of the Ministry on Monday evening, January eighteenth."

Instead of being delighted, as her husband hoped, she threw the invitation on the table with disdain, murmuring:

"What do you want me to do with that?"

"But, my dear, I thought you would be glad. You never go out, and this is such a fine opportunity. I had awful trouble to get it. Everyone wants to go; it is very select, and they are not giving many invitations to clerks. The whole official world will be there."

She looked at him with an irritated eye, and she said, impatiently:

"And what do you want me to put on my back?"

He had not thought of that; he stammered:

"Why, the dress you go to the theater in. It looks very well, to me."

He stopped, distracted, seeing that his wife was crying. Two great tears descended slowly from the corners of her eyes toward the corners of her mouth. He stuttered:

"What's the matter? What's the matter?"

But, by violent effort, she had conquered her grief, and she replied, with a calm voice, while she wiped her wet cheeks:

"Nothing. Only I have no dress and therefore I can't go to this ball. Give your card to some colleague whose wife is better equipped than I."

He was in despair. He resumed:

"Come, let us see, Mathilde. How much would it cost, a suitable dress, which you could use on other occasions, something very simple?"

She reflected several seconds, making her calculations and wondering also what sum she could ask without drawing on herself an immediate refusal and a frightened exclamation from the economical clerk.

Finally, she replied, hesitatingly:

"I don't know exactly, but I think I could manage it with four hundred francs."

He had grown a little pale, because he was laying aside just that amount to buy a gun and treat himself to a little shooting next summer on the plain of Nanterre, with several friends who went to shoot larks down there, of a Sunday.

But he said:

"All right. I will give you four hundred francs. And try to have a pretty dress."

The day of the ball drew near, and Mme. Loisel seemed sad, uneasy, anxious. Her dress was ready, however. Her husband said to her one evening:

"What is the matter? Come, you've been so queer these last three days."

And she answered:

"It annoys me not to have a single jewel, not a single stone, nothing to put on. I shall look like distress. I should almost rather not go at all."

He resumed:

"You might wear natural flowers. It's very stylish at this time of the year. For ten francs you can get two or three magnificent roses."

She was not convinced.

"No; there's nothing more humiliating than to look poor among other women who are rich."

But her husband cried:

"How stupid you are! Go look up your friend Mme. Forestier, and ask her to lend you some jewels. You're quite thick enough with her to do that."

She uttered a cry of joy:

"It's true. I never thought of it."

The next day she went to her friend and told of her distress.

Mme. Forestier went to a wardrobe with a glass door, took out a large jewel-box, brought it back, opened it, and said to Mme. Loisel:

"Choose, my dear."

She saw first of all some bracelets, then a pearl necklace, then a Venetian cross, gold and precious stones of admirable workmanship. She tried on the ornaments before the glass, hesitated, could not make up her mind to part with them, to give them back. She kept asking:

"Haven't you any more?"

"Why, yes. Look. I don't know what you like."

All of a sudden she discovered, in a black satin box, a superb necklace of diamonds, and her heart began to beat with an immoderate desire. Her hands trembled as she took it. She fastened it around her throat, outside her high-necked dress, and remained lost in ecstasy at the sight of herself.

Then she asked, hesitating, filled with anguish:

"Can you lend me that, only that?"

"Why, yes, certainly."

She sprang upon the neck of her friend, kissed her passionately, then fled with her treasure.

The day of the ball arrived. Mme. Loisel made a great success. She was prettier than them all, elegant, gracious, smiling, and crazy with joy. All the men looked at her, asked her name, endeavored to be introduced. All the attachés of the Cabinet wanted to waltz with her. She was remarked by the minister himself.

She danced with intoxication, with passion, made drunk by pleasure, forgetting all, in the triumph of her beauty, in the glory of her success, in a sort of cloud of happiness composed of all this homage, of all this admiration, of all these awakened desires, and of that sense of complete victory which is so sweet to a woman's heart.

She went away about four o'clock in the morning. Her husband had been sleeping since midnight, in a little deserted anteroom, with three other gentlemen whose wives were having a very good time. He threw over her shoulders the wraps which he had brought, modest wraps of common life, whose poverty contrasted with the elegance of the ball dress. She felt this, and wanted to escape so as not to be remarked by the other women, who were enveloping themselves in costly furs.

Loisel held her back.

"Wait a bit. You will catch cold outside. I will go and call a cab."

But she did not listen to him, and rapidly descended the stairs. When they were in the street they did not find a carriage; and they began to look for one, shouting after the cabmen whom they saw passing by at a distance.

They went down toward the Seine, in despair, shivering with cold. At last they found on the quay one of those ancient noctambulant coupés which, exactly as if they were ashamed to show their misery during the day, are never seen round Paris until after nightfall.

It took them to their door in the Rue des Martyrs, and once more, sadly, they climbed up homeward. All was ended, for her. And as to him, he reflected that he must be at the Ministry at ten o'clock.

She removed the wraps, which covered her shoulders, before the glass, so as once more to see herself in all her glory. But suddenly she uttered a cry. She had no longer the necklace around her neck!

Her husband, already half undressed, demanded:

"What is the matter with you?"

She turned madly towards him:

"I have—I have—I've lost Mme. Forestier's necklace."

He stood up, distracted.

"What!—how?—impossible!"

And they looked in the folds of her dress, in the folds of her cloak, in her pockets, everywhere. They did not find it.

He asked:

"You're sure you had it on when you left the ball?"

"Yes, I felt it in the vestibule of the palace."

"But if you had lost it in the street we should have heard it fall. It must be in the cab."

"Yes. Probably. Did you take his number?"

"No. And you, didn't you notice it?"

"No."

They looked, thunderstruck, at one another. At last Loisel put on his clothes.

"I shall go back on foot," said he, "over the whole route which we have taken to see if I can find it."

And he went out. She sat waiting on a chair in her ball dress, without strength to go to bed, overwhelmed, without fire, without a thought.

Her husband came back about seven o'clock. He had found nothing.

He went to Police Headquarters, to the newspaper offices, to offer a reward; he went to the cab companies—everywhere, in fact, whither he was urged by the least suspicion of hope.

She waited all day, in the same condition of mad fear before this terrible calamity.

Loisel returned at night with a hollow, pale face; he had discovered nothing.

"You must write to your friend," said he, "that you have broken the clasp of her necklace and that you are having it mended. That will give us time to turn round."

She wrote at his dictation.

At the end of a week they had lost all hope.

And Loisel, who had aged five years, declared:

"We must consider how to replace that ornament."

The next day they took the box which had contained it, and they went to the jeweler whose name was found within. He consulted his books.

"It was not I, madame, who sold that necklace; I must simply have furnished the case."

Then they went from jeweler to jeweler, searching for a necklace like the other, consulting their memories, sick both of them with chagrin and anguish.

They found, in a shop at the Palais Royal, a string of diamonds which seemed to them exactly like the one they looked for. It was worth forty thousand francs. They could have it for thirty-six.

So they begged the jeweler not to sell it for three days yet. And they made a bargain that he should buy it back for thirty-four thousand francs, in case they found the other one before the end of February.

Loisel possessed eighteen thousand francs which his father had left him. He would borrow the rest.

He did borrow, asking a thousand francs of one, five hundred of another, five louis here, three louis there. He gave notes, took up ruinous obligations, dealt with usurers and all the race of lenders. He compromised all the rest of his life, risked his signature without even knowing if he could meet it; and, frightened by the pains yet to come, by the black misery which was about to fall upon him, by the prospect of all the physical privations and of all the moral tortures which he was to suffer, he went to get the new necklace, putting down upon the merchant's counter thirty-six thousand francs.

When Mme. Loisel took back the necklace, Mme. Forestier said to her, with a chilly manner:

"You should have returned it sooner; I might have needed it."

She did not open the case, as her friend had so much feared. If she had detected the substitution, what would she have thought, what would she have said? Would she not have taken Mme. Loisel for a thief?

Mme. Loisel now knew the horrible existence of the needy. She took her part, moreover, all of a sudden, with heroism. That dreadful debt must be paid. She would pay it. They dismissed their servant; they changed their lodgings; they rented a garret under the roof.

She came to know what heavy housework meant and the odious cares of the kitchen. She washed the dishes, using her rosy nails on the greasy pots and pans. She washed the dirty linen, the shirts, and the dishcloths, which she dried upon a line; she carried the slops down to the street every morning, and carried up the water, stopping for breath at every landing. And, dressed like a woman of the people, she went to the fruiterer, the grocer, the butcher, her basket on her arm, bargaining, insulted, defending her miserable money sou by sou.

Each month they had to meet some notes, renew others, obtain more time.

Her husband worked in the evening making a fair copy of some tradesman's accounts, and late at night he often copied manuscript for five sous a page.

And this life lasted for ten years.

At the end of ten years, they had paid everything, everything, with the rates of usury, and the accumulations of the compound interest.

Mme. Loisel looked old now. She had become the woman of impoverished households—strong and hard and rough. With frowsy hair, skirts askew, and red hands, she talked loud while washing the floor with great swishes of water. But sometimes, when her husband was at the office, she sat down near the window, and she thought of that gay evening of long ago, of that ball where she had been so beautiful and so fêted.

What would have happened if she had not lost that necklace? Who knows? Who knows? How life is strange and changeful! How little a thing is needed for us to be lost or to be saved!

But, one Sunday, having gone to take a walk in the Champs Elysées to refresh herself from the labor of the week, she suddenly perceived a woman who was leading a child. It was Mme. Forestier, still young, still beautiful, still charming.

Mme. Loisel felt moved. Was she going to speak to her? Yes, certainly. And now that she had paid, she was going to tell her all about it. Why not?

She went up.

"Good-day, Jeanne."

The other, astonished to be familiarly addressed by this plain goodwife, did not recognize her at all, and stammered:

"But—madam!—I do not know— You must be mistaken."

"No. I am Mathilde Loisel."

Her friend uttered a cry.

"Oh, my poor Mathilde! How you are changed!"

"Yes, I have had days hard enough, since I have seen you, days wretched enough—and that because of you!"

"Of me! How so?"

"Do you remember that diamond necklace which you lent me to wear at the ministerial ball?"

"Yes. Well?"

"Well, I lost it."

"What do you mean? You brought it back."

"I brought you back another just like it. And for this we have been ten years paying. You can understand that it was not easy for us, us who had nothing. At last it is ended, and I am very glad."

Mme. Forestier had stopped.

"You say that you bought a necklace of diamonds to replace mine?"

"Yes. You never noticed it, then! They were very like."

And she smiled with a joy which was proud and naïve at once.

Mme. Forestier, strongly moved, took her two hands.

"Oh, my poor Mathilde! Why, my necklace was paste. It was worth at most five hundred francs!"

INTERPRETATION

This story ends with a surprising turn. The heroine, after years of privation and struggle caused by the loss of the borrowed necklace, learns that the jewels had, after all, been valueless. At first glance this revelation may seem to be a trick, just as the conclusion of "The Furnished Room" is a trick. To determine whether or not the conclusion of "The Necklace" is a trick, one should investigate the following questions:

1. Is the accidental fact that the jewels are paste used as a starting point from which the story develops, or is it merely a piece of trickery used to conclude the story (see Glossary, *coincidence*)? In other words, is there a really important difference between the fundamental fact that the jewels are paste, and the fact that the heroine eventually discovers them to be paste? Would there be an irony in the story even if the woman had never discovered the true nature of the jewels?

2. Waiving the question of the nature of the jewels: some people, having lost them, would have made a clean breast of the situation at once. Is the heroine's refusal to do so adequately motivated? Is the pride from which this refusal springs a true and admirable pride or merely a false pride? Or is it an ironical mixture of the two? The heroine's actions subsequent to the loss of the jewels are presumably conditioned by her character. Are these two elements logically related in the story?

3. Finally, does the fundamental meaning of the story depend on the fact of the loss of the jewels, whether paste or real? In other words, is not this the sort of woman who, in one way or another, would have wasted her life on some sort of vanity? (In this connection read the first paragraph of the story.) Does Maupassant not use the accident of the loss of the jewels as a means to speed up and intensify a process which is already inherent in the woman's character? If this can be maintained, then does not the falsity of the jewels become a kind of symbol for the root situation of the story? That is, does not the "falsity" of the jewels stand as a symbol for the falsity of the values by which the woman once lived?

4. Have we any evidence that the author intended to indicate a regeneration of the heroine?

An Occurrence at Owl Creek Bridge
AMBROSE BIERCE

A MAN stood upon a railroad bridge in northern Alabama, looking down into the swift water twenty feet below. The man's hands were behind his back, the wrists bound with a cord. A rope closely encircled his neck. It was attached to a stout cross-timber above his head

and the slack fell to the level of his knees. Some loose boards laid upon
the sleepers supporting the metals of the railway supplied a footing
for him and his executioners—two private soldiers of the Federal army,
directed by a sergeant who in civil life may have been a deputy sheriff.
At a short remove upon the same temporary platform was an officer
in the uniform of his rank, armed. He was a captain. A sentinel at
each end of the bridge stood with his rifle in the position known as
"support," that is to say, vertical in front of the left shoulder, the hammer resting on the forearm thrown straight across the chest—a formal
and unnatural position, enforcing an erect carriage of the body. It did
not appear to be the duty of these two men to know what was oc-
curring at the center of the bridge; they merely blockaded the two
ends of the foot planking that traversed it.

Beyond one of the sentinels nobody was in sight; the railroad ran
straight away into a forest for a hundred yards, then, curving, was lost
to view. Doubtless there was an outpost farther along. The other bank
of the stream was open ground—a gentle acclivity topped with a
stockade of vertical tree trunks, loopholed for rifles, with a single
embrasure through which protruded the muzzle of a brass cannon
commanding the bridge. Midway of the slope between the bridge
and fort were the spectators—a single company of infantry in line, at
"parade rest," the butts of the rifles on the ground, the barrels in-
clining slightly backward against the right shoulder, the hands crossed
upon the stock. A lieutenant stood at the right of the line, the point
of his sword upon the ground, his left hand resting upon his right.
Excepting the group of four at the center of the bridge, not a man
moved. The company faced the bridge, staring stonily, motionless.
The sentinels, facing the banks of the stream, might have been statues
to adorn the bridge. The captain stood with folded arms, silent, observing the work of his subordinates, but making no sign. Death is a
dignitary who when he comes announced is to be received with formal
manifestations of respect, even by those most familiar with him. In
the code of military etiquette silence and fixity are forms of deference.

The man who was engaged in being hanged was apparently about
thirty-five years of age. He was a civilian, if one might judge from his
habit, which was that of a planter. His features were good—a straight
nose, firm mouth, broad forehead, from which his long, dark hair was

combed straight back, falling behind his ears to the collar of his well-fitting frock coat. He wore a mustache and pointed beard, but no whiskers; his eyes were large and dark gray, and had a kindly expression which one would hardly have expected in one whose neck was in the hemp. Evidently this was no vulgar assassin. The liberal military code makes provision for hanging many kinds of persons, and gentlemen are not excluded.

The preparations being complete, the two private soldiers stepped aside and each drew away the plank upon which he had been standing. The sergeant turned to the captain, saluted and placed himself immediately behind that officer, who in turn moved apart one pace. These movements left the condemned man and the sergeant standing on the two ends of the same plank, which spanned three of the crossties of the bridge. The end upon which the civilian stood almost, but not quite, reached a fourth. This plank had been held in place by the weight of the captain; it was now held by that of the sergeant. At a signal from the former the latter would step aside, the plank would tilt and the condemned man go down between two ties. The arrangement commended itself to his judgment as simple and effective. His face had not been covered nor his eyes bandaged. He looked a moment at his "unsteadfast footing," then let his gaze wander to the swirling water of the stream racing madly beneath his feet. A piece of dancing driftwood caught his attention and his eyes followed it down the current. How slowly it appeared to move! What a sluggish stream!

He closed his eyes in order to fix his last thoughts upon his wife and children. The water, touched to gold by the early sun, the brooding mists under the banks at some distance down the stream, the fort, the soldiers, the piece of drift—all had distracted him. And now he became conscious of a new disturbance. Striking through the thought of his dear ones was a sound which he could neither ignore nor understand, a sharp, distinct, metallic percussion like the stroke of a blacksmith's hammer upon the anvil; it had the same ringing quality. He wondered what it was, and whether immeasurably distant or near by —it seemed both. Its recurrence was regular, but as slow as the tolling of a death knell. He awaited each stroke with impatience and—he knew not why—apprehension. The intervals of silence grew progres-

sively longer; the delays became maddening. With their greater in-
frequency the sounds increased in strength and sharpness. They hurt
his ear like the thrust of a knife; he feared he would shriek. What
he heard was the ticking of his watch.

He unclosed his eyes and saw again the water below him. "If I
could free my hands," he thought, "I might throw off the noose and
spring into the stream. By diving I could evade the bullets and, swimming vigorously, reach the bank, take to the woods and get away
home. My home, thank God, is as yet outside their lines; my wife
and little ones are still beyond the invader's farthest advance."

As these thoughts, which have here to be set down in words, were
flashed into the doomed man's brain rather than evolved from it the
captain nodded to the sergeant. The sergeant stepped aside.

Peyton Farquhar was a well-to-do planter, of an old and highly respected Alabama family. Being a slave owner and like other slave
owners a politician, he was naturally an original secessionist and
ardently devoted to the Southern cause. Circumstances of an imperious
nature, which it is unnecessary to relate here, had prevented him from
taking service with the gallant army that had fought the disastrous
campaigns ending with the fall of Corinth, and he chafed under the
inglorious restraint, longing for the release of his energies, the larger
life of the soldier, the opportunity for distinction. That opportunity, he
felt, would come, as it comes to all in war time. Meanwhile he did
what he could. No service was too humble for him to perform in aid
of the South, no adventure too perilous for him to undertake if consistent with the character of a civilian who was at heart a soldier, and
who in good faith and without too much qualification assented to at
least a part of the frankly villainous dictum that all is fair in love and
war.

One evening while Farquhar and his wife were sitting on a rustic
bench near the entrance to his grounds, a gray-clad soldier rode up
to the gate and asked for a drink of water. Mrs. Farquhar was only
too happy to serve him with her own white hands. While she was
fetching the water her husband approached the dusty horseman and
inquired eagerly for news from the front.

"The Yanks are repairing the railroads," said the man, "and are getting ready for another advance. They have reached the Owl Creek bridge, put it in order and built a stockade on the north bank. The commandant has issued an order, which is posted everywhere, declaring that any civilian caught interfering with the railroad, its bridges, tunnels or trains will be summarily hanged. I saw the order."

"How far is it to the Owl Creek bridge?" Farquhar asked.

"About thirty miles."

"Is there no force on this side the creek?"

"Only a picket post half a mile out, on the railroad, and a single sentinel at this end of the bridge."

"Suppose a man—a civilian and student of hanging—should elude the picket post and perhaps get the better of the sentinel," said Farquhar, smiling, "what could he accomplish?"

The soldier reflected. "I was there a month ago," he replied. "I observed that the flood of last winter had lodged a great quantity of driftwood against the wooden pier at this end of the bridge. It is now dry and would burn like tow."

The lady had now brought the water, which the soldier drank. He thanked her ceremoniously, bowed to her husband and rode away. An hour later, after nightfall, he re-passed the plantation, going northward in the direction from which he had come. He was a Federal scout.

As Peyton Farquhar fell straight downward through the bridge he lost consciousness and was as one already dead. From this state he was awakened—ages later, it seemed to him—by the pain of a sharp pressure up in his throat, followed by a sense of suffocation. Keen, poignant agonies seemed to shoot from his neck downward through every fiber of his body and limbs. These pains appeared to flash along well-defined lines of ramification and to beat with an inconceivably rapid periodicity. They seemed like streams of pulsating fire heating him to an intolerable temperature. As to his head, he was conscious of nothing but a feeling of fullness—of congestion. These sensations were unaccompanied by thought. The intellectual part of his nature was already effaced; he had power only to feel, and feeling was torment. He was conscious of motion. Encompassed in a luminous cloud, of which he was now merely the fiery heart, without material substance, he swung through unthinkable arcs of oscillation, like a vast pendulum. Then all at once, with terrible suddenness, the light about him shot upward with the noise of a loud plash; a frightful roaring was in his ears, and all was cold and dark. The power of thought was restored; he knew that the rope had broken and he had fallen into the stream. There was no additional strangulation; the noose about his neck was already suffocating him and kept the water from his lungs. To die of hanging at the bottom of a river!—the idea seemed to him ludicrous. He opened his eyes in the darkness and saw above him a gleam of light, but how distant, how inaccessible! He was still sinking, for the light became fainter and fainter until it was a mere glimmer. Then it began to grow and brighten, and he knew that he was rising toward the surface—knew it with reluctance, for he was now very comfortable. "To be hanged and drowned," he thought, "that is not so bad; but I do not wish to be shot. No; I will not be shot; that is not fair."

He was not conscious of an effort, but a sharp pain in his wrist apprised him that he was trying to free his hands. He gave the struggle his attention, as an idler might observe the feat of a juggler, without interest in the outcome. What splendid effort! What magnificent, what superhuman strength! Ah, that was a fine endeavor! Bravo! The cord fell away; his arms parted and floated upward, the hands dimly seen on each side in the growing light. He watched them with a new interest as first one and then the other pounced upon the noose at his neck. They tore it away and thrust it fiercely aside, its undulations resembling those of a water snake. "Put it back, put it back!" He thought he shouted these words to his hands, for the undoing of the noose had been succeeded by the direst pang that he had yet experienced. His neck ached horribly; his brain was on fire; his heart, which had been fluttering faintly, gave a great leap, trying to force itself out at his mouth. His whole body was racked and wrenched with an insupportable anguish! But his disobedient hands gave no heed to the command. They beat the water vigorously with quick, downward strokes, forcing him to the surface. He felt his head emerge; his eyes were blinded by the sunlight; his chest expanded convulsively, and with a supreme and crowning agony his lungs engulfed a great draught of air, which instantly he expelled in a shriek!

He was now in full possession of his physical senses. They were, indeed, preternaturally keen and alert. Something in the awful disturbance of his organic system had so exalted and refined them that they made record of things never before perceived. He felt the ripples upon his face and heard their separate sounds as they struck. He looked at the forest on the bank of the stream, saw the individual trees, the leaves and the veining of each leaf—saw the very insects upon them: the locusts, the brilliant-bodied flies, the gray spiders stretching their webs from twig to twig. He noted the prismatic colors in all the dewdrops upon a million blades of grass. The humming of the gnats that danced above the eddies of the stream, the beating of the dragonflies' wings, the strokes of the water spiders' legs, like oars which had lifted their boat—all these made audible music. A fish slid along beneath his eyes and he heard the rush of its body parting the water.

He had come to the surface facing down the stream; in a moment the visible world seemed to wheel slowly round, himself the pivotal point, and he saw the bridge, the fort, the soldiers upon the bridge, the captain, the sergeant, the two privates, his executioners. They were in silhouette against the blue sky. They shouted and gesticulated, pointing at him. The captain had drawn his pistol, but did not fire; the others were unarmed. Their movements were grotesque and horrible, their forms gigantic.

Suddenly he heard a sharp report and something struck the water smartly within a few inches of his head, spattering his face with spray. He heard a second report, and saw one of the sentinels with his rifle at his shoulder, a light cloud of blue smoke rising from the muzzle. The man in the water saw the eye of the man on the bridge gazing into his own through the sights of the rifle. He observed that it was a gray eye and remembered having read that gray eyes were keenest, and that all famous marksmen had them. Nevertheless, this one had missed.

A counter-swirl had caught Farquhar and turned him half round; he was again looking into the forest on the bank opposite the fort. The sound of a clear, high voice in a monotonous singsong now rang out behind him and came across the water with a distinctness that pierced and subdued all other sounds, even the beating of the ripples in his ears. Although no soldier, he had frequented camps enough to know the dread significance of that deliberate, drawling, aspirated chant;

the lieutenant on shore was taking a part in the morning's work. How coldly and pitilessly—with what an even, calm intonation, presaging, and enforcing tranquillity in the men—with what accurately measured intervals fell those cruel words:

"Attention, company! . . . Shoulder arms! . . . Ready! . . . Aim! . . . Fire!"

Farquhar dived—dived as deeply as he could. The water roared in his ears like the voice of Niagara, yet he heard the dulled thunder of the volley and, rising again toward the surface, met shining bits of metal, singularly flattened, oscillating slowly downward. Some of them touched him on the face and hands, then fell away, continuing their descent. One lodged between his collar and neck; it was uncomfortably warm and he snatched it out.

As he rose to the surface, gasping for breath, he saw that he had been a long time under water; he was perceptibly farther down stream —nearer to safety. The soldiers had almost finished reloading; the metal ramroads flashed all at once in the sunshine as they were drawn from the barrels, turned in the air, and thrust into their sockets. The two sentinels fired again, independently and ineffectually.

The hunted man saw all this over his shoulder; he was now swimming vigorously with the current. His brain was as energetic as his arms and legs; he thought with the rapidity of lightning.

"The officer," he reasoned, "will not make that martinet's error a second time. It is as easy to dodge a volley as a single shot. He has probably already given the command to fire at will. God help me, I cannot dodge them all!"

An appalling plash within two yards of him was followed by a loud, rushing sound, *diminuendo,* which seemed to travel back through the air to the fort and died in an explosion which stirred the very river to its deeps! A rising sheet of water curved over him, fell down upon him, blinded him, strangled him! The cannon had taken a hand in the game. As he shook his head free from the commotion of the smitten water he heard the deflected shot humming through the air ahead, and in an instant it was cracking and smashing the branches in the forest beyond.

"They will not do that again," he thought; "the next time they will use a charge of grape. I must keep my eye upon the gun; the smoke will apprise me—the report arrives too late; it lags behind the missile. That is a good gun."

Suddenly he felt himself whirled round and round—spinning like a top. The water, the banks, the forests, the now distant bridge, fort and men—all were commingled and blurred. Objects were represented by their colors only; circular horizontal streaks of color—that was all he saw. He had been caught in a vortex and was being whirled on with a velocity of advance and gyration that made him giddy and sick. In a few moments he was flung upon the gravel at the foot of the left bank of the stream—the southern bank—and behind a projecting point which concealed him from his enemies. The sudden arrest of his motion, the abrasion of one of his hands on the gravel, restored him, and he wept with delight. He dug his fingers into the sand, threw it over himself in handfuls and audibly blessed it. It looked like diamonds, rubies, emeralds; he could think of nothing beautiful which it did not resemble. The trees upon the bank were giant garden plants; he noted a definite order in their arrangement, inhaled the fragrance of their blooms. A strange, roseate light shone through the spaces among their trunks and the wind made in their branches the music of Aeolian harps. He had no wish to perfect his escape—was content to remain in that enchanting spot until retaken.

A whiz and rattle of grapeshot among the branches high above his head roused him from his dream. The baffled cannoneer had fired him a random farewell. He sprang to his feet, rushed up the sloping bank, and plunged into the forest.

All that day he traveled, laying his course by the rounding sun. The forest seemed interminable; nowhere did he discover a break in it, not even a woodman's road. He had not known that he lived in so wild a region. There was something uncanny in the revelation.

By nightfall he was fatigued, footsore, famishing. The thought of his wife and children urged him on. At last he found a road which led him in what he knew to be the right direction. It was as wide and straight as a city street, yet it seemed untraveled. No fields bordered it, no dwelling anywhere. Not so much as the barking of a dog suggested human habitation. The black bodies of the trees formed a straight wall on both sides, terminating on the horizon in a point, like a diagram in a lesson in perspective. Overhead, as he looked up through this rift in the wood, shone great golden stars looking unfamiliar and grouped in strange constellations. He was sure they were arranged in some order which had a secret and malign significance. The wood on either side was full of singular noises, among which—once, twice, and again—he distinctly heard whispers in an unknown tongue.

His neck was in pain and lifting his hand to it he found it horribly swollen. He knew that it had a circle of black where the rope had bruised it. His eyes felt congested; he could no longer close them. His tongue was swollen with thirst; he relieved its fever by thrusting it forward from between his teeth into the cold air. How softly the turf had carpeted the untraveled avenue—he could no longer feel the roadway beneath his feet!

Doubtless, despite his suffering, he had fallen asleep while walking, for now he sees another scene—perhaps he has merely recovered from a delirium. He stands at the gate of his own home. All is as he left it, and all bright and beautiful in the morning sunshine. He must have traveled the entire night. As he pushes open the gate and passes up the wide white walk, he sees a flutter of female garments; his wife, looking fresh and cool and sweet, steps down from the veranda to meet him. At the bottom of the steps she stands waiting, with a smile of ineffable joy, an attitude of matchless grace and dignity. Ah, how beautiful she is! He springs forward with extended arms. As he is about to clasp her he feels a stunning blow upon the back of the neck; a blinding white light blazes all about him with a sound like the shock of a cannon—then all is darkness and silence!

Peyton Farquhar was dead; his body, with a broken neck, swung gently from side to side beneath the timbers of the Owl Creek bridge.*

INTERPRETATION

This story, like "The Necklace" and "The Furnished Room," involves a surprise ending, an ironical turn. The basic question, then, which the story raises is this: Is the surprise ending justified; is it validated by the body of the story; is it, in other words, a mere trick, or is it expressive and functional?

Perhaps the best way to clear the ground for a consideration of this

---

* From *In the Midst of Life;* copyright, Albert & Charles Boni, Inc.

basic question is to raise another question which no doubt will occur to many readers of the story. Is it possible for a man in the last moment of his life to have a vision of the sort which Farquhar has as he falls from the bridge? Many people may be inclined to judge the story in terms of their acceptance or rejection of the psychological realism of this incident. But is it possible to have absolutely convincing evidence on this point? Isn't the fact of the vision something which, in itself, can be accepted without too much strain on the reader's credulity? But there is an even more important consideration to be taken into account. Even if we could arrive at a completely satisfying decision about the psychological realism of the incident, would this fact actually determine the nature of our judgment concerning the story? For reasons to be suggested below, it would not determine our judgment, and therefore preoccupation with this question is likely to prove a red herring—is likely to distract us from the real problem.

Suppose that we assume for the moment that the incident is psychologically valid; there remain these questions to be answered:

1. Why does the author withhold from the reader the knowledge that the dying man's vision is merely a vision?

2. Is any revelation of character accomplished thereby?

3. Does the withholding of this information throw any light on the development of a theme for the story?

4. There is an irony generated by the end of the story, but is it a meaningful irony?

A Piece of News
EUDORA WELTY

SHE HAD been out in the rain. She stood in front of the cabin fireplace, her legs wide apart, bending over, shaking her wet yellow head crossly, like a cat reproaching itself for not knowing better. She was talking to herself—only a small fluttering sound, hard to lay hold of in the sparsity of the room.

"The pouring-down rain, the pouring-down rain"—was that what she was saying over and over, like a song? She stood turning in little quarter turns to dry herself, her head bent forward and the yellow hair hanging out streaming and tangled. She was holding her skirt primly out to draw the warmth in.

Then, quite rosy, she walked over to the table and picked up a little bundle. It was a sack of coffee, marked "sample" in red letters, which she unwrapped from a wet newspaper. But she handled it tenderly.

"Why, how come he wrapped it in a newspaper!" she said, catching her breath, looking from one hand to the other. She must have been lonesome and slow all her life, the way things would take her by surprise.

She set the coffee on the table, just in the center. Then she dragged the newspaper by one corner in a dreamy walk across the floor, spread it all out, and lay down full length on top of it in front of the fire. Her little song about the rain, her cries of surprise, had been only a preliminary, only playful pouting with which she amused herself when she was alone. She was pleased with herself now. As she sprawled close to the fire, her hair began to slide out of its damp tangles and hung all displayed down her back like a piece of bargain silk. She closed her eyes. Her mouth fell into a deepness, into a look of unconscious cunning. Yet in her very stillness and pleasure she seemed to be hiding there, all alone. And at moments when the fire stirred and tumbled in the grate, she would tremble, and her hand would start out as if in impatience or despair.

Presently she stirred and reached under her back for the newspaper. Then she squatted there, touching the printed page as if it were fragile. She did not merely look at it—she watched it, as if it were unpredictable, like a young girl watching a baby. The paper was still wet in places where her body had lain. Crouching tensely and patting the creases away with small cracked red fingers, she frowned now and then at the blotched drawing of something and big letters that spelled a word underneath. Her lips trembled, as if looking and spelling so slowly had stirred her heart.

All at once she laughed.

She looked up.

"Ruby Fisher!" she whispered.

An expression of utter timidity came over her flat blue eyes and her soft mouth. Then a look of fright. She stared about. . . . What eye in the world did she feel looking in on her? She pulled her dress down tightly and began to spell through a dozen words in the newspaper.

The little item said:

"Mrs. Ruby Fisher had the misfortune to be shot in the leg by her husband this week."

As she passed from one word to the next she only whispered; she left the long word, "misfortune," until the last, and came back to it, then she said it all over out loud, like conversation.

"That's me," she said softly, with deference, very formally.

The fire slipped and suddenly roared in the house already deafening with the rain which beat upon the roof and hung full of lightning and thunder outside.

"You Clyde!" screamed Ruby Fisher at last, jumping to her feet. "Where are you, Clyde Fisher?"

She ran straight to the door and pulled it open. A shudder of cold brushed over her in the heat, and she seemed striped with anger and bewilderment. There was a flash of lightning, and she stood waiting, as if she half thought that would bring him in, a gun leveled in his hands.

She said nothing more and, backing against the door, pushed it closed with her hip. Her anger passed like a remote flare of elation. Neatly avoiding the table where the bag of coffee stood, she began to walk nervously about the room, as if a teasing indecision, an untouched mystery, led her by the hand. There was one window, and she paused now and then, waiting, looking out at the rain. When she was still, there was a passivity about her, or a deception of passivity, that was not really passive at all. There was something in her that never stopped.

At last she flung herself onto the floor, back across the newspaper, and looked at length into the fire. It might have been a mirror in the cabin, into which she could look deeper and deeper as she pulled her fingers through her hair, trying to see herself and Clyde coming up behind her.

"Clyde?"

But of course her husband, Clyde, was still in the woods. He kept a thick brushwood roof over his whisky still, and he was mortally afraid of lightning like this, and would never go out in it for anything.

And then, almost in amazement, she began to comprehend her predicament: it was unlike Clyde to take up a gun and shoot her.

She bowed her head toward the heat, onto her rosy arms, and began to talk and talk to herself. She grew voluble. Even if he heard about the coffee man, with a Pontiac car, she did not think he would shoot her. When Clyde would make her blue, she would go out onto the road, some car would slow down, and if it had a Tennessee license, the lucky kind, the chances were that she would spend the afternoon in the shed of the empty gin. (Here she rolled her head about on her arms and stretched her legs tiredly behind her, like a cat.) And if Clyde got word, he would slap her. But the account in the paper was wrong. Clyde had never shot her, even once. There had been a mistake made.

A spark flew out and nearly caught the paper on fire. Almost in fright she beat it out with her fingers. Then she murmured and lay back more firmly upon the pages.

There she stretched, growing warmer and warmer, sleepier and sleepier. She began to wonder out loud how it would be if Clyde shot her in the leg. . . . If he were truly angry, might he shoot her through the heart?

At once she was imagining herself dying. She would have a night-gown to lie in, and a bullet in her heart. Anyone could tell, to see her lying there with that deep expression about her mouth, how strange and terrible that would be. Underneath a brand-new night-gown her heart would be hurting with every beat, many times more than her toughened skin when Clyde slapped at her. Ruby began to cry softly, the way she would be crying from the extremity of pain; tears would run down in a little stream over the quilt. Clyde would be standing there above her, as he once looked, with his wild black hair hanging to his shoulders. He used to be very handsome and strong!

He would say, "Ruby, I done this to you."

She would say—only a whisper—"That is the truth, Clyde—you done this to me."

Then she would die; her life would stop right there.

She lay silently for a moment, composing her face into a look which would be beautiful, desirable, and dead.

Clyde would have to buy her a dress to bury her in. He would have to dig a deep hole behind the house, under the cedar, a grave. He would have to nail her up a pine coffin and lay her inside. Then he would have to carry her to the grave, lay her down and cover her up. All the time he would be wild, shouting, and all distracted, to think he could never touch her one more time.

She moved slightly, and her eyes turned toward the window. The white rain splashed down. She could hardly breathe, for thinking that this was the way it was to fall on her grave, where Clyde would come and stand, looking down in the tears of some repentance.

A whole tree of lightning stood in the sky. She kept looking out the window, suffused with the warmth from the fire and with the pity and beauty and power of her death. The thunder rolled.

Then Clyde was standing there, with dark streams flowing over the floor where he had walked. He poked at Ruby with the butt of his gun, as if she were asleep.

"What's keepin' supper?" he growled.

She jumped up and darted away from him. Then, quicker than lightning, she put away the paper. The room was dark, except for the firelight. From the long shadow of his steamy presence she spoke to him glibly and lighted the lamp.

He stood there with a stunned, yet rather good-humored look of delay and patience in his face, and kept on standing there. He stamped his mud-red boots, and his enormous hands seemed weighted with the rain that fell from him and dripped down the barrel of the gun. Presently he sat down with dignity in the chair at the table, making a little tumult of his rightful wetness and hunger. Small streams began to flow from him everywhere.

Ruby was going through the preparations for the meal gently. She stood almost on tiptoe in her bare, warm feet. Once as she knelt at the safe, getting out the biscuits, she saw Clyde looking at her and she smiled and bent her head tenderly. There was some way she began to move her arms that was mysteriously sweet and yet abrupt and tentative, a delicate and vulnerable manner, as though her breasts gave her pain. She made many unnecessary trips back and forth across the floor, circling Clyde where he sat in his steamy silence, a knife and fork in his fists.

"Well, where you been, anyway?" he grumbled at last, as she set the first dish on the table.

"Nowheres special."

"Don't you talk back to me. You been hitchhikin' again, ain't you?" He almost chuckled.

She gave him a quick look straight into his eyes. She had not even heard him. She was filled with happiness. Her hand trembled when she poured the coffee. Some of it splashed on his wrist.

At that he let his hand drop heavily down upon the table and made the plates jump.

"Some day I'm goin' to smack the livin' devil outa you," he said.

Ruby dodged mechanically. She let him eat. Then, when he had crossed his knife and fork over his plate, she brought him the newspaper. Again she looked at him in delight. It excited her even to touch the paper with her hand, to hear its quiet secret noise when she carried it, the rustle of surprise.

"A newspaper!" Clyde snatched it roughly and with a grabbing disparagement. "Where'd you git that? Hussy."

"Look at this-here," said Ruby in her small singsong voice. She opened the paper while he held it and pointed gravely to the paragraph.

Reluctantly, Clyde began to read it. She watched his damp bald head slowly bend and turn.

Then he made a sound in his throat and said, "It's a lie."

"That's what's in the newspaper about me," said Ruby, standing up straight. She took up his plate and gave him that look of joy.

He put his big crooked finger on the paragraph and poked at it.

"Well, I'd just like to see the place I shot you!" he cried explosively. He looked up, his face blank and bold.

But she drew herself in, still holding the empty plate, faced him straightened and hard, and they looked at each other. The moment filled full with their helplessness. Slowly they both flushed, as though with a double shame and a double pleasure. It was as though Clyde might really have killed Ruby, and as though Ruby might really have been dead at his hand. Rare and wavering, some possibility stood timidly like a stranger between them and made them hang their heads.

Then Clyde walked over in his water-soaked boots and laid the paper on the dying fire. It floated there a moment and then burst into flame. They stood still and watched it burn. The whole room was bright.

"Look," said Clyde suddenly. "It's a Tennessee paper. See 'Tennessee'? That wasn't none of you it wrote about." He laughed, to show that he had been right all the time.

"It was Ruby Fisher!" cried Ruby. "My name is Ruby Fisher!" she declared passionately to Clyde.

"Oho, it was another Ruby Fisher—in Tennessee," cried her husband. "Fool me, huh? Where'd you get that paper?" He spanked her good-humoredly across her backside.

Ruby folded her still trembling hands into her skirt. She stood stooping by the window until everything, outside and in, was quieted before she went to her supper.

It was dark and vague outside. The storm had rolled away to faintness like a wagon crossing a bridge.*

INTERPRETATION

At first glance this story may seem to be no story at all—merely a trivial incident, which is meaningless except as it may provoke our amusement: an all but illiterate girl happens, quite by accident, to come upon a newspaper story in which a girl with the same name as hers is shot by her husband. She goes off into a reverie in which she imagines that she has been shot by her own husband—imagines that she is really the girl of the newspaper story. This reverie is interrupted by the return of her husband, who reads the account, is for his own part momentarily shocked by the coincidence of names, but with an overriding common sense, throws the newspaper into the fire, and dismisses the incident.

Even the reader who tries to deal with the story sympathetically, who knows, for instance, the authority which the written word carries for many simple people, and who is willing to believe that the coincidence of names might really provoke in the simple girl the action ascribed to her in this story—even such a reader might feel that the story was finally pointless. That is, even if we feel that the motivation of the characters in the story is sound, we still may not be convinced

* From *A Curtain of Green;* copyright, 1942, by Doubleday, Doran & Company.

that the story has a "meaning" apart from its humorous commentary on the psychology of simple and primitive folk.

The story does have a meaning, but the author has been careful to dramatize it for us in terms of the action. Perhaps the most fruitful approach to a discussion of the meaning will take into account the dramatic, though gradual, presentation of this meaning.

In the first place, the girl and her husband, Ruby and Clyde, are isolated from the world which we know. Clyde Fisher keeps a still. He is an outlaw, and is properly suspicious of strangers. He and his wife live in a world which reverses most of the conventions of the ordinary world: it is a world in which, for example, guns are common and newspapers uncommon—mention in newspapers, least common of all.

Ruby, as the story opens, has just made a visit to that outside world, to get the sack of coffee. She comes back with the chance-acquired newspaper. Now that she is back inside her own house, the storm builds up the sense of her isolation. The storm has soaked her, and thus accounts for her idling over the newspaper before the fire; with its lightning and thunder, the storm supplies a background for the excited imaginings that possess her. But Miss Welty's use of the natural background is modest, probable, and subdued: the background remains background, yet contributes something to the story. Contrast this use of background with that made by O. Henry in "The Furnished Room."

Ruby, who "must have been lonesome and slow all her life," is first surprised when she sees her name, surprised and even delighted as a child is delighted. But her next reaction is fright: "What eye in the world did she feel looking in on her?" The isolation has been penetrated. She "pulled her dress down tightly"—as if her modesty were being violated.

The reader soon guesses the common-sense explanation of the matter —the explanation which after a few moments occurs to the husband Clyde when he comes in: the newspaper is referring to another Mrs. Ruby Fisher. But this is not the explanation which occurs in her bewilderment to the girl. The author, however, is not anxious to convince us of the strained and improbable psychology involved in the girl's belief that the newspaper account is true. The girl knows really that it is not true. She even reasons out to herself the impossibility of its being true; Clyde wouldn't do that. Indeed, there had been occasions which might have provoked a husband to shoot his wife, but Clyde had never shot her. Even if she told him about the coffee salesman,

Clyde would only strike her—he wouldn't shoot her. But the line which the author has Ruby take in arguing against the impossibility of the action suggests another motive which works against her making a realistic and common-sense dismissal of the newspaper story. It is exciting to imagine herself shot by Clyde—to imagine a Clyde who would shoot her. And after he had shot her, what would she be like, and what would he say, and do? The coincidence of names has stirred her imagination. It allows her—indeed, has seemed to force upon her—a new focus of attention in terms of which both she and Clyde take on new perspectives to each other. By being seen in a new role—reading about "herself" in the newspaper—she takes on the new role; she becomes somehow a stranger to her husband. Even her own body becomes something strange and new to her: "There was some way she began to move her arms that was mysteriously sweet and yet abrupt and tentative. . . ." Throughout the reverie she thinks of herself in a night-gown ("She would have a nightgown to lie in . . .") like a bride.

This sense of illumination in which old and familiar things, by acquiring an altered focus, become mysterious and strange, is a recurrent theme in fiction as it is a basic fact in human existence. A shocking and surprising incident, an emotional crisis, may very well force on us such an alteration of focus. For a person who lives in a suburban world, say, where newspapers and electrical toastmakers are familiar, and guns and whisky stills unfamiliar, such an alteration would hardly be effected by the coincidence of names in a scrap of newspaper. But the fact of the experience is universal. In this story, it comes about in terms consonant with the characters depicted in the story and with their situation, and the accident which brings it about for them is a— to us, ironically—trivial incident.

Ruby's reverie is broken by Clyde's prodding her with the gun. His act is the impingement of common sense, the return to reality. But, ironically, the fact that Clyde stands there with the gun in his hand ties the reverie to the reality. For a moment, to the girl, it almost seems that the imagined situation will become real.

We have seen how concretely—and delicately—the theme is developed. Equally noteworthy is the way the author has played down the ending of the story. The effect of the revelation on both Clyde and Ruby is given quietly, almost by suggestion.

1. Analyze the character of Clyde in relation to the ending of the story.

2. How is coincidence used in this story: is it used to set up the problem of the story or to solve the problem of the story?

3. Read "The Three Strangers," by Thomas Hardy. Compare the use made of coincidence in that story with the use made in "A Piece of News." In both stories what use is made of the fact that the characters are relatively primitive and simple? How necessary is this fact to the development of the theme in each of the stories? Write an analysis of "The Three Strangers" which will involve these points.

Mediators to the Goatherd

JAMES HINTON

SUNSET, and the goatherd still lay watching from the bluff above Javali Pass. Even though he was in the heart of the largest mass of uncharted mountain and forest in South Mexico, and the nearest hamlet three days' ride at a kill-horse pace, the goatherd felt that he was slowly but inexorably being pushed into a corner by mysterious man, by man the unwanted, the dangerous.

He felt himself menaced more than he usually did when men came within his sight. And without the infallibly sensitive nostrils and the ferocious stranger-hostility of his dogs, he felt himself crippled, particularly now, when up through the open parklike forest, up the steep trail from the hotland, there came a tall lean man, bearded, with a rifle in his *left* hand and a black serape hung from his *right* shoulder, and not moving openly in the middle of the trail, but stalking a little too much in line with the concealing pine trunks. He was at least five hundred yards away, but the goatherd knew him. He was an outlaw from the hotland, Sandoval; he lived in a lonely hut near Toro Muerto. His half-wild cattle roamed a mountainous forested domain long six days' ride, four days' wide, and when he could help it, Sandoval did not let others pasture in the domain of his cattle, least of all goats.

Though the sun was setting, the high-sierra air was still remarkably bright and clear; and so, of course, the goatherd thought of risking a shot. It was bound to cross his mind, for in the slow dangers every alternative crosses the mind of a wary man. And he was bound to think of it, for it was reasonable: first because at a distance Sandoval's repeating rifle had little advantage over his single-shot muzzle-loader; then because in a drawn-out sniping fight, his superior strength, swiftness, and marksmanship gave *him* the advantage; and last because at close range Sandoval would have an immense advantage in arms and stealth.

But it passed from his mind: he was a young man both pacific and cautious, and he was not yet certain that he would have to trade shots with Sandoval. Moreover, moving up to the pass from the other side, through the thicker bushier forest of the coastal slopes of the sierra, there came three men and five mules. One was a muleteer, a native of the coast. At almost a thousand yards the goatherd could tell that he was a *costeño:* his bolo was not in his belt but in a sheath hung from his shoulder, and his continually bowed head proved him a plainsman watching his clumsy feet on the steep rocky trail. The two riders were foreigners, for they wore boots and helmets, and even at a thousand yards the goatherd could see the brass stirrups, the arched little saddle-bows without pommels, the flaps on the pistol holsters.

Sandoval would come first, perhaps to kill, perhaps to threaten again. Then the foreigners would come, they would undoubtedly stop at his camp, for it was dusk and the next spring lay far away. And the goatherd intuitively saw how he might use the strangers either to defend himself from the outlaw or to gain the outlaw's friendship: he had known no man who feared and hated strangers more than the outlaw from Toro Muerto.

The goats had scattered, and as he went swiftly down through the open grassy forest to his camp in the hollow of Javali Pass, he cracked his whip in a series of accelerating pistol shots, which made the strays trot into groups, and the groups race into a solid panic-stricken herd of five thousand snow-white goats, from which there rose a vast multi-toned bleating.

He did not look at the huge jaguar skin that partially covered a cross carved into the trunk of the giant pine by the fire. He picked up the mangled dead dog and laid it in the distant clump of lupines beside the one that had died last night. Then he returned to couch himself by the fire, and kept flicking his new serape until it covered his old muzzle-loader without appearing to cover anything. With his hand loosely about the pistol grip, and his index finger on the trigger, he waited for the outlaw. His inky black eyes and the hidden barrel both

watched the same place, there where he most expected Sandoval to
appear.

It was intensely cold, the patches of snow in the open forest were
frozen hard. But pin points of sweat appeared on the goatherd's brow.
The nostrils of his small finely-shaped nose were white, and his whole
face taut. He realized that he had waited too long.

He was crippled without the keen-scented nostrils of his dogs, and
now Sandoval had turned his flank. Sandoval would know that he
was conscious of being watched, and he would keep him in suspense
until he did something foolish—like risking a flying shot as he rolled
rapidly over and over, with Sandoval pumping bullets into him from
behind a tree. But the goatherd just lay still, pin points of sweat ice-
cold on his hot skin: he knew that the outlanders were coming; besides, he had a certain fiber.

After Sandoval stopped moving, the goatherd could not see him at
all, he had been only a scarcely perceptible movement at the corner of
his right eye. The goatherd resisted. Finally Sandoval cleared his throat,
a sound distinctly different from any of the many small noises made
by the flocks—if one were minutely listening. Still the goatherd resisted, his sweaty fingers tight on the pistol grip.

Sandoval moved silently forward, in the corner of his eye the goatherd could see him, a dark stealthy motion.

"Well, goatherd, thanks to the jaguar, we meet quietly at close
range." Slow deep-toned mocking voice.

The goatherd turned his head sharply, careful to keep the rest of
his body absolutely still. He saw that the outlaw had put on his long
black serape, which just as effectively concealed the Winchester as his
own concealed the muzzle-loader. "Yes," said the goatherd in an indifferent voice, "my good dogs were killed. How goes it?" Lying still,
he nevertheless gave the impression of utmost wariness; this he knew,
but he could not help it.

Sandoval stood looking down at him from across the fire. Sometimes
his eyes seemed languidly half-closed; sometimes they seemed dangerously narrowed. In the dusk, in the faint firelight, they were filled
with a catlike expression of satiated superiority.

"Isn't it lucky we haven't our rifles?" he said. With voice and glance, with his whole being he luxuriously mocked the goatherd. "In sight," he added slyly.

"Ahh," said the goatherd, ignoring the last remark, "above all as my hands would be empty."

The outlaw mocked him with his soft throaty laughter. "Your hands would be fuller than mine, goatherd—old muzzle-loaders have thicker pistol grips than new repeating rifles."

In Sandoval's eyes the goatherd saw the threat growing, closing, tightening about him. "Look," he said, drawing his right hand, palm upward, from under the serape. "Empty."

Smiling slyly, the outlaw drew his rifle from under his long serape. "Now the thing is for ending."

"Then why didn't you shoot me from the tree?"

"I wanted to divert myself with you," said the outlaw. "This way I will feel more handsome when I kill you. My conscience, you know? Even though I told you clear if you came again I would shoot you."

"Well, why don't you?" said the goatherd seriously. He saw that this was exactly right, and he grew excited.

"Do you want me to kill you?"

"Not at all," said the goatherd. "Do you?"

"Not a great much."

"Well, don't then. . . . Sides to the rising and the sleeping of the sun you have pasture six days' ride, below to the hotland two and a half, up to the divide here half, and . . ."

"A day's ride, I told you clear," said the outlaw, and the goatherd saw that he had made a mistake.

"That was at Toro Muerto, and I thought up here, half a day's . . ."

"It would be a day's ride if I had told you in Totolapan."

Still worse, for now a malignant little line, a small horizontal wrinkle had appeared above the bridge of the outlaw's nose, adding malignance and cruelty to the mocking face. The goatherd's excitement passed into tense expectant fear. True, Sandoval still did not look mad, but the goatherd thought perhaps Sandoval killed without madness.

The outlaw's eyes narrowed further—with an expression of acute listening. Then the goatherd listened too. Sandoval crossed the fire and stood behind the goatherd. The dusk had not deepened, it had brightened; and the mighty black spears of fir were tipped pale green gold by the rising moon, and almost touching the dark bluff above Javali Pass, a great sparkling star was contracting and expanding as if it were breathing, and the flocks lay quiet now in the half-darkness. From the south came the sound of hoofbeats muffled in grass and pine needle, low-toned, somber.

II

When the strangers were within fifty yards of the fire, Sandoval spoke casually, perhaps with a shade of contempt: "It may be some people are always found empty-handed."

The goatherd eagerly slipped his hand under the blanket, and once more placed his index finger delicately on the trigger. Sandoval, he thought with quiet satisfaction, fears an unknown voyager more than he fears a familiar enemy. He wanted to look at the outlaw's face, but he felt that it would be imprudent to turn.

"Hola, amigos!" shouted the foremost rider in a Spanish both heavily accented and deeply gutturalized. The bluff heartiness of the voice was not quite convincing.

"Pass," cried the goatherd in a gay friendly tone. "Pass, señores, come warm yourselves by your servitor's fire."

Sandoval glanced curiously at the goatherd, but he himself remained silent. As he watched the outlanders, the expression of mocking superiority returned to his half-closed eyes.

The foremost rider dismounted and came forward with his great fat legs swinging in that "out-of-door" style of walking used only by city dwellers. He bristled with animal health and merriment, both seeming acquired manners rather than integral characteristics.

"Two shepherds with their flocks . . . huntsmen as well, as I see by the big skin hung there, a whopper! Alone with our mother nature . . . I envy you, amigos, I envy you!" He took a deep breath, and sighed noisily as he smote his big pink hands together in a gesture of enormous satisfaction. "I say, Yutsa, isn't it an immense temptation to forget all one's ambitious plotting and planning, spend the rest of one's days in this beautiful forest?" he said to the small slender companion who had joined him by the fire. Without waiting for a reply, he addressed himself to Sandoval: "And now, my good friend, what about some milk for the thirsty voyagers? A jug of warm sweet foaming milk, and what does one want with the finest wines? Get out the utensils," he said as an afterthought to the muleteer, who stood with a rope in his hands, staring defensively and with a great stupid embarrassment at the group by the fire.

"What!" cried the blond stranger with angry indignation when he saw the muleteer standing there so stupidly. "But what—what are you doing there? Do you expect the mules to unload themselves! Be about it now—flying, flying!"

"The mules . . . *sí,* Señor Steinman . . . the mules . . . there I go . . ." As the muleteer stared for another second at the blond alien, his stupid embarrassment increased unreasonably, and half-bewildered anger flickered across his blunt face. "There I go . . ." he mumbled rapidly as he began to fumble with the cargos. The goatherd was almost bound by tradition to help him. But his hands were skilled enough to untie hard knots and loosen the right ropes without looking, and as he helped the muleteer unload, he closely watched the three men. Yutsa had sat down by the fire, which was reflected in his glasses, giving him a solemn but remote and outlandish expression. Steinman had again requested the outlaw to milk the goats, but this time the request was said in a tone of good-natured command. The outlaw, leaning against the carved pine trunk, stared at the blond stranger with his eyes half-closed, and a languid mocking air to his face and the tilt of his head.

"If you would see . . ." he said in his slow mocking voice. He paused. "I don't know how."

"Don't know how!" echoed Steinman angrily. "Aren't you a goatherd?"

"I am not a goatherd," said Sandoval with a shade of contempt which was not lost upon the listening goatherd. "Are you?"

"Well, what are you if not a goatherd?" said Steinman belligerently.

"I am a man, sir, and you?"

The outlander clutched his pistol holster with a loud slap, a childishly dramatic gesture which he did not seem to realize nearly cost him his life. But Yutsa by the fire, and the goatherd unloading a little way off, they saw the muzzle of Sandoval's rifle as it moved up under his serape and pointed at Steinman's chest.

"Señor Steinman, let me have the altitude please," said Yutsa in his ludicrously broad Spanish, which he spoke as if experiencing difficulty in closing his mouth. The blond outlander seemed to think better of continuing his argument with the outlaw. "Eleven thousand seven hundred," he said. They began to talk in a strange gibbering tongue. "Weeshy, weeshy, weeshy, weesh," said Yutsa. "Bisgya, bisg, bisg, bisg," said Steinman.

Sandoval watched them from across the fire. There still remained between his eyes the little horizontal line which had appeared a moment ago; it gave him an expression full of malignant hatred.

"Who do you bring there?" whispered the goatherd to the muleteer.

"The little one is a Japanese, he looks for beetles all up and down the coast, and he climbs up the highest trees and stays there for hours waiting for the beetles with an instrument. The big one—some say he's American, others German, God may know. Some say they're making maps for an invasion, to protect us from the gringos you see, but what does it matter? they all come from the same country. I myself am from the coast, but finding myself very poor . . ."

"I knew you were from the coast a gunshot away," said the goatherd contemptuously. "The other rope—the *other* one, ox-foot! Now pull . . . *pull,* man! You pumpkin's head, you, how did you dare pass yourself off as a muleteer?"

"I did not, cousin, no!" whispered the muleteer, speaking rapidly and skipping his *d*'s and *s*'s. "I came as *mozo*—being ground down, one has to hire oneself out. The second day out from the village the muleteer left us. He said they were making maps for an invasion and scolding night and day. I was going too, but Steinman said he would kill me, all day long he grinds me, he doesn't give me enough to eat . . ."

They had finished unloading, and the goatherd interrupted his tearful whispers with a savage "Shut up!" Thinking of the foreigners, he grew angry.

"Have you got the pans out?" demanded Steinman.

"Pans . . . ?" echoed the muleteer stupidly, scratching his jet black hair, which stood stiffly on end. It was obvious that his master inspired in him such a feeling of fear, of uselessness, that he could not understand a simple command in his master's presence.

"Pans! can you not hear? . . . Pans, pans, pans!" Steinman's voice rose to an unreasonable shout.

The muleteer's eyes perspired with embarrassment. His expression indicated that he was on the verge of weeping with despair and humiliation, but he turned obediently and began to fumble with the packs.

"Do us the favor, *amigo*," said the blond stranger then to the goatherd. "Sell us a little milk."

The goatherd's finely shaped face paled as he replied with a sinking feeling: "I do not milk the she-goats now. If I milk them, the kids lose their strength and die of the cold."

"My God!" ejaculated the blond. "I suppose next you'll tell me you have no goat meat!"

"That is true. He-goats I have not enough, nor any she-goats not big with young or already with kids. Recently I took out and sold a flock." Against his desire, his tact forced him to give explanations, and he saw that he was losing his opportunity to fortify his new-sprung fraternity with the outlaw.

"Lies!" exclaimed the big stranger. He rose to his feet and began to stride rapidly back and forth in front of the fire. "No milk, no meat . . . then on what do you live!" he shouted, stretching out his arms, and looking from one mountaineer to the other.

"Look," said the goatherd, and he made as if to demonstrate on what he lived. He threw his new serape aside, swiftly picked up his old muzzle-loader, and curled his index finger about the trigger. "I shoot with my gun," he said.

"My God—you Mexicans are not fit to own this magnificent country!" cried Steinman, pretending that he had noticed neither the goatherd's threat nor his challenge. He tossed up his huge pink hands, and once more fell to striding back and forth in front of the fire.

"Hundreds of thousands of acres of splendid timber and pasture land, and yet you live houseless and nearly starve to death . . ." He grew eloquent, he poured over them great masses of contorted rhetoric, the more passionate he grew the more incomprehensible his oratory, until at last he was trying to smother them purely in his own harsh menacing gibberish.

The outlaw beckoned to the goatherd. "Look, pastor," he whispered,

"I am going to leave you for a moment—a little task." The goatherd saw that the outlaw, whatever else he intended, was testing his courage. And he noted with deep satisfaction that the outlaw had called him "pastor."

"Or it might be that you would do the little task," added Sandoval.

"It might be," said the goatherd.

"Some mule herb. There's a patch of it where the *madroño* lies across the trail to Toro Muerto."

"But . . ." The goatherd was discountenanced, and he glanced away with a sullen frown. "They die with agony," he said.

"It would be convenient—for you," said Sandoval. Meaningfully, he turned his sly half-closed eyes toward the flocks. The moonlight was descending into the hollow, and already it struck some of the standing goats' white backs and the he-goats' horns. The flocks were beginning to graze again.

The goatherd was undecided, his finely shaped lips tight.

"To the friendship of one mountaineer what is the good will of three outlanders?" said the outlaw softly. The malignant little line had returned to the bridge of his nose, and it increased the value of his overture.

"Agreed," said the goatherd, and he walked casually past the mules, toward the trail. His walk slowly accelerated, and when he disappeared into the moonless forest at the foot of the eastern bluff, he had fallen into the swift light stride which the watching outlaw knew could easily outstrip any man in the sierra. "Those Indians," he murmured to himself with pleasure.

Sandoval saw how the two outlanders exchanged glances when the goatherd left. Speculative glances. The blond probably speculating upon the extent of the superiority he had gained over the lone mountaineer, the Japanese speculating no doubt upon the meaning of the goatherd's departure. The tall Mexican leaned silently against his tree. He had forgotten about the jaguar skin behind him, but he was secretly satisfied to be leaning against the cross carved into the trunk. His half-closed eyes might have been looking steadily at the tips of yellow flame over the fire; they might have been looking through the thin flames at the two outlanders.

For over an hour the two outlanders sat together, talking the strange gibberish; painstakingly, and with much consultation of a shiny round instrument, drawing wavering meandering lines on a piece of paper already marked out with little squares and many other lines. Then they discussed the paper for a long time, and finally Steinman inclined his head slightly toward the outlaw. "Gisb, gisb, gisb, gisb," he said. "Weeshy, weesh," said the Japanese, and they were silent for some minutes. Casually then, Yutsa rose, pulled out a pack of cigarettes; he lit one, and, as an afterthought, offered one to Sandoval.

He noticed that the Japanese did not inhale the smoke, and he knew that for some time they had wanted to approach him. About what, he waited to see. He could feel that the immaculate little man before him was aware of being mocked, and that being mocked made not the slightest scratch on his pride.

"*Cuestas de la Desgracia . . .*" said the Japanese thoughtfully. "Why do they call them Hills of Misfortune?"

The outlaw was almost discountenanced. It was to Hills of Misfortune that the goatherd had gone, and they were called Hills of Misfortune precisely because of the poisonous herb that grew upon their slopes: nearly every year some unwary muleteer lost his whole caravan there.

Whether by some supernatural way of knowing things, or whether by supernatural keenness of hearing, he did not know; but for an instant Sandoval suspected that the strange little man before him knew where the goatherd had gone, and why. In the next instant, however, he realized that the Japanese was only leading on to another question. Still, he asked himself suspiciously, how would the Japanese know anything about the Hills of Misfortune, know even that they existed?

He languidly shrugged his shoulders. "Usually one knows only the reason for the names oneself gives to places," he said. "Like the pass here. Before the muleteers ever thought of crossing the sierra I used to shoot many javalis in this pass. So I called it Javali Pass, and that is what everyone calls it now."

The Japanese smiled, nodding his head and saying: "*Que bonito!* —how pretty!"

This was exactly right, and Sandoval was gratified; moreover, he was relieved to have successfully covered his flank. In his customary expression there was now, besides contempt for the physical aspects of Yutsa, what was an agreeable disposition toward him. Out of the corner of his eye, he saw the goatherd approaching, watched him steal toward the mules.

"What a poetic name! So full of hidden tales! And—where is the pass to these Hills of Misfortune?" asked the blond, with a coarse attempt at casualness.

Yutsa's glance fell. The outlaw languidly rolled his head, just as he might to indicate a direction, but actually indicating all points of the compass. As a matter of fact, the Misfortunes were too close to his hiding by Toro Muerto, and his suspicion increased. Steinman further spoiled the situation. "Well, *amigo*, you interest me; you know, you look like a pirate or a buccaneer of old. What do you do out here in the wilderness?"

Fortunately, Sandoval did not know the meaning of "pirate" or "buccaneer," but he understood the stranger's insincere clumsy overture. Steinman's lips parted over strong white teeth, the corners of his eyes crinkled; but the wide pale eyes did not smile. Sometimes he could see in them a certain mean imperiousness, but all in all they were far more strange and inscrutable than Yutsa's eyes. They were so pale and wide.

"If you would see . . ." he said slowly, then paused. "I hunt."

"And what do you hunt?" asked the Japanese.

"Deer, javali, . . . jaguar, puma, turkey. Sometimes I hunt my own cattle; they're just as wild as the deer."

"Your *own* cattle?" said Steinman. His tone was incredulous, affronted, and he could not keep contempt from it.

"Sometimes I hunt men," said the outlaw. Beyond the two outlanders, beyond the muleteer who was now taking his master's food from a wooden box, he saw the goatherd shaking the remnants of the herb out of his serape. He also saw that Yutsa's eyes were turned slightly, upon his countenance an air perhaps of wary listening, perhaps of thoughtfulness. The little man took his glasses off, wiped them, then held them up, not directly in front of his face, but a little to one side. Sandoval wondered whether he could see the goatherd reflected in the glasses.

Steinman forced a laugh, though his cheeks flushed. "Come," he

said with bluff superior familiarity, "be a good fellow, and tell us—
is the pass into those hills wide and hollow like this? or . . ."

"With myself anywhere near, its shape is such that you will not enter
it," said the outlaw. And the conversation died then in the reborn
tension.

The outlanders fell to eating, only Yutsa remembering the standard
courtesy of asking, "Is it not your pleasure to sup with us?" Steinman
ate with an outward show of enormous appetite, but he continually
hurled away scraps of food, and with ferocious exasperation complained
of the fare. Yutsa ate meagerly, not looking at what he ate, and apparently unaware of the fact that he was eating. The muleteer reached
furtively for his food, and Steinman watched closely every morsel that
both he and the Japanese took.

"Why should I be eating this dirty stale canned meat when there
are tons of fresh meat at my elbow!" said the big blond at last, flinging
away a half-emptied tin. With the air of a man who would have his
desires satisfied at any cost, he rose and faced the goatherd. "Now
look here, goatherd, by fair means or foul, I am going to finish my
supper with a nice fresh steak of goat. So, in the name of the hospitality for which you mountain people are famous throughout the
world, I ask you to kill us a goat." Apparently he thought this little
speech irresistible, for he finished with the smile of a man who knows
that by sheer charm of personality he has persuaded another to do
what he does not want to do.

The goatherd remained still, his arms crossed over his knees. He
was looking not at Steinman but at the outlaw. It struck him that
Sandoval was enjoying himself at the moment, enjoying himself exceedingly. The goatherd was silent.

"Say, didn't you hear me!" asked Steinman sharply, his pink cheeks
growing brick red.

"If you would see . . ." said the outlaw. "No."

Steinman stood glaring at the goatherd, who stared up from under
his brows at the outlander's waist. At the same time that the holster
flap snapped, the goatherd cocked the giant hammer of his muzzle-
loader. Apparently Yutsa had for some time past had his pistol on
the ground beside him, and now he picked it up and rested it sidewise

on his knee. He did not aim, and as he was gazing into the fire, his movement gave the impression of a casual absent-minded act.

At the goatherd's swift movement, Steinman half raised his hands, but for a moment the strife was in balance. Steinman's colorless eyes had become ferocious, and the little wrinkle between Sandoval's eyes had given to his face an expression of deadly malignance. The two mountaineers watched not Steinman but the Japanese.

Then Steinman continued the motion of his hands into an exasperated wave of his hands, and Yutsa said: "Let us go to bed."

III

The goatherd was roasting jerked venison over the fire. He paid no attention to the wide-awake outlanders. His cocked muzzle-loader lay beside him, but his only interest seemed to be in the roasting meat. Covertly, however, he sometimes glanced at the tethered mules. It was one of the fine saddle mules that was arching back and neck. It arched its neck as if it wanted to bite its chest.

Sandoval watched the outlanders. When the goatherd proffered him the stick, he took off the pieces impaled at the sharpened point, and he ate with his awkward right hand. The muleteer arose and came forward furtively, no doubt expecting the master to roughly bid him lie down. "Invite me, *amigos*. That whoreson doesn't give me enough to eat," he whispered.

The goatherd was going to let him pull some off the point of the stick, but Sandoval said: "No, give me the hot meat." He picked up the cold strips on the pine needles beside him, and he threw them at the feet of the muleteer. The muleteer's eyes watered with his stupid painful embarrassment as he stooped to pick them up. But when he squatted on his heels, he ravenously gulped down the half-chewed meat, and, just as a dog would, looked up at them for more.

The mountaineers ate meagerly. But after they were finished, the goatherd kept on roasting hard dark strips of venison. Sandoval plucked them off with his right hand and tossed them to the ground in front of the squatting muleteer, who snatched them up, stuffed them into his mouth, gulped them down, and looked up for more.

The goatherd no longer looked at the muleteer, but he could *feel* his stupid loathsome embarrassment. "Now go," he said.

The muleteer merely looked back with his eyes overflowing, and his embarrassment intensifying. "Enough, ox-foot!" said the goatherd irritably. "With this cold you'll die eating like that." The mules were now drawing in their necks as if unseen bridles were cruelly straining at their jaws. Thick viscous foam was growing on their muzzles.

A look of blind fear spread over the muleteer's blunt face. "Ahh, God!" he groaned. "The cold!"

"You'll wake up laughing with the cold," said the outlaw, mocking him with his queer low-toned laughter.

"Ahh!" groaned the muleteer, fearfully.

One of the mules fell down and began a noisy struggle to rise. The goatherd's nostrils whitened, he sat staring with very tight lips at the fire.

"Now you'll catch it, now he'll *kill* you," murmured the outlaw to the startled muleteer. Probably Steinman thought that the mules were merely rolling about to scratch the sweat-caked hair on their backs, for he did not look up. Sandoval thought that perhaps the Japanese knew what was happening.

When one of the mules began to give forced panting grunts, Steinman suddenly sat up. "What have the mules got?" he said sharply to the horrified muleteer.

"Got . . . ? Yes, Señor Steinman, the mules . . . there I go." He rose awkwardly, he walked clumsily over to the mules. "It looks as if they're ill," he said in a terrified voice, scratching his jet black hair which stood stiffly on end. Steinman hastily drew on his boots. Talking excited gibberish to the Japanese, he took his riding whip and went rapidly to the mules, his step curiously short, effeminate. When they did not rise but only lay panting, he shouter louder, he whipped their foaming muzzles, furiously kicked their distended bellies. Gesticulating, shouting furious gibberish, he walked back and forth between the beasts and the fire, questioning both the muleteer and the Japanese. He slapped the muleteer's face, shook his fist at the mountaineers, in a passionate voice thundered explosive menacing words. The flocks stared at him for a moment with their stupid short-sighted gazes, they gave popping sneezes followed at once by a deprecatory jerk of their heads, and then went on chewing with incredible rapidity.

Sandoval still leaned against his tree, the malignant little line once more between his eyes. The goatherd sat looking into the fire, resisting the tension, resisting with all his fiber the unbearable desire to leap up screaming and bury his teeth in the raving stranger's cheekbone. He was not watching Yutsa as he should have been. The Japanese was staring thoughtfully into space, but he seemed a little surprised.

"You *dog—you* will pay!" shouted Steinman at last in Spanish, shaking his huge pink fist in the outlaw's face. For the first time Sandoval uncovered his rifle; he dug the muzzle into Steinman's barrel-like middle, and then he lunged. Steinman ran and threw himself upon his sleeping bag, where he cried hysterically and beat the pillow with his two huge fists. Suddenly he was silent.

"Take my boots off," he said thickly to the muleteer. Sandoval moved his right hand to catch the muleteer's eye, and then he shook his head menacingly, raising the muzzle of his rifle. The muleteer stood as if paralyzed, his yellow face contorted with blind overpowering fear.

"Take my boots off!" screamed the blond giant, turning over. The outlaw made a motion as if to extract from an invisible sheath hung from his shoulder an invisible bolo. The muleteer snatched his bolo out of the sheath.

"What do you want?" asked Steinman in the uncontrolled voice of a mad adolescent.

"Whatever *you* want," whispered the muleteer. He appeared to be on the verge of fainting.

Steinman leaped to his feet, drawing from his riding whip a needle-like two-foot blade. "I am a swordsman! . . . scientifically trained . . . !" he screamed as he feinted and lunged. The muleteer fell over backwards, and the blond giant stumbled over him. Then the muleteer sprang up and fled into the moonlit forest with the master galloping after him.

Soon he brought him back, one of his big pink hands squeezing the cowering blubbering muleteer by the scruff of the neck. After the muleteer had pulled his boots off, Steinman, as if speaking to a small child he had just whipped, said: "Now don't ever tell me 'whatever you want' again. And just for that, you drag the mules away, drag them to the bluff, else I'll beat you."

The moon was high overhead, and the flocks were restless. On moonlit nights they obliged the goatherd to stay awake, for the herd broke up into many straying handfuls, and when handfuls wandered too far, the jaguar became their herder. He would consolidate them by a series of hollow feline grunts uttered in crescendo, by sudden sharp whistles, but always with sounds not used within the last few minutes, with sounds that would fall upon them with uttermost surprise. Now the whole flock was drawing hesitantly toward the fire. The leader stopped, the whole flock stopped. Two bearded he-goats standing side by side rose up on their hind legs, turned their heads as they came down so that their horns met with a shock as of two heavy stones smitten together. A few he-goats pushed through the front ranks and moved a few steps nearer, followed at once by the whole flock. Nearer and nearer they came with their short-sighted, slightly cross-eyed, inquisitive gazes, making a clicking sound with their hoofs as of a man cracking his knuckles. "Ugh!" cried the goatherd, as if he had been given a mighty blow on the stomach. They knocked each other down in their haste to flee, and as he continued crying, "Ugh! ugh! ugh!" they fell into a mad panic-stricken flight down the moonlit forest. In a minute the tightly knit flock was staring silently at him from the other side of the hollow.

Above the murmuring sound of the fire, he could hear the muleteer grunting and cursing as he tugged at the dead mules' tails. He wished he would stop his animal-like struggling and grunting. It irritated him more and more to think of the fool trying to drag the mules away, particularly as he went about it in such a senseless way; and he would have been glad to see the poor numbskull escape. He turned to look at Sandoval's tree, but the outlaw, whom he had not seen leave, had not yet returned. Taking several strips of jerked venison and a piece of jaguar meat, he walked lightly toward the muleteer, guardedly watching the figures lying by the·fire.

"Here, pumpkin's head," he whispered contemptuously, thrusting the meat nearly into the muleteer's face. "Be going now. In the morning your master is going to saddle you with the three cargos and then whip you dead. As you go, chew this jaguar meat for your cowardice. At noon eat one strip of venison, at sundown another. Day after tomorrow, eat one for breakfast, one for dinner, one for supper. There's one for your breakfast the third day, and you'll sup in the village. Now be going before they stop you. By dawn you'll have half a day's start."

"Yes?" said the muleteer stupidly. "Yes . . . the jaguar meat for . . . one for each meal, you say?"

"Be going!" hissed the goatherd.

"I go," said the muleteer. For the first time since the goatherd had seen him, he spoke with the mind of a man. And he hurried up the slope, body ungracefully forward and head down, after the manner of plainsmen in the mountain.

The goats were again pressing about the camp, nibbling at the strangers' cargos. The goatherd tossed a glowing ember whirling through the air, and they swarmed off, their twenty thousand hoofs sounding like a hurricane sweeping through the grassy forest.

Sandoval did not return until the moon was about half way between the zenith and the western horizon. He had been gone about six hours, and now, of a sudden, he was once more leaning against his tree. The goatherd noticed at once that he had two rifles, for the outlaw made no attempt to conceal them.

"Where is the *costeño?*"

The goatherd explained to him, and Sandoval was displeased.

"I wanted to give him your rifle," he said.

"Pretty soon I'll have to be asking you about the breath I draw," said the goatherd with sudden anger. His eyes did not waver, though Sandoval stared at him darkly.

"Pretty soon you may not have any breath to draw," whispered the outlaw.

The goatherd frowned impatiently. "What did you want to give him my rifle for?"

"So that he could ambush his master."

"And what would I do without my rifle?" asked the goatherd. He wanted that repeating rifle right away.

"Could you overtake him and return here by dawn?"

"The ox-foot's been gone only since midnight."

"You'll have to talk to him," said the outlaw as he handed the rifle to the goatherd.

The goatherd stole between the trees, his pace slowly increasing. Up the steepness he went swiftly, his body straight, head poised. It was the swiftest pace he had ever seen, and in the outlaw's sly half-smile there was something of pleasure. The queer part of him was that though he was a goatherd, he did not seem to lie. "The Indian," murmured Sandoval. He tossed an ember at the encroaching goats, and then he comforted himself against his tree.

There was no sign of dawn when the goatherd returned. His pace gradually slackened, and he stole slowly into the camp.

"Did you animate him?" asked Sandoval, who was eating venison.

"He was trembling with anger," whispered the goatherd. "Those aliens must have cast a spell over him, and the jaguar meat broke the spell. You would not have known him. He was a man, trembling with a man's anger."

"It's good enough the rifle fires only one shot at a time," said Sandoval. "It should close the trail, and I don't want people crossing here any more. Those muleteers—talk, talk, talk. I've turned back three families this season."

"How?" whispered the goatherd, thinking of the closed trail.

"The Japanese will reach the coast, and he will talk. Then people will be afraid to come this way any more."

"The big one will be less afraid of us in the day," said the goatherd after a while.

When the strangers awoke, they seemed to take the muleteer's disappearance for granted, and they breakfasted without a single word. The mountaineers did not understand the silence, and their wariness increased. Steinman particularly made them overly suspicious.

The silence was not broken until the outlanders had finished their meal and made packs of their bedding and food. Then Yutsa spoke. "Will you do us the favor of keeping our baggage for us meanwhile we send up a muleteer to pick it up?"

"If you would see . . ." slowly answered the outlaw. "No."

For an instant the eyes behind the lenses brightened dangerously.

Then they went off without a word, but with many a guarded look.

The mountaineers watched them until they disappeared at the upper end of the pass. Then they followed, and watched the two booted figures vanishing into the coastal-slope forests below.

They returned to examine the cargo—more to see what the strangers had than to see what they might find profitable to themselves. "Those strangers . . ." said the goatherd calculatingly. "If one of them gets out alive, he will tell the other one's government, and then there will be an invasion. He said we were not fit to live here. It makes no difference who kills them, so long as they're killed a good way from here. But the thing is to kill none or kill both, true?"

They picked out blankets, clothes, cans; they picked out what pleased their fancy, without jealousy or quarreling. Most of the cargo was merely corn for the mules.

"It may be," said the outlaw, staring curiously at the goatherd.

"I haven't eaten a grain of corn since the rains," said the goatherd. He heated some in an aluminum pan over the fire. When it began to turn inside out, he crunched it eagerly. Sandoval continued to look at him curiously, and then he too began to eat roasted corn grains.

"I'm weary of venison and turkey. Let's kill a young she-goat. We'll fill it full of boiled maize, then roast it."

"I'd like some goat meat," said the outlaw. He rose and stretched himself. "I'll be back by night, and so have it ready. Maybe I'll find some wild *aguacates*." He went off with his cat-light step. He always moved as if he were stalking something. Usually he was.

The goatherd kept on eating corn. He was richly satisfied with himself until for some reason unknown he thought of a dark stealthy motion between the trees. As if a mouse had thrust its cold whiskered nose into his ear, an icy little tremor went down his spine. He went on eating corn, but his gaze had changed, as if he had been suddenly stricken with fever. He did not know whether he had seen the stealthy motion or whether he had remembered it from yesterday. Obliquely he glanced at his new rifle leaning against Sandoval's tree. It was gone.

The goatherd rose swiftly to consolidate the flock, to do his counting, and at the same time pick out a fat young she-goat. The thick white wheel of goats turned faster and faster, as he whirled the noose faster over his head. *"Shepedi, shepedi, shepedi!"* he cried. *"Shepedi,*

shepedi, shepedi!" He was an Indian from Oaxaca with pin points of sweat ice-cold on his fine Zapotec face.*

INTERPRETATION

1. The main conflict in this story is, of course, that between the goatherd and the outlaw. What are the secondary conflicts and how are they related to the main conflict?

2. In how far does the desire of the two mountaineers to maintain their isolation and their freedom merge into a sort of patriotism? In the case of the goatherd? In the case of the outlaw, Sandoval? How is this dramatized in the relation of the two men to the outlanders?

3. Is the ending a surprise ending? Is it a trick ending? How is the ending of the story related to the central conflict in the story?

4. Can one say that the story involves, among other things, a study in manliness? Consider in this connection the characters of Yutsa, Steinman, and the muleteer; the emphasis placed on the cringing servility of the muleteer; the attempt on the part of the goatherd to infuse courage into him, and the emphasis placed on Sandoval's pride. Does Sandoval have a code? What is it?

5. How does the last sentence of the story help to define the author's attitude toward the goatherd? What is that attitude? Relate this to the total intention of the author in telling this story.

War

LUIGI PIRANDELLO

THE PASSENGERS who had left Rome by the night express had had to stop until dawn at the small station of Fabriano in order to continue their journey by the small old-fashioned local joining the main line with Sulmona.

At dawn, in a stuffy and smoky second-class carriage in which five people had already spent the night, a bulky woman in deep mourning was hoisted in—almost like a shapeless bundle. Behind her—puffing and moaning, followed her husband—a tiny man, thin and weakly, his face death-white, his eyes small and bright and looking shy and uneasy.

Having at last taken a seat he politely thanked the passengers who

* From the *Southern Review,* copyright, 1942; by permission of the author.

had helped his wife and who had made room for her; then he turned round to the woman trying to pull down the collar of her coat, and politely inquired:

"Are you all right, dear?"

The wife, instead of answering, pulled up her collar again to her eyes, so as to hide her face.

"Nasty world," muttered the husband with a sad smile.

And he felt it his duty to explain to his traveling companions that the poor woman was to be pitied for the war was taking away from her her only son, a boy of twenty to whom both had devoted their entire life, even breaking up their home at Sulmona to follow him to Rome, where he had to go as a student, then allowing him to volunteer for war with an assurance, however, that at least for six months he would not be sent to the front and now, all of a sudden, receiving a wire saying that he was due to leave in three days' time and asking them to go and see him off.

The woman under the big coat was twisting and wriggling, at times growling like a wild animal, feeling certain that all those explanations would not have aroused even a shadow of sympathy from those people who—most likely—were in the same plight as herself. One of them, who had been listening with particular attention, said:

"You should thank God that your son is only leaving now for the front. Mine has been sent there the first day of the war. He has already come back twice wounded and been sent back again to the front."

"What about me? I have two sons and three nephews at the front," said another passenger.

"Maybe, but in our case it is our *only* son," ventured the husband.

"What difference can it make? You may spoil your only son with excessive attentions, but you cannot love him more than you would all your other children if you had any. Paternal love is not like bread that can be broken into pieces and split amongst the children in equal shares. A father gives *all* his love to each one of his children without discrimination, whether it be one or ten, and if I am suffering now for my two sons, I am not suffering half for each of them but double . . ."

"True . . . true . . ." sighed the embarrassed husband, "but suppose (of course we all hope it will never be your case) a father has two sons at the front and he loses one of them, there is still one left to console him . . . while . . ."

"Yes," answered the other, getting cross, "a son left to console him but also a son left for whom he must survive, while in the case of the father of an only son if the son dies the father can die too and put an end to his distress. Which of the two positions is the worse? Don't you see how my case would be worse than yours?"

"Nonsense," interrupted another traveler, a fat, red-faced man with bloodshot eyes of the palest gray.

He was panting. From his bulging eyes seemed to spurt inner violence of an uncontrolled vitality which his weakened body could hardly contain.

"Nonsense," he repeated, trying to cover his mouth with his hand so as to hide the two missing front teeth. "Nonsense. Do we give life to our children for our own benefit?"

The other travelers stared at him in distress. The one who had had his son at the front since the first day of the war sighed: "You are right. Our children do not belong to us, they belong to the Country. . . ."

"Bosh," retorted the fat traveler. "Do we think of the Country when we give life to our children? Our sons are born because . . . well, because they must be born and when they come to life they take our own life with them. This is the truth. We belong to them but they never belong to us. And when they reach twenty they are exactly what we were at their age. We too had a father and mother, but there were so many other things as well . . . girls, cigarettes, illusions, new ties . . . and the Country, of course, whose call we would have answered—when we were twenty—even if father and mother had said no. Now at our age, the love of our Country is still great, of course, but stronger than it is the love for our children. Is there any one of us here who wouldn't gladly take his son's place at the front if he could?"

There was a silence all round, everybody nodding as to approve.

"Why then," continued the fat man, "shouldn't we consider the feelings of our children when they are twenty? Isn't it natural that at their age they should consider the love for their Country (I am speaking of decent boys, of course) even greater than the love for us? Isn't it natural that it should be so, as after all they must look upon us as upon old boys who cannot move any more and must stay at home? If Country exists, if Country is a natural necessity, like bread, of which each of us must eat in order not to die of hunger, somebody must go to defend it. And our sons go, when they are twenty, and they don't want tears, because if they die, they die inflamed and happy (I am speaking, of course, of decent boys). Now, if one dies young and happy, without having the ugly sides of life, the boredom of it, the pettiness, the bitterness of disillusion . . . what more can we ask for him? Everyone should stop crying; everyone should laugh, as I do . . . or at least thank God—as I do—because my son, before dying, sent me a message saying that he was dying satisfied at having ended his life in the best way he could have wished. That is why, as you see, I do not even wear mourning. . . ."

He shook his light fawn coat as to show it; his livid lip over his missing teeth was trembling, his eyes were watery and motionless, and soon after he ended with a shrill laugh which might well have been a sob.

"Quite so . . . quite so . . ." agreed the others.

The woman who, bundled in a corner under her coat, had been sitting and listening had—for the last three months—tried to find in the words of her husband and her friends something to console her in her deep sorrow, something that might show her how a mother should resign herself to send her son not even to death but to a prob-ably dangerous life. Yet not a word had she found amongst the many which had been said . . . and her grief had been greater in seeing that nobody—as she thought—could share her feelings.

But now the words of the traveler amazed and almost stunned her. She suddenly realized that it wasn't the others who were wrong and could not understand her but herself who could not rise up to the same height of those fathers and mothers willing to resign themselves, without crying, not only to the departure of their sons but even to their death.

She lifted her head, she bent over from her corner trying to listen with great attention to the details which the fat man was giving to his companions about the way his son had fallen as a hero, for his

King and his Country, happy and without regrets. It seemed to her that she had stumbled into a world she had never dreamt of, a world so far unknown to her and she was so pleased to hear everyone joining in congratulating that brave father who could so stoically speak of his child's death.

Then suddenly, just as if she had heard nothing of what had been said and almost as if waking up from a dream, she turned to the old man, asking him:

"Then . . . is your son really dead?"

Everybody stared at her. The old man, too, turned to look at her, fixing his great, bulging, horribly watery light gray eyes, deep in her face. For some little time he tried to answer, but words failed him. He looked and looked at her, almost as if only then—at that silly, incongruous question—he had suddenly realized at last that his son was really dead—gone for ever—for ever. His face contracted, became horribly distorted, then he snatched in haste a handkerchief from his pocket and, to the amazement of everyone, broke into harrowing, heart-rending, uncontrollable sobs.*

INTERPRETATION

This story is peculiarly lacking in action, it seems, if by action we mean physical action. After the fat woman has been "hoisted" into the compartment and her shy, apologetic husband has climbed in after her, there is no physical movement indicated except the wriggling and twisting of the fat woman under her coat, the attempt of the old man to cover his mouth with his hand when he talks in order to conceal the fact that two of his teeth are missing, his shaking of his fawn-colored overcoat to show that he does not wear mourning, the fat woman's bending forward to listen to the old man, the turning of all eyes upon the woman when she finally asks the old man about his son, and the contortion of the old man's face as he tries to answer. These physical actions are important in the story, but their importance lies in the fact that they are clues to the feelings and attitudes of the persons involved in the story. They do not, in other words, actually constitute the plot.

The plot itself is constituted of the conflicts among the various atti-

* From *The Medals and Other Stories;* copyright by E. P. Dutton & Co., Inc., publishers in the United States.

tudes held by the characters toward the subject: the giving of children
to the country. The form, then, is almost the form of a debate—different points of view are stated and argued, one after another. But this is
not a debate for the mere sake of debate. The persons involved are
persons for whom the issue is very real; they have sons in the war, and
one man, the old man in the fawn-colored overcoat, has already lost
his son. That is, the debate is dramatically meaningful for the partici-
pants.

The two extreme positions in the debate are held by the fat woman
and the old man. The fat woman says nothing, but we know what
her position is: "The woman under the big coat was twisting and
wriggling, at times growling like a wild animal, feeling certain that all
those explanations would not have aroused even a shadow of sympathy
from those people who—most likely—were in the same plight as herself." Her grief has a kind of immediacy, like physical pain; it is beyond reasoning or discussion; she can only twist as in pain or utter
meaningless animal-like sounds. The other extreme position, that of
the old man whose son has been actually killed, is the most fully
stated. He argues that one does not, in the first place, have children for
one's own benefit; that, in the second place, a son, being young and
idealistic, is more drawn by love of country than by love of parents;
that if a son dies for his country he dies happy—if he is "decent"; that
one who dies young and happy has been spared the ugly side of life,
boredom, pettiness, disillusion; that, therefore, a parent whose son has
died heroically should be happy and laugh, as he says he does, or
should at least thank God. That is, the old man has completely argued
away, philosophized away, all of the fundamental sense of loss and
grief. Such are the two extremes of attitude.

Now, the *plot pattern* (see Glossary) of the story depends upon the
opposition between these two extreme views. But it is not a static
opposition—a mere statement of difference. Both views are modified.

First, the fat woman, who had been unable to take consolation from
her husband or her friends, because, as she felt, nobody could share her
feelings, begins to take consolation from the words of the stranger. He
has actually lost a son, and therefore he must know, must be able to
share, her own feelings. He must be wise, because his loss is greater
than hers, for her son is yet alive. Furthermore, the very violence of
the old man's position, its difference from all the views given her by
husband and friends, its absolute denial of grief by its heroic terms,
make her feel that she has "stumbled into a world she had never

dreamt of." It seems incredible to her that a man whose son is really dead can speak thus of his loss. So "almost as if waking up from a dream" she asks him: "Then . . . is your son really dead?"

Presumably, if the man should say, simply, "Yes, he is dead," she would be prepared to accept, for the moment at least, his position. If the man could assure her once more that the son is "really" dead, then she could try to imitate his heroic attitude. She, too, would be able to face the fact of death.

But her question, which provides the climax, the focal point of the story, reveals something to the old man, just as his previous words have revealed something to her. So, as in the first place, we find her position modified by him, we find now, in the second place, his position modified by her. When she utters the words "really dead" everybody "stares" at her—as though she had said something out of place, something impolite and embarrassing, as though she had divulged some horrible and shocking secret. The old man stares at her too, and cannot answer. For the first time, he realizes that his son is "really dead—gone for ever—for ever." He is caught now in the abject, animal-like, unreasoning misery, in which she had previously been held, and bursts into sobs.

The story, then, depends on a conflict between the basic, personal, unformulable emotion on the one hand, and systems, codes, reason, ideal compensations, and interpretations on the other. There is here an ironical contrast, an irreconcilable contrast—or a contrast, which if reconcilable is reconcilable only by the greatest effort. The equilibrium of the man who has made the reconciliation is upset, we see, by the slightest touch, by the woman's "silly, incongruous question," but a question which is fundamental. Are we to assume, therefore, that the author is simply saying that codes, systems, reason, obligations, ideals do not matter, that the only thing which matters is the fact of personal emotion? It would not seem to be the case. If that were the case, why would he illustrate the powerful appeal which the old man's words make to the woman who is sunk in grief? No, it seems that the author is putting, in dramatic terms, a basic conflict in human experience—is saying that the two terms of the opposition are always in existence and that neither can be ignored. (Compare the author's attitude toward his theme with that of Hawthorne toward the theme of "The Birthmark." See pp. 87, 105–106.)

Let us turn again to the pattern of the story. We have said that we find a movement away from the two extreme positions, a process of mutual modification focused, finally, on the question which the woman asks the old man. In other words, we have, in a sense, two "stories" within a story—the story of the woman's change of attitude and the story of the old man's change of attitude. Each of the two persons seems, when introduced, to be firmly fixed in a special attitude. How are we to account for the changes? Are the changes prepared for and made acceptable in the story?

The author devotes some analysis to the woman's change. It is the novelty, the heroic quality, of the consolation which the old man offers, the fact that he, having really lost a son will "understand" her, which attract her. But we have no such explicit analysis of the change on the part of the old man. His change of attitude comes as a surprise. But does he not overstate his case in the earlier part of the story? Is there not an inkling of the fact that he is trying to argue against himself rather than against other people? Is there not a hint of hysteria? In this connection one might investigate the following sentence, which comes just after he has said that he does not even wear mourning: "He shook his light fawn coat as to show it; his livid lip over his missing teeth was trembling, his eyes were watery and motionless, and soon after he ended with a shrill laugh which might well have been a sob." Then, we may take the attitude of the woman herself as a kind of preparation for the old man's final change. She represents, as it were, the opposite pole of experience, but an undeniable pole.

The foregoing analysis of the story is not complete. Certain other questions are important for a full interpretation and for an understanding of the author's method.

1. What is the importance of the physical actions in the story? We have said that they offer clues to the feelings and attitudes of the characters. How is this true? How, for instance, is the fact that the old man at first tries to cover his mouth but later forgets to do so significant?

2. What is the significance of the words which are italicized in the following sentence: "The old man, too, turned to look at her, fixing his great, bulging, *horribly* watery light gray eyes, *deep* in her face."

3. The following version of the story would be inferior to the present version: The old man's son is merely at the front. He argues with the other people in the compartment, and persuades them, as in the present version of the story. At a station, he receives a telegram saying that his son has been killed and bursts into "heart-rending, uncontrolla-

ble sobs," while they stare at him in amazement. Why would this version be inferior to the story as given?

The Face

LOUIS MOREAU

THE HUBS made a hollow knocking sound as our wagon rolled down the road in monotony. My mother sat beside me on the front seat of our canvas-covered wagon. We were in the hills of east Texas and were moving toward south Louisiana. A tub of hot coals set upon four brickbats in the wagon bed made us comfortable.

To our left was a small patch of plowed ground, separated from the road by a rail fence. Not far beyond this stood a strip of naked trees through which the sun could be seen as it sank near the horizon, a huge ball of yellow fire. There was no sound except the squeak of harness and the noise of the wagon rolling slowly along.

Farther ahead there was more plowed ground. A pair of horses' heads could be seen over the rail fence. At that place two men were leaning against the fence and were talking to each other across it.

"I wonder if the man is telling your father we are on the wrong road," said my mother.

"I hope not," I answered.

"Let us talk about something cheerful, Son."

"Are you afraid?"

My mother did not answer but shrugged her shoulders and kept looking ahead at the two men talking at the fence. She seemed enveloped in some feeling all her own. She had spells of despondency I could not quite understand.

I looked at her out of the corner of my eye, for I feared she would begin again. She was not skinny and nervous looking, as most women are who get on your nerves with their petty fears. She was stout and vigorous looking and her eyes were calm, sometimes dreamy. Although we once lived in the Bayou Jack country, where there were ferocious beasts, and she was not afraid to live there, yet I have seen her upset over trifles. What makes her that way? I would think.

"Won't you be glad when we get back home and you can go hunting in the swamp with your father, and we can eat peaches and figs out of our trees in the yard? You don't remember our home very well, do you, Son?"

"Not very."

"Well, our home is—well, it is just home," she said, trying to be gay. "Don't you remember the time that we thought you were lost and your grandfather found you asleep in the cornfield?"

"How old was I?"

"Three. You little crocodile, we've been gone eleven years." Then with dreamy eyes she was silent. "Wouldn't you like to see your grandfather again?"

"Yes," I answered.

"I know he will be glad to see us."

The monotonous thudding of the wheels reigned again for a moment; then my mother said in a lonely voice, "Isn't it funny about home, how everything wants to go back to it. Is it magic?"

I sat there not paying much attention to her, listening to the wagon hubs as the wagon lumbered on, feeling as though a burden was upon me as long as she talked.

My father, whom we were nearing, stood up straight, faced us, and twirled his mustache. I thought I could see the gleam in his gray-blue eyes.

When we drew near he called out to me to stop and said: "We are among friends from our home parish." Then, addressing the man who stood on the other side of the fence, he said, "This is my big family, my wife and my son."

The man's name was George Monin.

He and my parents talked for a while; then he started unhitching his horses. My father said to me, "You may start your snails over the hill. We will be waiting for you beyond it."

On the far side of the hill was a narrow lane which followed a winding creek leading west of the road. My father and his friend had passed us and were waiting there. We all followed the lane and shortly came to a three-room, unpainted house, almost hidden behind a bend in the line of trees. This house was even more lonely than the road.

The man's wife was thin, and careworn. She held out her hand to my mother, then embraced her and wept, as all women who have lived in the lonely hills of Texas weep when meeting a stranger.

"They are from Avoyelles and speak French!" her husband said. At this she redoubled her tears for joy. After a while the two women were talking and laughing.

"Let me unhitch your team," said our friend to my father. He busied himself at this courtesy and would not let me or my father help him. He was so glad to see us that it seemed he could not do enough for us.

Then as he worked I observed his face. It was flushed red from excitement. But I perceived something peculiar about it, since I was free to examine it without his noticing me.

In my childhood fancy I thought the face looked the way it did for a purpose. Although he could not have been more than forty-two, he was wrinkled, but his wrinkles were not those of sun, dust, or wind. I saw on closer observation that the reddish tint was a natural one only darkened by the stimulation of blood to his face. The cheekbones were high and flat. The eyes were bulging and restless; the mouth was nervous. It was such a face as I have seen in nightmares in which the monster was gentle and of good intent.

Soon after dark we were eating the simple but wholesome meal of a country home: chicken gumbo, rice, long slices of homemade bread with sweet milk, which Mrs. Monin served to us out of a large bowl.

Somewhat restless, perhaps, because of the peaceful atmosphere, and the uninteresting conversation about crops and the weather, I sought escape by examining the interior of the dining room. Over the fireplace, in which was a low fire, hung an old-fashioned picture. On the mantel I saw an old-fashioned clock that was not running. Then I found myself counting the doors, three of them, one opening into the kitchen, another giving access to the side porch, and a third, which led into the sitting room. Over each of these hung a large rifle.

We got up after supper and went into the living room, where a warm fire burned in the hearth. My mother walked in just ahead of my father. "Have you asked Mr. Monin about the road?" she said.

"Why, yes—I had forgotten to tell you—we are off the main road, but can regain it by cutting across a wood about a day's drive from here."

My mother sighed contentedly and soon was engaged in talking to Mrs. Monin.

I sat near the men.

"How long have you been away from Louisiana?" my father asked George Monin.

"Eleven years."

"So have I."

"Avoyelles is all right, I guess," said George Monin looking fixedly into the fire.

My father said, "It's got its good and its bad."

They went on talking about a wealthy doctor there who owned nearly all the land, who made nearly all the money, owned a large cotton gin, and swindled all the farmers.

"He was worse than Nick Reshaum," said my father.

"A lot worse."

"Nick got sent to the pen about the time we left there, didn't he?"

"Right after that," said George Monin. And my father said, "I heard he had escaped."

"He did, after a couple of months."

"Did you ever know him?"

"No, but I knew a brother of his, a blacksmith."

"So did I. Melville?"

"Yes, Melville, the blacksmith," answered George Monin.

"Melville used to trade at my store," said my father. "Pretty straight guy."

"Melville was as square-shooting a man as I want to meet. He wasn't anything at all like Nick. Didn't even look like him."

"He used to help Nick break out of jail," my father added.

"One time he forged a key just like the jail key and gave it to Nick when Nick was in jail. That way, Nick could get out at night and come back before daybreak. If Melville had made him stay in he might've made a man out of him. Melville was too good."

"But that Nick!" said my father.

"Yeh, that Nick!" And the two men laughed.

"Did you ever hear about the night he got married?"

"He eloped on a stolen horse with a brand new saddle and blanket on it."

My father laughed. "Some devil of a man for that peace-loving country. I heard he'd had a scuffle with Sheriff Tom Butler when he had escaped jail and Tom caught him and took him back. When they got to the cell he threw Tom down, picked him up and threw him in the cell; then he locked him in and took the key off with him. They had to break the door to get Tom Butler out. Some people say he killed a guard in escaping the penitentiary."

George Monin's face looked strange in the fire and lamplight. It was strange to see his bulging eyes sparkling with humor. "Some devil!" he said, and he and my father laughed and the sound of their voices seemed to grow dimmer and dimmer. The room was growing stuffy. I could barely keep my eyes open. Soon I was asleep.

The next morning my mother awoke me at sunrise. "Get up and eat," she said; "we will soon be leaving."

My father and George Monin were in the lot hitching the wagon. In nearly an hour we were climbing in, ready to leave. It was as though with our departure there would come a calamity to the Monins. As my mother started to step up into the wagon, the lonely, careworn little woman threw her arms about her neck and began to sob like a child. Her husband, a look of wistful sadness on his red face, stood by not knowing what to do or say. My father came up to him and offered his hand. George Monin took it and with a heavy voice said, "Please . . . do stay longer . . . couldn't you stay one more day?"

My father shook his head with a kindly smile. "I wish we could stay longer, Mr. Monin, but we've been on the road for three weeks, already."

George Monin slapped my father on the shoulder. He had a pitiful expression on his face. "Wait a minute," he said, and went off toward the smoke house. He returned with a bundle of fresh sausage which he had wrapped for us in some thick paper. "You might need this when you get home," he laughed, then added, "to remember me by."

He opened the gate and we passed onto the road. As we went by him I caught a lasting impression of his face. Somehow I felt that that face would follow me through life—looking for something I had.

Once more the hubs knocked with the wheels rolling towards home. Late that afternoon we camped at a spot which had been designated as being four miles from the edge of the wood.

The next morning my father said to my mother, "Where are those buckshot shells?" My mother began searching under some things.

"What do you want them for?" I asked him.

"Safety."

"Is it—p-panthers?"

"Hush, Son," my mother interposed; "you were born in a panther country."

We lost the way three times because the tracks left by the rare traffic were so dim. At these times we were rather uneasy, for men have been known to get lost and die of distraction and starvation in places much smaller than this. At almost sundown we came to an open place which showed no connection with the forest. "We are out of the wilderness," my father said, then pointing ahead, "There is the road. In three days we will be in Louisiana."

We drove the wagon off the road and stopped on the bank of a creek, to camp for the night. With nothing about us but naked trees, a creek, the setting sun, the vacant, chilly atmosphere, and perhaps because we so suddenly found ourselves without any visible obstacles, I did not know how to feel. As I helped my father unhitch and put the blankets on the horses I looked over and saw my mother sitting in the back of the wagon, looking down into the tub of hot coals.

I went over and said to her, "Do you feel bad, Mamma?"

"No," she answered.

"Are you thinking about home?"

"No."

"Then, Mamma, why do you sit like that, without anything to say? . . . Are you sad?"

"Go and get me some hickory branches for the tub, Son," she said calmly.

Dusk began to fall and to envelop our solitary little camp with gloom. I went and got the wood and brought it to her. Then I put some oats for the horses in a trough fastened behind the wagon. I called them and they came and ground up the oats between their teeth with monotonous crunching.

I thought I heard a sound on the road. I looked there and saw a buggy stopping, with a man in it peering at us through the trees. After a while he turned his horse and drove off the road in our direction.

It was George Monin.

"Hello, there!" exclaimed my father going to him. The man got out of the buggy. He had not said a word.

"What brings you here?" asked my father.

"My friend," replied George Monin with an uneasy sigh, "you see me in trouble."

"Yes?"

Just then my mother who had been inside the wagon came out. "Why, hello, Mr. ——"

"Doesn't it occur to you who I am?" the man was saying.

My father thought a while, then looked into his face. His lips flickered with a smile of familiarity. For a moment it seemed as though a grin strayed over George Monin's face.

"You are Nick Reshaum," said my father.

"I am."

The words mingled with the crunching of oats in the horse trough. After some hesitation the man who had spoken them looked up at the bare trees, then down at his toes. "You know—of course—there's a price on my head—a thousand dollars, I think," he said haltingly.

My father laughed. "Ha! Nick, I wouldn't turn you in for my wagon full of money."

With tears streaming down his cheeks and his face suffused with mingled joy and sadness, Nick Reshaum bowed his head, repeating, "My friends—my friends . . ."

He was in a hurry to go back home to his wife, but my parents prevailed upon him to stay with us. That night in the dim lamplight under the wagon canvas he told us his story. I don't remember all of it. Perhaps it was fatigue, perhaps it was the oily smell of the lamp, or the look in his face that made me forget most of the story and go to sleep before it was finished. I can only remember that he spoke of loneliness in his boyhood, of stealing, of switching cattle brands. I remember he said to my father, "You're a square-shooter. I've known you a long time but you haven't known me. I've heard a lot of good things about you. That's why I trust you. . . . I've learned that jails and penitentiaries are not the only prisons a man can be in. . . . Some day they'll hang me, I know. . . ."

The next morning when I awoke, my father was standing by our horses, and was looking toward the road. I thought of our friend and looked about me. I did not see him. My father said something to my mother and she made an exclamation such as a woman makes when she is both shocked and hurt.

"Where is he—what has happened?" I cried out.

"He is gone," said my father calmly. There was a heavy look on his face.

"Did he take anything?" I asked.

"Nothing but his horse and buggy," said my father.

"Oh, Son, how could you!" my mother exclaimed to me; and she hid her face and sobbed, "He has gone like this—into those woods—in the dark . . ."

Oftentimes while my mother was ironing, or when she was bent over the stove, and I had just thrown an armful of wood into the wood box, she has looked at me and said in her tender, wisful voice, "I wonder if Mr. Reshaum ever got through those woods, or if a panther killed him. Do you think, perhaps, he got lost and died away out there alone with his horse?"

"I don't know, Mamma," I would answer, "but wasn't he a queer man, wasn't his face the most peculiar thing you ever saw?"

"Wasn't it!" my mother would say; "I think I would like to forget him, but somehow I can't. I wonder what makes us remember people though we try to forget them. Can't you tell me that, Son?"

Where anyone else would have been merely surprised or astonished she had been heartbroken and permanently impressed. I felt very near her.

Fifteen years after that my mother died.

As the years are passing I am gradually forgetting Nick Reshaum— the man—but his face will never leave me. As in my childhood I am yet bewildered before it. And while his face is there in my thoughts, I think I feel something present about me, and I am shaken with a violent and tragic desire to be again near that which is tender, and comforting—but impossible to reach. Then I am swept back into the deceitful materiality about me. And, here, let me digress to contend that substance is faithless; in it my senses lead me about as a blind man—and I am deceived; for here is something I can lay my hand upon and feel, and it is proved a fraud; but yonder is a dream, a desire, or yet a faint image only touched by the last sigh of sad memory—and I am drawn to it as though by some overpowering machine of the Universe——

Nick Reshaum, what has become of you! *

INTERPRETATION

"The Face" is a story about homesickness. We see that this is true on a perfectly literal level early in the story. A family which has had a hard time in east Texas is finally on the way back home to Louisiana. The mother, in particular, looks forward to seeing her family, to eating fruit from her own fruit trees, to speaking her own language again. "Is it magic?" she asks about this mysterious attachment which she feels. The impressionable child, who, long afterwards as a grown man, tells the story, does not clearly remember the Louisiana home, but he can share his mother's feeling. On the journey back, they meet another Louisiana family, but a family which, as they discover, cannot go back. In one sense the little incident of the meeting with the outlaw family may seem rather trivial and tame. Nothing in particular happens. We do learn why the man cannot go back, and this does heighten the sense of homesickness. In terms of plot, the only thing that happens is that the boy's father promises not to turn the stranger over to the law. But is this the point of the story? What is the rather slight plot being used to do? We see that the story continues for several paragraphs after the plot action is over. We must, therefore, try to determine whether this section of the story has any proper function. In this connection we should ask ourselves the following questions:

1. What is the function of the last conversation between the mother and son concerning Nick Reshaum, in the paragraph beginning, "Oftentimes while my mother was ironing . . . "?

2. What is the importance of the statement, which is emphasized by its bald isolation, that the mother died fifteen years after the event of the story?

3. What is the function of the last paragraph? What is the importance of the statement that the boy, now grown up, is gradually for-

* Copyright, 1936, *The Southern Review;* reprinted by permission of the author.

getting Nick, the man, but cannot forget Nick's face? Does this imply that the face has come to have some symbolic meaning? What is the importance of the phrase "deceitful materiality" and of the flat contention—observe how boldly this is stated—that "substance is faithless"?

4. What does the last sentence of the story, the appeal addressed to Nick Reshaum, mean?

Do not, in fact, the answers to these questions lead us to the conclusion that the story is not about homesickness upon the merely literal level, but about another kind of homesickness, a homesickness for a state of being, for a world to which no one can ever go back? Try to define more particularly this other, more fundamental and inclusive, homesickness, for which the literal homesickness treated in the story stands, in the end, as a symbol.

After arriving at a definition of the theme of the story, go back and study the function of the "face." Why is it described as such a face as appears in the boy's nightmares in which "the monster was gentle and of good intent"? What significance for the theme appears in the fact that Nick Reshaum has committed a crime which forbids him to go back home? Can it be said that this, in a way, implies that everyone commits a crime which forbids him to return to his "home"?

What Character Reveals

AS THE preceding stories and their accompanying interpretations should have made abundantly evident, this section, in calling especial attention to the problem of character in fiction, introduces nothing which is in principle new. We have seen that it is impossible to talk about the stories in Section II without going into a detailed discussion of character: Various actions are performed; are these actions "in character"? Do they conform to a certain logic inherent in the nature of the people who are supposed to perform them? Are they psychologically valid? And we have seen, furthermore, that in order to discuss the preceding stories we have had to ask other questions which involve character: Are the actions performed in these stories significant in terms of character? Do they reveal character? Or do they effect changes in the inner lives of the characters?

Yet, though the problems of plot and character in fiction are inextricably interwoven, the title of Section II may not be wholly arbitrary. The emphasis on the plot element in these stories has given us an opportunity to focus our attention on a number of basic problems. The stories examined range from those in which the plot involves violent physical action to those in which the plot as such is no more than an apparently trivial incident. Yet, as we have seen, significance and even dramatic intensity are not restricted to the complicated plot, or to the plot which involves violent action. The story with a slight plot may achieve both. We have also had an opportunity, in examining these stories, to investigate the problem of the surprise ending— the ending which reveals an unexpected turn in events and produces some sort of shock in the reader. This device is constantly employed by writers of fiction and, as we have seen, may be thoroughly legitimate, but its legitimacy depends upon whether or not the shock is significant in terms of the rest of the story; it is clearly unjustified when it is used merely to titillate the reader or to supply him with a gratuitous surprise.

In the stories presented in Section III, there is also a considerable range of types, and certainly a considerable variation in the delicacy and firmness of character delineation. All the stories, however, may be used as examples of the problems involved in character delineation. Even the first story in this section, Poe's "The Fall of the House of Usher," usually described as an "atmosphere story," may be fruitfully approached from the standpoint of the author's method of handling the central character.

The Fall of the House of Usher
EDGAR ALLAN POE

DURING the whole of a dull, dark, and soundless day in the autumn of the year, when the clouds hung oppressively low in the heavens, I had been passing alone, on horseback, through a singularly dreary tract of country; and at length found myself, as the shades of the evening drew on, within view of the melancholy House of Usher. I know not how it was—but, with the first glimpse of the building, a sense of insufferable gloom pervaded my spirit. I say insufferable; for the feeling was unrelieved by any of that half-pleasurable, because poetic, sentiment with which the mind usually receives even the sternest natural images of the desolate or terrible. I looked upon the scene before me— upon the mere house, and the simple landscape features of the domain, upon the bleak walls, upon the vacant eye-like windows, upon a few rank sedges, and upon a few white trunks of decayed trees—with an utter depression of soul which I can compare to no earthly sensation more properly than to the after-dream of the reveler upon opium; the bitter lapse into everyday life, the hideous dropping off of the veil. There was an iciness, a sinking, a sickening of the heart, an unre- deemed dreariness of thought which no goading of the imagination could torture into aught of the sublime. What was it—I paused to think —what was it that so unnerved me in the contemplation of the House of Usher? It was a mystery all insoluble; nor could I grapple with the shadowy fancies that crowded upon me as I pondered. I was forced to fall back upon the unsatisfactory conclusion, that while, beyond doubt, there *are* combinations of very simple natural objects which have the power of thus affecting us, still the analysis of this power lies among considerations beyond our depth. It was possible, I reflected, that a mere different arrangement of the particulars of the scene, of the details of the picture, would be sufficient to modify, or perhaps to annihilate, its capacity for sorrowful impression; and acting upon this idea, I reined my horse to the precipitous brink of a black and lurid tarn that lay in unruffled luster by the dwelling, and gazed down— but with a shudder even more thrilling than before—upon the remodeled and inverted images of the gray sedge, and the ghastly tree stems, and the vacant and eye-like windows.

Nevertheless, in this mansion of gloom I now proposed to myself a sojourn of some weeks. Its proprietor, Roderick Usher, had been one of my boon companions in boyhood; but many years had elapsed since our last meeting. A letter, however, had lately reached me in a distant part of the country—a letter from him—which in its wildly importunate nature had admitted of no other than a personal reply. The MS. gave evidence of nervous agitation. The writer spoke of acute bodily illness, of a mental disorder which oppressed him, and of an earnest desire to see me, as his best and indeed his only personal friend, with a view of attempting by the cheerfulness of my society, some alleviation of his malady. It was the manner in which all this, and much more, was said—it was the apparent *heart* that went with his request—which allowed me no room for hesitation; and I accordingly obeyed forthwith what I still considered a very singular summons.

Although as boys we had been even intimate associates, yet I really knew little of my friend. His reserve had been always excessive and habitual. I was aware, however, that his very ancient family had been noted, time out of mind, for a peculiar sensibility of temperament, displaying itself, through long ages, in many works of exalted art, and manifested of late in repeated deeds of munificent yet unobtrusive charity, as well as in a passionate devotion to the intricacies, perhaps even more than to the orthodox and easily recognizable beauties, of musical science. I had learned, too, the very remarkable fact that the stem of the Usher race, all time-honored as it was, had put forth at no period any enduring branch; in other words, that the entire family lay in the direct line of descent, and had always, with very trifling and very temporary variation, so lain. It was this deficiency, I considered, while running over in thought the perfect keeping of the character of the premises with the accredited character of the people, and while speculating upon the possible influence which the one, in the long lapse of centuries, might have exercised upon the other—it was this deficiency, perhaps, of collateral issue, and the consequent un-deviating transmission from sire to son of the patrimony with the name, which had, at length, so identified the two as to merge the original title of the estate in the quaint and equivocal appellation of the "House of Usher"—an appellation which seemed to include, in the minds of the peasantry who used it, both the family and the family mansion.

I have said that the sole effect of my somewhat childish experiment, that of looking down within the tarn, had been to deepen the first singular impression. There can be no doubt that the consciousness of the rapid increase of my superstition—for why should I not so term it?—served mainly to accelerate the increase itself. Such, I have long known, is the paradoxical law of all sentiments having terror as a basis. And it might have been for this reason only, that, when I again up-lifted my eyes to the house itself, from its image in the pool, there grew in my mind a strange fancy—a fancy so ridiculous, indeed, that I but mention it to show the vivid force of the sensations which op-pressed me. I had so worked upon my imagination as really to believe that about the whole mansion and domain there hung an atmosphere peculiar to themselves and their immediate vicinity: an atmosphere which had no affinity with the air of heaven, but which had reeked up from the decayed trees, and the gray wall, and the silent tarn: a pestilent and mystic vapor, dull, sluggish, faintly discernible, and leaden-hued.

Shaking off from my spirit what *must* have been a dream, I scanned more narrowly the real aspect of the building. Its principal feature seemed to be that of an excessive antiquity. The discoloration of ages had been great. Minute fungi overspread the whole exterior, hanging in a fine tangled webwork from the eaves. Yet all this was apart from any extraordinary dilapidation. No portion of the masonry had fallen; and there appeared to be a wild inconsistency between its still perfect adaptation of parts and the crumbling condition of the individual stones. In this there was much that reminded me of the specious total- -

ity of old woodwork which had rotted for long years in some neglected vault, with no disturbance from the breath of the external air. Beyond this indication of excessive decay, however, the fabric gave little token of instability. Perhaps the eye of a scrutinizing observer might have discovered a barely perceptible fissure, which, extending from the roof of the building in front, made its way down the wall in a zigzag direction, until it became lost in the sullen waters of the tarn.

Noticing these things, I rode over a short causeway to the house. A servant in waiting took my horse, and I entered the Gothic archway of the hall. A valet, of stealthy step, thence conducted me, in silence, through many dark and intricate passages in my progress to the studio of his master. Much that I encountered on the way contributed, I know not how, to heighten the vague sentiments of which I have already spoken. While the objects around me—while the carvings of the ceilings, the somber tapestries of the walls, the ebon blackness of the floors, and the phantasmagoric armorial trophies which rattled as I strode, were but matters to which, or to such as which, I had been accustomed from my infancy—while I hesitated not to acknowledge how familiar was all this—I still wondered to find how unfamiliar were the fancies which ordinary images were stirring up. On one of the staircases, I met the physician of the family. His countenance, I thought, wore a mingled expression of low cunning and perplexity. He accosted me with trepidation and passed on. The valet now threw open a door and ushered me into the presence of his master.

The room in which I found myself was very large and lofty. The windows were long, narrow, and pointed, and at so vast a distance from the black oaken floor as to be altogether inaccessible from within. Feeble gleams of encrimsoned light made their way through the trellised panes, and served to render sufficiently distinct the more prominent objects around; the eye, however, struggled in vain to reach the remoter angles of the chamber, or the recesses of the vaulted and fretted ceiling. Dark draperies hung upon the walls. The general furniture was profuse, comfortless, antique, and tattered. Many books and musical instruments lay scattered about, but failed to give any vitality to the scene. I felt that I breathed an atmosphere of sorrow. An air of stern, deep, and irredeemable gloom hung over and pervaded all.

Upon my entrance, Usher arose from a sofa on which he had been lying at full length, and greeted me with a vivacious warmth which had much in it, I at first thought, of an overdone cordiality—of the constrained effort of the *ennuyé* man of the world. A glance, however, at his countenance, convinced me of his perfect sincerity. We sat down; and for some moments, while he spoke not, I gazed upon him with a feeling half of pity, half of awe. Surely man had never before so terribly altered in so brief a period as had Roderick Usher! It was with difficulty that I could bring myself to admit the identity of the wan being before me with the companion of my early boyhood. Yet the character of his face had been at all times remarkable. A cadaverousness of complexion; an eye large, liquid, and luminous beyond comparison; lips somewhat thin and very pallid, but of a surpassingly beautiful curve; a nose of a delicate Hebrew model, but with a breadth of nostril unusual in similar formations; a finely molded chin, speaking, in its want of prominence, of a want of moral energy; hair of a more than weblike softness and tenuity; these features, with an inordinate expansion above the regions of the temple, made up altogether a countenance not easily to be forgotten. And now in the mere exaggeration of the prevailing character of these features, and of the expression they were wont to convey, lay so much of change that I doubted to whom I spoke. The now ghostly pallor of the skin, and the now miraculous luster of the eye, above all things startled and even awed me. The silken hair, too, had been suffered to grow all unheeded, and as, in its wild gossamer texture, it floated rather than fell about the face, I could not, even with effort, connect its arabesque expression with any idea of simple humanity.

In the manner of my friend I was at once struck with an incoherence, an inconsistency; and I soon found this to arise from a series of feeble and futile struggles to overcome an habitual trepidancy, an excessive nervous agitation. For something of this nature I had indeed been prepared, no less by his letter than by reminiscences of certain boyish traits, and by conclusions deduced from his peculiar physical conformation and temperament. His action was alternatively vivacious and sullen. His voice varied rapidly from a tremulous indecision (when the animal spirits seemed utterly in abeyance) to that species of energetic concision—that abrupt, weighty, unhurried, and hollow-sounding enunciation—that leaden, self-balanced and perfectly modulated guttural utterance—which may be observed in the lost drunkard, or the irreclaimable eater of opium, during the periods of his most intense excitement.

It was thus that he spoke of the object of my visit, of his earnest desire to see me, and of the solace he expected me to afford him. He entered, at some length, into what he conceived to be the nature of his malady. It was, he said, a constitutional and a family evil, and one for which he despaired to find a remedy—a mere nervous affection, he immediately added, which would undoubtedly soon pass off. It displayed itself in a host of unnatural sensations. Some of these, as he detailed them, interested and bewildered me: although, perhaps, the terms and the general manner of the narration had their weight. He suffered much from a morbid acuteness of the senses; the most insipid food was alone endurable; he could wear only garments of a certain texture; the odors of all flowers were oppressive; his eyes were tortured by even a faint light; and there were but peculiar sounds, and these from stringed instruments, which did not inspire him with horror.

To an anomalous species of terror I found him a bounden slave. "I shall perish," said he, "I *must* perish in this deplorable folly. Thus, thus, and not otherwise, shall I be lost. I dread the events of the future, not in themselves, but in their results. I shudder at the thought of any, even the most trivial, incident, which may operate upon this intolerable agitation of soul. I have, indeed, no abhorrence of danger, except in its absolute effect—in terror. In this unnerved—in this pitiable condition, I feel that the period will sooner or later arrive when I must abandon life and reason together, in some struggle with the grim phantasm, FEAR."

I learned moreover at intervals, and through broken and equivocal hints, another singular feature of his mental condition. He was enchained by certain superstitious impressions in regard to the dwelling which he tenanted, and whence, for many years, he had never ventured forth—in regard to an influence whose supposititious force was conveyed in terms too shadowy here to be restated—an influence which some peculiarities in the mere form and substance of his family mansion, had, by dint of long sufferance, he said, obtained over his spirit—an effect which the physique of the gray walls and turrets, and of the dim tarn into which they all looked down, had, at length, brought about upon the morale of his existence.

He admitted, however, although with hesitation, that much of the peculiar gloom which thus afflicted him could be traced to a more natural and far more palpable origin—to the severe and long-continued illness, indeed to the evidently approaching dissolution, of a tenderly beloved sister—his sole companion for long years, his last and only relative on earth. "Her decease," he said, with a bitterness which I can never forget, "would leave him (him the hopeless and the frail) the last of the ancient race of the Ushers." While he spoke, the lady Madeline (for so was she called) passed slowly through a remote portion of the apartment, and, without having noticed my presence, disappeared. I regarded her with an utter astonishment not unmingled with dread, and yet I found it impossible to account for such feelings. A sensation of stupor oppressed me, as my eyes followed her retreating steps. When a door, at length, closed upon her, my glance sought instinctively and eagerly the countenance of the brother; but he had buried his face in his hands, and I could only perceive that a far more than ordinary wanness had overspread the emaciated fingers through which trickled many passionate tears.

The disease of the lady Madeline had long baffled the skill of her physicians. A settled apathy, a gradual wasting away of the person, and frequent although transient affections of a partially cataleptical character, were the unusual diagnosis. Hitherto she had steadily borne up against the pressure of her malady, and had not betaken herself finally to bed; but, on the closing in of the evening of my arrival at the house, she succumbed (as her brother told me at night with inexpressible agitation) to the prostrating power of the destroyer; and I learned that the glimpse I had obtained of her person would thus probably be the last I should obtain—that the lady, at least while living, would be seen by me no more.

For several days ensuing, her name was unmentioned by either Usher or myself; and during this period I was busied in earnest endeavors to alleviate the melancholy of my friend. We painted and read together; or I listened, as if in a dream, to the wild improvisation of his speaking guitar. And thus, as a closer and still closer intimacy admitted me more unreservedly into the recesses of his spirit, the more

bitterly did I perceive the futility of all attempt at cheering a mind
from which darkness, as if an inherent positive quality, poured forth
upon all objects of the moral and physical universe, in one unceasing
radiation of gloom.

I shall ever bear about me a memory of the many solemn hours I
thus spent alone with the master of the House of Usher. Yet I should
fail in any attempt to convey an idea of the exact character of the
studies, or of the occupations, in which he involved me, or led me
the way. An excited and highly distempered ideality threw a sulphur-
ous luster over all. His long improvised dirges will ring forever in
my ears. Among other things, I hold painfully in mind a certain singular perversion and amplification of the wild air of the last waltz of
Von Weber. From the paintings over which his elaborate fancy
brooded, and which grew, touch by touch, into vagueness at which
I shuddered the more thrillingly because I shuddered knowing not
why;—from these paintings (vivid as their images now are before me)
I would in vain endeavor to educe more than a small portion which
should lie within the compass of merely written words. By the utter
simplicity, by the nakedness of his designs, he arrested and overawed
attention. If ever mortal painted an idea, that mortal was Roderick
Usher. For me at least, in the circumstances then surrounding me,
there arose, out of the pure abstractions which the hypochondriac contrived to throw upon his canvas, an intensity of intolerable awe, no
shadow of which felt I ever yet in the contemplation of the certainly
glowing yet too concrete reveries of Fuseli.

One of the phantasmagoric conceptions of my friend, partaking not
so rigidly of the spirit of abstraction, may be shadowed forth, although
feebly, in words. A small picture presented the interior of an im-
mensely long and rectangular vault or tunnel, with low walls, smooth,
white, and without interruption or device. Certain accessory points of
the design served well to convey the idea that this excavation lay at
an exceeding depth below the surface of the earth. No outlet was observed in any portion of its vast extent, and no torch or other artificial
source of light was discernible; yet a flood of intense rays rolled
throughout, and bathed the whole in a ghastly and inappropriate
splendor.

I have just spoken of that morbid condition of the auditory nerve which rendered all music intolerable to the sufferer, with the exception of certain effects of stringed instruments. It was, perhaps, the narrow limits to which he thus confined himself upon the guitar, which gave birth, in great measure, to the fantastic character of his performances. But the fervid *facility* of his impromptus could not be so accounted for. They must have been, and were, in the notes, as well as in the words of his wild fantasias (for he not unfrequently accompanied himself with rhymed verbal improvisations), the result of that intense mental collectedness and concentration to which I have previously alluded as observable only in particular moments of the highest artificial excitement. The words of one of these rhapsodies I have easily remembered. I was, perhaps, the more forcibly impressed with it, as he gave it, because, in the under or mystic current of its meaning, I fancied that I perceived, and for the first time, a full consciousness, on the part of Usher, of the tottering of his lofty reason upon her throne. The verses, which were entitled "The Haunted Palace," ran very nearly, if not accurately, thus:

I

In the greenest of our valleys
By good angels tenanted,
Once a fair and stately palace—
Radiant palace—reared its head.
In the monarch Thought's dominion,
It stood there;
Never seraph spread a pinion
Over fabric half so fair.

II

Banners yellow, glorious, golden,
On its roof did float and flow,
(This—all this—was in the olden
Time long ago)
And every gentle air that dallied,
In that sweet day,
Along the ramparts plumed and pallid,
A winged odor went away.

III

Wanderers in that happy valley
Through two luminous windows saw

Spirits moving musically
  To a lute's well-tunèd law,
Round about a throne where, sitting,
  Porphyrogene,
In state his glory well befitting,
  The ruler of the realm was seen.

IV

And all with pearl and ruby glowing
  Was the fair palace door,
Through which came flowing, flowing, flowing,
  And sparkling evermore,
A troop of Echoes whose sweet duty
  Was but to sing,
In voices of surpassing beauty,
  The wit and wisdom of their king.

V

But evil things, in robes of sorrow,
  Assailed the monarch's high estate;
(Ah, let us mourn, for never morrow
  Shall dawn upon him, desolate!)
And round about his home the glory
  That blushed and bloomed
Is but a dim-remembered story
  Of the old time entombed.

VI

And travelers now within that valley
  Through the red-litten windows see
Vast forms that move fantastically
  To a discordant melody;
While, like a ghastly rapid river,
  Through the pale door
A hideous throng rush out forever,
  And laugh—but smile no more.

I well remember that suggestions arising from this ballad led us into a train of thought, wherein there became manifest an opinion of Usher's which I mention not so much on account of its novelty (for other men have thought thus) as on account of the pertinacity with which he maintained it. This opinion, in its general form, was that of the sentience of all vegetable things. But in his disordered fancy the idea had assumed a more daring character, and trespassed, under certain conditions, upon the kingdom of inorganization. I lack words to express the full extent, or the earnest *abandon* of his persuasion. The belief, however, was connected (as I have previously hinted) with the gray stones of the home of his forefathers. The conditions of the sentience had been here, he imagined, fulfilled in the method of collocation of these stones—in the order of their arrangement, as well as in that of the many fungi which overspread them, and of the decayed trees which stood around—above all, in the long undisturbed endurance of this arrangement, and in its reduplication in the still waters of the tarn. Its evidence—the evidence of the sentience—was to be seen, he said (and I here started as he spoke), in the gradual yet certain condensation of an atmosphere of their own about the waters and the walls. The result was discoverable, he added, in that silent, yet importunate and terrible influence which for centuries had molded the destinies of his family, and which made *him* what I now saw him —what he was. Such opinions need no comment, and I will make none.

Our books—the books which, for years, had formed no small portion of the mental existence of the invalid—were, as might be supposed, in strict keeping with this character of phantasm. We pored together over such works as the Ververt and Chartreuse of Gresset; the Belphegor of Machiavelli; the Heaven and Hell of Swedenborg; the Subterranean Voyage of Nicholas Klimm by Holberg; the Chiromancy of Robert Flud, of Jean D'Indaginé, and of De la Chambre; the Journey into the Blue Distance of Tieck; and the City of the Sun of Campanella. One favorite volume was a small octavo edition of the *Directorium Inquisitorium,* by the Dominican Eymeric de Gironne; and there were passages in Pomponius Mela, about the old African Satyrs and Ægipans, over which Usher would sit dreaming for hours. His chief delight, however, was found in the perusal of an exceedingly rare and curious book in quarto Gothic—the manual of a forgotten church—the *Vigiliæ Mortuorum Secundum Chorum Ecclesiæ Maguntinæ.*

I could not help thinking of the wild ritual of this work, and of its probable influence upon the hypochondriac, when one evening, having informed me abruptly that the lady Madeline was no more, he stated his intention of preserving her corpse for a fortnight (previously to its final interment) in one of the numerous vaults within the main walls of the building. The worldly reason, however, assigned for this singular proceeding was one which I did not feel at liberty to dispute. The brother had been led to his resolution (so he told me) by consideration of the unusual character of the malady of the deceased, of certain obtrusive and eager inquiries on the part of her medical men, and of the remote and exposed situation of the burial-ground of the family. I will not deny that when I called to mind the sinister countenance of the person whom I met upon the staircase, on the day of my arrival at the house, I had no desire to oppose what I regarded as at best but a harmless, and by no means an unnatural, precaution.

At the request of Usher, I personally aided him in the arrangements for the temporary entombment. The body having been encoffined, we two alone bore it to its rest. The vault in which we placed it (and which had been so long unopened that our torches, half smothered in its oppressive atmosphere, gave us little opportunity for investigation) was small, damp, and entirely without means of admission for light; lying, at great depth, immediately beneath that portion of the building in which was my own sleeping apartment. It had been used, apparently, in remote feudal times, for the worst purposes of a donjon-keep, and in later days as a place of deposit for powder, or some other highly combustible substance, as a portion of its floor, and the whole interior of a long archway through which we reached it, were carefully sheathed with copper. The door, of massive iron, had been also similarly protected. Its immense weight caused an unusually sharp grating sound, as it moved upon its hinges.

Having deposited our mournful burden upon trestles within this region of horror, we partially turned aside the yet unscrewed lid of the coffin, and looked upon the face of the tenant. A striking similitude between the brother and sister now first arrested my attention; and Usher divining, perhaps, my thoughts, murmured out some few words from which I learned that the deceased and himself had been twins, and that sympathies of a scarcely intelligible nature had always existed between them. Our glances, however, rested not long upon the dead—for we could not regard her unawed. The disease which had thus entombed the lady in the maturity of youth, had left, as usual in all maladies of a strictly cataleptical character, the mockery of a faint blush upon the bosom and the face, and that suspiciously lingering smile upon the lip which is so terrible in death. We replaced and screwed down the lid, and, having secured the door of iron, made our way, with toil, into the scarcely less gloomy apartments of the upper portion of the house.

And now, some days of bitter grief having elapsed, an observable change came over the features of the mental disorder of my friend. His ordinary manner had vanished. His ordinary occupations were neglected or forgotten. He roamed from chamber to chamber with hurried, unequal, and objectless step. The pallor of his countenance had assumed, if possible, a more ghastly hue—but the luminousness of his eye had utterly gone out. The once occasional huskiness of his tone was heard no more; and a tremulous quaver, as if of extreme terror, habitually characterized his utterance. There were times, indeed, when I thought his unceasingly agitated mind was laboring with some oppressive secret, to divulge which he struggled for the necessary courage. At times, again, I was obliged to resolve all into the mere inexplicable vagaries of madness, for I beheld him gazing upon vacancy for long hours, in an attitude of the profoundest attention, as if listening to some imaginary sound. It was no wonder that his condition terrified—that it infected me. I felt creeping upon me, by slow yet certain degrees, the wild influences of his own fantastic yet impressive superstitions.

It was, especially, upon retiring to bed late in the night of the seventh or eighth day after the placing of the lady Madeline within the donjon, that I experienced the full power of such feelings. Sleep came not near my couch, while the hours waned and waned away. I struggled to reason off the nervousness which had dominion over me. I endeavored to believe that much, if not all, of what I felt was due to the bewildering influence of the gloomy furniture of the room—of the dark and tattered draperies which, tortured into motion by the breath of a rising tempest, swayed fitfully to and fro upon the walls, and rustled uneasily about the decorations of the bed. But my efforts were fruitless. An irrepressible tremor gradually pervaded my frame; and at length there sat upon my very heart an incubus of utterly causeless alarm. Shaking this off with a gasp and a struggle, I up-lifted myself upon the pillows, and, peering earnestly within the in-tense darkness of the chamber, hearkened—I know not why, except that an instinctive spirit prompted me—to certain low and indefinite sounds which came, through the pauses of the storm, at long intervals, I knew not whence. Overpowered by an intense sentiment of horror, unaccountable yet unendurable, I threw on my clothes with haste (for I felt that I should sleep no more during the night) and endeavored to arouse myself from the pitiable condition into which I had fallen, by pacing rapidly to and fro through the apartment.

I had taken but few turns in this manner, when a light step on an adjoining staircase arrested my attention. I presently recognized it as that of Usher. In an instant afterward he rapped with a gentle touch at my door, and entered, bearing a lamp. His countenance was, as usual, cadaverously wan—but, moreover, there was a species of mad hilarity in his eyes—an evidently restrained hysteria in his whole de-meanor. His air appalled me—but anything was preferable to the solitude which I had so long endured, and I even welcomed his pres-ence as a relief.

"And you have not seen it?" he said abruptly, after having stared about him for some moments in silence—"you have not then seen it?—but, stay! you shall." Thus speaking, and having carefully shaded his lamp, he hurried to one of the casements, and threw it freely open to the storm.

The impetuous fury of the entering gust nearly lifted us from our feet. It was, indeed, a tempestuous yet sternly beautiful night, and one wildly singular in its terror and its beauty. A whirlwind had ap-parently collected its force in our vicinity; for there were frequent and violent alterations in the direction of the wind; and the exceeding density of the clouds (which hung so low as to press upon the turrets of the house) did not prevent our perceiving the lifelike velocity with which they flew careering from all points against each other, without passing away into the distance. I say that even their exceeding density did not prevent our perceiving this; yet we had no glimpse of the moon or stars, nor was there any flashing forth of the lightning. But the under surfaces of the huge masses of agitated vapor, as well as all terrestrial objects immediately around us, were glowing in the unnatural light of a faintly luminous and distinctly visible gaseous exhalation which hung about and enshrouded the mansion.

"You must not—you shall not behold this!" said I, shudderingly, to Usher, as I led him with a gentle violence from the window to a seat. "These appearances, which bewilder you, are merely electrical phenomena not uncommon—or it may be that they have their ghastly origin in the rank miasma of the tarn. Let us close this casement; the air is chilling and dangerous to your frame. Here is one of your favorite romances. I will read, and you shall listen;—and so we will pass away this terrible night together."

The antique volume which I had taken up was the *Mad Trist* of Sir Launcelot Canning; but I had called it a favorite of Usher's more in sad jest than in earnest; for, in truth, there is little in its uncouth and unimaginative prolixity which could have had interest for the lofty and spiritual ideality of my friend. It was, however, the only book immediately at hand; and I indulged a vague hope that the excitement which now agitated the hypochondriac might find relief (for the history of mental disorder is full of similar anomalies) even in the extremeness of the folly which I should read. Could I have judged, indeed, by the wild overstrained air of vivacity with which he hearkened, or apparently hearkened, to the words of the tale, I might well have congratulated myself upon the success of my design.

I had arrived at that well-known portion of the story where Ethelred, the hero of the Trist, having sought in vain for peaceable admission into the dwelling of the hermit, proceeds to make good an entrance by force. Here, it will be remembered, the words of the narrative run thus:

"And Ethelred, who was by nature of a doughty heart, and who was now mighty withal, on account of the powerfulness of the wine which he had drunken, waited no longer to hold parley with the hermit, who, in sooth, was of an obstinate and maliceful turn, but, feeling the rain upon his shoulders, and fearing the rising of the tempest, uplifted his mace outright, and with blows made quickly room in the plankings of the door for his gauntleted hand; and now pulling therewith sturdily, he so cracked, and ripped, and tore all asunder, that the noise of the dry and hollow-sounding wood alarumed and reverberated through-out the forest."

At the termination of this sentence I started, and for a moment paused; for it appeared to me (although I at once concluded that my excited fancy had deceived me)—it appeared to me that from some very remote portion of the mansion there came, indistinctly, to my ears, what might have been, in its exact similarity of character, the echo (but a stifled and dull one certainly) of the very cracking and ripping sound which Sir Launcelot had so particularly described. It was, beyond doubt, the coincidence alone which had arrested my attention; for, amid the rattling of the sashes of the casements, and the ordinary commingled noises of the still increasing storm, the sound, in itself, had nothing, surely, which should have interested or disturbed me. I continued the story:

"But the good champion Ethelred, now entering within the door, was sore enraged and amazed to perceive no signal of the maliceful hermit; but, in the stead thereof, a dragon of a scaly and prodigious demeanor, and of a fiery tongue, which sate in guard before a palace of gold, with a floor of silver; and upon the wall there hung a shield of shining brass with this legend enwritten—

Who entereth herein, a conqueror hath bin;
Who slayeth the dragon, the shield he shall win.

And Ethelred uplifted his mace, and struck upon the head of the dragon, which fell before him, and gave up his pesty breath, with a shriek so horrid and harsh, and withal so piercing, that Ethelred had fain to close his ears with his hands against the dreadful noise of it, the like whereof was never before heard."

Here again I paused abruptly, and now with a feeling of wild amazement; for there could be no doubt whatever that, in this instance, I did actually hear (although from what direction it proceeded I found it impossible to say) a low and apparently distant, but harsh, protracted, and most unusual screaming or grating sound—the exact counterpart of what my fancy had already conjured up for the dragon's unnatural shriek as described by the romancer.

Oppressed, as I certainly was, upon the occurrence of this second and most extraordinary coincidence, by a thousand conflicting sensations, in which wonder and extreme terror were predominant, I still retained sufficient presence of mind to avoid exciting, by any observation, the sensitive nervousness of my companion. I was by no means certain that he had noticed the sounds in question; although, assuredly, a strange alteration had during the last few minutes taken place in his demeanor. From a position fronting my own, he had gradually brought round his chair, so as to sit with his face to the door of the chamber; and thus I could but partially perceive his features, although I saw that his lips trembled as if he were murmuring inaudibly. His head had dropped upon his breast—yet I knew that he was not asleep, from the wide and rigid opening of the eye as I caught a glance of it in profile. The motion of his body, too, was at variance with this idea—for he rocked from side to side with a gentle yet constant and uniform sway. Having rapidly taken notice of all this, I resumed the narrative of Sir Launcelot, which thus proceeded:

"And now, the champion having escaped from the terrible fury of the dragon, bethinking himself of the brazen shield, and of the breaking up of the enchantment which was upon it, removed the carcass from out of the way before him, and approached valorously over the silver pavement of the castle to where the shield was upon the wall; which in sooth tarried not for his full coming, but fell down at his feet upon the silver floor, with a mighty great and terrible ringing sound."

No sooner had these syllables passed my lips, than—as if a shield of brass had indeed, at the moment, fallen heavily upon a floor of silver—I became aware of a distinct, hollow, metallic and clangorous, yet apparently muffled reverberation. Completely unnerved, I leaped to my feet; but the measured rocking movement of Usher was undisturbed. I rushed to the chair in which he sat. His eyes were bent fixedly before him, and throughout his whole countenance there reigned a stony rigidity. But, as I placed my hand upon his shoulder, there came a strong shudder over his whole person; a sickly smile quivered about his lips; and I saw that he spoke in a low, hurried, and gibbering murmur, as if unconscious of my presence. Bending closely over him, I at length drank in the hideous import of his words.

"Not hear it?—yes, I hear it, and *have* heard it. Long—long—long—

many minutes, many hours, many days, have I heard it—yet I dared not—oh, pity me, miserable wretch that I am!—I dared not—*I dared not speak! We have put her living in the tomb!* Said I not that my senses were acute? I *now* tell you that I heard her first feeble movements in the hollow coffin. I heard them—many, many days ago—yet I dared not—*I dared not speak!* And now—tonight—Ethelred—ha! ha! —the breaking of the hermit's door, and the death-cry of the dragon, and the clangor of the shield!—say, rather, the rending of her coffin, and the grating of the iron hinges of her prison, and her struggles within the coppered archway of the vault! Oh, whither shall I fly? Will she not be here anon? Is she not hurrying to upbraid me for my haste? Have I not heard her footsteps on the stair? Do I not distinguish that heavy and horrible beating of her heart? Madman!"— here he sprang furiously to his feet, and shrieked out his syllables, as if in the effort he were giving up his soul—*"Madman! I tell you that she now stands without the door!"*

As if in the superhuman energy of his utterance there had been found the potency of a spell, the huge antique panels to which the speaker pointed drew slowly back, upon the instant, their ponderous and ebony jaws. It was the work of the rushing gust—but then without the doors there *did* stand the lofty and enshrouded figure of the lady Madeline of Usher. There was blood upon her white robes, and the evidence of some bitter struggle upon every portion of her emaciated frame. For a moment she remained trembling and reeling to and fro upon the threshold—then, with a low moaning cry, fell heavily inward upon the person of her brother, and, in her violent and now final death agonies, bore him to the floor a corpse, and a victim to the terrors he had anticipated.

From that chamber, and from that mansion, I fled aghast. The storm was still abroad in all its wrath as I found myself crossing the old causeway. Suddenly there shot along the path a wild light, and I turned to see whence a gleam so unusual could have issued; for the vast house and its shadows were alone behind me. The radiance was that of the full, setting, and blood-red moon, which now shone vividly through that once barely discernible fissure, of which I have before spoken as extending from the roof of the building, in a zigzag direction, to the base. While I gazed, this fissure rapidly widened—there came a fierce breath of the whirlwind—the entire orb of the satellite burst at once upon my sight—my brain reeled as I saw the mighty walls rushing asunder—there was a long tumultuous shouting sound like the voice of a thousand waters—and the deep and dank tarn at my feet closed sullenly and silently over the fragments of the House of Usher.

INTERPRETATION

This is a story of horror, and the author has used nearly every kind of device at his disposal in order to stimulate a sense of horror in the reader: not only is the action itself horrible but the descriptions of the decayed house, the gloomy landscape in which it is located, the furnishings of its shadowy interior, the ghastly and unnatural storm— all of these are used to build up in the reader the sense of something mysterious and unnatural. Within its limits, the story is rather successful in inducing in the reader the sense of nightmare; that is, if the reader allows himself to enter into the mood of the story, the mood infects him rather successfully.

But one usually does not find nightmares pleasant, and though there is an element of horror in many of the great works of literature— Dante's *Inferno,* Shakespeare's tragedies—still, we do not value the sense of horror for its own sake. What is the meaning, the justification of the horror in this story? Does the story have a meaning, or is the horror essentially meaningless, horror aroused for its own sake?

In the beginning of the story, the narrator says of the House of Usher that he experienced "a sense of insufferable gloom," a feeling which had nothing of that "half-pleasurable, because poetic, sentiment with which the mind usually receives even the sternest natural images of the desolate or terrible. . . . It was a mystery all insoluble. . . ." Does the reader feel, with regard to the story as a whole, what the narrator in the story feels toward the house in the story?

One point to determine is the quality of the horror—whether it is merely vague and nameless, or an effect of a much more precise and special imaginative perception. Here, the description which fills the story will be helpful: the horror apparently springs from a perception of decay, a decay which constitutes a kind of life-in-death, monstrous because it represents death and yet pulsates with a special vitality of its own. For example, the house itself gets its peculiar *atmosphere* (see

Glossary) from its ability apparently to defy reality: to remain intact and yet seem to be completely decayed in every detail. By the same token, Roderick Usher has a wild vitality, a preternatural acuteness and sensitiveness which itself springs from the fact that he is sick unto death. Indeed, Roderick Usher is more than once in the story compared to the house, and by more subtle hints, by implications of descriptive detail, throughout the story, the house is identified with its heir and owner. For example, the house is twice described as having "vacant eye-like windows"—the house, it is suggested, is like a man. Or, again, the mad song, which Roderick Usher sings with evident reference to himself, describes a man under the *allegory* (see Glossary) of a house. To repeat, the action of the story, the description, and the symbolism, consistently insist upon the horror as that which springs from the unnatural and monstrous. One might reasonably conclude that the "meaning" of the story lies in its perception of the dangers of divorcement from reality and the attempt to live in an unreal world of the past, or in any private and abstract world of thought. Certainly, elements of such a critique are to be found in the story. But their mere presence there does not in itself justify the pertinacious and almost loving care with which Poe conjures up for us the sense of the horrors of the dying House of Usher.

One may penetrate perhaps further into the question by considering the relation of the horror to Roderick Usher himself. The story is obviously his story. It is not Madeline's—in the story she hardly exists for us as a human being—nor is it the narrator's story, though his relation to the occupants of the doomed House of Usher becomes most important when we attempt to judge the ultimate success or failure of the story.

Roderick Usher, it is important to notice, recognizes the morbidity of the life which he is leading. Indeed, he even calls his persistence in carrying on his mode of living in the house a deplorable "folly." And yet one has little or no sense in the story that Roderick Usher is actually making any attempt to get away from the haunting and oppressive gloom of the place. Actually, there is abundant evidence that he is in love with "the morbid acuteness of the senses" which he has cultivated in the gloomy mansion, and that in choosing between this and the honest daylight of the outside world, there is but one choice for him. But, in stating what might be called the moral issue of the story in such terms as these, we have perhaps already overstated it. The reader gets no sense of struggle, no sense of real choice at all. Rather, Roderick Usher impresses the reader as being as thoroughly doomed as the decaying house in which he lives.

One may go further with this point: we hardly take Roderick Usher seriously as a real human being at all. Even on the part of the narrator who tells us that Usher has been one of his intimate companions in boyhood, there is little imaginative identification of his interests and feelings with those of Usher. At the beginning of the story, the narrator admits that he "really knew little" of his friend. Even his interest in Usher's character tends to be what may be called a "clinical" interest. Now, baffled by the vague terrors and superstitions that beset Roderick Usher, he is able to furnish us, not so much a reading of his friend's character as a list of symptoms and aberrations. Usher is a medical case, a fascinating case to be sure, a titillatingly horrible case, but merely another case after all.

In making these points, we are really raising questions that have to do with the limits of tragedy. The tragic protagonist must be a man who engages our own interests and hopes and fears as a Macbeth or a Lear, of superhuman stature though these be, engages them. We must not merely look on from without. Even if the interest is an overwhelming psychological interest, it is not enough. Eugene O'Neill perhaps falls into the same error in handling his protagonist in *The Emperor Jones*. We see the overlayings of civilization progressively torn from the big confident Negro, until at the end he is reduced to an impotent wreck, at the mercy of the primitive superstitions which he himself had thought he had put away. But the play is hardly a tragedy; for there is no imaginative identification of ourselves with the protagonist; there is merely an outside interest, clinical observation.*

In the case of Roderick Usher, then, there is on our part little imaginative sympathy and there is, on his own part, very little struggle. The story lacks tragic quality. One can go farther: the story lacks even pathos—that is, a feeling of pity, as for the misfortune of a weak person, or the death of a child. To sum up, Poe has narrowed the fate of his protagonist from a universal thing into something special and even peculiar, and he has played up the sense of gloom and monstrous derangement so heavily that free will and rational decision hardly exist in the nightmare world which he describes. The horror is rela-

---

* The question of the sick or mad protagonist will receive further discussion in connection with William Faulkner's "A Rose for Emily," pp. 410-14.

tively meaningless—it is generated for its own sake; and one is inclined to feel that Poe's own interest in the story was a morbid interest.

1. In this story and in the "Portrait of Henry Hastings," the character of each man is revealed to a large extent by a description of the house in which he lives. In which case is this done the more successfully? Can it be said that "The Fall of the House of Usher" suffers from overwriting?

2. Can one justify the conclusion of the story against the charge that it is melodramatic?

3. The song which Roderick Usher sings may be said to describe the same situation as that described in the story as a whole, to embody the same atmosphere, and to contain the same theme. Does the story "say" anything which the poem does not "say" in more concentrated form? If so, what?

Tennessee's Partner

BRET HARTE

I DO NOT think that we ever knew his real name. Our ignorance of it certainly never gave us any social inconvenience, for at Sandy Bar in 1854 most men were christened anew. Sometimes these appellatives were derived from some distinctiveness of dress, as in the case of "Dungaree Jack"; or from some peculiarity of habit, as shown in "Saleratus Bill," so called from an undue proportion of that chemical in his daily bread; or from some unlucky slip, as exhibited in "The Iron Pirate," a mild, inoffensive man, who earned that baleful title by his unfortunate mispronunciation of the term "iron pyrites." Perhaps this may have been the beginning of a rude heraldry; but I am constrained to think that it was because a man's real name in that day rested solely upon his own unsupported statement. "Call yourself Clifford, do you?" said Boston, addressing a timid newcomer with infinite scorn; "hell is full of such Cliffords!" He then introduced the unfortunate man, whose name happened to be really Clifford, as "Jay-bird Charley"—an unhallowed inspiration of the moment that clung to him ever after.

But to return to Tennessee's Partner, whom we never knew by any other than this relative title. That he had ever existed as a separate and distinct individuality we only learned later. It seems that in 1853 he left

Poker Flat to go to San Francisco, ostensibly to procure a wife. He never got any farther than Stockton. At that place he was attracted by a young person who waited upon the table at the hotel where he took his meals. One morning he said something to her which caused her to smile not unkindly, to somewhat coquettishly break a plate of toast over his up-turned, serious, simple face, and to retreat to the kitchen. He followed her, and emerged a few moments later, covered with more toast and victory. That day week they were married by a justice of the peace, and returned to Poker Flat. I am aware that something more might be made of this episode, but I prefer to tell it as it was current at Sandy Bar—in the gulches and barrooms—where all sentiment was modified by a strong sense of humor.

Of their married felicity but little is known, perhaps for the reason that Tennessee, then living with his partner, one day took occasion to say something to the bride on his own account, at which, it is said, she smiled not unkindly and chastely retreated—this time as far as Marysville, where Tennessee followed her, and where they went to housekeeping without the aid of a justice of the peace. Tennessee's Partner took the loss of his wife simply and seriously, as was his fashion. But to every-body's surprise, when Tennessee one day returned from Marysville, without his partner's wife—she having smiled and retreated with some-body else—Tennessee's Partner was the first man to shake his hand and greet him with affection. The boys who had gathered in the cañon to see the shooting were naturally indignant. Their indignation might have found vent in sarcasm but for a certain look in Tennessee's Part-ner's eye that indicated a lack of humorous appreciation. In fact, he was a grave man, with a steady application to practical detail which was un-pleasant in a difficulty.

Meanwhile a popular feeling against Tennessee had grown up on the Bar. He was known to be a gambler; he was suspected to be a thief. In these suspicions Tennessee's Partner was equally compromised; his continued intimacy with Tennessee after the affair above quoted could only be accounted for on the hypothesis of a copartnership of crime. At last Tennessee's guilt became flagrant. One day he overtook a stranger on his way to Red Dog. The stranger afterward related that Tennessee beguiled the time with interesting anecdote and reminiscence, but illogi-cally concluded the interview in the following words: "And now, young man, I'll trouble you for your knife, your pistols, and your money. You see your weppings might get you into trouble at Red Dog, and your money's a temptation to the evilly disposed. I think you said your address was San Francisco. I shall endeavor to call." It may be stated here that Tennessee had a fine flow of humor, which no business preoccupation could wholly subdue.

This exploit was his last. Red Dog and Sandy Bar made common cause against the highwayman. Tennessee was hunted in very much the same fashion as his prototype, the grizzly. As the toils closed around him, he made a desperate dash through the Bar, emptying his revolver at the crowd before the Arcade Saloon, and so on up Grizzly Cañon; but at its farther extremity he was stopped by a small man on a gray horse. The men looked at each other a moment in silence. Both were fearless, both self-possessed and independent; and both types of a civilization that in the seventeenth century would have been called heroic, but in the nineteenth simply "reckless."

"What have you got there?—I call," said Tennessee, quietly.

"Two bowers and an ace," said the stranger, as quietly, showing two revolvers and a bowie knife.

"That takes me," returned Tennessee; and, with this gambler's epigram, he threw away his useless pistol, and rode back with his captor.

It was a warm night. The cool breeze which usually sprang up with the going down of the sun behind the chaparral-crested mountain was that evening withheld from Sandy Bar. The little cañon was stifling with heated resinous odors, and the decaying driftwood on the Bar sent forth faint, sickening exhalations. The feverishness of day and its fierce passions still filled the camp. Lights moved restlessly along the bank of the river, striking no answering reflection from its tawny current. Against the blackness of the pines the windows of the old loft above the express office stood out staringly bright; and through their curtainless panes the loungers below could see the forms of those who were even then deciding the fate of Tennessee. And above all this, etched on the dark firmament, rose the Sierra, remote and passionless, crowned with remoter passionless stars.

The trial of Tennessee was conducted as fairly as was consistent with a judge and jury who felt themselves to some extent obliged to justify, in their verdict, the previous irregularities of arrest and indictment. The law of Sandy Bar was implacable, but not vengeful. The excitement and personal feeling of the chase were over; with Tennessee safe in their hands, they were ready to listen patiently to any defense, which they were already satisfied was insufficient. There being no doubt in their own minds, they were willing to give the prisoner the benefit of any that might exist. Secure in the hypothesis that he ought to be hanged on general principles, they indulged him with more latitude of defense than his reckless hardihood seemed to ask. The judge appeared to be more anxious than the prisoner, who, otherwise unconcerned, evidently took a grim pleasure in the responsibility he had created. "I don't take any hand in this yer game," had been his invariable, but good-humored reply to all questions. The judge—who was also his captor—for a moment vaguely regretted that he had not shot him "on sight" that morning, but presently dismissed this human weakness as unworthy of the judicial mind. Nevertheless, when there was a tap at the door, and it was said that Tennessee's Partner was there on behalf of the prisoner, he was admitted at once without question. Perhaps the younger members of the jury, to whom the proceedings were becoming irksomely thoughtful, hailed him as a relief.

For he was not, certainly, an imposing figure. Short and stout, with a square face, sunburned into a preternatural redness, clad in a loose duck "jumper" and trousers streaked and splashed with red soil, his aspect under any circumstances would have been quaint, and was now even ridiculous. As he stooped to deposit at his feet a heavy carpetbag he was carrying, it became obvious, from partially developed legends and inscriptions, that the material with which his trousers had been patched had been originally intended for a less ambitious covering. Yet he advanced with great gravity, and after having shaken the hand of each person in the room with labored cordiality, he wiped his serious perplexed face on a red bandana handkerchief, a shade lighter than his complexion, laid his powerful hand upon the table to steady himself, and thus addressed the judge:

"I was passin' by," he began, by way of apology, "and I thought I'd just step in and see how things was gittin' on with Tennessee thar—my pardner. It's a hot night. I disremember any sich weather before on the Bar."

He paused a moment, but nobody volunteering any other meteoro-
logical recollection, he again had recourse to his pocket handkerchief,
and for some moments mopped his face diligently.

"Have you anything to say on behalf of the prisoner?" said the judge
finally.

"Thet's it," said Tennessee's Partner, in a tone of relief. "I come yar as
Tennessee's pardner—knowing him nigh on four year, off and on, wet
and dry, in luck and out o' luck. His ways ain't aller my ways, but thar
ain't any p'ints in that young man, thar ain't any liveliness as he's been
up to, as I don't know. And you sez to me, sez you—confidential-like,
and between man and man—sez you, 'Do you know anything in his
behalf?' and I sez to you, sez I—confidential-like, as between man and
man—'What should a man know of his pardner?'"

"Is this all you have to say?" asked the judge impatiently, feeling,
perhaps, that a dangerous sympathy of humor was beginning to human-
ize the court.

"Thet's so," continued Tennessee's Partner. "It ain't for me to say
anything agin' him. And now, what's the case? Here's Tennessee wants
money, wants it bad, and doesn't like to ask it of his old pardner. Well,
what does Tennessee do? He lays for a stranger, and he fetches that
stranger; and you lays for *him,* and you fetches *him;* and the honors is
easy. And I put it to you, bein' a fa'r-minded man, and to you, gentlemen all, as fa'r-minded men, ef this isn't so."

"Prisoner," said the judge, interrupting, "have you any questions to
ask this man?"

"No! no!" continued Tennessee's Partner, hastily. "I play this yer
hand alone. To come down to the bedrock, it's just this: Tennessee, thar,
has played it pretty rough and expensive-like on a stranger, and on this
yer camp. And now, what's the fair thing? Some would say more, some
would say less. Here's seventeen hundred dollars in coarse gold and
a watch,—it's about all my pile,—and call it square!" And before a
hand could be raised to prevent him, he had emptied the contents of the
carpetbag upon the table.

For a moment his life was in jeopardy. One or two men sprang to their
feet, several hands groped for hidden weapons, and a suggestion to
"throw him from the window" was only overridden by a gesture from

the judge. Tennessee laughed. And apparently oblivious of the excitement, Tennessee's Partner improved the opportunity to mop his face again with his handkerchief.

When order was restored, and the man was made to understand, by the use of forcible figures and rhetoric, that Tennessee's offense could not be condoned by money, his face took a more serious and sanguinary hue, and those who were nearest to him noticed that his rough hand trembled slightly on the table. He hesitated a moment as he slowly returned the gold to the carpetbag, as if he had not yet entirely caught the elevated sense of justice which swayed the tribunal, and was perplexed with the belief that he had not offered enough. Then he turned to the judge, and saying, "This yer is a lone hand, played alone, and without my pardner," he bowed to the jury and was about to withdraw, when the judge called him back:

"If you have anything to say to Tennessee, you had better say it now."

For the first time that evening the eyes of the prisoner and his strange advocate met. Tennessee smiled, showed his white teeth, and saying, "Euchred, old man!" held out his hand. Tennessee's Partner took it in his own, and saying, "I just dropped in as I was passin' to see how things was gettin' on," let the hand passively fall, and adding that "it was a warm night," again mopped his face with his handkerchief, and without another word withdrew.

The two men never again met each other alive. For the unparalleled insult of a bribe offered to Judge Lynch—who, whether bigoted, weak, or narrow, was at least incorruptible—firmly fixed in the mind of that mythical personage any wavering determination of Tennessee's fate; and at the break of day he was marched, closely guarded, to meet it at the top of Marley's Hill.

How he met it, how cool he was, how he refused to say anything, how perfect were the arrangements of the committee, were all duly reported, with the addition of a warning moral and example to all future evil-doers, in the *Red Dog Clarion,* by its editor, who was present, and to whose vigorous English I cheerfully refer the reader. But the beauty of that midsummer morning, the blessed amity of earth and air and sky, the awakened life of the free woods and hills, the joyous renewal and promise of Nature, and above all, the infinite serenity that thrilled through each, was not reported, as not being a part of the social lesson.

And yet, when the weak and foolish deed was done, and a life, with its possibilities and responsibilities, had passed out of the misshapen thing that dangled between earth and sky, the birds sang, the flowers bloomed, the sun shone, as cheerily as before; and possibly the *Red Dog Clarion* was right.

Tennessee's Partner was not in the group that surrounded the ominous tree. But as they turned to disperse, attention was drawn to the singular appearance of a motionless donkey cart halted at the side of the road. As they approached, they at once recognized the venerable Jenny and the two-wheeled cart as the property of Tennessee's Partner, used by him in carying dirt from his claim; and a few paces distant the owner of the equipage himself, sitting under a buckeye tree, wiping the perspiration from his glowing face. In answer to an inquiry, he said he had come for the body of the "diseased," "if it was all the same to the committee." He didn't wish to "hurry anything"; he could "wait." He was not working that day; and when the gentlemen were done with the "diseased," he would take him. "Ef thar is any present," he added, in his simple, serious way, "as would care to jine in the fun'l, they kin come." Perhaps it was from a sense of humor, which I have already intimated was a feature of Sandy Bar—perhaps it was from something even better than that, but two thirds of the loungers accepted the invitation at once.

It was noon when the body of Tennessee was delivered into the hands of his partner. As the cart drew up to the fatal tree, we noticed that it contained a rough oblong box,—apparently made from a section of sluicing,—and half filled with bark and the tassels of pine. The cart was further decorated with slips of willow, and made fragrant with buckeye blossoms. When the body was deposited in the box, Tennessee's Partner drew over it a piece of tarred canvas, and gravely mounting the narrow seat in front, with his feet upon the shafts, urged the little donkey forward. The equipage moved slowly on, at that decorous pace which was habitual with Jenny even under less solemn circumstances. The men—half curiously, half jestingly, but all good-humoredly—strolled along beside the cart, some in advance, some a little in the rear of the homely catafalque. But whether from the narrowing of the road or some present sense of decorum, as the cart passed on, the company fell to the rear in couples, keeping step, and otherwise assuming the external show of a formal procession. Jack Folinsbee, who had at the outset played a funeral march in dumb show upon an imaginary trombone, desisted from a lack of sympathy and appreciation—not having, perhaps, your true humorist's capacity to be content with the enjoyment of his own fun.

The way led through Grizzly Cañon, by this time clothed in funereal drapery and shadows. The redwoods, burying their moccasined feet in the red soil, stood in Indian file along the track, trailing an uncouth benediction from their bending boughs upon the passing bier. A hare, surprised into helpless inactivity, sat upright and pulsating in the ferns by the roadside, as the cortège went by. Squirrels hastened to gain a secure outlook from higher boughs; and the bluejays, spreading their wings, fluttered before them like outriders, until the outskirts of Sandy Bar were reached, and the solitary cabin of Tennessee's Partner.

Viewed under more favorable circumstances, it would not have been a cheerful place. The unpicturesque site, the rude and unlovely outlines, the unsavory details, which distinguish the nest-building of the California miner, were all here, with the dreariness of decay superadded. A few paces from the cabin there was a rough enclosure, which, in the brief days of Tennessee's Partner's matrimonial felicity, had been used as a garden, but was now overgrown with fern. As we approached it, we were surprised to find that what we had taken for a recent attempt at cultivation was the broken soil about an open grave.

The cart was halted before the enclosure, and rejecting the offers of assistance with the same air of simple self-reliance he had displayed throughout, Tennessee's Partner lifted the rough coffin on his back, and deposited it unaided within the shallow grave. He then nailed down the board which served as a lid, and mounting the little mound of earth beside it, took off his hat and slowly mopped his face with his handkerchief. This the crowd felt was a preliminary to speech, and they disposed themselves variously on stumps and boulders, and sat expectant.

"When a man," began Tennessee's Partner slowly, "has been running free all day, what's the natural thing for him to do? Why, to come home. And if he ain't in a condition to go home, what can his best friend do? Why, bring him home. And here's Tennessee has been running free, and we brings him home from his wandering." He paused and picked up a fragment of quartz, rubbed it thoughtfully on his sleeve and went on: "It ain't the first time I've packed him on my back, as you see'd me now. It ain't the first time that I brought him to this yer cabin when he couldn't help himself; it ain't the first time that I and Jinny have waited for him on yon hill, and picked him up and so fetched him home, when he couldn't speak and didn't know me. And now that it's the last time, why"—he paused, and rubbed the quartz gently on his sleeve—"you see it's sort of rough on his pardner. And now, gentlemen," he added abruptly, picking up his long-handled shovel, "the fun'l's over; and my thanks, and Tennessee's thanks, to you for your trouble."

Resisting any proffers of assistance, he began to fill in the grave, turning his back upon the crowd, that after a few moments' hesitation gradually withdrew. As they crossed the little ridge that hid Sandy Bar from view, some, looking back, thought they could see Tennessee's Partner, his work done, sitting upon the grave, his shovel between his knees, and his face buried in his red bandana handkerchief. But it was argued by others that you couldn't tell his face from his handkerchief at that distance, and this point remained undecided.

In the reaction that followed the feverish excitement of that day, Tennessee's Partner was not forgotten. A secret investigation had cleared him of any complicity in Tennessee's guilt, and left only a suspicion of his general sanity. Sandy Bar made a point of calling on him, and proffering various uncouth but well-meant kindnesses. But from that day his rude health and great strength seemed visibly to decline; and when the rainy season fairly set in, and the tiny grass blades were beginning to peep from the rocky mound above Tennessee's grave, he took to his bed.

One night, when the pines beside the cabin were swaying in the storm and trailing their slender fingers over the roof, and the roar and rush of the swollen river were heard below, Tennessee's Partner lifted his head from the pillow, saying, "It is time to go for Tennessee; I must put Jinny in the cart"; and would have risen from his bed but for the restraint of his attendant. Struggling, he still pursued his singular fancy: "There, now, steady, Jinny—steady, old girl. How dark it is! Look out for the ruts—and look out for him, too, old gal. Sometimes, you know, when he's blind drunk, he drops down right in the trail. Keep on straight up to the pine on the top of the hill. Thar! I told you so!—thar he is—coming this way, too—all by himself, sober, and his face a-shining. Tennessee! Pardner!"

And so they met.*

INTERPRETATION

This is a story about the loyalty of one man for his friend, Tennessee, a man who, by all commonly accepted standards, could have no claim on loyalty. On two counts Tennessee has forfeited all reasonable claim on his friend's loyalty: first, he has stolen his friend's wife, and second, he has been caught red-handed, given a fair trial, and convicted of highway robbery. But in spite of this forfeiture his partner tries to save him from execution and when he fails in this, claims the body and buries it with his own hands.

Tennessee's Partner, the author makes plain, is a simple, untutored, and rough man, a member of a community which, taken as a whole, is simple, untutored, and rough. His act of loyalty is all the more touching since it springs from such an unpromising background, a background which, at first glance, would appear to offer no encouragement for tenderness and sensitivity. There is an element of surprise, consequently, in the author's revelation of this idealism in Tennessee's Partner. This surprise is obviously a part of the author's intended effect. The use of the unlikely background and of the rough, simple character, gives several related effects: a rebuke to moral snobbery; an emphasis on the pathos inherent in the situation; a guarantee of the genuineness of the emotion—Tennessee's Partner is too simple and uncouth to adopt a pose.

The use of such a contrast between the idealism of the hero and his roughness, is in itself, of course, perfectly legitimate. The contrast derives from one of the basic facts of human nature: the fact that goodness and decency are not confined to the cultivated and educated members of society. Many writers have made use of this special type of contrast and for the same complex of effects for which Bret Harte strives here. The poet Wordsworth, for instance, constantly affirms the basic goodness and sensitivity of common human nature, and makes the unexpected revelation of it the focal point of many of his poems. Or, to take an instance from contemporary writers, the student may consider the work of Ernest Hemingway in which his "tough" and

* By permission of Houghton Mifflin Company.

"hard-boiled" characters reveal a sensitivity which belies their apparent callousness (see pp. 320–323).

There is nothing wrong, we may judge, either with the general idea in itself (the theme), or with the particular situation in which Bret Harte finds the theme embodied. But neither theme nor situation as such can guarantee the success of a story. Other factors must be considered. For instance, we are entitled to ask ourselves whether Tennessee's Partner is credible in the action which he performs. In asking ourselves whether his character as portrayed is convincing, it is not enough to decide that such persons have performed such acts in real life. Rather, we must decide whether the character of Tennessee's Partner, as Bret Harte has delineated it for us in this story, is actually convincing in the magnanimous action which he is made to perform. That is, we must decide whether Bret Harte has made us understand the psychological steps by which the man arrives at his action, an action which, we discover, comes with some surprise to the other members of the community.

What is Tennessee's Partner like as he first appears in the story? We do not even know his name, but this situation was not uncommon in a society where many were trying to conceal their past lives. He is merely "Tennessee's Partner." But early in the story occurs an incident which ordinarily strains partnerships past the breaking point. Tennessee runs off with his partner's wife. A little later, when the wife deserts Tennessee for another man, the two friends renew their partnership as if nothing had happened, even though the whole town had turned out for the expected shooting.

Why does Bret Harte use this incident? He obviously uses it to prepare for the scene which he considers to be the *climax* (see Glossary) of his story—the scene of the "funeral service." Certainly, if Tennessee's Partner can so readily forgive Tennessee for stealing his wife, he may be expected to perform the easier task of burying his friend. So far as character is concerned, then, the funeral scene is really an anticlimax. But why does Tennessee's Partner forgive Tennessee so easily for the wife-stealing? The matter is never explained, and we learn nothing of the state of mind which led the partner to the decision. In other words, Bret Harte has dodged the real psychological issue of his story: the conflict in the mind of the partner between his affection for Tennessee on the one hand, and, on the other, his attachment to his wife and his outraged honor which the primitive community expects him to avenge with bloodletting.

One might defend the motivation of the story by saying that Bret Harte simply was not interested in dealing with the wife-stealing incident in detail, but *was* interested in the burial of Tennessee. This is all very well, in one sense: an author does have the right to select the incidents on which he cares to focus attention. But his selection must have its basis in some logic, and, in this case, it is a logic of character; that is, Harte is dealing with the partner's attitude toward the perfidious Tennessee. Apparently, Bret Harte's intended strategy was this: by touching lightly on the wife situation he hoped to lull the reader into an acceptance of an easy solution of the psychological problem involved in it, and then hoped to use the reader's acceptance of it as a preparation for the climax. But if a reader does not accept the easy solution of this problem, then the rest of the story will seem false.

What else does Bret Harte give us in preparation for the climax? He gives us the scene of the attempted bribery. The purpose of this scene seems to be to indicate a certain characteristic of the partner: his naïveté with regard to the conventions of society, to the nature of law, and even to the concept of abstract justice itself. Apparently, he honestly sees the situation into which Tennessee has fallen as one which can be settled by a money payment. The stranger will be compensated for his losses and will be given something for his trouble. Perhaps there is the implication that he is attempting to bribe the court; certainly, the violent reaction of the bystanders would indicate this assumption, though the judge apparently realizes the childlike nature of the man's mind. Indeed, the judge proceeds to give the man a lecture on the nature of law: "The man was made to understand . . . that Tennessee's offense could not be condoned by money." But another purpose of the scene is to develop the idea of the partner's fidelity: he is willing to sacrifice his "pile" for his friend. Furthermore, the fidelity suggested by the scene is a kind of doglike devotion which takes no account of abstract matters such as the moral character of Tennessee or the nature of his offense.

But does this incident represent a real development of the idea first suggested to the reader by the incident of the partner's forgiveness of Tennessee for the wife-stealing? One would be inclined to suppose that it is more credible that a man should put up money to help a friend than that he should sacrifice his wife to his friend's pleasure and accept smilingly the insult to his personal honor. If this is true, then the court incident is again anticlimatic; it does not represent a true progression. Moreover, if the partner is a man who sees things in very concrete personal terms (as the bribery incident indicates), does this court scene afford any real clarification of the forgiveness of Tennessee for the wife-stealing? For, presumably, the relation of the man to his wife is also a personal, concrete relation, not merely an abstract and conventional relation. Moreover, if one rationalizes the whole incident of the forgiveness, by saying that the partner regarded his wife as merely a chattel (and remember the author has given us no basis for making this supposition), then the whole meaning of his act of forgiveness is lost, for the conflict—between personal affection for his friend on the one hand, and personal honor and personal affection for his wife on the other—disappears from the situation.

For what, after all, does this court incident intend to prepare us? It is, of course, not merely for the incident of the burial, as such. For someone among the rough citizenry would have buried the hanged man in any case, and perhaps with a kind of elemental pity. (Tennessee, has, for instance, certain qualities which would extort special admiration in this primitive community—a courage and coolness, which are dramatized several times in the story.) The intended high point in the story is the funeral oration, which Tennessee's Partner delivers to the camp. It is here that our full sense of the pathos is supposed to emerge.

But if such pathos is to emerge to the full, and is to be meaningful, the author must have convinced us (1) that it is logical for this particular character to deliver the oration under the circumstances and (2) that this oration brings to focus elements of interpretation and meaning implicit in previous incidents.

But there are more difficulties. First, would the partner, as his character has been prepared for in earlier pages of the story, have made such a speech to the members of the community who had turned out, purely from curiosity, to see what he would do? A man whose life had been dominated by a merely personal attachment to his friend and who had been completely incapable of understanding why his friend had to be hanged (as indicated by the bribery scene), would more probably have felt a sullen resentment against the men who had done his friend to death for, in his eyes, no good reason. At least, he would probably have wanted privacy for his sorrow.* (He can be under no illusion that the spectators have come out of love for Tennessee.)

Second, assuming that the partner would have delivered the ora-

---

* Compare the partner's attitude with that of the mother in Tennyson's poem, "Rizpah," or with that of the mother in Maupassant's story, "La Mère Sauvage."

tion, would he have said what Bret Harte makes him say? For example, would he have apologized to the spectators and have thanked them for their trouble? (Notice that Bret Harte does not intend for us to take this as the bitter irony of a hurt man, but as a manifestation of a kind of Christlike forgiveness. The partner is almost too good to be true.) And notice, further, in this connection, what Bret Harte has the partner say in his delirium as he dies of a broken heart. Here, even the language becomes unrealistic; it is entirely out of the partner's idiom. For example, would he have said: "There, now, steady, Jinny,— steady, old girl. How dark it is!" Isn't it more likely that he would have said: "It's dark as hell." Or: "God-a-mighty, it's dark!" Why does Bret Harte break out of the partner's idiom? Because Bret Harte is straining for a highly emotional effect, and feeling that the realistic language is not good enough, he resorts to "poeticizing" the character. In other words, he is not willing to let the case rest on its own merits. The same thing is true of the symbolic reference, in the dying speech, to the pine tree on the top of the hill.

But other examples of such strain are to be found earlier in the story— take, for example, the description of nature as the partner carries the body to the place of burial: "The way led through Grizzly Cañon, by this time clothed in funereal drapery and shadows. The redwoods, burying their moccasined feet in the red soil, stood in Indian file along the track, trailing an uncouth benediction from their bending boughs upon the passing bier." Nature, apparently, is sympathetic with the partner's grief. Like him, it can give only an "uncouth benediction," but it expresses its brooding sympathy as best it can. One recognizes that a writer may legitimately use description of nature as a device for defining the atmosphere of a piece of fiction, or may even use it as specific symbolism. But it should be quite clear that Bret Harte here is not using it legitimately. It is used here to give a false heightening to the pathos of the scene, and the language in which the description is couched is as "poeticized" as is the language of the partner's dying speech. For example, the description of the redwoods "burying their moccasined feet in the red soil" is completely irrelevant and represents an attempt at fanciful decoration; it is another instance of the author's straining for effects which, he seems to feel, are not adequately supported by the situation in itself.*

* Compare Bret Harte's use of nature here with the use made of the references to the storm in "A Piece of News," p. 144, or to the use of nature made by Chekhov in "The Lament," pp. 247–48.

The presence of this straining for an emotional effect is one of the surest symptoms that one is dealing with a case of *sentimentality* (see Glossary). In its general sense sentimentality may be defined as an emotional response in excess of the occasion. We speak of a person who weeps at some trivial occurrence as being sentimental. Such a person lacks a sense of proportion and gets a morbid enjoyment from an emotional debauch for its own sake. When we apply the term to a piece of literature, a story, for instance, we usually mean that the author intends for the reader to experience an intense emotion which is actually not justified by the materials of the story.

One symptom of sentimentality is, as we have said, the author's straining to heighten and prettify and poeticize his language quite apart from the dramatic issues involved in the story.

A second symptom frequently to be found is "editorializing" on the part of the author—pointing out to the reader what he should feel, nudging the reader to respond—devices which would not be necessary if the story could make its own case. (For example, Bret Harte comments on the hanging of Tennessee as follows: "And yet, when the weak and foolish deed was done, and a life, with its possibilities and responsibilities, had passed out of the misshapen thing that dangled between earth and sky, the birds sang, the flowers bloomed, the sun shone, as cheerily as before. . . .")

A third symptom is the tendency to dodge the real issues which should prepare for the final effect of a story. That is, an author who is primarily concerned with giving the emotional effect may not be too scrupulous about the means adopted to that end. For example, in this story Bret Harte is so thoroughly obsessed with the pathos of the partner's loyalty that he has devoted no thought to the precise nature of the basis of that loyalty. As has already been pointed out, he does not bring the wife-stealing episode into real focus. Either he was so little interested in the psychology of the situation that he did not investigate it, or he was aware that the issues involved were too complicated for him to handle in terms of the scheme which he had laid down for the story.

The reading of this story raises some such question as this: Has not Bret Harte taken a theme which, perhaps, he had seen successfully employed for pathetic effects in other fiction, and attempted to trick it out with a new romantic setting, touches of local color (such as descriptions of the community and bits of dialect), and poeticized writing, without ever grounding the story in a presentation of the real psychological issues involved?

1. Compare the relation of Tennessee and his partner with that of Dravot and Peachey in "The Man Who Would Be King." How does Kipling avoid sentimentality?

2. Is O. Henry's "The Furnished Room" guilty of sentimentality? Compare the "editorializing" of O. Henry with that of Bret Harte. What is the function of the "editorializing" in each case?

The Outcasts of Poker Flat
BRET HARTE

AS MR. JOHN OAKHURST, gambler, stepped into the main street of Poker Flat on the morning of the twenty-third of November, 1850, he was conscious of a change in its moral atmosphere since the preceding night. Two or three men, conversing earnestly together, ceased as he approached, and exchanged significant glances. There was a Sabbath lull in the air, which, in a settlement unused to Sabbath influences, looked ominous.

Mr. Oakhurst's calm, handsome face betrayed small concern in these indications. Whether he was conscious of any predisposing cause was another question. "I reckon they're after somebody," he reflected; "likely it's me." He returned to his pocket the handkerchief with which he had been whipping away the red dust of Poker Flat from his neat boots, and quietly discharged his mind of further conjecture.

In point of fact, Poker Flat was "after somebody." It had lately suffered the loss of several thousand dollars, two valuable horses, and a prominent citizen. It was experiencing a spasm of virtuous reaction, quite as lawless and ungovernable as any of the acts that had provoked it. A secret committee had determined to rid the town of all improper persons. This was done permanently in regard to two men who were then hanging from the boughs of a sycamore in the gulch, and temporarily in the banishment of certain other objectionable characters. I regret to say that some of these were ladies. It is but due to the sex, however, to state that their impropriety was professional, and it was only in such easily established standards of evil that Poker Flat ventured to sit in judgment.

Mr. Oakhurst was right in supposing that he was included in this category. A few of the committee had urged hanging him as a possible example and a sure method of reimbursing themselves from his pockets of the sums he had won from them. "It's agin justice," said Jim Wheeler, "to let this yer young man from Roaring Camp—an entire stranger— carry away our money." But a crude sentiment of equity residing in the breasts of those who had been fortunate enough to win from Mr. Oakhurst overruled this narrower local prejudice.

Mr. Oakhurst received his sentence with philosophic calmness, none the less coolly that he was aware of the hesitation of his judges. He was too much of a gambler not to accept fate. With him life was at best an uncertain game, and he recognized the usual percentage in favor of the dealer.

A body of armed men accompanied the deported wickedness of Poker Flat to the outskirts of the settlement. Besides Mr. Oakhurst, who was known to be a coolly desperate man, and for whose intimidation the armed escort was intended, the expatriated party consisted of a young woman familiarly known as "The Duchess"; another who had won the title of "Mother Shipton"; and "Uncle Billy," a suspected sluice-robber and confirmed drunkard. The cavalcade provoked no comments from the spectators, nor was any word uttered by the escort. Only when the gulch which marked the uttermost limit of Poker Flat was reached, the leader spoke briefly and to the point. The exiles were forbidden to return at the peril of their lives.

As the escort disappeared, their pent-up feelings found vent in a few hysterical tears from the Duchess, some bad language from Mother Shipton, and a Parthian volley of expletives from Uncle Billy. The philosophic Oakhurst alone remained silent. He listened calmly to Mother Shipton's desire to cut somebody's heart out, to the repeated statements of the Duchess that she would die in the road, and to the alarming oaths that seemed to be bumped out of Uncle Billy as he rode forward. With the easy good humor characteristic of his class, he insisted upon exchanging his own riding-horse, "Five-Spot," for the sorry mule which the Duchess rode. But even this act did not draw the party into any closer sympathy. The young woman readjusted her somewhat draggled plumes with a feeble, faded coquetry; Mother Shipton eyed the possessor of "Five-Spot" with malevolence, and Uncle Billy included the whole party in one sweeping anathema.

The road to Sandy Bar—a camp that, not having as yet experienced the regenerating influences of Poker Flat, consequently seemed to offer some invitation to the emigrants—lay over a steep mountain range. It was distant a day's severe travel. In that advanced season the party soon passed out of the moist, temperate regions of the foothills into the dry, cold, bracing air of the Sierras. The trail was narrow and difficult. At noon the Duchess, rolling out of her saddle upon the ground, declared her intention of going no farther, and the party halted.

The spot was singularly wild and impressive. A wooded amphitheater, surrounded on three sides by precipitous cliffs of naked granite, sloped gently toward the crest of another precipice that overlooked the valley. It was, undoubtedly, the most suitable spot for a camp, had camping been advisable. But Mr. Oakhurst knew that scarcely half the journey to Sandy Bar was accomplished, and the party were not equipped or provisioned for delay. This fact he pointed out to his companions curtly, with a philosophic commentary on the folly of "throwing up their hand before the game was played out." But they were furnished with liquor, which in this emergency stood them in place of food, fuel, rest, and pre-science. In spite of his remonstrances, it was not long before they were more or less under its influence. Uncle Billy passed rapidly from a belli-cose state into one of stupor, the Duchess became maudlin, and Mother Shipton snored. Mr. Oakhurst alone remained erect, leaning against a rock, calmly surveying them.

Mr. Oakhurst did not drink. It interfered with a profession which required coolness, impassiveness, and presence of mind, and, in his own language, he "couldn't afford it." As he gazed at his recumbent fellow exiles, the loneliness begotten of his pariah trade, his habits of life, his very vices, for the first time seriously oppressed him. He bestirred him-self in dusting his black clothes, washing his hands and face, and other acts characteristic of his studiously neat habits, and for a moment forgot his annoyance. The thought of deserting his weaker and more pitiable companions never perhaps occurred to him. Yet he could not help feel-ing the want of that excitement which, singularly enough, was most conducive to that calm equanimity for which he was notorious. He looked at the gloomy walls that rose a thousand feet sheer above the circling pines around him; at the sky, ominously clouded, at the valley below, already deepening into shadow; and, doing so, suddenly he heard his own name called.

A horseman slowly ascended the trail. In the fresh, open face of the newcomer Mr. Oakhurst recognized Tom Simson, otherwise known as "The Innocent," of Sandy Bar. He had met him some months before over a "little game," and had, with perfect equanimity, won the entire fortune—amounting to some forty dollars—of that guileless youth. After the game was finished, Mr. Oakhurst drew the youthful speculator behind the door and thus addressed him: "Tommy, you're a good little man, but you can't gamble worth a cent. Don't try it over again." He then handed him his money back, pushed him gently from the room, and so made a devoted slave of Tom Simson.

There was a remembrance of this in his boyish and enthusiastic greeting of Mr. Oakhurst. He had started, he said, to go to Poker Flat to seek his fortune. "Alone?" No, not exactly alone; in fact (a giggle), he had run away with Piney Woods. Didn't Mr. Oakhurst remember Piney? She that used to wait on the table at the Temperance House? They had been engaged a long time, but old Jake Woods had objected, and so they had run away, and were going to Poker Flat to be married, and here they were. And they were tired out, and how lucky it was they had found a place to camp, and company. All this the Innocent delivered rapidly, while Piney, a stout, comely damsel of fifteen, emerged from behind the pine tree, where she had been blushing unseen, and rode to the side of her lover.

Mr. Oakhurst seldom troubled himself with sentiment, still less with propriety; but he had a vague idea that the situation was not fortunate. He retained, however, his presence of mind sufficiently to kick Uncle Billy, who was about to say something, and Uncle Billy was sober enough to recognize in Mr. Oakhurst's kick a superior power that would not bear trifling. He then endeavored to dissuade Tom Simson from delaying further, but in vain. He even pointed out the fact that there was no provision, nor means of making a camp. But, unluckily, the Innocent met this objection by assuring the party that he was provided with an extra mule loaded with provisions, and by the discovery of a rude attempt at a log house near the trail. "Piney can stay with Mrs. Oakhurst," said the Innocent, pointing to the Duchess, "and I can shift for myself."

Nothing but Mr. Oakhurst's admonishing foot saved Uncle Billy from bursting into a roar of laughter. As it was, he felt compelled to retire up the cañon until he could recover his gravity. There he confided the joke to the tall pine trees, with many slaps of his leg, contortions of his face, and the usual profanity. But when he returned to the party, he found them seated by a fire—for the air had grown strangely chill and the sky overcast—in apparently amicable conversation. Piney was actually talking in an impulsive girlish fashion to the Duchess, who was listening with an interest and animation she had not shown for many days. The Innocent was holding forth, apparently with equal effect, to Mr. Oakhurst, and Mother Shipton, who was actually relaxing into amiability. "Is this yer a d—d picnic?" said Uncle Billy, with inward scorn, as he surveyed the sylvan group, the glancing firelight, and the tethered animals in the foreground. Suddenly an idea mingled with the alcoholic fumes that disturbed his brain. It was apparently of a jocular nature, for he felt impelled to slap his leg again and cram his fist into his mouth.

As the shadows crept slowly up the mountain, a slight breeze rocked the tops of the pine trees and moaned through their long and gloomy aisles. The ruined cabin, patched and covered with pine boughs, was set apart for the ladies. As the lovers parted, they unaffectedly exchanged a kiss, so honest and sincere that it might have been heard above the swaying pines. The frail Duchess and the malevolent Mother Shipton were probably too stunned to remark upon this last evidence of simplicity, and so turned without a word to the hut. The fire was replenished, the men lay down before the door, and in a few minutes were asleep.

Mr. Oakhurst was a light sleeper. Toward morning he awoke benumbed and cold. As he stirred the dying fire, the wind, which was now blowing strongly, brought to his cheek that which caused the blood to leave it—snow!

He started to his feet with the intention of awakening the sleepers, for there was no time to lose. But turning to where Uncle Billy had been lying, he found him gone. A suspicion leaped to his brain, and a curse to his lips. He ran to the spot where the mules had been tethered—

they were no longer there. The tracks were already rapidly disappearing in the snow.

The momentary excitement brought Mr. Oakhurst back to the fire with his usual calm. He did not waken the sleepers. The Innocent slumbered peacefully, with a smile on his good-humored, freckled face; the virgin Piney slept beside her frailer sisters as sweetly as though attended by celestial guardians; and Mr. Oakhurst, drawing his blanket over his shoulders, stroked his mustaches and waited for the dawn. It came slowly in a whirling mist of snowflakes that dazzled and confused the eye. What could be seen of the landscape appeared magically changed. He looked over the valley, and summed up the present and future in two words, "Snowed in!"

A careful inventory of the provisions, which, fortunately for the party, had been stored within the hut, and so escaped the felonious fingers of Uncle Billy, disclosed the fact that with care and prudence they might last ten days longer. "That is," said Mr. Oakhurst, *sotto voce* to the Innocent, "if you're willing to board us. If you ain't—and perhaps you'd better not—you can wait till Uncle Billy gets back with provisions." For some occult reason, Mr. Oakhurst could not bring himself to disclose Uncle Billy's rascality, and so offered the hypothesis that he had wandered from the camp and had accidentally stampeded the animals. He dropped a warning to the Duchess and Mother Shipton, who of course knew the facts of their associate's defection. "They'll find out the truth about us *all* when they find out anything," he added significantly, "and there's no good frightening them now."

Tom Simson not only put all his worldly store at the disposal of Mr. Oakhurst, but seemed to enjoy the prospect of their enforced seclusion. "We'll have a good camp for a week, and then the snow'll melt, and we'll all go back together." The cheerful gayety of the young man and Mr. Oakhurst's calm infected the others. The Innocent, with the aid of pine boughs, extemporized a thatch for the roofless cabin, and the Duchess directed Piney in the rearrangement of the interior with a taste and tact that opened the blue eyes of that provincial maiden to their fullest extent. "I reckon now you're used to fine things at Poker Flat," said Piney. The Duchess turned away sharply to conceal something that reddened her cheeks through their professional tint, and Mother Shipton requested Piney not to "chatter." But when Mr. Oakhurst returned from a weary search for the trail, he heard the sound of happy laughter echoed from the rocks. He stopped in some alarm, and his thoughts first naturally reverted to the whisky, which he had prudently cached. "And yet it don't somehow sound like whisky," said the gambler. It was not until he caught sight of the blazing fire through the still blinding storm, and the group around it, that he settled to the conviction that it was "square fun."

Whether Mr. Oakhurst had cached his cards with the whisky as something debarred the free access of the community, I cannot say. It was certain that, in Mother Shipton's words, he "didn't say 'cards' once" during that evening. Haply the time was beguiled by an accordion, produced somewhat ostentatiously by Tom Simson from his pack. Notwithstanding some difficulties attending the manipulation of this instrument, Piney Woods managed to pluck several reluctant melodies from its keys, to an accompaniment by the Innocent on a pair of bone castanets. But the crowning festivity of the evening was reached in a rude camp-meeting hymn, which the lovers, joining hands, sang with great earnestness and vociferation. I fear that a certain defiant tone and Covenanter's swing to its chorus, rather than any devotional quality, caused it speedily to infect the others, who at last joined in the refrain:

> I'm proud to live in the service of the Lord,
> And I'm bound to die in His army.

The pines rocked, the storm eddied and whirled above the miserable group, and the flames of their altar leaped heavenward, as if in token of the vow.

At midnight the storm abated, the rolling clouds parted, and the stars glittered keenly above the sleeping camp. Mr. Oakhurst, whose professional habits had enabled him to live on the smallest possible amount of sleep, in dividing the watch with Tom Simson, somehow managed to take upon himself the greater part of that duty. He excused himself to the Innocent by saying that he had "often been a week without sleep." "Doing what?" asked Tom. "Poker!" replied Oakhurst sententiously. "When a man get a streak of luck—nigger luck—he don't get tired. The luck gives in first. Luck," continued the gambler reflectively, "is a mighty queer thing. All you know about it for certain is that it's bound to change. And it's finding out when it's going to change that makes you. We've had a streak of bad luck since we left Poker Flat—you come along, and slap you get into it, too. If you can hold your cards right along you're all right. For," added the gambler, with cheerful irrelevance—

> I'm proud to live in the service of the Lord,
> And I'm bound to die in His army.

The third day came, and the sun, looking through the white-curtained valley, saw the outcasts divide their slowly decreasing store of provisions for the morning meal. It was one of the peculiarities of that mountain climate that its rays diffused a kindly warmth over the wintry landscape, as if in regretful commiseration of the past. But it revealed drift on drift of snow piled high around the hut—a hopeless, uncharted, trackless sea of white lying below the rocky shores to which the castaways still clung. Through the marvelously clear air the smoke of the pastoral village of Poker Flat rose miles away. Mother Shipton saw it, and from a remote pinnacle of her rocky fastness hurled in that direction a final malediction. It was her last vituperative attempt, and perhaps for that reason was invested with a certain degree of sublimity. It did her good, she privately informed the Duchess. "Just you go out there and cuss, and see." She then set herself to the tasking of amusing "the child," as she and the Duchess were pleased to call Piney. Piney was no chicken, but it was a soothing and original theory of the pair thus to account for the fact that she didn't swear and wasn't improper.

When night crept up again through the gorges, the reedy notes of the accordion rose and fell in fitful spasms and long-drawn gasps by the flickering campfire. But music failed to fill entirely the aching void left by insufficient food, and a new diversion was proposed by Piney—storytelling. Neither Mr. Oakhurst nor his female companions caring to relate their personal experiences, this plan would have failed too, but for the Innocent. Some months before he had chanced upon a stray copy of Mr. Pope's ingenious translation of the Iliad. He now proposed to narrate the principal incidents of that poem—having thoroughly mastered the argument and fairly forgotten the words—in the current vernacular of Sandy Bar. And so for the rest of that night the Homeric demigods again walked the earth. Trojan bully and wily Greek wrestled in the winds, and the great pines in the cañon seemed to bow to the wrath of the son of Peleus. Mr. Oakhurst listened with quiet satisfaction. Most especially was he interested in the fate of "Ashheels," as the Innocent persisted in denominating the "swift-footed Achilles."

So, with small food and much of Homer and the accordion, a week passed over the heads of the outcasts. The sun again forsook them, and again from leaden skies the snowflakes were sifted over the land. Day by day closer around them drew the snowy circle, until at last they looked from their prison over drifted walls of dazzling white, that towered twenty feet above their heads. It became more and more difficult to replenish their fires, even from the fallen trees beside them, now half hidden in the drifts. And yet no one complained. The lovers turned from the dreary prospect and looked into each other's eyes, and were happy. Mr. Oakhurst settled himself coolly to the losing game before him. The Duchess, more cheerful than she had been, assumed the care of Piney. Only Mother Shipton—once the strongest of the party—seemed to sicken and fade. At midnight on the tenth day she called Oakhurst to her side. "I'm going," she said, in a voice of querulous weakness, "but don't say anything about it. Don't waken the kids. Take the bundle from under my head, and open it." Mr. Oakhurst did so. It contained Mother Shipton's rations for the last week, untouched. "Give 'em to the child," she said, pointing to the sleeping Piney. "You've starved yourself," said the gambler. "That's what they call it," said the woman querulously, as she lay down again, and, turning her face to the wall, passed quietly away.

The accordion and the bones were put aside that day, and Homer was forgotten. When the body of Mother Shipton had been committed to the snow, Mr. Oakhurst took the Innocent aside, and showed him a pair of snowshoes, which he had fashioned from the old packsaddle. "There's one chance in a hundred to save her yet," he said, pointing to Piney; "but it's there," he added, pointing toward Poker Flat. "If you can reach there in two days she's safe." "And you?" asked Tom Simson. "I'll stay here," was the curt reply.

The lovers parted with a long embrace. "You are not going, too?" said the Duchess, as she saw Mr. Oakhurst apparently waiting to accompany him. "As far as the cañon," he replied. He turned suddenly and kissed the Duchess, leaving her pallid face aflame, and her trembling limbs rigid with amazement.

Night came, but not Mr. Oakhurst. It brought the storm again and the whirling snow. Then the Duchess, feeding the fire, found that some-one had quietly piled beside the hut enough fuel to last a few days longer. The tears rose to her eyes, but she hid them from Piney.

The women slept but little. In the morning, looking into each other's faces, they read their fate. Neither spoke, but Piney, accepting the position of the stronger, drew near and placed her arm around the Duchess's waist. They kept this attitude for the rest of the day. That night the storm reached its greatest fury, and, rending asunder the protecting pines, invaded the very hut.

Toward morning they found themselves unable to feed the fire, which gradually died away. As the embers slowly blackened, the Duchess crept closer to Piney, and broke the silence of many hours: "Piney, can you pray?" "No, dear," said Piney simply. The Duchess, without knowing exactly why, felt relieved, and, putting her head upon Piney's shoulder, spoke no more. And so reclining, the younger and purer pillowing the head of her soiled sister upon her virgin breast, they fell asleep.

The wind lulled as if it feared to waken them. Feathery drifts of snow, shaken from the long pine boughs, flew like white-winged birds, and settled about them as they slept. The moon through the rifted clouds looked down upon what had been the camp. But all human stain, all trace of earthly travail, was hidden beneath the spotless mantle mercifully flung from above.

They slept all day that day and the next, nor did they waken when voices and footsteps broke the silence of the camp. And when pitying fingers brushed the snow from their wan faces, you could scarcely have told from the equal peace that dwelt upon them which was she that had sinned. Even the law of Poker Flat recognized this, and turned away, leaving them still locked in each other's arms.

But at the head of the gulch, on one of the largest pine trees, they found the deuce of clubs pinned to the bark with a bowie knife. It bore the following, written in pencil in a firm hand:

†

BENEATH THIS TREE

LIES THE BODY

OF

JOHN OAKHURST,

WHO STRUCK A STREAK OF BAD LUCK
ON THE 23RD OF NOVEMBER 1850,
AND
HANDED IN HIS CHECKS
ON THE 7TH DECEMBER, 1850.

✝

And pulseless and cold, with a Derringer by his side and a bullet in his heart, though still calm as in life, beneath the snow lay he who was at once the strongest and yet the weakest of the outcasts of Poker Flat.*

INTERPRETATION

1. The theme of this story, like that of "Tennessee's Partner," is that decency, sensitivity, and goodness may appear in the most unpromising surroundings and in the most unpromising characters; that there is, in human nature, a basic virtue. As in "Tennessee's Partner," the question here is not whether the theme is true or false. Certainly, it is a theme which is worth serious consideration, if we can judge by the poets and fiction writers who have adopted it. The question is, rather, this: has Harte oversimplified the theme, has he rendered it too easily, has he sentimentalized the story? In the light of these questions, write an analysis of this story, touching on the following points: (a) the suddenness of the "conversion" of the Duchess and Mother Shipton; (b) the motivation of Oakhurst; (c) the excessive innocence of the "Innocent"; (d) the use of nature; (e) the author's editorializing and humor.

2. Compare the theme of this story with that of "The Man Who Would Be King."

The Poor Relation's Story
CHARLES DICKENS

HE WAS very reluctant to take precedence of so many respected members of the family, by beginning the round of stories they were to relate as they sat in a goodly circle by the Christmas fire; and he modestly suggested that it would be more correct if "John our esteemed host" (whose health he begged to drink) would have the kindness to begin.

* By permission of Houghton Mifflin Co.

For as to himself, he said he was so little used to lead the way that really—— But as they all cried out here, that he must begin, and agreed with one voice that he might, could, would, and should begin, he left off rubbing his hands, and took his legs out from under his armchair and did begin.

I have no doubt (said the poor relation) that I shall surprise the assembled members of our family, and particularly John our esteemed host to whom we are so much indebted for the great hospitality with which he has this day entertained us, by the confession I am going to make. But, if you do me the honor to be surprised at anything that falls from a person so unimportant in the family as I am, I can only say that I shall be scrupulously accurate in all I relate.

I am not what I am supposed to be. I am quite another thing. Perhaps before I go further, I had better glance at what I *am* supposed to be.

It is supposed, unless I mistake—the assembled members of our family will correct me if I do, which is very likely (here the poor relation looked mildly about him for contradiction)—that I am nobody's enemy but my own. That I never met with any particular success in anything. That I failed in business because I was unbusinesslike and credulous—in not being prepared for the interested designs of my partner. That I failed in love, because I was ridiculously trustful—in thinking it impossible that Christiana could deceive me. That I failed in my expectations from my Uncle Chill, on account of not being as sharp as he could have wished in worldly matters. That, through life, I have been rather put upon and disappointed in a general way. That I am at present a bachelor of between fifty-nine and sixty years of age, living on a limited income in the form of a quarterly allowance, to which I see that John our esteemed host wishes me to make no further allusion.

The supposition as to my present pursuits and habits is to the following effect.

I live in a lodging in the Clapham Road—a very clean back room, in a very respectable house—where I am expected not to be at home in the day time, unless poorly; and which I usually leave in the morning at nine o'clock, on pretense of going to business. I take my breakfast— my roll and butter, and my half pint of coffee—at the old established coffee shop near Westminster Bridge; and then I go into the City—I don't know why—and sit in Garraway's Coffee House, and on 'Change, and walk about, and look into a few offices and countinghouses where some of my relations or acquaintance are so good as to tolerate me, and where I stand by the fire if the weather happens to be cold. I get through the day in this way until five o'clock, and then I dine: at a cost, on the average, of one and three pence. Having still a little money to spend on my evening's entertainment, I look into the old-fashioned coffee shop as I go home, and take my cup of tea, and perhaps my bit of toast. So, as the large hand of the clock makes its way round to the morning hour again, I make my way round to the Clapham Road again, and go to bed when I get to my lodging—fire being expensive, and being objected to by the family on account of its giving trouble and making a dirt.

Sometimes, one of my relations or acquaintances is so obliging as to ask me to dinner. Those are holiday occasions, and then I generally walk in the Park. I am a solitary man, and seldom walk with anybody. Not that I am avoided because I am shabby; for I am not at all shabby, having always a very good suit of black on (or rather Oxford mixture, which has the appearance of black and wears much better); but I have got into a habit of speaking low, and being rather silent, and my spirits are not high, and I am sensible that I am not an attractive companion.

The only exception to this general rule is the child of my first cousin, little Frank. I have a particular affection for that child, and he takes very kindly to me. He is a diffident boy by nature; and in a crowd he is soon run over, as I may say, and forgotten. He and I, however, get on exceedingly well. I have a fancy that the poor child will in time succeed to my peculiar position in the family. We talk but little; still, we understand each other. We walk about, hand in hand; and without much speaking he knows what I mean, and I know what he means. When he was very little indeed, I used to take him to the windows of the toy shops, and show him the toys inside. It is surprising how soon he found out that I would have made him a great many presents if I had been in circumstances to do it.

Little Frank and I go and look at the outside of the Monument—he is very fond of the Monument—and at the Bridges, and at all the sights that are free. On two of my birthdays, we have dined on à-la-mode beef, and gone at half-price to the play, and been deeply interested. I was once

walking with him in Lombard Street, which we often visit on account
of my having mentioned to him that there are great riches there—he is
very fond of Lombard Street—when a gentleman said to me as he
passed by, "Sir, your little son has dropped his glove." I assure you, if
you will excuse my remarking on so trivial a circumstance, this accidental mention of the child as mine, quite touched my heart and brought
the foolish tears to my eyes.

When little Frank is sent to school in the country, I shall be very
much at a loss what to do with myself, but I have the intention of walk·
ing down there once a month and seeing him on a half holiday. I am
told he will then be at play upon the Heath; and if my visits should be
objected to, as unsettling the child, I can see him from a distance without his seeing me, and walk back again. His mother comes of a highly
genteel family, and rather disapproves, I am aware, of our being too
much together. I know that I am not calculated to improve his retiring
disposition; but I think he would miss me beyond the feeling of the
moment if we were wholly separated.

When I die in the Clapham Road, I shall not leave much more in
this world than I shall take out of it; but, I happen to have a miniature
of a bright-faced boy, with a curling head, and an open shirt frill waving
down his bosom (my mother had it taken for me, but I can't believe
that it was ever like), which will be worth nothing to sell, and which
I shall beg may be given to Frank. I have written my dear boy a little
letter with it, in which I have told him that I felt very sorry to part from
him, though bound to confess that I knew no reason why I should remain here. I have given him some short advice, the best in my power,
to take warning of the consequences of being nobody's enemy but his
own; and I have endeavored to comfort him for what I fear he will
consider a bereavement, by pointing out to him, that I was only a
superfluous something to everyone but him; and that having by some
means failed to find a place in this great assembly, I am better out of it.

Such (said the poor relation, clearing his throat and beginning to
speak a little louder) is the general impression about me. Now, it is a
remarkable circumstance, which forms the aim and purpose of my
story, that this is all wrong. This is not my life, and these are not my
habits. I do not even live in the Clapham Road. Comparatively speaking, I am very seldom there. I reside, mostly, in a—I am almost ashamed

to say the word, it sounds so full of pretension—in a Castle. I do not mean that it is an old baronial habitation, but still it is a building always known to everyone by the name of a Castle. In it, I preserve the particulars of my history; they run thus:

It was when I first took John Spatter (who had been my clerk) into partnership, and when I was still a young man of not more than five-and-twenty, residing in the house of my Uncle Chill, from whom I had considerable expectations, that I ventured to propose to Christiana. I had loved Christiana a long time. She was very beautiful, and very winning in all respects. I rather mistrusted her widowed mother, who I feared was of a plotting and mercenary turn of mind; but, I thought as well of her as I could, for Christiana's sake. I never had loved anyone but Christiana, and she had been all the world, and oh, far more than all the world, to me, from our childhood!

Christiana accepted me with her mother's consent, and I was rendered very happy indeed. My life at my Uncle Chill's was of a spare dull kind, and my garret chamber was as dull, and bare, and cold, as an upper prison room in some stern northern fortress. But, having Christiana's love, I wanted nothing upon earth. I would not have changed my lot with any human being.

Avarice was, unhappily, my Uncle Chill's master-vice. Though he was rich, he pinched, and scraped, and clutched, and lived miserably. As Christiana had no fortune, I was for some time a little fearful of confessing our engagement to him; but, at length I wrote him a letter, saying how it all truly was. I put it into his hand one night, on going to bed.

As I came downstairs next morning, shivering in the cold December air; colder in my uncle's unwarmed house than in the street, where the winter sun did sometimes shine, and which was at all events enlivened by cheerful faces and voices passing along; I carried a heavy heart toward the long, low breakfast room in which my uncle sat. It was a large room with a small fire, and there was a great bay window in it which the rain had marked in the night as if with the tears of houseless people. It stared upon a raw yard, with a cracked stone pavement, and some rusted iron railings half uprooted, whence an ugly outbuilding, that had once been a dissecting room (in the time of the great surgeon who had mortgaged the house to my uncle), stared at it.

We rose so early always, that at that time of the year, we breakfasted by candle light. When I went into the room, my uncle was so contracted by the cold, and so huddled together in his chair behind the one dim candle, that I did not see him until I was close to the table.

As I held out my hand to him, he caught up his stick (being infirm, he always walked about the house with a stick), and made a blow at me, and said, "You fool!"

"Uncle," I returned, "I didn't expect you to be so angry as this." Nor had I expected it, though he was a hard and angry old man.

"You didn't expect!" said he; "when did you ever expect? When did you ever calculate, or look forward, you contemptible dog?"

"These are hard words, Uncle!"

"Hard words? Feathers, to pelt such an idiot as you with," said he. "Here! Betsy Snap! Look at him!"

Betsy Snap was a withered, hard-favored, yellow old woman—our only domestic—always employed at this time of the morning, in rubbing my uncle's legs. As my uncle adjured her to look at me, he put his lean grip on the crown of her head, she kneeling beside him, and turned her face toward me. An involuntary thought connecting them both with the Dissecting Room, as it must often have been in the surgeon's time, passed across my mind in the midst of my anxiety.

"Look at the sniveling milksop!" said my uncle. "Look at the baby! This is the gentleman who, people say, is nobody's enemy but his own. This is the gentleman who can't say no. This is the gentleman who was making such large profits in his business that he must needs take a partner, t'other day. This is the gentleman who is going to marry a wife without a penny, and who falls into the hands of Jezebels who are speculating on my death!"

I knew, now, how great my uncle's rage was; for nothing short of his being almost beside himself would have induced him to utter that concluding word, which he held in such repugnance that it was never spoken or hinted at before him on any account.

"On my death," he repeated, as if he were defying me by defying his own abhorrence of the word. "On my death—death—Death! But I'll spoil the speculation. Eat your last under this roof, you feeble wretch, and may it choke you!"

You may suppose that I had not much appetite for the breakfast to which I was bidden in these terms; but I took my accustomed seat. I saw that I was repudiated henceforth by my uncle; still I could bear that very well, possessing Christiana's heart.

He emptied his basin of bread and milk as usual, only that he took it on his knees with his chair turned away from the table where I sat. When he had done, he carefully snuffed out the candle; and the cold, slate-colored, miserable day looked in upon us.

"Now, Mr. Michael," said he, "before we part, I should like to have a word with these ladies in your presence."

"As you will, sir," I returned; "but you deceive yourself, and wrong us cruelly, if you suppose that there is any feeling at stake in this contract but pure, disinterested, faithful love."

To this, he only replied, "You lie!" and not one other word.

We went, through half-thawed snow and half-frozen rain, to the house where Christiana and her mother lived. My uncle knew them very well. They were sitting at their breakfast, and were surprised to see us at that hour.

"Your servant, ma'am," said my uncle to the mother. "You divine the purpose of my visit, I dare say, ma'am. I understand there is a world of pure, disinterested, faithful love cooped up here. I am happy to bring it all it wants, to make it complete. I bring you your son-in-law, ma'am —and you, your husband, miss. The gentleman is a perfect stranger to me, but I wish him joy of his wise bargain."

He snarled at me as he went out, and I never saw him again.

It is altogether a mistake (continued the poor relation) to suppose that my dear Christiana, overpersuaded and influenced by her mother, married a rich man, the dirt from whose carriage wheels is often, in these changed times, thrown upon me, as she rides by. No, no. She married me.

The way we came to be married rather sooner than we intended, was this. I took a frugal lodging and was saving and planning for her sake, when one day she spoke to me with great earnestness, and said:

"My dear Michael, I have given you my heart. I have said that I loved you, and I have pledged myself to be your wife. I am as much yours through all changes of good and evil as if we had been married on the day when such words passed between us. I know you well, and know that if we should be separated and our union broken off, your whole life would be shadowed, and all that might, even now, be stronger in your character for the conflict with the world would then be weakened to the shadow of what it is!"

"God help me, Christiana!" said I. "You speak the truth."

"Michael!" said she, putting her hand in mine, in all maidenly devotion, "let us keep apart no longer. It is but for me to say that I can live contented upon such means as you have, and I well know you are happy. I say so from my heart. Strive no more alone; let us strive together. My dear Michael, it is not right that I should keep secret from you what you do not suspect, but what distresses my whole life. My mother—without considering that what you have lost, you have lost for me, and on the assurance of my faith—sets her heart on riches and urges another suit upon us, to my misery. I cannot bear this, for to bear it is to be untrue to you. I would rather share your struggles than look on. I want no better home than you can give me. I know that you will aspire and labor with a higher courage if I am wholly yours, and let it be so when you will!"

I was blest indeed, that day, and a new world opened to me. We were married in a very little while, and I took my wife to our happy home. That was the beginning of the residence I have spoken of; the Castle we have ever since inhabited together, dates from that time. All our children have been born in it. Our first child—now married—was a little girl, whom we called Christiana. Her son is so like little Frank, that I hardly know which is which.

The current impression as to my partner's dealings with me is also quite erroneous. He did not begin to treat me coldly, as a poor simpleton, when my uncle and I so fatally quarreled; nor did he afterwards gradually possess himself of our business and edge me out. On the contrary, he behaved to me with the utmost good faith and honor.

Matters between us took this turn: On the day of my separation from my uncle, and even before the arrival at our countinghouse of my trunks (which he sent after me, *not* carriage paid), I went down to our room of business, on our little wharf, overlooking the river; and there I told John Spatter what had happened. John did not say, in reply, that rich old relatives were palpable facts, and that love and sentiment were moonshine and fiction. He addressed me thus:

"Michael," said John, "we were at school together, and I generally had the knack of getting on better than you, and making a higher reputation."

"You had, John," I returned.

"Although," said John, "I borrowed your books and lost them; borrowed your pocket money, and never repaid it; got you to buy my damaged knives at a higher price than I had given for them new; and to own to the windows that I had broken."

"All not worth mentioning, John Spatter," said I, "but certainly true."

"When you were first established in this infant business, which promises to thrive so well," pursued John, "I came to you, in my search for almost any employment, and you made me your clerk."

"Still not worth mentioning, my dear John Spatter," said I; "still, equally true."

"And finding that I had a good head for business, and that I was really useful *to* the business, you did not like to retain me in that capacity, and thought it an act of justice soon to make me your partner."

"Still less worth mentioning than any of those other little circumstances you have recalled, John Spatter," said I; "for I was, and am, sensible of your merits and my deficiencies."

"Now, my good friend," said John, drawing my arm through his, as he had had a habit of doing at school; while two vessels outside the windows of our countinghouse—which were shaped like the stern windows of a ship—went lightly down the river with the tide, as John and I might then be sailing away in company, and in trust and confidence, on our voyage of life; "let there, under these friendly circumstances, be a right understanding between us. You are too easy, Michael. You are nobody's enemy but your own. If I were to give you that damaging character among our connection, with a shrug, and a shake of the head, and a sigh; and if I were further to abuse the trust you place in me—"

"But you never will abuse it at all, John," I observed.

"Never!" said he; "but I am putting a case—I say, and if I were further to abuse that trust by keeping this piece of our common affairs in the dark, and this other piece in the light, and again this other piece in the twilight, and so on, I should strengthen my strength, and weaken your weakness, day by day, until at last I found myself on the high road to fortune, and you left behind on some bare common, a hopeless number of miles out of the way."

"Exactly so," said I.

"To prevent this, Michael," said John Spatter, "or the remotest chance of this, there must be perfect openness between us. Nothing must be concealed, and we must have but one interest."

"My dear John Spatter," I assured him, "that is precisely what I mean."

"And when you are too easy," pursued John, his face glowing with friendship, "you must allow me to prevent that imperfection in your nature from being taken advantage of, by anyone; you must not expect me to humor it—"

"My dear John Spatter," I interrupted, "I *don't* expect you to humor it. I want to correct it."

"And I too," said John.

"Exactly so!" cried I. "We both have the same end in view; and, honorably seeking it, and fully trusting one another, and having but one interest, ours will be a prosperous and happy partnership."

"I am sure of it!" returned John Spatter. And we shook hands most affectionately.

I took John home to my Castle, and we had a very happy day. Our partnership throve well. My friend and partner supplied what I wanted, as I had foreseen that he would; and by improving both the business and myself, amply acknowledged any little rise in life to which I had helped him.

I am not (said the poor relation, looking at the fire as he slowly rubbed his hands) very rich, for I never cared to be that; but I have enough, and am above all moderate wants and anxieties. My Castle is not a splendid place, but it is very comfortable, and it has a warm and cheerful air, and is quite a picture of Home.

Our eldest girl, who is very like her mother, married John Spatter's eldest son. Our two familes are closely united in other ties of attachment. It is very pleasant of an evening, when we are all assembled together—which frequently happens—and when John and I talk over old times, and the one interest there has always been between us.

I really do not know, in my Castle, what loneliness is. Some of our children or grandchildren are always about it, and the young voices of my descendants are delightful—oh, how delightful!—to me to hear. My dearest and most devoted wife, ever faithful, ever loving, ever helpful and sustaining and consoling, is the priceless blessing of my house; from whom all its other blessings spring. We are rather a musical family, and when Christiana sees me, at any time, a little weary or depressed, she steals to the piano and sings a gentle air she used to sing when we were first betrothed. So weak a man am I, that I cannot bear to hear it from any other source. They played it once, at the Theater, when I was there with little Frank; and the child said wondering, "Cousin Michael, whose hot tears are these that have fallen on my hand!"

Such is my Castle, and such are the real particulars of my life therein preserved. I often take little Frank home there. He is very welcome to my grandchildren, and they play together. At this time of the year— the Christmas and New Year time—I am seldom out of my Castle. For, the associations of the season seem to hold me there, and the precepts of the season seem to teach me that it is well to be there.

"And the Castle is—" observed a grave, kind voice among the company.

"Yes, my Castle," said the poor relation, shaking his head as he still looked at the fire, "is in the Air. John our esteemed host suggests its situation accurately. My Castle is in the Air! I have done. Will you be so good as to pass the story."

INTERPRETATION

1. Define the character of "the poor relation." What light does his story throw upon (a) what the world thinks of him, (b) what he thinks of the world, and (c) what he thinks of himself? What is the basic irony of his life as he sees it? Has life robbed him by leaving him only a "castle in the air," or, contrary to the opinion of other people, has life given him the only secure "castle"?

2. What about the surprise ending of this story? Is it grounded in the character and situation as presented in the story?

3. Read the essay "Dream Children," by Charles Lamb. Compare its theme and general mood with that of "The Poor Relation's Story." The essay, too, involves a situation and some narrative, and has, in one sense, a surprise ending. What aspects of structure make it an essay and not a story?

4. Is "The Poor Relation's Story" sentimental? In connection with this, one should investigate the following questions:

(*a*) Are we convinced that the poor relation would have told such a story at this Christmas gathering? For example, such statements as these would, no doubt, be embarrassing to the company of successful people: "It is supposed . . . that I am nobody's enemy but my own. That I never met with any particular success in anything. That I failed in business because I was unbusinesslike and credulous. . . . That I failed in my expectations from my Uncle Chill. . . . That, through life, I have been rather put upon and disappointed in a general way." Is he sincere in his general mildness and reluctance to take precedence—"in knowing his place"—or, is he being really ironical with the intention of embarrassing and rebuking his successful and "charitable" kinsmen? If this is not the motivation of the telling of the story, what is the motivation? Is the story motivated by a desire to appeal to the sympathy of the rich relations? Or is there any particular motivation indicated?

(*b*) Does not our acceptance of the story as unsentimental depend, to some extent at least, on its being grounded firmly in the character? Compare the story, on this point, with "The Lament," by Chekhov, p. 242.

(*c*) Are the last four paragraphs, with their references to "hot tears," loneliness, and the "grave, kind voice" of some unspecified member of the company, an obvious straining to play on our feelings more than the situation seems to merit? For example, would a child of the age of "little Frank" have spoken such a sentence as: "Whose hot tears are these that have fallen on my hand?"

(*d*) What is the intended meaning of the sentence toward the end of the story: "For, the associations of the season [Christmas] seem to hold me there [in the Castle], and the precepts of the season seem to teach me that it is well to be there"?

The Lament
ANTON CHEKHOV

IT IS twilight. A thick wet snow is slowly twirling around the newly lighted street lamps, and lying in soft thin layers on roofs, on horses' backs, on people's shoulders and hats. The cabdriver Iona Potapov is quite white, and looks like a phantom; he is bent double as far as a human body can bend double; he is seated on his box; he never makes a move. If a whole snowdrift fell on him, it seems as if he would not find it necessary to shake it off. His little horse is also quite white, and remains motionless; its immobility, its angularity, and its straight wooden-looking legs, even close by, give it the appearance of a ginger-bread horse worth a *kopek*. It is, no doubt, plunged in deep thought. If you were snatched from the plow, from your usual gray surroundings, and were thrown into this slough full of monstrous lights, unceasing noise, and hurrying people, you too would find it difficult not to think.

Iona and his little horse have not moved from their place for a long while. They left their yard before dinner, and up to now, not a fare. The evening mist is descending over the town, the white lights of the lamps replacing brighter rays, and the hubbub of the street getting louder. "Cabby for Viborg way!" suddenly hears Iona. "Cabby!"

Iona jumps, and through his snow-covered eyelashes sees an officer in a greatcoat, with his hood over his head.

"Viborg way!" the officer repeats. "Are you asleep, eh? Viborg way!"

With a nod of assent Iona picks up the reins, in consequence of which layers of snow slip off the horse's back and neck. The officer seats himself in the sleigh, the cabdriver smacks his lips to encourage his horse, stretches out his neck like a swan, sits up, and, more from habit than necessity, brandishes his whip. The little horse also stretches its neck, bends its wooden-looking legs, and makes a move undecidedly.

"What are you doing, werewolf!" is the exclamation Iona hears from the dark mass moving to and fro, as soon as they have started.

"Where the devil are you going? To the r-r-right!"

"You do not know how to drive. Keep to the right!" calls the officer angrily.

A coachman from a private carriage swears at him; a passerby, who has run across the road and rubbed his shoulder against the horse's nose, looks at him furiously as he sweeps the snow from his sleeve. Iona shifts about on his seat as if he were on needles, moves his elbows as if he were trying to keep his equilibrium, and gapes about like someone suffocating, who does not understand why and wherefore he is there.

"What scoundrels they all are!" jokes the officer; "one would think they had all entered into an agreement to jostle you or fall under your horse."

Iona looks round at the officer, and moves his lips. He evidently wants to say something, but the only sound that issues is a snuffle.

"What?" asks the officer.

Iona twists his mouth into a smile, and with an effort says hoarsely: "My son, *barin,* died this week."

"Hm! What did he die of?"

Iona turns with his whole body toward his fare, and says:

"And who knows! They say high fever. He was three days in the hospital, and then died. . . . God's will be done."

"Turn round! The devil!" sounds from the darkness. "Have you popped off, old doggie, eh? Use your eyes!"

"Go on, go on," says the officer, "otherwise we shall not get there by tomorrow. Hurry up a bit!"

The cabdriver again stretches his neck, sits up, and, with a bad grace, brandishes his whip. Several times again he turns to look at his fare, but the latter has closed his eyes, and apparently is not disposed to listen. Having deposited the officer in the Viborg, he stops by the tavern, doubles himself up on his seat, and again remains motionless, while the snow once more begins to cover him and his horse. An hour, and another. . . . Then, along the footpath, with a squeak of galoshes, and quarreling, come three young men, two of them tall and lanky, the third one short and humpbacked.

"Cabby, to the Police Bridge!" in a cracked voice calls the humpback. "The three of us for two *griveniks!*"

Iona picks up his reins, and smacks his lips. Two *griveniks* is not a fair price, but he does not mind whether it is a *rouble* or five *kopeks* —to him it is all the same now, so long as they are fares. The young men, jostling each other and using bad language, approach the sleigh, and all three at once try to get onto the seat; then begins a discussion as to which two shall sit and who shall be the one to stand. After wrangling, abusing each other, and much petulance, it is at last decided that the humpback shall stand, as he is the smallest.

"Now then, hurry up!" says the humpback in a twanging voice, as he takes his place and breathes in Iona's neck. "Old furry! Here, mate, what a cap you have! There is not a worse one to be found in all Petersburg! . . ."

"He-he!—he-he!" giggles Iona. "Such a . . ."

"Now you, 'such a,' hurry up, are you going the whole way at this pace? Are you? . . . Do you want it in the neck?"

"My head feels like bursting," says one of the lanky ones. "Last night at the Donkmasovs, Vaska and I drank the whole of four bottles of cognac."

"I don't understand what you lie for," says the other lanky one angrily; "you lie like a brute."

"God strike me, it's the truth!"

"It's as much the truth as that a louse coughs!"

"He, he," grins Iona, "what gay young gentlemen!"

"Pshaw, go to the devil!" says the humpback indignantly.

"Are you going to get on or not, you old pest? Is that the way to drive? Use the whip a bit! Go on, devil, go on, give it to him well!"

Iona feels at his back the little man wriggling, and the tremble in his voice. He listens to the insults hurled at him, sees the people, and little by little the feeling of loneliness leaves him. The humpback goes on swearing until he gets mixed up in some elaborate six-foot oath, or chokes with coughing. The lankies begin to talk about a certain Nadejda Petrovna. Iona looks round at them several times; he waits for a temporary silence, then, turning round again, he murmurs:

"My son . . . died this week."

"We must all die," sighs the humpback, wiping his lips after an attack of coughing. "Now, hurry up, hurry up! Gentlemen, I really cannot go any farther like this! When will he get us there?"

"Well, just you stimulate him a little in the neck!"

"You old pest, do you hear, I'll bone your neck for you! If one

treated the like of you with ceremony one would have to go on foot!
Do you hear, old serpent Gorinytch! Or do you not care a spit?"

Iona hears rather than feels the blows they deal him.

"He, he," he laughs. "They are gay young gentlemen, God bless 'em!"

"Cabby, are you married?" asks a lanky one.

"I? He, he, gay young gentlemen! Now I have only a wife and the
moist ground. . . . He, ho, ho . . . that is to say, the grave. My son
has died, and I am alive. . . . A wonderful thing, death mistook the
door . . . instead of coming to me, it went to my son. . . ."

Iona turns round to tell them how his son died, but at this moment,
the humpback, giving a little sigh, announces, "Thank God, we have
at last reached our destination," and Iona watches them disappear
through the dark entrance. Once more he is alone, and again surrounded by silence. . . . His grief, which has abated for a short while,
returns and rends his heart with greater force. With an anxious and
hurried look, he searches among the crowds passing on either side of
the street to find whether there may be just one person who will listen
to him. But the crowds hurry by without noticing him or his trouble.
Yet it is such an immense, illimitable grief. Should his heart break
and the grief pour out, it would flow over the whole earth, so it seems,
and yet no one sees it. It has managed to conceal itself in such an insignificant shell that no one can see it even by day and with a light.

Iona sees a hall porter with some sacking, and decides to talk to him.

"Friend, what sort of time is it?" he asks.

"Past nine. What are you standing here for? Move on."

Iona moves on a few steps, doubles himself up, and abandons himself to his grief. He sees it is useless to turn to people for help. In less
than five minutes he straightens himself, holds up his head as if he
felt some sharp pain, and gives a tug at the reins; he can bear it no
longer. "The stables," he thinks, and the little horse, as if it understood, starts off at a trot.

About an hour and a half later Iona is seated by a large dirty stove.
Around the stove, on the floor, on the benches, people are snoring;
the air is thick and suffocatingly hot. Iona looks at the sleepers, scratches
himself, and regrets having returned so early.

"I have not even earned my fodder," he thinks. "That's what's my trouble. A man who knows his job, who has had enough to eat, and his horse too, can always sleep peacefully."

A young cabdriver in one of the corners half gets up, grunts sleepily, and stretches towards a bucket of water.

"Do you want a drink?" Iona asks him.

"Don't I want a drink!"

"That's so? Your good health! But listen, mate—you know, my son is dead. . . . Did you hear? This week, in the hospital. . . . It's a long story."

Iona looks to see what effect his words have, but sees none—the young man has hidden his face and is fast asleep again. The old man sighs, and scratches his head. Just as much as the young one wants to drink, the old man wants to talk. It will soon be a week since his son died, and he has not been able to speak about it properly to anyone. One must tell it slowly and carefully; how his son fell ill, how he suffered, what he said before he died, how he died. One must describe every detail of the funeral, and the journey to the hospital to fetch the dead son's clothes. His daughter Anissia has remained in the village—one must talk about her too. Is it nothing he has to tell? Surely the listener would gasp and sigh, and sympathize with him? It is better, too, to talk to women; although they are stupid, two words are enough to make them sob.

"I'll go and look after my horse," thinks Iona; "there's always time to sleep. No fear of that!"

He puts on his coat, and goes to the stables to his horse; he thinks of the corn, the hay, the weather. When he is alone, he dares not think of his son; he can speak about him to anyone, but to think of him, and picture him to himself, is unbearably painful.

"Are you tucking in?" Iona asks his horse, looking at its bright eyes; "go on, tuck in, though we've not earned our corn, we can eat hay. Yes! I am too old to drive—my son could have, not I. He was a first-rate cabdriver. If only he had lived!"

Iona is silent for a moment, then continues:

"That's how it is, my old horse. There's no more Kuzma Ionitch. He has left us to live, and he went off pop. Now let's say, you had a foal, you were the foal's mother, and suddenly, let's say, that foal went and left you to live after him. It would be sad, wouldn't it?"

The little horse munches, listens, and breathes over its master's hand. . . .

Iona's feelings are too much for him, and he tells the little horse the whole story.

INTERPRETATION

This story, like "Tennessee's Partner," deals with a pathetic situation. An old cabdriver, who has lost his son, can find no one in the world to whom he can confide his grief, and in the end goes out to the stable to tell his horse. In writing this story an author would almost certainly confront the danger of sentimentality. In considering this story, particularly after having read "Tennessee's Partner," one is interested in seeing what means Chekhov uses to avoid sentimentalizing his material.

One of the most obvious things which the reader notices in looking back on this story is the objective and neutral presentation. The author seems to be presenting scenes and actions to us without weighting them in favor of one interpretation or another.

For instance, consider his use of nature. In "Tennessee's Partner," as has been pointed out, Bret Harte uses nature to set a mood. But the use here—say in the first paragraph of "The Lament"—is different on two counts. First, Chekhov gives us the picture of the lonely scene on the street corner at evening, with the snow falling on the old cabdriver and the little horse. The fact of isolation is suggested, but there is no appeal to our sympathies either by poeticized language, as is the case in "Tennessee's Partner," or by editorial comment. Indeed, when Chekhov does depart from the straight, neutral, objective description, the effect is to play down the appeal to our sympathy rather than to insist upon it. For example, the suggestion is that the scene is scarcely real: "The cabdriver . . . is quite white, and looks like a phantom." And the "little horse is also quite white, and remains motionless; its immobility, its angularity, and its straight wooden-looking legs, even close by, give it the appearance of a gingerbread horse worth a kopek." The comparisons to the phantom and to the gingerbread horse serve to make the scene vivid and particular. But phantoms and gingerbread horses are fantastic things which do not feel or suffer and can make no appeal to sympathy. In other words, the scene, though it does give a sense of isolation, an effect which is important in the story of the cabdriver, is ostensibly pointed *away* from the appeal for sympathy and not *toward* it; Chekhov seems to say that he will be willing to rest his case on its own merits. The second way in which Chekhov's use of nature differs from that of Bret Harte in "Tennessee's Partner" is this: the function of the scene in "The Lament" is purely preparatory; the function in "Tennessee's Partner" is to seduce the reader into a proper response when he comes to the crucial point in the story.

The objective and neutral presentation, of which we have spoken in connection with the first paragraph of the story, continues through the various incidents which constitute the action.

The cabman picks up a fare who seems to be friendly and conversational. Apparently the cabman is encouraged enough by the friendliness of the officer to make a remark that his son has just died. But Chekhov does not indicate at this point the true meaning of the son's death to the cabman. Chekhov merely tells us that he "twists his mouth into a smile, and with an effort says hoarsely" that the boy is dead. This description of how the cabman says the words is our first revelation of his feelings, but we notice that the description is objective, and, indeed, somewhat ambiguous. What does the smile mean? Obviously, we can take it to be, in part, a response of gratitude for the officer's friendliness which comes in contrast to the isolation of the original scene. But the smile, like the comparisons to the phantom and the gingerbread horse in the first scene, tends to play down, rather than up, any direct appeal to our sympathy with the cabman as a grief-stricken man. At any rate, when the cabman, further encouraged by the officer's perfunctory expression of curiosity, takes his attention from his driving and begins to give some details of the son's death, he is interrupted by an irate protest from the darkness. And the officer then tells him to hurry, and forbids further conversation by leaning back and shutting his eyes.

It is worth noting that such information as we have been given about the cabman's feelings has come to us *dramatically*—that is, we have had it only in terms of his speech and not by commentary. By the same token, our information is incomplete. The basic motivation of the cabman has only been hinted at; it has not been fully revealed. Thus the dramatic presentation and the development of the reader's suspense here go hand in hand.

The motivation is further developed in the next scene, when the cabman tries, with unfriendly and boisterous passengers, to open the same subject. Their attitude toward him, too, emphasizes his own isolation. He tries to humor them in their drunkenness, and flatter them. In part, this behavior, no doubt, may be taken as an effort to get on

good terms with his fares and as an indication of his humble position
in society: but in part it may be taken as an indication of his willingness to accept any humiliation in order to tell his story. Thus, his behavior dramatically suggests the overpowering necessity which compels
him to tell his story. (One should notice how, even here, Chekhov
continues to play down the pathos of Iona: the young men are not
necessarily cruel, but may be merely drunken and thoughtless.)

After the young men get out and the cabman is again left alone,
Chekhov introduces his first explicit statement of the situation: "His
grief, which has abated for a short while, returns and rends his heart
with greater force. With an anxious and a hurried look, he searches
among the crowds passing on either side of the street to find if there
may be just one person who will listen to him." In other words, Chekhov has been cunning enough to validate the situation dramatically,
before he commits himself to the overt statement. Unlike similar
statements in the Bret Harte story, which attempt to prod the reader's
sympathies, this statement summarizes what the intelligent reader has
already been able to infer. But, of course, it is not merely a summary.
It analyzes the state of mind of the cabman: as long as he has had
any kind of human contact, even an unpleasant one, as with the drunken
youths, his grief has abated, but now that he is completely alone, it
returns with added force. Now he is even compelled to get out of the
cab and seek conversation.

But the attempt to engage the porter in conversation fails, and the
cabman finally returns to the stables. There, at least, one would expect
him to be able to find some sympathy among his own kind and class.
But even here he is forced back upon himself.

This sets the stage for the second piece of analysis of the cabman's
state of mind. Chekhov now, for the first time, gives us some of the
details of the son's death. But not merely as information. He gives
them as preparation for the question which is wrung from the heart
of the old man by the realization that no one will listen to him: "Was
it nothing he had to tell?"

This seems to be the summary of the old man's feelings—his incom-
prehension of the world, and his loneliness in it. If this were all, however, the story could come to a proper close after the old man's next
thought: "I'll go and look at my horse . . . there's always time to sleep.
No fear of that!"

But the situation is a little more complicated than this. Therefore,
we have the last bit of analysis, which is now fully prepared for. Iona

tries to think of the corn, the hay, and the weather. Presumably, he is going out to see about his horse, but really, we learn, he thinks of these things and goes out to his horse, simply because he cannot bear to be alone with the thought of his loss. The impulse to go to the stable does not depend on any conscious decision to tell the horse his troubles. He is fulfilling an unconscious need. This need is unconscious, but it colors even the way in which he begins to talk to the horse: "Are you tucking in?" He talks as if the horse were a child. But the unconscious need is so great that before he has uttered more than a sentence or two, he is back to the subject of his son. And once he has started talking with the horse, he begins to explain to the horse what he had been unable to explain to anyone else. But we may note that not only what he says to the horse is important, but the way in which he speaks: he adopts the careful, patient tone of explanation which a father might take to a young child: "Now, let's say, you had a foal, you were the foal's mother . . ."

This whole episode, though it has been perfectly prepared for by all preceding incidents and by the psychological analysis in the story, comes with an *ironical* shock of surprise. It is a surprise because the cabman's decision to go out to the stables is presented, on the surface at least, as a routine matter: the good cabman goes out to look after his horse. It is ironical, because it offers a commentary on a world in which one human being can find human sympathy only from a beast. Furthermore, this irony itself is shocking, for Chekhov has so presented the world of the story that it does not seem entirely vindictive and cruel. Some of the people who do not listen are simply preoccupied with their own affairs, or worn out with their own work. Yet this apparently normal world, in which there is a mixture of attitudes, turns out to be a world which does drive the man, seeking human sympathy, to the beast in the stable. And this turns out to be the theme of the story.

1. Comment on the use of the comparison of the old man to a swan in the fifth paragraph.

2. Comment on the function of these lines in helping supply preparation for the last scene (p. 245): ". . . he can bear it no longer. 'The stables,' he thinks . . . starts off at a trot."

3. In the last scene, Chekhov gives us Iona, a simple man, speaking in his full simplicity. This is a device for pathetic effect. Bret Harte uses a similar device in the funeral speech and in the dying speech of

the partner. Why is the device successful in one instance, and unsuccessful in the other?

The Secret Life of Walter Mitty
JAMES THURBER

"WE'RE GOING through!" The Commander's voice was like thin ice breaking. He wore his full-dress uniform, with the heavily braided white cap pulled down rakishly over one cold gray eye. "We can't make it, sir. It's spoiling for a hurricane, if you ask me." "I'm not asking you, Lieutenant Berg," said the Commander. "Throw on the power lights! Rev her up to 8,500! We're going through!" The pounding of the cylinders increased; ta-pocketa-pocketa-pocketa-*pocketa-pocketa*. The Commander stared at the ice forming on the pilot window. He walked over and twisted a row of complicated dials. "Switch on No. 8 auxiliary!" he shouted. "Switch on No. 8 auxiliary!" repeated Lieutenant Berg. "Full strength in No. 3 turret!" shouted the Commander. "Full strength in No. 3 turret!" The crew, bending to their various tasks in the huge, hurtling eight-engined Navy hydroplane, looked at each other and grinned. "The Old Man'll get us through," they said to one another. "The Old Man ain't afraid of Hell!" . . .

"Not so fast! You're driving too fast!" said Mrs. Mitty. "What are you driving so fast for?"

"Hmm?" said Walter Mitty. He looked at his wife, in the seat beside him, with shocked astonishment. She seemed grossly unfamiliar, like a strange woman who had yelled at him in a crowd. "You were up to fifty-five," she said. "You know I don't like to go more than forty. You were up to fifty-five." Walter Mitty drove on toward Waterbury in silence, the roaring of the SN202 through the worst storm in twenty years of Navy flying fading in the remote, intimate airways of his mind. "You're tensed up again," said Mrs. Mitty. "It's one of your days. I wish you'd let Dr. Renshaw look you over."

Walter Mitty stopped the car in front of the building where his wife went to have her hair done. "Remember to get those overshoes while I'm having my hair done," she said. "I don't need overshoes," said Mitty. She put her mirror back into her bag. "We've been all through that,"

she said, getting out of the car. "You're not a young man any longer."
He raced the engine a little. "Why don't you wear your gloves? Have
you lost your gloves?" Walter Mitty reached in a pocket and brought
out the gloves. He put them on, but after she had turned and gone into
the building and he had driven on to a red light, he took them off again.
"Pick it up, brother!" snapped a cop as the light changed, and Mitty
hastily pulled on his gloves and lurched ahead. He drove around the
streets aimlessly for a time, and then he drove past the hospital on his
way to the parking lot.

. . . "It's the millionaire banker, Wellington McMillan," said the
pretty nurse. "Yes?" said Walter Mitty, removing his gloves slowly.
"Who has the case?" "Dr. Renshaw and Dr. Benbow, but there are two
specialists here, Dr. Remington from New York and Dr. Pritchard-
Mitford from London. He flew over." A door opened down a long,
cool corridor and Dr. Renshaw came out. He looked distraught and
haggard. "Hello, Mitty," he said. "We're having the devil's own time
with McMillan, the millionaire banker and close personal friend of
Roosevelt. Obstreosis of the ductal tract. Tertiary. Wish you'd take a
look at him." "Glad to," said Mitty.

In the operating room there were whispered introductions: "Dr. Remington, Dr. Mitty. Dr. Pritchard-Mitford, Dr. Mitty." "I've read your
book on streptothricosis," said Pritchard-Mitford, shaking hands. "A
brilliant performance, sir." "Thank you," said Walter Mitty. "Didn't
know you were in the States, Mitty," grumbled Remington. "Coals to
Newcastle, bringing Mitford and me up here for a tertiary." "You are
very kind," said Mitty. A huge, complicated machine, connected to
the operating table, with many tubes and wires, began at this moment
to go pocketa-pocketa-pocketa. "The new anaesthetizer is giving away!"
shouted an interne. "There is no one in the East who knows how to fix
it!" "Quiet, man!" said Mitty, in a low, cool voice. He sprang to the
machine, which was now going pocketa-pocketa-queep-pocketa-queep.
He began fingering delicately a row of glistening dials. "Give me a
fountain pen!" he snapped. Someone handed him a fountain pen. He
pulled a faulty piston out of the machine and inserted the pen in its
place. "That will hold for ten minutes," he said. "Get on with the
operation." A nurse hurried over and whispered to Renshaw, and Mitty
saw the man turn pale. "Coreopsis has set in," said Renshaw nervously.

"If you would take over, Mitty?" Mitty looked at him and at the craven figure of Benbow, who drank, and at the grave, uncertain faces of the two great specialists. "If you wish," he said. They slipped a white gown on him; he adjusted a mask and drew on thin gloves; nurses handed him shining . . .

"Back it up, Mac! Look out for that Buick!" Walter Mitty jammed on the brakes. "Wrong lane, Mac," said the parking-lot attendant, looking at Mitty closely. "Gee. Yeh," muttered Mitty. He began cautiously to back out of the lane marked "Exit Only." "Leave her sit there," said the attendant. "I'll put her away." Mitty got out of the car. "Hey, better leave the key." "Oh," said Mitty, handing the man the ignition key. The attendant vaulted into the car, backed it up with insolent skill, and put it where it belonged.

They're so damn cocky, thought Walter Mitty, walking along Main Street; they think they know everything. Once he had tried to take his chains off, outside New Milford, and he had got them wound around the axles. A man had had to come out in a wrecking car and unwind them, a young, grinning garage man. Since then Mrs. Mitty always made him drive to a garage to have the chains taken off. The next time, he thought, I'll wear my right arm in a sling; they won't grin at me then. I'll have my right arm in a sling and they'll see I couldn't possibly take the chains off myself. He kicked at the slush on the sidewalk. "Overshoes," he said to himself, and he began looking for a shoe store.

When he came out into the street again, with the overshoes in a box under his arm, Walter Mitty began to wonder what the other thing was his wife had told him to get. She had told him, twice before they set out from their house for Waterbury. In a way he hated these weekly trips to town—he was always getting something wrong. Kleenex, he thought, Squibb's, razor blades? No. Toothpaste, toothbrush, bicarbonate, carborundum, initiative and referendum? He gave it up. But she would remember it. "Where's the what's-its-name?" she would ask. "Don't tell me you forgot the what's-its-name." A newsboy went by shouting something about the Waterbury trial.

. . . "Perhaps this will refresh your memory." The District Attorney suddenly thrust a heavy automatic at the quiet figure on the witness stand. "Have you ever seen this before?" Walter Mitty took the gun and examined it expertly. "This is my Webley-Vickers 50.80," he said calmly. An excited buzz ran around the courtroom. The judge rapped for order. "You are a crack shot with any sort of firearms, I believe?" said the District Attorney, insinuatingly. "Objection!" shouted Mitty's attorney. "We have shown that the defendant could not have fired the shot. We have shown that he wore his right arm in a sling on the night of the fourteenth of July." Walter Mitty raised his hand briefly and the bickering attorneys were stilled. "With any known make of gun," he said evenly, "I could have killed Gregory Fitzhurst at three hundred feet *with my left hand*." Pandemonium broke loose in the courtroom. A woman's scream rose above the bedlam and suddenly a lovely, dark-haired girl was in Walter Mitty's arms. The District Attorney struck at her savagely. Without rising from his chair, Mitty let the man have it on the point of the chin. "You miserable cur!" . . .

"Puppy biscuit," said Walter Mitty. He stopped walking and the buildings of Waterbury rose up out of the misty courtroom and surrounded him again. A woman who was passing laughed. "He said 'Puppy biscuit,'" she said to her companion. "That man said 'Puppy biscuit' to himself." Walter Mitty hurried on. He went into an A. & P., not the first one he came to but a smaller one farther up the street. "I want some biscuit for small, young dogs," he said to the clerk. "Any special brand, sir?" The greatest pistol shot in the world thought a moment. "It says 'Puppies Bark for It' on the box," said Walter Mitty.

His wife would be through at the hairdresser's in fifteen minutes, Mitty saw in looking at his watch, unless they had trouble drying it; sometimes they had trouble drying it. She didn't like to get to the hotel first; she would want him to be there waiting for her as usual. He found a big leather chair in the lobby, facing a window, and he put the over-shoes and the puppy biscuit on the floor beside it. He picked up an old copy of *Liberty* and sank down into the chair. "Can Germany Conquer the World through the Air?" Walter Mitty looked at the pictures of bombing planes and of ruined streets.

. . . "The cannonading has got the wind up in young Raleigh, sir," said the sergeant. Captain Mitty looked up at him through tousled hair. "Get him to bed," he said wearily, "with the others. I'll fly alone." "But you can't, sir," said the sergeant anxiously. "It takes two men to handle that bomber and the Archies are pounding hell out of the air.

Von Richtman's circus is between here and Saulier." "Somebody's got to get that ammunition dump," said Mitty. "I'm going over. Spot of brandy?" He poured a drink for the sergeant and one for himself. War thundered and whined around the dugout and battered at the door. There was a rending of wood and splinters flew through the room. "A bit of a near thing," said Captain Mitty carelessly. "The box barrage is closing in," said the sergeant. "We only live once, sergeant," said Mitty, with his faint, fleeting smile. "Or do we?" He poured another brandy and tossed it off. "I never see a man could hold his brandy like you, sir," said the sergeant. "Begging your pardon, sir." Captain Mitty stood up and strapped on his huge Webley-Vickers automatic. "It's forty kilometers through hell, sir," said the sergeant. Mitty finished one last brandy. "After all," he said softly, "what isn't?" The pounding of the cannon increased; there was the rat-tat-tatting of machine guns, and from somewhere came the menacing pocketa-pocketa-pocketa of the new flame-throwers. Walter Mitty walked to the door of the dugout humming *"Après de Ma Blonde."* He turned and waved to the sergeant. "Cheerio!" he said. . . .

Something struck his shoulder. "I've been looking all over this hotel for you," said Mrs. Mitty. "Why do you have to hide in this old chair? How did you expect me to find you?" "Things close in," said Walter Mitty vaguely. "What?" Mrs. Mitty said. "Did you get the what's-its-name? The puppy biscuit? What's in that box?" "Overshoes," said Mitty. "Couldn't you have put them on in the store?" "I was thinking," said Walter Mitty. "Does it ever occur to you that I am sometimes thinking?" She looked at him. "I'm going to take your temperature when I get you home," she said.

They went out through the revolving doors that made a faintly derisive whistling sound when you pushed them. It was two blocks to the parking lot. At the drugstore on the corner she said, "Wait here for me. I forgot something. I won't be a minute." She was more than a minute. Walter Mitty lighted a cigarette. It began to rain, rain with sleet in it. He stood up against the wall of the drugstore, smoking. . . . He put his shoulders back and his heels together. "To hell with the handkerchief," said Walter Mitty scornfully. He took one last drag on his cigarette and snapped it away. Then, with that faint, fleeting smile playing about his lips, he faced the firing squad; erect and motionless,

proud and disdainful, Walter Mitty the Undefeated, inscrutable to the
last.*

INTERPRETATION

There is humor of various kinds in some of the stories which have
preceded this one: in "Old Red," for example; in "A Piece of News";
and even in a story like "The Man Who Would Be King" there are
humorous elements like the contract drawn up between Peachey and
Dravot. This story, however, is more purely humorous than any which
have preceded it. On what is the humor based? Is it rooted in character?

1. Attempt to define Mr. Mitty's character. Granting that his day-
dreaming is exaggerated, is the exaggeration, like that of a good cartoonist, justified?

2. How has the author suggested the kind of figure which Mr. Mitty
cuts in the world's eyes?

3. Consider the function of the following items in making for the
humorous effect: Mr. Mitty's fondness for the syllables "pocketa-
pocketa" as expressive of certain sounds; the *alliteration* (see Glossary)
involved in such phrases as "sir, said the sergeant"; the use, in the
parts of the story which recount Mitty's various fantasies, of *clichés*
(see Glossary) drawn from thriller stories.

4. What is the author's attitude toward Mr. Mitty? Obviously, he
regards him as amusing, but is his attitude essentially kindly? Harsh?
Sympathetic? Or what? How does the attitude express itself in the
way the story is told; that is, what is the *tone* (see Glossary) of the
story?

5. "The Poor Relation's Story" recounts the story of a man who
presented one side to the world, but carried on a very different secret
life of his own. Compare and contrast the intention of Dickens in
this story with that of Thurber in his story of Mr. Mitty. Notice particularly the difference in tone between the two stories. (For another
comparison of this type, the student might consider "Old Mr. Marblehall," p. 472.)

* From *The New Yorker;* by permission of the author.

Two Little Soldiers
GUY DE MAUPASSANT
(Translated by Emma Brescia Warren)

EVERY SUNDAY, as soon as they were free, the two little soldiers would set out walking.

They turned to the right on leaving the barracks, and crossed Courbevoie with long, quick strides, as if on military march; then, on passing the last houses, they continued at a calmer pace, on the bare, dusty road which leads to Bezons.

They were little and thin, lost in their coats, which were too big and too long, with sleeves which covered the hands, bothered by the too-big red trousers, which forced them to separate their legs if they wanted to walk fast. And under the tall, stiff shakos, one could scarcely see a small bit of face, two poor hollow Breton faces, simple with an almost animal-like innocence, with calm, sweet blue eyes.

They never spoke during the walk, the same idea, which took the place of conversation, stirring in their heads; for they had found, at the edge of the little woods of Champioux, a place which reminded them of their home, and they felt at ease nowhere else.

At the crossing of the roads of Colombes and Chatou, on arriving under the trees, they would take off their shakos, which weighed on the head, and dry their brows.

They always stopped a little on the bridge of Bezons to look at the Seine. They would stay there two or three minutes, bent over, leaning on the parapet; or they would consider the great basin of Argenteuil, where glided the white, leaning sails of the clippers, which, perhaps, reminded them of the Breton sea, the port of Vannes, whose neighbors they were, and of the boats which went on across Morbihan, toward the open sea.

As soon as they had crossed the Seine, they would buy their provisions from the shops of the pork butcher and the baker, and from the town wine shop. A piece of sausage, four sous' worth of bread, and a liter of *petit-bleu*, carried in handkerchiefs, constituted their supply. But as soon as they had left the village, they would slow their pace, and begin to talk.

Before them a barren plain, spotted here and there with a clump of trees, led to the woods, the little woods which, they thought, resembled those of Kermarivan. Blades of oats bordered the narrow path, lost in the fresh verdure of the coming crops; and Jean Kerderen would always say to Luc le Ganidec, "It's just like near Plunivon."

"Yes, it's just like it."

They would go on, side by side, their spirits filled with vague remembrances of their own country, full of awakened images, naïve images like the colored pictures one buys for a sou. They would see again the corner of a field, a hedge, a bit of heath, a crossroads, a granite cross.

Every time, too, they would stop near a stone which marked the boundary of a property, because it looked somewhat like the dolmen of Locneuven.

On reaching the first clump of trees, Luc le Ganidec would break off a switch, a hazel switch; and he would begin, quite gently, to peel back the bark, thinking of the people back home.

Jean Kerderen carried the provisions.

From time to time, Luc would mention a name, or recall an episode of childhood, briefly in order to give them time to dream. And their own country, the dear, faraway country, would repossess them little by little, would envelop them, would send to them, across the distance, its forms, its noises, its known horizons, its odors, the odor of the green heath where the sea air ran.

They no longer smelled the exhalations of the Parisian stables by which the earth of the suburbs is manured, but the perfume of the blooming thorn broom which the salt breeze gathers and carries away. And the sails of the boats appearing above the banks seemed to them the sails of coasting vessels seen beyond the long plain which stretched from their homes to the edge of the waves.

They walked slowly, Luc le Ganidec and Jean Kerderen, happy and sad, haunted by a sweet melancholy, the slow and penetrating melancholy of a caged animal that remembers.

And by the time Luc had finished peeling the bark from the thin switch, they would have arrived at the corner of the woods where they had lunch every Sunday.

They would find the two bricks which they had hidden in a thicket, and would light a little fire of twigs to cook their sausage on the point of a knife.

And when they had finished, eaten their bread to the last crumb and drunk their wine to the last drop, they would remain seated in the grass, side by side, not speaking, eyes far away, eyelids heavy, fingers crossed as at mass, their red legs stretched out beside the poppies of the field; and the leather of their shakos and the brass of their buttons shining under the burning sun would make the larks overhead stop singing.

Toward noon, they would begin to turn their glance, now and then, toward the village of Bezons, for the milkmaid.

Every Sunday she passed before them on her way to milk the cow and bring it home, the only cow in the neighborhood out at grass. It was pastured in a small field at the edge of the woods, beyond them.

They would soon see the girl, the only human being moving on the plain, and they would feel gladdened by the brilliant reflections thrown by the tin bucket under the flame of the sun. They never spoke to her. They were merely glad to see her, without realizing why.

She was a great, vigorous girl, reddened and burned by the heat of bright days, a great, bold girl of the Parisian countryside.

One time, seeing them seated at the accustomed place, she said to them, "Hello—so you're always here?"

Luc le Ganidec, the more daring, stammered: "Yes, we're here to rest."

That was all. But the following Sunday, she laughed on seeing them, laughing with the patronizing benevolence of a shrewd woman who understood their timidity, and asked: "What are you doing like that? Are you watching the grass grow?"

Luc, brightening, smiled too: "Maybe."

She replied: "What! It doesn't go fast."

Still laughing, he said: "Well, no."

She went on. But on returning with her pail full of milk, she stopped in front of them again, and said to them: "Do you want a drop? It'll remind you of home."

With the instinctive knowledge of belonging to the same stock, perhaps far from home herself, she had divined and touched their feeling.

They were both moved.

Then she poured out some milk, not without difficulty, into the neck of the bottle in which they had carried the wine; and Luc drank first, in little sips, stopping now and then to see that he didn't get more than his share. Then he gave the bottle to Jean.

She remained standing before them, her hands on her hips, the pail on the ground at her feet, glad for the pleasure she had given them.

Then, going away, she called: "Well, so long till Sunday!"

And as long as they could see her, their eyes followed her tall silhouette which receded, which diminished, which seemed to sink into the verdure of the earth.

When, the next week, they left the barracks, Jean said to Luc, "Shouldn't we buy her something nice?"

And they were embarrassed before the problem of choosing a tidbit for the milkmaid.

Luc thought of a piece of pork sausage, but Jean, because he loved sweets, preferred some candy. His idea carried, and they bought at a grocer's two sous' worth of white and red bonbons.

They ate their lunch faster than usual, agitated by their expectancy.

Jean saw her first. "There she is," he said.

Luc replied: "Yes. There she is."

On seeing them, still far off, she laughed, and called: "Is it going to suit you?"

They answered together: "How about you?"

Then she chatted with them, speaking of simple things which interested them, the weather, the crops, the folks she worked for.

They scarcely dared to offer their bonbons which melted gently in Jean's pocket.

Luc at last nerved himself and murmured, "We've brought you something."

"What is it?" she demanded.

Then Jean, red to the ears, reached for the thin cone of paper, and held it out to her.

She began eating the little pieces of candy which she rolled from one cheek to the other, and which made bumps under the flesh. The two soldiers, seated before her, regarded her, moved and enchanted.

Then she went to milk her cow and, on returning, again gave them some milk.

They thought of her all week and spoke of her many times. The next Sunday she sat down beside them to chat longer, and all three, side by side, their eyes far away, their knees held in clasped hands, recounted little events and little details of the villages where they had been born, while the cow, over there, seeing that the girl had stopped on the way, stretched out her heavy head, with the damp nostrils, and lowed protractedly to call her.

The girl soon accepted the invitation to eat a little with them and to drink a little wine. Often she would bring them some plums in her pocket, for the plum season had come. Her presence enlivened the two little Breton soldiers, who chattered like two birds.

Now, on a Tuesday, Luc le Ganidec asked for leave, something which he had never done before, and did not return until ten in the evening.

Jean, disturbed, racked his head for the reason for his comrade's absence.

The following Friday, Luc, having borrowed ten sous from his cot neighbor, asked and obtained permission for another leave of some hours.

And when he set out with Jean for the Sunday walk, he had a roguish, nervous air, all changed. Kerderen did not understand, but he vaguely suspected something, without guessing what it might be.

They didn't speak a word until they had reached the usual place, where they had worn out the grass by always sitting in the same spot; and they ate slowly. Neither one was hungry.

Soon the girl appeared. They watched her coming as they did every Sunday. When she was near, Luc got up and took two steps. She set her pail on the ground, and embraced him. She embraced him passionately, throwing her arms about his neck, without concerning herself with Jean, without noticing that he was there, without seeing him.

And he felt lost, poor Jean, so lost that he did not understand it, his soul agitated, his heart broken.

Then the girl sat near Luc, and they began to chatter.

Jean did not look at them. He divined now why his comrade had gone out twice during the week, and he felt within himself a burning sadness, a sort of wound, that rending which treacheries make.

Luc and the girl got up to go together to change the cow.

Jean followed them with his eyes. He saw them move away, side by side. His comrade's red trousers made a blazing spot in the path. It was Luc who picked up the mallet and drove in the stake which held the animal.

The girl sank down to milk, while he absently caressed the animal's sharp backbone. Then they left the pail on the grass, and disappeared under the trees.

Jean saw nothing more than the wall of leaves through which they had entered; and he felt so troubled that, had he tried to rise, he would certainly have fallen.

He stayed still, stupefied by amazement and suffering, with a suffering deep and simple. He longed to weep, to get away, to hide, never to see anybody again.

Suddenly, he saw them coming out of the thicket. They came slowly holding hands, the way engaged couples do in the villages. It was Luc who carried the pail.

They kissed again at parting, and the girl, after having cast a friendly farewell and a knowing smile to Jean, went away. She did not think of offering him any milk that day.

The two little soldiers remained side by side, motionless as always, silent and calm, the placidity of their faces showing nothing of what troubled their hearts. The sun set. The cow, sometimes, lowed, regarding them from the distance.

At the usual hour, they got up to return.

Luc was peeling a switch. Jean carried the empty bottle. He left it at the wine shop of Bezons. Then they reached the bridge, and, as every Sunday, stopped at the middle for some moments to watch the water flow.

Jean leaned forward; he leaned forward more and more on the iron balustrade, as though he had seen something in the current which attracted him.

Luc said to him: "Maybe you'd like a drink of it?"

As he spoke the last word, Jean's head overbalanced his body, the lifted legs described a circle in the air, and the little red and blue soldier fell like a stone, entered the water, and disappeared.

Luc, his throat paralyzed with anguish, tried in vain to cry out. He saw something moving farther on; then his comrade's head broke the surface of the river, only to disappear again.

Farther on yet, he saw, again, a single hand which reached from the water, and plunged in again. That was all.

The boatmen who came hurrying did not find the body that day.

Luc returned to the barracks alone, running, his head in a whirl, and told of the accident, his eyes and voice full of tears, blowing his nose from time to time: "He leaned—he—he leaned—so far—so far his head tumbled over—and—and—look at him falling there—he's falling—"

He could not go on, his emotion strangled him so. If he had only known—

INTERPRETATION

1. This story, unlike the stories preceding it in this section, does not present a fully rounded portrait of an individual. But, as the title indicates, the story is concerned with a matter of character. In investigating this matter, the student may ask these questions: (*a*) In what ways are the two soldiers alike? (*b*) In what ways are they different? (Actually, a small amount of space is devoted to direct character delineation, but the author has planted certain leads and indications here and there in the story.)

2. The tightness of the bond between the two little soldiers is obviously an important factor in the story. The author has not stated this explicitly, either by commentary or by giving what is going on inside the minds of the characters. But would the boys have been such close friends at home? Consider in this regard the importance of such items as these: (*a*) They choose for their walks a road through country that reminds them of home. (*b*) The peasant girl offers the milk with the suggestion that it will taste like home. (*c*) The author describes them: "They were little and thin, lost in their coats, which were too big and too long." (*d*) They never converse while they take their walk but go straight on "the same idea . . . stirring in their heads." After investigating these items, does not one feel that Maupassant is trying to suggest a relationship, which is not easy to define, but which lies at the heart of the story? It is, obviously, a relationship based on a kind of loneliness and homesickness, almost animal-like in the sense

that it is not founded on any intellectual communion or shared ideas. Attempt to define this relationship further.

3. The problem raised in the foregoing paragraph concerns the similarities of the two little soldiers. But what are their differences? Maupassant has quietly suggested some of the differences. For instance, he says that Jean always carries the package on their walks, while Luc idly peels a hazel switch. What are some of the other indications?

4. Are we convinced that Jean would feel that Luc's private meetings with the girl amounted to a kind of "treachery"? To what extent is the word justified?

5. Is Jean's death a suicide? If so, in what sense? Is it calculated? Is there any motivation for it?

6. Whose story is this, Jean's or Luc's? In this connection, what is the significance of the last sentence of the story?

7. Just before the death of Jean, we are given the following sentences: "Luc was peeling a switch. Jean carried the empty bottle." What is the significance of the sentences in this place? Does the word *empty* have any special significance here?

Love and James K. Polk
GRIFFITH BEEMS

FOR MORE than a year, several, in fact, possibly even for three years—in the beginning she had so little noticed that she was no longer certain—she had had these dreams, or experiences; for they were more unpleasant experiences than dreams. She would close her eyes and the activities of her mind would fitfully subside and she would be almost asleep when she was among the peering, crowding, wavering, lurid flicker of innumerable faceless faces, punily and ambiguously monstrous, and she awoke, stifling, without having been asleep. After the experience, sleep would be hours in coming. Whatever the original cause of these dreams, and they were probably related to the strains of teaching (for eleven years she had instructed at James K. Polk High School and this semester had 161 students in American History), it was certain that the dreams had been much more frequent and annoying during the recent months in which Mr. Herr, the chemistry instructor, had been writing to her. This Thursday morning, like the other recent Thursday mornings, there would be a letter from him in the mailbox downstairs, another stupid abject letter, full of protestation and egotism, but now while the water for an egg and for her coffee was coming to a boil and she was having her shower, Martha Flint had a joyous premonition. The absence of the dream foretold the absence of the letter. Such an interpretation was perhaps not scientific but there it was: she had a fixed premonition that the letter would not be in the mailbox this morning and inordinately enjoyed her solitary breakfast and second cup of coffee in consequence.

She rode down in the automatic elevator with impatience. Through the star-shaped perforations of the mailbox, the key gripped tightly in her hand, she could see the letter, a stiff solid letter. So much for premonition. A blaze of exasperation, of undischarged and frustrate scolding, made the tears start. She was doubly angry, angry because he dared to write to her, angry because her premonition had failed. She had not stopped him after the first letter and the business went on, kindness and the slightest pity always being exploited. It had to stop. She knew with a certainty equal to her original premonition, without looking inside, that the letter was from him. She left the box unopened, the letter untouched.

Except for his letter-writing and for his stratagem at lunch time of coming into the school cafeteria five or so minutes late and making the crowded condition the excuse for asking to sit with Gertrude Apfel and Lillian Ferrara, the assistant librarian, and herself, Mr. Herr had not made himself into an acute problem. Mr. Herr had every reason to be hangdog and timid; he was married and living with his wife and he had two little girls. He had written that Mrs. Herr was in love with an unemployed musician, who called at the apartment three days a week and gave the little girls piano lessons, and that it had been going on for years, and that he was hopelessly and miserably unhappy. As it didn't matter to Martha one way or the other, she hadn't had to decide whether these were the delusions of a morbid jealousy or the truth. But Martha Flint had a strong sense of the secretness and inviolability of her own life, from which Mr. Herr benefited, and if these things were true it was a cruel situation, caught between an unfaithful wife and responsibility to his little girls—perhaps even worse than the cruelty was the humiliation —and Martha, who ignored the letters, had respected Mr. Herr's unsought confidences. There had been a kind of humaneness, of matured tolerance, in putting up with the man, but this Thursday noon, remembering her morning's irritation and rather than confront his furtive fluttering stare, usually risked at the moment that he was putting food into his mouth, she went his own stratagem one better and came into the cafeteria fifteen minutes late. He was already seated with Gertrude and Lillian. Keeping her back turned, she found another table. But in the midst of her chocolate cake, there was Gertrude and Mr. Herr following, smiling. Mr. Herr was a stooped, excessively bony, nearsighted man, with a thick upper lip and a stubby reddish-brown mustache, the left bristles predeterminately askew.

"What are you doing over here by yourself?" Gertrude demanded.

Mr. Herr's skeletal shoulders were fidgeting and he smiled. There was something pale and uncertain and puffy about his smile—like painfully smiling through a blister, Gertrude had remarked.

"Oh, hello," Martha said. "I didn't see you. I'm in a tearing hurry today."

Gertrude, who was a large woman, with cropped hair, not in the least concerned that Martha was in a tearing hurry, settled solidly into the opposite chair. "What are you in a hurry about?" Mr. Herr, for whom there was no chair, crossed his feet and dangled a fist on the table, then unwound, and putting a foot on the rung of Martha's chair, abruptly swung and leaned on her chair back. Martha's shoulders flinched. If he touches me, she thought, I don't care, I can't help it (the fork stirred in her hand), if he leans over and touches me, I'll turn round and jab— jab. She waited. The back of his hand touched, passed brushingly, along her shoulder blades. He had never touched her before.

"I've half a dozen references to do in the library before next period," she said.

Mr. Herr edged closer. "What's the good news, if any, with you this morning?" Beneath the audacity he was frightened. "Has anything happened?" His hand brushed her shoulder blade again. She knew that he was referring to the letter in the mailbox.

"Nothing of the slightest interest to me," she said sharply, trying to turn her head and speak her annoyance into his face; but he moved farther behind her.

Gertrude noticed. "Here," she commanded, holding up her lunch check. "Be an angel and get me another cup of coffee. Cream," she called after him. "Don't forget." Her eyes shone with impatience. "Why did you snap so? I thought you were going to bite his head off."

"Who?"

"Herr."

Martha twirled her plate. It occurred to her that if she were going to stop Mr. Herr's letter-writing, as she had decided that morning in front of the mailbox, one way would be to lean forward and confide to Trudie, "I've a letter from him at home. I'll bring it tomorrow." In a few days the talk would pursue him through offices, halls, and classrooms like his own shadow, grown longer and more pervasive. Having been the first to ridicule him, she would be almost entirely absolved. Trudie's fleshy large face demanded and her eyes were avid. "He annoys me," Martha said, with a sense of prevaricating on her own behalf rather than Mr. Herr's, "hanging over the back of my chair like that."

"Come clean, Martha. That isn't everything." Already, between the tables, Mr. Herr was hurrying back. Trudie scowled. She was acquainted with Martha's aggravating reticences. "I thought at the very least he must have pinched you," she grumbled. Being large, she particularly resented being pinched.

"Sorry. But he didn't."

Mr. Herr was back. "Be an angel again," Gertrude commanded impatiently, "and fly away." She motioned with her hand. "Fly." Mr. Herr did not want to fly. He smiled weakly to show that he was not offended by her rudeness, opened his mouth to reply, hesitated, then looked hurt, then defeated, then embarrassed, closed his mouth and went. Martha had not looked at him. She envied Trudie her brutality.

She immediately encountered it herself. For getting to the bottom of affairs, after fifteen years of teaching, Gertrude believed in direct questions. "Has that heel been pestering you?"

"Oh, Trudie."

"Has he?"

"No," Martha lied.

"He gets crushes, you know. He's the one that was responsible for Miss Hostetler being transferred to Benjamin Franklin. One of the junior highs saw them at a downtown movie theater together."

Mr. Herr in his letters had already tried to explain away Miss Hostetler. Martha remembered the talk. Being transferred had forced Miss

Hostetler to give up that dark narrow apartment which she had talked up as a bargain for so many years, and to re-establish her tidy ingrown existence, all because, as Trudie had then said, she probably thought that she could save thirty-five cents by allowing Mr. Herr to take her to the movies. No one had actually supposed that she had permitted Mr. Herr any familiarities. Martha had twice been in Miss Hostetler's apartment to tea, that darkish corridorlike apartment, formidably decorated with Miss Hostetler's dead brother's collection of fish specimens. If only they had been birds, Lillian had whispered, Miss Hostetler could have worn them in her hat. While the student bus boy, whose coming had interrupted the conversation, stacked the dishes on the table, Martha remembered Lillian and Gertrude and herself, that long-ago afternoon at tea, simultaneously overcome by the varnished sand shark mounted on oak above the mantel. They had nudged each other, but contained themselves, except for solemnly setting down their three teacups, one after another, and then as solemnly picking them up again. Still amused, Martha wondered whether Mr. Herr had ever gotten far enough with Miss Hostetler to have encountered the sand shark. How light-hearted and rude they had been, she thought half-enviously, studying Trudie's impatient chunky frowning face across the table, as silly that afternoon at Miss Hostetler's tea as three high-school girls. They had grown older; they had grown apart; and irresponsible light-heartedness would never return.

The boy carried away the dishes.

"He's beginning to follow you around," Gertrude warned.

"Don't be middle-aged."

"You'll see."

"If he ever pestered me," Martha announced sharply, rising, "I'd make mince meat of him."

The letter in the mailbox, when she read it that evening after correcting the day's history papers, interested her slightly more than had its predecessors. "Dear Miss Flint," it began.

"I am writing this from 317D. You do not know the satisfaction that it gives me to be sitting at your desk and in your chair too. I have locked the door but if anyone should come in I will tell them that I am working in here because the light is better. Can you understand what I mean? It is true.

"The other evening at home, while I did not know where my wife was, I wrote this: 'I always write about my own troubles. I must be sinking Miss Flint in my own unhappiness. I must show her that I think of her myself aside. When I think of her, leaving myself out, I imagine that she was deeply in love with a man but that for some good reason they were not able to marry. She has never forgotten him. That is why she has these headaches. If she would forget this man a little and notice the real world that is all around her with its new possibilities, the headaches would go away. To do that would not be disloyal. People should be loyal up to a certain point and after that point has been passed they are no longer bound.' I should like to discuss this with you and hear your views.

"My wife said that she had been to the movies. Would you believe her after what I have written to you?

"I cannot tell whether you think my letters interesting or not. You do not let anything show in your face. I could easily write to you every day. I mean that I have the impulse.

"There are other times that I think you do not know what love is. Whenever I think that it makes me very unhappy. Then I try to put the thought out of my mind and be happy again. No one likes unhappiness.

"Does it seem to you that I understand you? I think about you so much and turn my thoughts about you over and over in my mind until at times I am confused and then at other times I seem to understand you very well, like the other evening. You are unhappy too. If I listen I can almost hear a voice that says that to me. There is so much that I could say but I will not dwell on that, Martha. By coming to this desk I can kiss the places where your hands have been. What do you think it is that I am doing? Faithfully, Daniel G. Herr."

It was the reference to headaches that interested her. He was wrong; she seldom had them. Headaches must have been the version of her dreams that had reached him. Why couldn't a woman have headaches, or buy a radio, or attend summer school, without being suspected of needing a man? The "headaches" explained his attentions, she thought, exasperatedly blaming Trudie. Two years before, when they had been much closer, she had confided her annoying dreams to Trudie and she had never forgotten that paralyzed unexpected terror-stricken moment, a month and a half later, when Mr. Engle, the principal, casually inquired about her insomnia. Gertrude had blabbed to the whole school and in time even began reporting back the various interpretations that had been made. In her way Gertrude was thorough. Fortunately Mr. Levine, who had majored in abnormal psychology at Columbia and was the authority at James K. Polk, although now he was teaching geometry, had explained the flittering objects as children's heads and faces, and said that fear dreams by teachers of their students were common. It was as satisfactory an explanation as any, and Martha rather accepted it and hoped that her colleagues did too, but Mr. Levine might have suggested whatnot disgraceful interpretation, and Martha had never forgiven Trudie.

Had Trudie been blabbing round the little that she knew about George Fitts? She had never suspected it for the reason, principally, that there was nothing derogatory to tell. She and George had gone together for six years and after various stewings and fussings and telling him twenty times or more that she would not marry him and being told that she had to or he wouldn't go on seeing her, George abruptly stopped seeing her. That had been almost five years ago. When she thought of him now she remembered mostly the skinny hairy legs dashing round the squash racquet court. Possibly Gertrude had told what she knew and Mr. Herr had received a version but (she glanced at the letter again) it seemed more likely that he was, as he said, "imagining" this man that she had "loved." If Mr. Herr had made much of an effort, she thought scornfully, he could have discovered her views on marriage; they were no secret; she had stated them frequently. If a woman were on the plain side and frankly admitted as much, it wasn't likely that exactly the man she wanted would ever present himself, and she could either do without or accept a substitute. There it was in a nutshell. George would have been a substitute and she preferred to do without. The whole world, including Mr. Herr and the eighty-seven other teachers, male and female, at James K. Polk, could know that for the asking.

Martha thought of herself as an efficient quiet person, who knew her subject, maintained discipline, wore her clothes well, and kept her troubles, if she had any, to herself. Among the women over thirty-five at James K. Polk, she privately considered herself the most attractive. Certainly she had the best figure. Perhaps she should attribute Mr. Herr's attentions to her figure (she overlooked as a possible explanation her disposition to keep her troubles, and other people's, to herself). But why did she attract such a poor sort of man? Mr. Herr was wishy-washy, ineffectual, an obvious weakling. His entire letter breathed an unpleasant atmosphere of self-absorption and egotism. The one masculine thing about him was his handwriting. It was large and confident, each character developed to the last quirk. The signature was even bolder and more confident, almost a flourish. "You are unhappy too." Martha could see him admiring that as a master stroke. It was one of those generalizations such as fortune tellers use, or charlatan psychologists. Of course she was unhappy, like everyone else, no more and no less. She would have liked to reply: I have read your letter and am not in the least affected by it, except disagreeably.

Replying to the letter was out of the question. She was dealing with a potential crank or maniac, she reminded herself, and in Mr. Engle's office there was a lengthy file card, headed by her name and underneath a section, among others, called "Deportment," which was related to tenure, pension rights, and her future. A teacher in the public schools could not take risks like an ordinary person. Miss Hostetler was an example. The affair had been entirely innocent, Mr. Herr had written, and she was eight years his senior and had asked him to help her freshen up her German. Martha disliked him for putting the blame off on Miss Hostetler, and she reflected disdainfully that in these lonely-heart affairs, it was always six of one and half a dozen of the other, especially with a man like Herr. Seriously, with Herr daring to touch her and Gertrude becoming suspicious, the business had to stop. She had to speak to him, without being overheard and without permitting him to answer back and without leaving the slightest appearance of indiscretion, and speak conclusively.

By Monday morning Martha had worked out every detail, rehearsed every word. The school library was a long open room, parallel with assembly, seldom crowded, and she had an open period between ten and ten forty-five that she frequently spent there, and she had noticed that during the five minutes between bells at the end of the period Mr. Herr usually wandered restlessly through. At ten-forty Martha crossed to the big dictionary, which stood apart between the windows on a rotatable steel standard, and busying herself, covertly watched the doorway. Mr. Herr came in, questing nearsightedly, and finally encountering her standing alone between the windows, her eyes intently on him, he stopped. His hand went up uncertainly to the book that he was carrying under his arm. Martha beckoned imperiously. She did not allow him to utter a word.

"Pretend to be reading," she commanded, pointing at random at the open dictionary page. There was no one near and she leaned close to him. "Don't look up or show the slightest surprise. Now listen. I mean every word. I don't care anything about you, or your letters, or your personal difficulties. I want nothing to do with you. Absolutely nothing. I've had too much already. If you continue writing letters to me, or anything else, by so much as lifting a finger, I'm going straight to Mr. Engle. This is your warning. Don't forget it. Anything that happens after this will be strictly on your own head. Now don't you forget it."

Mr. Herr's bony knuckle and forefinger pointing meaninglessly on the dictionary page were trembling, and as she finished, instead of straightening, his breath rushed out in a sort of sobbing sigh. Martha, glancing swiftly round, would have liked to shake him. If she walked away, he would remain slumped there like a reprimanded schoolboy. Martha came still closer to him and examined the open page. "The word is oblique," she said, pointing to it, and then suddenly she put her hand over his and forced her thumbnail into his flesh. "Brace up." He straightened and lifting his hand which no longer was trembling stared at it. Martha, aghast at her act, had a further sickening rush of fear: he would carry his hand to his lips, and kiss it, openly there, because she had touched his hand. But he only stared at it (the imprint of her nail was distinct by the knuckle). Much perturbed, Martha walked away.

That noon Mr. Herr came into the cafeteria late again, but he walked past the three of them with his tray and stopped at the long table frequented by Mr. Levine and his coterie. There was so much discussion at the long table, clamoring and laughing, with Mr. Levine leading and Mr. Herr being questioned, and a paper could be seen passing from hand to hand, that Martha became apprehensive and Trudie glanced over her shoulder at every shriek from Miss Baron, unbearably curious. Finally Gertrude called and Miss Saugerties, wadding the note, tossed it over. It was scribbled on cheap ruled paper in a boy's hand. "Quit stalling! Girls give me a big pain! BE THERE. Thrills! Thrills!" the words were each twice underlined. It was the same note that Mr. Herr had shown them a week or two before. A girl in one of his classes had dropped it on his desk. "Why has he been carrying it all this time?" Lillian wondered. They were mystified by the hilarity at the long table. Mr. Herr, as quickly as he could, escaped, and when Trudie and Lillian went over, Martha followed.

"It's just an ordinary note," Gertrude complained, returning it to Miss Saugerties.

Mr. Levine, the cause of the storm, sprawled out, one arm embracing the chair back on his left, the other the chair back on his right, laughing and showing his strong teeth. "It's a love declaration," he insisted sarcastically. Miss Baron in the chair on his left, stimulated by proximity, shook his coat lapel and shrieked, "It is not." "He's been saying that all period," explained Miss Saugerties in the chair on his right, dragging her finger out of the grip that Mr. Levine, behind the cover of the chair back, had suddenly caught on it. "Can women live without love?" shrilled Mr. Delano from the far end of the table, climaxing his daring with a blat of laughter. The table was in stitches of nervous hilarity.

"He's been teasing Mr. Herr unmercifully," Miss Saugerties cried.

"Not a bit of it," shouted Mr. Levine. "I've been expounding psychology. Mr. Herr was merely the scientific occasion—"

"Shut up," Miss Baron shrieked, snatching at the handkerchief in his breast pocket. "We've done nothing but listen to you."

"Listen again then," said Mr. Levine, turning his back on the overstimulated Miss Baron. "I'll put it up to Miss Apfel. She understands these things."

"Not me," Gertrude objected, reddening. She did not like embittered Albert Levine who, disappointed at not becoming a psychiatrist, was not afraid to state publicly that he despised teachers and teaching at James K. Polk. He had pinched Gertrude and she had demanded an explanation. "Insolence," he answered. She was afraid of him.

"I put it up to Miss Apfel," Mr. Levine announced, silencing them. "Listen again. I'm serious. Our friend Herr said that his class was filing out when he heard the sound of a struggle and turning round he saw Virginia Agramonte standing in front of him." Virginia was large, hulking, stupid, and boy-crazy. "Three boys were struggling with her and grabbing at her hand. Virginia opened her hand, looking deep into Mr. Herr's eyes the while, and let fall the note. She fled. The three boys followed her." Mr. Levine paused and looked round him impatiently. "Have I recreated the scene? Do you get it? It was a love declaration. Don't laugh." Mr. Levine had been building on the incongruity between the robustious Virginia and Mr. Herr. "I'm serious." He frowned at their laughter. "The note shows that others consider Agramonte worthy of attention. She gives our Mr. Herr the note. It was to show our Mr. Herr that she was worthy of attention, his attention. Isn't it clear?" It was the impossibility of a woman's making advances to Mr. Herr that was clear. "Don't you think it was a love declaration, Miss Apfel?"

Gertrude had been laughing. She was unprepared. She reddened again.

"Psychology tells us," he admonished her, pursuing her embarrassment, "'that when you as a woman love you have to express that love. Direct expression is forbidden you by convention. What do you do if you are a woman? You express yourself symbolically. Like Agramonte—"

Martha slipped away. Mr. Levine respected her, she felt, and always let her alone. As for symbolic acts—Martha still remembered too sharply the complete vindictiveness with which she had dug her thumbnail into Mr. Herr to believe in symbolic nonsense. But she was ashamed to have laughed. She knew more, had adequate reason to pity him, and yet she had laughed like the rest. For the first time, while she reproved herself, she experienced compassion for him. If in his miserable pathetic way, Mr. Herr was actually in love with her and suffering (his hand had trembled) she understood and pitied the tortured sensitivity with which he had had to bear Mr. Levine's malice.

Late the next day, Tuesday afternoon after classes, Martha had been delayed, talking with Lillian in the teachers' room, and they agreed to meet for dinner and afterwards go to the movie at the State. Martha's text was not in her locker and she supposed that she had left it on the desk in her classroom. It was only at the door of 317D that it occurred to her, since it was late, that Mr. Herr might be inside writing to her (defying her warning), sitting at her desk and saturating himself, or whatever he did, in her chair, and she had a flash of premonitory anger that she could not walk into her own classroom after hours without being apprehensive. She braced herself to confront him, and opening the door resolutely, she started, but it was not Mr. Herr at the desk—it was only little ugly Désirée McCord, who suddenly began rumbling the pencil sharpener on the window sill.

"What are you doing in here, Désirée?" she inquired sharply. The girl's name was an irritating affectation, for Désirée was box-jawed and murky-skinned, with a colony of moles on her throat, but pretensions in names had to be respected by teachers. Désirée, in signing her papers, always included the two *accents aigus*.

"Sharpening a pencil," said Désirée, craning at Martha over her shoulder and cranking.

"I asked why you were doing it in here?"

"I'm waiting for Maria Kolodna."

Martha was brusquely suspicious. "You know the classrooms are not meeting places," she scolded. "You can't wait for Maria in here. Now get out, Désirée. I won't have this."

The girl, in going, wriggled unnecessarily and scraped the classroom chairs. Whenever she averted her face, she wrinkled and unwrinkled her nose in a sullen sniff. "Mr. Herr was looking for you," she said at the door, and fled.

Martha whirled, angered by the impertinence in the girl's tone, but Désirée had gone, and then at the meaning of the words there rose up in her a gasp, a stifling breathlessness, and a giddiness and rigidity like that of horror. On the desk when she looked, there was the textbook as she had remembered leaving it, but between the pages lay folded an unfamiliar sheet of white paper. "I cannot go on this way," was typewritten on the sheet, without address or signature. Martha understood it all in an instant. Mr. Herr had sneaked and slunk around in the hall outside 317D (she couldn't imagine that man handling or brazening a situation properly) until Désirée and Maria had been made suspicious. As soon as he tiptoed out, looking like a thief, Désirée, the more daring, had investigated, read the note, been surprised by Martha's return, jumped away from the desk, and started cranking the pencil sharpener. Martha's tears started, scalding with mortification, but first, before giving way, Martha locked the door, and then when she sat down and buried her hot face in her arms she was unable to cry. The sobbing would not come and she sat there in parched burning dry anger. There was bitterness, a rankling poignancy, in that he said that he loved her—she had almost come to believe it—and he had done this to her. No doubt he had sup-

posed that she would be the first to open the book but what right had
he to suppose that. The criminal carelessness, the stupidity of the man.
He would have to answer for this. If Désirée's suspicions had started, in
a week the whole school, including the teachers, would be squirming in
identical suspicions. She was being rushed headlong into embarrassment, scandal, and disaster. How had she been involved? She was innocent. Not even a civil word to him, scarcely that. And yet it was happening—the whispering and spying and covert laughter crowding
around her. They were being entangled together, and she did not want
it, and forbade it, and fought against it, and yet it was happening. Like
Miss Hostetler. She was being destroyed, her position and world toppling,
and for what, for what? Not Mr. Herr, whom she despised. There came
a surge of revolting fear and she was no longer the capable self-sufficient
Miss Flint. She was screamingly afraid of him (whatever else she did,
she had to get away from him, avoid him, never confront him) because
walking toward her or smiling or speaking she was afraid of him. She
was afraid of the excitement and unpredictability of his emotion. His
voice would break, his hand would tremble, and in her desperation
(gouging his hand to stop its trembling) she would have to say something, do something—she was afraid of what she would say and do.
She would be unable to control herself. There was something wrong
with her. Mr. Herr knew it. He recognized it in a queer psychotic way
(he was a weakling) and he was taking advantage of it. It was impossible to defend herself because there was something wrong with her.
Mr. Herr understood and she did not. She could be driven into horrible things. This was the beginning of horrible things. She closed her
eyes but immediately there was the dim reddish light, like that of a photographer's darkroom, and in it the peering jiggling batlike objects of
her dream, but this time they were shiny black and each distinct, like
eyes without cornea or iris, and the alive eyes lurked far back, darting
spasmodically among themselves, although by exerting all her force she
steadied them and almost stopped them in their places. But when they
had stopped the strain by which she held them exhausted her, and the
eyes revived and enlarged and came toward her in spiraling red-tinged
sickening pulsations. She opened her eyes (the pulsations disappeared)
but the surging of her fear mounted higher, then burst upon her in a
horror of helplessness and stultification, of inward withering and dying.

The authority, the power, by which she lived and dominated her classes was gone. "I have lost my strength," she thought in the penetrating rigidifying catalepsis of her horror. "I no longer have the power to face them. I am ended." Despairingly she saw the classroom, the late afternoon dusk in the two windows and the school chairs with broad mysterious encircling yellow arms. "I shall have to give this up," she thought with despairing force and insight. "I shall have to give up teaching and go away. I shall have to give everything up and go away before it is too late." And having reached this, the extreme of her conscious fears, her sobs broke and she began to cry.

By dinnertime she was more rational. She was immediately going to Mr. Engle. Mr. Herr had been warned; he had transgressed the warning; she had no alternative but to go to Mr. Engle. Otherwise the encroaching process would only resume, a longer note tomorrow, a letter on Thursday. Before leaving her apartment to meet Lillian, Martha tied up his letters in a packet, using unromantic kitchen string, preparatory to delivering them to Mr. Engle in the morning. She reassured herself by doubting whether Désirée's remark had the significance that she had first given it. Throughout dinner she had to resist telling Lillian, who was generally sensible and sympathetic, but Lillian and Gertrude lived together and everything that Lillian knew Gertrude eventually wormed out of her. At the movies she felt unaccountably dull and sluggish but that night she again had the dream, and after she had finally fallen asleep, she had another dream in which she was falling into a morass of black pitch. She felt Wednesday morning, she told herself, as if she had been dragged through the wringer. But the decision had been made. She was going to Mr. Engle and the sense of a decision irrevocably made cleared away the clouds of her foreboding. At school she promptly arranged with Mr. Engle's secretary for an appointment at the first available time, three o'clock.

At noon Mr. Herr did not come into the cafeteria and his unexplained absence set Martha to contemplating Mr. Engle's probable behavior. Mr. Engle was notoriously cautious and before acting he was addicted to what he called a thorough investigation, which included such subsidiary inquiries as the attitude of the Superintendent, the Board, the city machine, the possibility of religious or racial uproar, and the state of the promotions list. Martha wanted the matter settled that afternoon. She wanted the whole nightmarish business concluded. That required, she abruptly perceived (yesterday's dread of confronting him vanished) that Mr. Herr be spoken to in Mr. Engle's office in her presence that afternoon. She went directly to Mr. Herr's room, off the chemistry lab, and rapped sharply on the door. She did not have to arrange or rehearse the meeting as she had done that in the library. Mr. Herr was looking out the window.

"Have you a free period at three o'clock?"

Swinging round agitatedly, Mr. Herr said yes.

"Be at Mr. Engle's office at twenty minutes after three."

The closing of the door was as sharp as her rap. She had confronted him and escaped. It did not occur to her that Mr. Herr might not recognize her authority.

At five minutes after three, in a sharp constrained voice, her hands clasped on the packet of Mr. Herr's letters, Martha was relating the matter to Mr. Engle succinctly and clearly. Mr. Engle pressed his lips together and shook his head in constant silent disapproval as she proceeded. Mr. Engle had unruly gray hair, thickly tossed and ruffled above his right forehead, a florid complexion, and slouching heavy thickset shoulders. He listened with his hand raised, either shaking his head commiseratingly or stroking with his hand behind his ear, and the steely bow of his steel-rimmed glasses, disappearing behind the ear, made a white welt across the floridness of his flesh.

"You've done exactly right, Miss Flint," he assured her. He had a deep voice, hoarse and impaired, that whispered if he tried to raise it. He patted his neck when reflecting and lifted his head when he spoke. "You've made the matter very easy to deal with by coming to me in the early stages. I compliment you on your discretion."

Martha waited for him to continue. She expected condemnation of Mr. Herr. "These things are regrettable." He patted.

"What are you going to do?" she demanded.

"Miss Flint," he said hoarsely, "we want to protect you. We want you to feel protected. We don't want to have you molested again."

"I should hope not," Martha said sharply.

"But these things call for some thought, some thinking over, Miss Flint." He went on talking, but never denouncing Mr. Herr, and she suddenly realized that Mr. Engle considered her overwrought and that in his hoarse unmodulatable voice he was endeavoring to soothe her and that the reason for his infuriating evasiveness was simply that he was not ready to believe her. He thought she might be a lying trouble-making hysterical woman. She had never before been suspected of hysteria. It made her constrained and intense and lucid.

"I see that you have brought the letters with you," Mr. Engle said. "That's good. I want to look through them very carefully. Written proof is always excellent to have."

"You misunderstand me," Martha said coldly. "I am not here to ask that Mr. Herr be dismissed, or formally disciplined, or to submit proof. I want Mr. Herr to cease writing to me. That is all. I do not see that that calls for thinking over, or investigation, or proof. I want Mr. Herr called in and in my presence ordered to stop writing these letters. Surely, that is very simple, Mr. Engle."

"Possibly, possibly," he agreed. "Ah. Ah. Coming back to these letters. Of course, naturally you have read them. What's eating the man, Miss Flint? Does he say? Or wait. Tell me first, plainly, are there any—any improper passages—objectionable—disgusting, that is?"

"Did I make that complaint?"

"But you might—out of modesty—"

"I've told you the entire story, Mr. Engle."

"Domestic difficulties? Is that it?"

"I said they were love letters."

Mr. Engle stared. He found this description singularly unenlighten-ing. "I shall have to read them myself," he decided finally. "I should want to do that in any case."

"I see no need for you to read them. They were written to me in con-fidence."

"Miss Flint—"

"I'm complaining because the letters were written. It isn't what's in them. It's the fact that they were written at all. Can't you understand that, Mr. Engle?"

There was a pause, during which Mr. Engle scowled, and the note of expostulation having dried his throat, he swallowed several times. "You're being inconsistent," he charged. "You appeal to me and then you won't co-operate."

"I want you to have Mr. Herr in here. If there is any doubt in your mind as to the truth of my story, question him. He will admit every bit of it."

"What makes you so sure?"

"I am sure. He'll admit it."

"Well," said Mr. Engle, turning away. "You may be sure but I'm not. I can take no action unless you allow me to read these letters. I will not be led into a business like this blindfold. That's final, Miss Flint."

In the slouching of his body, the relaxing of his heavy chin, there was ponderous and bureaucratic finality. She might equally well have attempted to pick him up and carry him away on her shoulders, but knowing, Martha persisted. She disputed hotly. Mr. Engle was reiterating for the twentieth time that she was inconsistent when his telephone rang. "What is he doing here?" Mr. Engle inquired hoarsely into the telephone.

"I asked him to come," Martha said quickly.

Mr. Engle put down the telephone with a vicious wrench and strode to the door. "Come in, Herr." As soon as the door had closed, "Do you know what this is all about? You've got Miss Flint very excited— alarmed. She's the one that sent for you, understand. I didn't." Mr. Engle returned to his chair. "Come away from the door, man," he commanded irritably.

Martha had risen, tightly holding the packet of letters tied with kitchen string. She struggled through a dense implacable moment.

"Mr. Herr, is it true that for the past five or six weeks you have been writing to me?"

Mr. Herr stood inside the door, stooped and deferential, looked about him like a nearsighted person who has lost his glasses, although he was wearing them, and put his hand uncertainly to the edge of his coat. Before replying he left the door. As he walked across the room toward her, the dread returned: he was going to do something silly, romantic, or embarrassing, like seizing her hand and then she would—but he stopped and only laid his bony knuckles on the desk edge opposite and stared at her apprehensively. "Yes," he said.

"Did I ever ask you to write to me?"

"No."

"What kind of letters were they?"

Mr. Herr's lips, the puffy upper one from the lower, parted, teeth gaped in his open mouth, and he stared at her resistingly. She had the letters clasped against her breast. "You have surely read them," he remonstrated, vaguely complaining, pleading, and shrinking too.

"Say it," Martha commanded imperiously. "Go on and say what they were."

"They were love letters."

"There, you see," Martha cried, wheeling to Mr. Engle. "You see." She was vindicated. She was exultant. She was reckless. He admitted that he loved her. "I told you he would admit it. You see." Mr. Engle principally saw a dangerously overwrought woman. "Sit down, both of you, please," he commanded hoarsely.

"One more question," Martha cried. "Why did you write to me? Why, out of all the women here—why out of all did you pick on me?" The furtive withdrawal of Mr. Herr's eyes disconcerted her. "Why did you pick on me—to annoy?"

Instead of answering her straightforwardly, instead of meeting her eyes as he had done, Mr. Herr in obedience to Mr. Engle had put out his hand behind him for the chair and was sitting down. He did not answer or look up again.

"Sit down, Miss Flint. Please."

"Why?" Martha insisted passionately, but she sat down.

"Never mind why," put in Mr. Engle, who had a politician's intuition and who was becoming suspicious of Miss Flint's discretion. "Never mind the whys and wherefores. Listen to me, Herr. I can't tell you how surprised and shocked I was when Miss Flint brought this tale to me. Could hardly believe it in fact. Didn't believe it in fact. You can ask Miss Flint. You know you can't do this sort of thing and get away with it. I don't have to read you a lecture. Miss Flint is preserving your letters and if this ever recurs she will bring them to me and I'll start disciplinary proceedings. Miss Flint has been remarkably decent about this. She only wants me to give you a warning this time. I am warning you. Do you understand, Herr?"

Mr. Herr, without looking up, nodded.

"At your age this sort of thing is childish. You've a good record and you're risking everything, pension, future, good name. You've got a wife and children, man. You can't pursue whims, you know. An infatuation like this. In the circumstances it's ridiculous, nothing but ridiculous."

Mr. Herr nodded.

It is not ridiculous, Martha retorted silently.

"The next time that you sit down to write a letter to Miss Flint just remember that you're writing the letter to me. Because that's where the letter is going. Understand?"

Mr. Herr nodded again.

His record is not good, she thought. There's Miss Hostetler.

"What's eating you, anyway? What makes you do things like this? Is there trouble at home? Aren't you happy?"

Mr. Herr's head and high stooped shoulders bowed lower in the chair and noticing the occasional spasmodic twitching of the reddish-brown mustache and the working of his mouth, she foresaw that he was going to lean forward, under Mr. Engle's urging, his head in his arms, and sob out the whole miserable story of Mrs. Herr and the unemployed musician, sob it out unnecessarily and humiliatingly, and to Mr. Engle's avid satisfaction.

"Are you in trouble, man?"

She forbade him to answer. His unhappiness was a secret that he had confided to her. She had protected and defended it and if he broke down now and weakly blurted it out, she would forever despise him. She stared anxiously at Mr. Herr, sunken in his chair, and concentrated her force and forbade him to speak of his unhappiness. She forbade him to complain against his wife. Certain things are inviolable, Martha thought tensely, formulating the words with which Mr. Herr should reply.

Mr. Herr answered dejectedly. "I don't know," he said in a low voice. "I guess I'm a fool."

You're not a fool, Martha contradicted angrily. Don't humiliate yourself by saying that. But she did not have to despise him.

"Why not talk about it, man. Miss Flint would like to know too."

Mr. Herr shook his head, stubbornly Martha thought.

"You haven't anything more to say to him, have you, Miss Flint?"

"Yes I have," Martha said rising, the letters still in her hand, while Mr. Engle vigorously frowned at her. "Why did he pick on me?"

"Because I'm a fool," Mr. Herr said bitterly, not lifting his head. "Because I thought you would understand."

"All right," put in Mr. Engle hurriedly. "All right. You sit where you are, Herr," although Mr. Herr had not stirred. "I don't want you following Miss Flint into the halls." Mr. Engle rose. "And you, Miss Flint. This matter has serious possibilities. If he should write to you again, or do anything else, I don't want you to exercise the slightest discretion. Come to me immediately and with everything. Don't even open his letters. That's a command. You hear that, Herr?"

Martha resented the command. Like Mr. Herr, she nodded. She walked out of the office resentful and depressed.

The next morning Martha opened her eyes wide on the familiar gray half-past-seven daylight. It was Thursday morning and she had not had the dream. She turned, snuggling on her arm, to enjoy for a moment longer the brisk awakening joyousness. How swiftly the night had passed, as if blown away by a breath, and Martha amused herself by huffing away the night three times, and decided that she was going to walk to school this morning instead of the bus. Under the shower, hurrying, she had a sudden startled premonition, and she hurried through breakfast, rushing so that she would have the twenty minutes to walk and rushing too, she knew, because of a new reckless insurgent expectation, a preposterous notion, a dread. He had known. If he had the prescience of a true lover he had known and would write to her again. There was even pleasure in delaying, in slowly pulling on gloves, glancing the unnecessary second time in the mirror, and riding down on the automatic elevator. Through the star-shaped perforations, there it was (it did not surprise her), a stiff white envelope, and a complete confirmation of the infallibility of premonition. Martha opened the box, read the writing, scrutinized the postmark. The letter had been stamped at nine o'clock the previous evening. The sending was deliberate. And then suddenly, staring at that bold masculine handwriting, it became surprising; it became the most surprising thing that had ever happened, this letter that he had written and that she was not going to carry to Mr. Engle; it became portentous and unbetrayable and defiant. She remembered that she had been rushing: that she had an extra twenty minutes. In the apartment she read it a second time and a third and at the last possible minute, hastily putting the letter away to read that night undisturbed, Miss Martha Flint (not thinking of Miss Hostetler) caught the bus for James K. Polk.*

INTERPRETATION

"Love and James K. Polk," like the other stories in this section, raises special problems of character. But in most of the stories in this section the character of the hero or heroine does not seem to undergo a basic change. To take a simple instance, in "The Poor Relation's Story" the main character simply tells a story which defines his own fundamental attitude toward life. The attitude itself has, presumably, been in existence for a long time. In "Old Red" the hero comes to an understanding of himself and his situation—of his relationship to other people—but the situation itself is not new. It simply becomes sharpened under the circumstances of the story. In "The Lament" there is the same process of gradual revelation of the character's condition and a growing realization on the part of the character, but again the revelation progresses in a "straight line" to the scene in the stables. In the present story, on the other hand, the character undergoes an apparent reversal of attitude; the progression of revelation is not in a straight line, but takes a sharp and surprising turn at the very end. That is, Miss Flint, who has dreaded the appearance of the letter in the first scene of the story, and who has taken drastic steps to prevent Mr. Herr from writing to her again, has come, in the last scene of the story, to welcome the letter, which she will read, against the principal's orders, and will not turn over to him. This story, then, involves a rather marked development, a change, in character. The basic questions to be asked with regard to this story center around this development of character. Is the development, however surprising it may seem at the end, convincing to the reader? Has it been logically prepared for? In other words, is Martha Flint, in the surprising last scene of the story, the same Martha Flint with whom we have become acquainted earlier? The following specific questions present themselves:

1. What part does Mr. Engle's attitude have in bringing about the change on the part of Miss Flint?
2. What part does Mr. Herr's attitude in the scene in the principal's office have in bringing about the change on the part of Miss Flint?

* Copyright, 1939, *The Southern Review;* reprinted by permission of the author.

3. What does Miss Flint mean when, concerning Mr. Herr, she thinks: "If he had the prescience of a true lover he had known and would write to her again."

4. What importance in determining Miss Flint's final attitude do such characters as Trudie, Mr. Levine, Désirée, and Lillian have?

SECTION IV

What Theme Reveals

IN THE stories of the preceding sections, the matter of theme has come up again and again in connection with our interpretations of the handling of plot or the handling of character. It is not enough to say of a story merely that it presents a coherent account of action, or, approaching it from another standpoint, that it gives us a valid account of a human being's mind and personality. Fiction is more than reporting, as we have seen; and it presents more than mere case histories such as might come from a psychologist's notebook. The good story has a meaning—it says something—it has significance. Bret Harte is trying to tell us, we say, that human virtue is to be found in the most unlikely places and under the most unpromising conditions. Or, we say that the theme of Pirandello's "War" is that the fact of death and loss breaks through all of man's attempts to rationalize and compensate for it.

This is true. But we are not to conclude, of course, that a "good" theme insures a good story, or that we can enjoy only those stories in whose themes we have a partisan's interest. We are not even to conclude that a good story expresses its theme in the most emphatic and most unequivocal terms possible; for, if this were true, the best story would be the story which took its theme for a text, reduced the "story" to the simplest and thinnest illustration possible, and then relentlessly pounded home the moral.

But we go to literature for something more than a collection of moralizations on life, and the relation of a piece of fiction to its theme is a complicated one. It is on this latter point that it is easiest to go astray. The most tempting account of the relation of the story to its theme is that which explains the story as merely an *illustration* of the theme: accordingly the story gives a concrete instance of the generalization, and furthermore, it recommends the abstract generalization to us by clothing it in emotional terms. The danger of this account is twofold: it overemphasizes the didactic element in fiction and thus distorts the writer's intention; more important still, it neglects the fact that the organization of the story, if it is valid, does much more than illustrate—it qualifies and modifies the theme. The form of the story states the theme so precisely that for an *exact* statement of it we must turn to the whole body of the story itself. The brief, condensed statements of the "theme" which we use may serve well enough as a sort of shorthand account of a quite complicated matter. But they are not equivalent to the story itself, and they are not equivalent, *even in terms of statement.* If we want to know precisely what "The Man Who Would Be King" says, we must read the story. Anything less is merely a reduced paraphrase.

It is for this reason that an examination of the stories that follow with special attention to theme is not to be thought of as an exercise in moral-hunting. The stories included in this section range from some which state their themes almost as simply as does a parable to others in which the theme may appear to be hidden—almost perversely buried —within the dramatization of the story. The student, in studying these stories, must not be content to arrive at what he feels to be the theme of the story in question: it is fully as important for him to ask himself why the author has chosen his particular way of stating his theme.

Christ in Flanders
HONORÉ DE BALZAC

AT A TIME somewhat indeterminate in Brabantine history, connection between the island of Cadzant and the coast of Flanders was kept up by a boat used for passengers to and fro. The capital of the island, Middleburg, afterward so celebrated in the annals of Protestantism, counted then hardly two or three hundred hearths. Rich Ostend was then an unknown harbor, flanked by a village thinly peopled by a few fisherfolk, and poor dealers, and pirates who plied their trade with impunity. Nevertheless, the borough of Ostend, composed of about twenty houses and three hundred cottages, cabins, and hovels—made with the remains of wrecked ships—rejoiced in a governor, a militia, a gallows, a convent, and a burgomaster, in fact, all the institutions of advanced civilization. Who was reigning at that time in Brabant, Belgium, and Flanders? On this point tradition is mute.

Let us admit that this story is strangely imbued with that vagueness, indefiniteness, and love of the marvelous which the favorite orators of Flemish vigils love to intermingle in their legends, as varied in poetry as they are contradictory in detail. Told from age to age, repeated from hearth to hearth, by grandmothers and by storytellers night and day, this chronicle has received each century a different coloring. Like those buildings planned according to the architectural caprice of each epoch, whose dark, crumbling masses are a pleasure to poets alone, this legend would drive commentators, and wranglers over facts, words, and dates, to desperation. The narrator believes in it, as all superstitious souls in Flanders have believed in it, without being for that reason either more learned or more weak-minded. Admitting the impossibility of harmonizing all the different versions, here is the story, stripped perhaps of its romantic naïveté—for this it is impossible to reproduce—but still, with its daring statements disproved by history, and its morality approved by religion, its fantastic flowers of imagination, and hidden sense which the wise can interpret each to his own liking. Let each one seek his pasture herein and take the trouble to separate the good grain from the tares.

The boat which served to carry over the passengers from the island of Cadzant to Ostend was just about to leave the village. Before undoing the iron chain which held his boat to a stone on the little jetty where people embarked, the skipper blew his horn several times to call the loiterers, for this journey was his last. Night was coming on, the last fires of the setting sun scarcely gave enough light to distinguish the coast of Flanders or the tardy passengers on the island wandering along the earthen walls which surrounded the fields or among the tall reeds of the marshes. The boat was full. "What are you waiting for? Let us be off!" they cried. Just then a man appeared a few steps from the jetty. The pilot, who had neither heard nor seen him approaching, was somewhat surprised. The passenger seemed to have risen from the earth on a sudden. He might have been a peasant sleeping in a field, waiting for the hour for starting, whom the horn had wakened up. Was it a thief, or was it someone from the Customs House or police? When he arrived on the jetty to which the boat was moored, seven persons who were standing in the stern hastened to sit down on the benches, in order to have them to themselves and prevent the stranger from seating himself among them. It was a sudden instinctive feeling, one of those aristocratic instincts which suggest themselves to rich people. Four of these personages belonged to the highest nobility of Flanders.

First of all, there was a young cavalier, with two beautiful greyhounds, wearing over his long hair a cap decked with jewels. He clinked his gilded spurs, and now and again curled his mustache, as he cast disdainful looks at the rest of the freight.

Then there was a proud damosel, who carried a falcon on her wrist and spoke only to her mother or to an ecclesiastic of high rank, a relative, no doubt. These persons made as much noise talking together as if they were the only people on the boat. All the same, next to them sat a man of great importance in the country, a fat merchant from Bruges, enveloped in a large mantle. His servant, armed to the teeth, kept by his side two bags full of money. Beside them was a man of science, a doctor of the University of Louvain, with his clerk. These people, who all despised one another, were separated from the bows by the rower's bench.

When the late passenger put his foot into the boat he gave a swift look at the stern, but when he saw no room there he went to seek a place among the people in the bows. It was the poor who sat there. At the sight of a man bareheaded, whose brown cloth coat and fine linen shirt had no ornament, who held in his hand neither hat nor cap, with neither purse nor rapier at his girdle, all took him for a burgomaster— a good and gentle man, like one of those old Flemings whose nature and simple character have been so well rendered by the painters of their country. The poor passengers welcomed the stranger with a respectful demeanor, which excited mocking whispers among the people in the stern. An old soldier, a man of toil and trouble, gave him his place on the bench, and sat himself at the end of the boat, keeping himself steady by putting his feet against one of the transverse beams which knit the planks together like the backbone of a fish.

A young woman, a mother with her little child, who seemed to belong to the working class of Ostend, moved back to make room for the newcomer. In this movement there was no trace either of servility or disdain. It was merely a mark of that kindliness by which the poor, who know so well how to appreciate a service, show their frank and natural disposition—so simple and obvious in the expression of all their qualities, good or bad.

The stranger thanked them with a gesture full of nobility, and sat down between the young mother and the old soldier. Behind him was a peasant with his son, ten years old. A poor old woman, with a wallet almost empty, old and wrinkled, and in rags—a type of misery and neglect—lay in the prow, crouched upon a coil of ropes. One of the rowers, an old sailor, who had known her when she was rich and beautiful, had let her get in for what the people so beautifully call "the love of God." "Thank you kindly, Thomas," the old woman had said; "I will say two *Paters* and two *Aves* for you in my prayers this evening."

The skipper blew his horn once more, looked at the silent country, cast the chain into his boat, ran along the side to the helm, took the tiller, and stood erect; then, having looked at the sky, called out in a loud voice to the rowers, when they were well in the open sea, "Row hard, make haste; the sea smiles evilly—the witch! I feel the swell at the helm and the storm at my wound." These words, spoken in the language of the sea—a tongue only understood of those accustomed to the sound of the waves—gave to the oars a hastened but ever-cadenced movement, as different from the former manner of rowing as the gallop of a horse from its trot. The fine people sitting at the stern took pleasure in seeing the sinuous arms, the bronzed faces with eyes of fire, the distended muscles, and the different human forms working in unison, just to get *them* the quicker over this narrow strait. So far from being sorry for their labor, they pointed out the rowers to each other, and laughed at the grotesque expressions which their exertion printed on their anxious faces. In the prow the soldier, the peasant, and the old woman regarded the mariners with that kind of compassion natural to people who, living by toil, know its hard anguish and feverish fatigue. Besides, being accustomed to life in the open air, they all divined by the look of the sky the danger which threatened them; so *they* were serious. The young mother was rocking her child to sleep, singing to it some old hymn of the church.

"If we *do* get over," said the old soldier to the peasant, "God will have taken a deal of trouble to keep us alive."

"Ah! He is master," said the old woman; "but I think it is His good pleasure to call us to Himself. Do you see that light, there?" and by a gesture of the head she pointed out the setting sun. Bands of fire streaked vividly the brown-red tinted clouds, which seemed just about to unchain a furious wind. The sea gave forth a suppressed murmur, a sort of internal groan, something like the growling of a dog whose anger will not be appeased.

After all Ostend was not far off. Just now the sky and the sea showed one of those sights to which it is impossible for words or painting to give longer duration than they have in reality. Human creations like powerful contrasts, so artists generally demand from nature its most brilliant aspects, despairing perhaps to be able to render the great and beautiful poetry of her ordinary appearance, although the human soul is often as profoundly moved by calm as by motion, by the silence as much as by the storm.

There was one moment when everyone on the boat was silent and gazed on the sea and sky, whether from presentiment or in obedience to that religious melancholy which comes over nearly all of us at the hour of prayer, at the fall of day, at the moment when nature is silent and the bells speak. The sea cast up a faint, white glimmer, but changing like the color of steel; the sky was mostly gray; in the west, long, narrow spaces looked like waves of blood, whereas in the east, glittering lines, marked as by a fine pencil, were separated from one another by clouds, folded like the wrinkles on an old man's forehead. Thus the sea and the sky formed a neutral background, everything in half tints, which made the fires of the setting sun glare ominously. The face of nature inspired a feeling of terror. If it is allowable to interweave the daring hyperboles of the people into the written language, one might repeat what the soldier said, "Time is rolling away," or what the peasant answered, that the sky had the look of a hangman. All of a sudden the wind rose in the west, and the skipper, who never ceased to watch the sea, seeing it swell toward the horizon, cried, "Ho, ho!" At this cry the sailors stopped immediately, and let their oars float.

"The skipper is right," said Thomas. The boat, borne on the top of a huge wave, seemed to be descending to the bottom of the gaping sea. At this extraordinary movement and this sudden rage of the ocean the people in the stern turned pale, and gave a terrible cry, "We perish!"

"Not yet," answered the skipper quietly. At this moment the clouds were rent in twain by the force of the wind exactly above the boat. The gray masses spread out with ominous quickness from east to west, and the twilight, falling straight down through a rent made by the storm wind, rendered visible every face. The passengers, the rich and the noble, the sailors and the poor, all stopped one moment in astonishment at the aspect of the last comer. His golden hair, parted in the middle on his tranquil, serene forehead, fell in many curls on his shoulders, and outlined against the gray sky a face sublime in its gentleness, radiant with divine love. He did not despise death; he was certain not to perish. But if at first the people at the stern had forgotten for an instant the tempest whose implacable fury menaced them, they soon returned to their selfish sentiments and lifelong habits.

"It's lucky for him, that dolt of a burgomaster, that he does not know the danger we are all in. There he stands like a dog, and doesn't seem to mind dying," said the doctor.

Hardly had he completed this judicious remark when the tempest unchained its legions; wind blew from every side, the boat spun round like a top, and the sea swamped it.

"Oh, my poor child! my child! who will save my child?" cried the mother, in a heartrending voice.

"You yourself," replied the stranger. The sound of this voice penetrated the heart of the young woman and put hope therein. She heard this sweet word, in spite of the raging of the storm, in spite of the shrieks of the passengers.

"Holy Virgin of Perpetual Succor, who art at Antwerp, I promise you twenty pounds of wax and a statue if you will only get me out of this," cried the merchant, falling on his knees upon his bags of gold.

"The Virgin is no more at Antwerp than she is here," replied the doctor.

"She is in heaven," said a voice, which seemed to come forth from the sea.

"Who spoke?"

"The devil," said the servant; "he's mocking the Virgin of Antwerp."

"Shut up with your blessed Virgin," said the skipper to the passengers; "take hold of the bowls and help me get the water out of the boat. As to you," he continued, addressing the sailors, "row hard, we have a moment's grace, and in the devil's name, who has left you in this world until now, let us be our own Providence. This little strip of water is horribly dangerous, I know from thirty years' experience. Is this evening the first time I have had a storm to deal with?" Then standing at the helm, the skipper continued to look alternately at the boat, the sea, and the sky.

"The skipper mocks at everything," said Thomas in a low voice.

"Will God let *us* die with these wretched people?" asked the proud damosel of the handsome cavalier.

"No! no! Noble damsel, listen to me." He put his arm round her waist, and spoke in her ear. "I can swim—don't say anything about it; I will take you by your beautiful hair and bring you safely to the shore; but I can save you only."

The damosel looked at her old mother; the dame was on her knees asking absolution from the bishop, who was not listening to her. The cavalier read in the eyes of his beautiful mistress some faint sentiment of filial piety, so he said to her in a low voice, "Submit yourself to the will of God; if He wishes to call your mother to Himself, it will doubtless be for her happiness—in the other world," he added, in a voice still lower, "and for ours in this."

The dame Rupelmonde possessed seven fiefs, besides the barony of Gâvres. The damosel listened to the voice of life, to the interests of love, speaking through the mouth of the handsome adventurer, a young miscreant, who haunted churches, seeking for prey—either a girl to marry or else good ready money.

The bishop blessed the waves and ordered them to be calm, not knowing exactly what to do; he was thinking of his concubine awaiting him with a delicate feast, perhaps at this moment in her bath perfuming herself, or arraying herself in velvet, and fastening on her necklaces and jewels. So far from thinking of the powers of the Church, and consoling these Christians, and exhorting them to trust in God, the perverse bishop mingled worldly regrets and words of lust with the sacred words of the Breviary.

The light, which lit up the pale faces, showed all their varying expressions, when the boat was borne up into the air by a wave, or cast down to the bottom of the abyss; then, shaken like a frail leaf, a plaything of the autumn wind, it cracked its shell, and seemed nigh to break altogether. Then there were horrible cries alternating with awful silence.

The demeanor of the people seated in the prow of the boat contrasted singularly with that of the rich and powerful in the stern. The young mother strained her child to her bosom every time that the waves threatened to engulf the frail bark; but she held to the hope with which the words of the stranger had filled her heart: each time she turned her eyes toward this man she drank in from his face a new faith, the strong faith of a weak woman, the faith of a mother. Living by the divine word, the word of love, which had gone forth from this man, the simple creature awaited trustfully the fulfillment of the sort of promise he had given her, and scarcely feared the tempest any more. Sticking to the side of the boat, the soldier ceased not to contemplate this singular being, on whose impassibility he sought to model his own rough, tanned face, bringing into play all his intelligence and strength of will, whose powerful springs had not been vitiated in the course of a passive mechanical life. He was emulous to show himself tranquil and calm, after the manner of this superior courage; he ended by identifying himself in some measure with the secret principle of its interior power. Then his imagination became an instinctive fanaticism, a love without limit, a faith in this man, like that enthusiasm which soldiers have for their commander when he is a man of power, surrounded with the glory of victories, marching in the midst of the splendid prestige of genius. The poor old woman said in a low voice, "Ah! what a miserable sinner I am! Have I not suffered enough to expiate the pleasures of my youth? Miserable one, why hast thou led the gay life of a Frenchwoman? Why hast thou consumed the goods of God with the people of the Church, the goods of the poor 'twixt the drink shop and the pawn shop? Ah! how wicked I was! Oh! my God! my God! let me finish my hell in this world of misery. Holy Virgin, Mother of God, take pity on me."

"Console yourself, mother, God is not a Lombard; although I have killed here and there good people and wicked, I do not fear for the resurrection."

"Ah! Sir, how happy they are, those beautiful ladies who are near the bishop, holy man!" the old woman went on; "they will have absolution from their sins. Oh! if I could only hear the voice of a priest saying to me, 'Your sins are forgiven you,' I could believe him."

The stranger turned toward her, and his look, full of charity, made her tremble. "Have faith," he said, "and you will be saved."

"May God reward you, good sir," she answered. "If you speak truly, I will go for you and for me on a pilgrimage to Our Lady of Loretto, barefooted."

The two peasants, father and son, remained silent, resigned, and submitting to the will of God, as people accustomed to follow instinctively, like animals, the convulsions of nature.

So on one side there were riches, pride, knowledge, debauchery, crime, all human society such as it is made by arts, thought, and education, the world and its laws; but also on this side, only shrieks, terror, the struggles of a thousand conflicting feelings, with horrible doubt —naught but the anguish of fear. And, towering above these, one powerful man, the skipper of the boat, doubting nothing, the chief, the fatalist king, making his own Providence, crying out for bailing bowls and not on the Virgin to save him, defying the storm, and wrestling with the sea, body to body.

At the other end of the boat, the weak: The mother, holding to her bosom a little child, who smiled at the storm. A wanton once gay, now given over to horrible remorse. A soldier, scarred with wounds, without other reward than his mutilated life, as a price for indefatigable devotion—he had hardly a morsel of bread, steeped in tears; all the same, he laughed at everything, and marched on without care, happy when he could drown his glory at the bottom of a pot of beer, or was telling stories thereof to wondering children; he commended gaily to God the care of his future. Lastly, two peasants, people of toil and weariness, labor incarnate, the work on which the world lives; these simple creatures were guileless of thought and its treasures, but ready to lose themselves utterly in a belief; having a more robust faith, in that they had never discussed or analyzed it; virgin natures, in whom conscience had remained pure and feeling strong. Contrition, misery, love, work had exercised, purified, concentrated, disculpated their will, the only thing which in man resembles that which sages call the soul.

When the boat, piloted by the marvelous dexterity of the skipper,

came almost in view of Ostend, fifty paces from the shore, it was
driven back by the convulsion of the storm, and suddenly began to
sink. The stranger with the light upon his face then said to this little
world of sorrow, "Those who have faith shall be saved; let them follow
me." This man stood up and walked with a firm step on the waves. At
once the young mother¹ took her child² in her arms and walked with
him on the sea. The soldier³ suddenly stood at attention, saying in his
rough language, "By my pipe! I follow you to the devil." Then, without seeming astonished, he marched on the sea.

The old prostitute,⁴ believing in the omnipotence of God, followed
the man, and walked on the sea. The two⁵⁻⁶ peasants said, "As they are
walking on the sea, why should not *we?*" So they got up and hastened
after the others, walking on the sea.

Thomas wished to do likewise; but his faith wavered, and he fell
several times into the sea, but got out again; and after three failures
he too walked upon the sea.

The daring pilot stuck like a leech to the bottom of his boat. The
merchant had faith, and had risen, but he wanted to take his gold with
him, and his gold took him to the bottom of the sea. Mocking at the
charlatan and the imbeciles who listened to him, at the moment when
he saw the stranger proposing to the passengers to walk on the sea, the
man of science began to laugh, and was swallowed up in the ocean.
The damosel was drawn down into the abyss by her lover. The bishop
and the old lady went to the bottom, heavy with sin perhaps, heavier
still with unbelief and confidence in false images; heavy with devotional practices, light of alms and true religion.

The faithful troop, who trod with firm, dry feet on the plain of
the raging waters, heard around them the horrible howling of the
storm; great sheets of water broke in their path; irresistible force rent
the ocean in twain. Through the mist these faithful ones perceived
on the shore a little feeble light, which flickered in the window of a
fisherman's cabin. Each one as he marched bravely toward this light
seemed to hear his neighbor crying through the roaring sea, "Courage!" Nevertheless, absorbed each in his own danger, no one said a
single word. And so they reached the shore. When they were all seated
at the hearth of the fisherman, they sought in vain the guide who had
a light upon his face. From his seat upon the summit of a rock, at the

base of which the hurricane had cast the pilot clinging to his plank with all the strength of a sailor in the throes of death, the MAN descended, picked up the shipwrecked man almost dashed to pieces; then he said, as he held out a helping hand over his head, "It is well this once, but do as thou *hast* done no more; the example would be too bad." He took the mariner on his shoulders, and carried him to the fisherman's cottage. He knocked for the unfortunate man, so that someone would open the door of this humble refuge to him; then the Savior disappeared.

In this place the sailors built the Convent of Mercy, where were long to be seen the prints that the feet of JESUS CHRIST had, it was said, left on the sand.

Afterward, when the French entered Belgium, some monks took away with them this precious relic, the testimony of the last visit JESUS ever paid to the earth.

INTERPRETATION

In previous sections, we have already read stories which illustrate a variety of ways in which fiction may embody its idea, or theme. The present story shows one of the simplest of all methods. It is a method similar to that found in fables and parables. In a parable, for instance, the idea, or truth, is presented by a simple narrative in which the events, persons, and the like, of the narrative are understood as being directly equivalent to elements involved in the statement of the truth. For example, let us look at the parable of the sower, in the Gospel according to Saint Mark:

Hearken; Behold, there went out a sower to sow:
And it came to pass, as he sowed, some fell by the way side, and the fowls of the air came and devoured it up.
And some fell on stony ground, where it had not much earth; and immediately it sprang up, because it had no depth of earth:
But when the sun was up, it was scorched; and because it had no root, it withered away.
And some fell among thorns, and the thorns grew up, and choked it, and it yielded no fruit.
And other fell on good ground, and did yield fruit that sprang up and increased; and brought forth, some thirty, and some sixty, and some an hundred.

Later, Jesus explains and interprets the parable to his disciples:

The sower soweth the word.

And these are they by the way side, where the word is sown; but when they have heard, Satan cometh immediately, and taketh away the word that was sown in their hearts.

And these are they likewise which are sown on stony ground; who, when they have heard the word, immediately receive it with gladness;

And have no root in themselves, and so endure but for a time: afterward, when affliction or persecution ariseth for the word's sake, immediately they are offended.

And these are they which are sown among thorns; such as hear the word,

And the cares of this world, and the deceitfulness of riches, and the lusts of other things entering in, choke the word, and it becometh unfruitful.

And these are they which are sown on good ground; such as hear the word, and receive it, and bring forth fruit, some thirtyfold, some sixty, and some an hundred.

In the parable itself, we observe, no more is presented than is absolutely required to illustrate the idea. The sower is *any* sower; strictly speaking, he has no character, for he exhausts his function in the parable merely in the act of scattering the seed. *Setting* (see Glossary) is reduced to a minimum; simply the stony ground, the thorny ground, and the good ground are specified. The events are summarized as economically as possible. Actually, the parable is a kind of metaphor, or image, of a basic truth which in reality may assume many forms. For example, the "affliction or persecution" which "ariseth for the word's sake" might assume many forms, and the reaction of the person whose heart, like the stony ground, could give no deep root to the seed, might take many different forms. Ordinarily, fiction is concerned with these specific, individual forms—character, event, experience—and does not content itself with presenting merely the basic image as detached from the details of the particular instance. The story of a man whose heart was like stony ground and whose faith withered under the scorching sun of persecution would be presented as the story of a particular man, living in a particular place and time. The psychological stages in the struggle between faith and persecution would be indicated.

But despite the fact that ordinary fiction, as contrasted with parable or fable, is intensely concerned with specific persons and the circumstantiality of experience, all fiction implies a meaningfulness beyond the particular instances which it presents. The meanings involved in characters and events can be extended to apply to other characters and events. The problems and issues and decisions involved in a particular piece of fiction are not limited to that situation and those persons. For example, in "War," by Pirandello, the conflict between the attitude of the fat woman and that of the old man does not appear, in life, merely in the case of persons whose sons are in an army. It appears in all cases of grief and bereavement. And the pathetic isolation of the cabdriver in "The Lament" can be observed in all sorts and conditions of people.

But the way in which fiction embodies its meaning will vary from story to story. Some stories, like "The Birthmark," will approach the method of the parable, in that only the aspect of the characters and events which is directly involved in the meaning will be presented; there will not be, in such cases, much circumstantiality, for the character, or event, tends to "stand for something," for an idea, rather than to be fully developed as an individual person or as a particular event with its own complications. Such a story tends to be *allegorical* (see Glossary). Usually, such stories are relatively simple, because the complexities of individual character and particular event are purged away; once one has grasped the key idea everything falls into its pattern. But in some stories of this general type, such as "In the Penal Colony," by Kafka, which we shall come to later (p. 441), there is great complication and obscurity because the idea behind the allegory is a complicated one and because the "key" is difficult to come by.

At the other extreme we find stories in which the individual and circumstantial aspects are so strongly emphasized that we do not discover any point-to-point equivalents as in fables, parables, and allegories. In such cases the meaning is more generalized. We "get the drift" toward the basic idea, as it were, but many particular events or aspects of character may serve no other purpose than to convince us of the reality of a person or situation. For example, in "Old Red," when the old man goes fishing on the pond, the action is simply in line with the old man's passion for sport, and has no definite allegorical meaning such as one attaches to certain events in "The Birthmark." We finally grasp the conflict between old Mister Maury and the world, not through any special individual event, but through a patterning of events which, in themselves, might be ordinary and meaningless enough. The story "Old Red" does conclude with a symbol which points up the theme, the symbol of the fox, but many stories do not depart from the realistic treatment; in such cases we simply follow the pattern of event and of motivation to an understanding of the idea; we simply "get the general drift."

In "Christ in Flanders," however, we have a story which approaches the method of the parable. The persons are presented only in so far as some one aspect of character is involved in the meaning. For instance, the merchant is fat and has two large money bags guarded by an armed servant. The man of science laughs at the stranger's preposterous suggestion that the passengers walk on the sea. The pretty damosel, with the falcon on her wrist, hearkens to the whispered temptation of the cavalier. The old soldier is a little more fully presented, but even in his case, we know merely the central fact, the "key" trait, of the character. We are given, in each case, just the aspect of character which means salvation or damnation in the shipwreck, the crucial trait. Thus, the representation of character is simplified to a point where we have little more than a series of equivalents, almost as strict as in allegory: the man of science is pride of intellect; the soldier, fidelity and courage; the damosel and cavalier, pleasure; the merchant, avarice; and so on. Finally, the boatload of people seems to be an image of the world, the high and the low, all confronted by the fact of death.

1. What is the significance of the first two paragraphs of the story? What does the author gain, if anything, by not plunging immediately into the narrative with the third paragraph?

2. What is the basic theme of the story? What are the subsidiary themes associated with this basic theme?

3. Why does Jesus save the skipper, who had not obeyed His command?

The Death of the Dauphin
ALPHONSE DAUDET

THE LITTLE DAUPHIN is sick; the little Dauphin is going to die. In all the churches of the realm the Blessed Sacrament is exposed night and day, and tall candles are burning for the recovery of the royal child. The streets in the old residence are sad and silent, the bells no longer ring, and carriages go at a foot pace. About the palace the curious citizens watch, through the iron grilles, the porters with gilt paunches talking in the courtyards with an air of importance.

The whole chateau is in commotion. Chamberlains, majordomos, run hastily up and down the marble staircases. The galleries are full of pages and of courtiers in silk garments, who go from group to group asking news in undertones. On the broad steps weeping maids of honor greet one another with low courtesies, wiping their eyes with pretty embroidered handkerchiefs.

In the orangery there is a great assemblage of long-robed doctors. Through the windows they can be seen flourishing their long black sleeves and bending majestically their hammerlike wigs. The little Dauphin's governor and equerry walk back and forth before the door, awaiting the decision of the faculty. Scullions pass them by without saluting them. The equerry swears like a heathen, the governor recites lines from Horace. And meanwhile, in the direction of the stables one hears a long, plaintive neigh. It is the little Dauphin's horse, calling sadly from his empty manger.

And the king? Where is *monseigneur* the king? The king is all alone in a room at the end of the chateau. Majesties do not like to be seen weeping. As for the queen, that is a different matter. Seated at the little Dauphin's pillow, her lovely face is bathed in tears, and she sobs aloud before them all, as a linen-draper's wife might do.

In his lace-bedecked crib the little Dauphin, whiter than the cushions upon which he lies, is resting now with closed eyes. They think that he sleeps; but no. The little Dauphin is not asleep. He turns to his mother, and seeing that she is weeping, he says to her:

"Madame queen, why do you weep? Is it because you really believe that I am going to die?"

The queen tries to reply. Sobs prevent her from speaking.

"Pray do not weep, madame queen; you forget that I am the Dauphin, and that dauphins cannot die like this."

The queen sobs more bitterly than ever, and the little Dauphin begins to be alarmed.

"I say," he says, "I don't want Death to come and take me and I will find a way to prevent his coming here. Let them send at once forty very strong troopers to stand guard around our bed! Let a hundred big guns watch night and day with matches lighted, under our windows! And woe to Death if it dares approach us!"

To please the royal child the queen makes a sign. In a moment they hear the big guns rumbling through the courtyard; and forty tall troopers, halberds in hand, take their places about the room. They are all old soldiers with gray mustaches. The little Dauphin claps his hands when he sees them. He recognizes one of them and calls him:

"Lorrain! Lorrain!"

The soldier steps forward toward the bed.

"I love you dearly, my old Lorrain. Let me see your big sword. If Death tries to take me you must kill him, won't you?"

"Yes, *monseigneur,*" Lorrain replies. And two great tears roll down his bronzed cheeks.

At that moment the chaplain approaches the little Dauphin and talks with him for a long time in a low voice, showing him a crucifix. The little Dauphin listens with an expression of great surprise, then, abruptly interrupting him, he says:

"I understand what you say, *monsieur l'abbé;* but tell me, couldn't my little friend Beppo die in my place, if I gave him a lot of money?"

The chaplain continues to speak in a low voice, and the little Dauphin's expression becomes more and more astonished.

When the chaplain has finished, the little Dauphin replies with a deep sigh:

"All this that you tell me is very sad, *monsieur l'abbé;* but one thing consoles me, and that is that up yonder, in the paradise of the stars, I shall still be the Dauphin. I know that the good Lord is my cousin, and that He cannot fail to treat me according to my rank."

Then he adds, turning to his mother:

"Let them bring me my richest clothes, my doublet of white ermine, and my velvet slippers! I wish to make myself handsome for the angels, and to enter paradise in the costume of a Dauphin."

A third time the chaplain leans toward the little Dauphin and talks to him for a long time in a low voice. In the midst of his harangue, the royal child angrily interrupts:

"Why, then, to be Dauphin is to be nothing at all!"

And, refusing to listen to anything more, the little Dauphin turns toward the wall and weeps bitterly.

INTERPRETATION

1. Is the ironical "point" of the story weakened or strengthened by the pathos of the little Dauphin's death? How does the author pre-

vent the ironical parable from turning into a story of the pathos of a hurt and bewildered child?

2. In this regard consider such matters as the following: (*a*) the author's maintenance of a detached objectivity; (*b*) the amount of attention given to the various activities in and about the palace; (*c*) the fact that the story ends on a note of petulance as the little Dauphin weeps in childish disappointment.

3. Where does the story find its real center? If the implied ironical commentary does not fall primarily on the little Dauphin, where does it fall?

{Filboid Studge, the Story of a Mouse that} Helped

SAKI (HECTOR HUGH MUNRO)

"I WANT to marry your daughter," said Mark Spayley with faltering eagerness. "I am only an artist with an income of two hundred a year, and she is the daughter of an enormously wealthy man, so I suppose you will think my offer a piece of presumption."

Duncan Dullamy, the great company inflator, showed no outward sign of displeasure. As a matter of fact, he was secretly relieved at the prospect of finding even a two-hundred-a-year husband for his daughter Leonore. A crisis was rapidly rushing upon him, from which he knew he would emerge with neither money nor credit; all his recent ventures had fallen flat, and flattest of all had gone the wonderful new breakfast food, Pipenta, on the advertisement of which he had sunk such huge sums. It could scarcely be called a drug on the market; people bought drugs, but no one bought Pipenta.

"Would you marry Leonore if she were a poor man's daughter?" asked the man of phantom wealth.

"Yes," said Mark, wisely avoiding the error of overprotestation. And to his astonishment Leonore's father not only gave his consent, but suggested a fairly early date for the wedding.

"I wish I could show my gratitude in some way," said Mark with genuine emotion. "I'm afraid it's rather like the mouse proposing to help the lion."

"Get people to buy that beastly muck," said Dullamy, nodding savagely at a poster of the despised Pipenta, "and you'll have done more than any of my agents have been able to accomplish."

"It wants a better name," said Mark reflectively, "and something distinctive in the poster line. Anyway, I'll have a shot at it."

Three weeks later the world was advised of the coming of a new breakfast food, heralded under the resounding name of "Filboid Studge." Spayley put forth no pictures of massive babies springing up with funguslike rapidity under its forcing influence, or of representatives of the leading nations of the world scrambling with fatuous eagerness for its possession. One huge somber poster depicted the damned in Hell suffering a new torment from their inability to get at the Filboid Studge which elegant young fiends held in transparent bowls just beyond their reach. The scene was rendered even more gruesome by a subtle suggestion of the features of leading men and women of the day in the portrayal of the Lost Souls; prominent individuals of both political parties, Society hostesses, well-known dramatic authors and novelists, and distinguished aeroplanists were dimly recognizable in that doomed throng; noted lights of the musical-comedy stage flickered wanly in the shades of the Inferno, smiling still from force of habit, but with the fearsome smiling rage of baffled effort. The poster bore no fulsome allusions to the merits of the new breakfast food, but a single grim statement ran in bold letters along its base: "They cannot buy it now."

Spayley had grasped the fact that people will do things from a sense of duty which they would never attempt as a pleasure. There are thousands of respectable middle-class men who, if you found them unexpectedly in a Turkish bath, would explain in all sincerity that a doctor had ordered them to take Turkish baths; if you told them in return that you went there because you liked it, they would stare in pained wonder at the frivolity of your motive. In the same way, whenever a massacre of Armenians is reported from Asia Minor, everyone assumes that it has been carried out "under orders" from somewhere or another; no one seems to think that there are people who might *like* to kill their neighbors now and then.

And so it was with the new breakfast food. No one would have eaten Filboid Studge as a pleasure, but the grim austerity of its advertisement drove housewives in shoals to the grocers' shops to clamor for an immediate supply. In small kitchens solemn pigtailed daughters helped depressed mothers to perform the primitive ritual of its preparation. On the breakfast tables of cheerless parlors it was partaken of in silence. Once the womenfolk discovered that it was thoroughly unpalatable, their zeal in forcing it on their households knew no bounds. "You haven't eaten your Filboid Studge!" would be screamed at the appetiteless clerk as he hurried weariedly from the breakfast table, and his evening meal would be prefaced by a warmed-up mess which would be explained as "your Filboid Studge that you didn't eat this morning." Those strange fanatics who ostentatiously mortify themselves, inwardly and outwardly, with health biscuits and health garments, battened aggressively on the new food. Earnest spectacled young men devoured it on the steps of the National Liberal Club. A bishop who did not believe in a future state preached against the poster, and a peer's daughter died from eating too much of the compound. A further advertisement was obtained when an infantry regiment mutinied and shot its officers rather than eat the nauseous mess; fortunately, Lord Birrell of Blatherstone, who was War Minister at the moment, saved the situation by his happy epigram, that "Discipline to be effective must be optional."

Filboid Studge had become a household word, but Dullamy wisely realized that it was not necessarily the last word in breakfast dietary; its supremacy would be challenged as soon as some yet more unpalatable food should be put on the market. There might even be a reaction in favor of something tasty and appetizing, and the Puritan austerity of the moment might be banished from domestic cookery. At an opportune moment, therefore, he sold out his interests in the article which had brought him in colossal wealth at a critical juncture, and placed his financial reputation beyond the reach of cavil. As for Leonore, who was now an heiress on a far greater scale than ever before, he naturally found her something a vast deal higher in the husband market than a two-hundred-a-year poster designer. Mark Spayley, the brainmouse who had helped the financial lion with such untoward effect, was left to curse the day he produced the wonder-working poster.

"After all," said Clovis, meeting him shortly afterwards at his club, "you have this doubtful consolation, that 'tis not in mortals to countermand success." *

INTERPRETATION

1. What advantages does the parable-like form of this story afford the author in his satire on some aspects of modern society?
2. In what is the humor of the story rooted? Is the irony too heavy-handed?
3. Justify the surprise ending of the story. The surprise ending is prepared for by what?

The Killers

ERNEST HEMINGWAY

THE DOOR of Henry's lunchroom opened and two men came in. They sat down at the counter.

"What's yours?" George asked them.

"I don't know," one of the men said. "What do you want to eat, Al?"

"I don't know," said Al. "I don't know what I want to eat."

Outside it was getting dark. The street light came on outside the window. The two men at the counter read the menu. From the other end of the counter Nick Adams watched them. He had been talking to George when they came in.

"I'll have a roast pork tenderloin with apple sauce and mashed potatoes," the first man said.

"It isn't ready yet."

"What the hell do you put it on the card for?"

"That's the dinner," George explained. "You can get that at six o'clock."

George looked at the clock on the wall behind the counter.

"It's five o'clock."

"The clock says twenty minutes past five," the second man said.

"It's twenty minutes fast."

* From *The Short Stories of Saki;* by permission of the Viking Press, Inc., New York.

"Oh, to hell with the clock," the first man said. "What have you got to eat?"

"I can give you any kind of sandwiches," George said. "You can have ham and eggs, bacon and eggs, liver and bacon, or a steak."

"Give me chicken croquettes with green peas and cream sauce and mashed potatoes."

"That's the dinner."

"Everything we want's the dinner, eh? That's the way you work it."

"I can give you ham and eggs, bacon and eggs, liver—"

"I'll take ham and eggs," the man called Al said. He wore a derby hat and a black overcoat buttoned across the chest. His face was small and white and he had tight lips. He wore a silk muffler and gloves.

"Give me bacon and eggs," said the other man. He was about the same size as Al. Their faces were different, but they were dressed like twins. Both wore overcoats too tight for them. They sat leaning forward, their elbows on the counter.

"Got anything to drink?" Al asked.

"Silver beer, bevo, ginger ale," George said.

"I mean you got anything to *drink?*"

"Just those I said."

"This is a hot town," said the other. "What do they call it?"

"Summit."

"Ever hear of it?" Al asked his friend.

"No," said the friend.

"What do you do here nights?" Al asked.

"They eat the dinner," his friend said. "They all come here and eat the big dinner."

"That's right," George said.

"So you think that's right?" Al asked George.

"Sure."

"You're a pretty bright boy, aren't you?"

"Sure," said George.

"Well, you're not," said the other little man. "Is he, Al?"

"He's dumb," said Al. He turned to Nick. "What's your name?"

"Adams."

"Another bright boy," Al said. "Ain't he a bright boy, Max?"

"The town's full of bright boys," Max said.

George put the two platters, one of ham and eggs, the other of bacon and eggs, on the counter. He set down two side dishes of fried potatoes and closed the wicket into the kitchen.

"Which is yours?" he asked Al.

"Don't you remember?"

"Ham and eggs."

"Just a bright boy," Max said. He leaned forward and took the ham and eggs. Both men ate with their gloves on. George watched them eat.

"What are *you* looking at?" Max looked at George.

"Nothing."

"The hell you were. You were looking at me."

"Maybe the boy meant it for a joke, Max," Al said.

George laughed.

"*You* don't have to laugh," Max said to him. "*You* don't have to laugh at all, see?"

"All right," said George.

"So he thinks it's all right." Max turned to Al. "He thinks it's all right. That's a good one."

"Oh, he's a thinker," Al said. They went on eating.

"What's the bright boy's name down the counter?" Al asked Max.

"Hey, bright boy," Max said to Nick. "You go around on the other side of the counter with your boy friend."

"What's the idea?" Nick asked.

"There isn't any idea."

"You better go around, bright boy," Al said. Nick went around behind the counter.

"What's the idea?" George asked.

"None of your damn business," Al said. "Who's out in the kitchen?"

"The nigger."

"What do you mean the nigger?"

"The nigger that cooks."

"Tell him to come in."

"What's the idea?"

"Tell him to come in."

"Where do you think you are?"

"We know damn well where we are," the man called Max said. "Do we look silly?"

"You talk silly," Al said to him. "What the hell do you argue with this kid for? Listen," he said to George, "tell the nigger to come out here."

"What are you going to do to him?"

"Nothing. Use your head, bright boy. What would we do to a nigger?"

George opened the slit that opened back into the kitchen. "Sam," he called. "Come in here a minute."

The door to the kitchen opened and the nigger came in. "What was it?" he asked. The two men at the counter took a look at him.

"All right, nigger. You stand right there," Al said.

Sam, the nigger, standing in his apron, looked at the two men sitting at the counter. "Yes, sir," he said. Al got down from his stool.

"I'm going back to the kitchen with the nigger and bright boy," he said. "Go on back to the kitchen, nigger. You go with him, bright boy." The little man walked after Nick and Sam, the cook, back into the kitchen. The door shut after them. The man called Max sat at the counter opposite George. He didn't look at George but looked in the mirror that ran along back of the counter. Henry's had been made over from a saloon into a lunch counter.

"Well, bright boy," Max said, looking into the mirror, "why don't you say something?"

"What's it all about?"

"Hey, Al," Max called, "bright boy wants to know what it's all about."

"Why don't you tell him?" Al's voice came from the kitchen.

"What do you think it's all about?"

"I don't know."

"What do you think?"

Max looked into the mirror all the time he was talking.

"I wouldn't say."

"Hey, Al, bright boy says he wouldn't say what he thinks it's all about."

"I can hear you, all right," Al said from the kitchen. He had propped open the slit that dishes passed through into the kitchen with a catsup bottle. "Listen, bright boy," he said from the kitchen to George. "Stand a little further along the bar. You move a little to the left, Max." He was like a photographer arranging for a group picture.

"Talk to me, bright boy," Max said. "What do you think's going to happen?"

George did not say anything.

"I'll tell you," Max said. "We're going to kill a Swede. Do you know a big Swede named Ole Andreson?"

"Yes."

"He comes here to eat every night, don't he?"

"Sometimes he comes here."

"He comes here at six o'clock, don't he?"

"If he comes."

"We know all that, bright boy," Max said. "Talk about something else. Ever go to the movies?"

"Once in a while."

"You ought to go to the movies more. The movies are fine for a bright boy like you."

"What are you going to kill Ole Andreson for? What did he ever do to you?"

"He never had a chance to do anything to us. He never even seen us."

"And he's only going to see us once," Al said from the kitchen.

"What are you going to kill him for, then?" George asked.

"We're killing him for a friend. Just to oblige a friend, bright boy."

"Shut up," said Al from the kitchen. "You talk too goddamn much."

"Well, I got to keep bright boy amused. Don't I, bright boy?"

"You talk too damn much," Al said. "The nigger and my bright boy are amused by themselves. I got them tied up like a couple of girl friends in a convent."

"I suppose you were in a convent."

"You never know."

"You were in a kosher convent. That's where you were."

George looked up at the clock.

"If anybody comes in you tell them the cook is off, and if they keep after it, you tell them you'll go back and cook yourself. Do you get that, bright boy?"

"All right," George said. "What you going to do with us afterward?"

"That'll depend," Max said. "That's one of those things you never know at the time."

George looked up at the clock. It was a quarter past six. The door from the street opened. A street-car motorman came in.

"Hello, George," he said. "Can I get supper?"

"Sam's gone out," George said. "He'll be back in about half an hour."

"I'd better go up the street," the motorman said. George looked at the clock. It was twenty minutes past six.

"That was nice, bright boy," Max said. "You're a regular little gentleman."

"He knew I'd blow his head off," Al said from the kitchen.

"No," said Max. "It ain't that. Bright boy is nice. He's a nice boy. I like him."

At six-fifty-five George said: "He's not coming."

Two other people had been in the lunchroom. Once George had gone out to the kitchen and made a ham-and-egg sandwich "to go" that a man wanted to take with him. Inside the kitchen he saw Al, his derby hat tipped back, sitting on a stool beside the wicket with the muzzle of a sawed-off shotgun resting on the ledge. Nick and the cook were back to back in the corner, a towel tied in each of their mouths. George had cooked the sandwich, wrapped it up in oiled paper, put it in a bag, brought it in, and the man had paid for it and gone out.

"Bright boy can do everything," Max said. "He can cook and everything. You'd make some girl a nice wife, bright boy."

"Yes?" George said. "Your friend, Ole Andreson, isn't going to come."

"We'll give him ten minutes," Max said.

Max watched the mirror and the clock. The hands of the clock marked seven o'clock, and then five minutes past seven.

"Come on, Al," said Max. "We better go. He's not coming."

"Better give him five minutes," Al said from the kitchen.

In the five minutes a man came in, and George explained that the cook was sick.

"Why the hell don't you get another cook?" the man asked. "Aren't you running a lunch counter?" He went out.

"Come on, Al," Max said.

"What about the two bright boys and the nigger?"

"They're all right."

"You think so?"

"Sure. We're through with it."

"I don't like it," said Al. "It's sloppy. You talk too much."

"Oh, what the hell," said Max. "We got to keep amused, haven't we?"

"You talk too much, all the same," Al said. He came out from the kitchen. The cut-off barrels of the shotgun made a slight bulge under the waist of his too tight-fitting overcoat. He straightened his coat with his gloved hands.

"So long, bright boy," he said to George. "You got a lot of luck."

"That's the truth," Max said. "You ought to play the races, bright boy."

The two of them went out the door. George watched them, through the window, pass under the arc light and cross the street. In their tight overcoats and derby hats they looked like a vaudeville team. George went back through the swinging door into the kitchen and untied Nick and the cook.

"I don't want any more of that," said Sam, the cook. "I don't want any more of that."

Nick stood up. He had never had a towel in his mouth before.

"Say," he said. "What the hell?" He was trying to swagger it off.

"They were going to kill Ole Andreson," George said. "They were going to shoot him when he came in to eat."

"Ole Andreson?"

"Sure."

The cook felt the corners of his mouth with his thumbs.

"They all gone?" he asked.

"Yeah," said George. "They're gone now."

"I don't like it," said the cook. "I don't like any of it at all."

"Listen," George said to Nick. "You better go see Ole Andreson."

"All right."

"You better not have anything to do with it at all," Sam, the cook, said. "You better stay way out of it."

"Don't go if you don't want to," George said.

"Mixing up in this ain't going to get you anywhere," the cook said. "You stay out of it."

"I'll go see him," Nick said to George. "Where does he live?"

The cook turned away.

"Little boys always know what they want to do," he said.

"He lives up at Hirsch's rooming house," George said to Nick.

"I'll go up there."

Outside the arc light shone through the bare branches of a tree. Nick walked up the street beside the car tracks and turned at the next arc light down a side street. Three houses up the street was Hirsch's rooming house. Nick walked up the two steps and pushed the bell. A woman came to the door.

"Is Ole Andreson here?"

"Do you want to see him?"

"Yes, if he's in."

Nick followed the woman up a flight of stairs and back to the end of a corridor. She knocked on the door.

"Who is it?"

"It's somebody to see you, Mr. Andreson," the woman said.

"It's Nick Adams."

"Come in."

Nick opened the door and went into the room. Ole Andreson was lying on the bed with all his clothes on. He had been a heavyweight prizefighter and he was too long for the bed. He lay with his head on two pillows. He did not look at Nick.

"What was it?" he asked.

"I was up at Henry's," Nick said, "and two fellows came in and tied up me and the cook, and they said they were going to kill you."

It sounded silly when he said it. Ole Andreson said nothing.

"They put us out in the kitchen," Nick went on. "They were going to shoot you when you came in to supper."

Ole Andreson looked at the wall and did not say anything.

"George thought I better come and tell you about it."

"There isn't anything I can do about it," Ole Andreson said.

"I'll tell you what they were like."

"I don't want to know what they were like," Ole Andreson said. He looked at the wall. "Thanks for coming to tell me about it."

"That's all right."

Nick looked at the big man lying on the bed.

"Don't you want me to go and see the police?"

"No," Ole Andreson said. "That wouldn't do any good."

"Isn't there something I could do?"

"No. There ain't anything to do."

"Maybe it was just a bluff."

"No. It ain't just a bluff."

Ole Andreson rolled over toward the wall.

"The only thing is," he said, talking toward the wall, "I just can't make up my mind to go out. I been in here all day."

"Couldn't you get out of town?"

"No," Ole Andreson said. "I'm through with all that running around."

He looked at the wall.

"There ain't anything to do now."

"Couldn't you fix it up some way?"

"No. I got in wrong." He talked in the same flat voice. "There ain't anything to do. After a while I'll make up my mind to go out."

"I better go back and see George," Nick said.

"So long," said Ole Andreson. He did not look toward Nick. "Thanks for coming around."

Nick went out. As he shut the door he saw Ole Andreson with all his clothes on, lying on the bed looking at the wall.

"He's been in his room all day," the landlady said downstairs. "I guess he don't feel well. I said to him: 'Mr. Andreson, you ought to go out and take a walk on a nice fall day like this,' but he didn't feel like it."

"He doesn't want to go out."

"I'm sorry he don't feel well," the woman said. "He's an awfully nice man. He was in the ring, you know."

"I know it."

"You'd never know it except from the way his face is," the woman said. They stood talking just inside the street door. "He's just as gentle."

"Well, good-night, Mrs. Hirsch," Nick said.

"I'm not Mrs. Hirsch," the woman said. "She owns the place. I just look after it for her. I'm Mrs. Bell."

"Well, good-night, Mrs. Bell," Nick said.

"Good-night," the woman said.

Nick walked up the dark street to the corner under the arc light, and then along the car tracks to Henry's eating house. George was inside, back of the counter.

"Did you see Ole?"

"Yes," said Nick. "He's in his room and he won't go out."

The cook opened the door from the kitchen when he heard Nick's voice.

"I don't even listen to it," he said and shut the door.

"Did you tell him about it?" George asked.

"Sure. I told him but he knows what it's all about."

"What's he going to do?"

"Nothing."

"They'll kill him."

"I guess they will."

"He must have got mixed up in something in Chicago."

"I guess so," said Nick.

"It's a hell of a thing."

"It's an awful thing," Nick said.

They did not say anything. George reached down for a towel and wiped the counter.

"I wonder what he did?" Nick said.

"Double-crossed somebody. That's what they kill them for."

"I'm going to get out of this town," Nick said.

"Yes," said George. "That's a good thing to do."

"I can't stand to think about him waiting in the room and knowing he's going to get it. It's too damned awful."

"Well," said George, "you better not think about it." *

* By permission of Charles Scribner's Sons.

INTERPRETATION

There are certain fairly obvious points to be made about the technique of this story. It breaks up into one long scene and three short scenes. Indeed, the method is so thoroughly scenic that not over three or four sentences are required to make the transitions. The focus of narration is objective throughout, practically all information being conveyed in simple realistic dialogue. In the first scene the revelation of the. mission of the gangsters is accomplished through a few significant details—the fact that the gangsters eat with gloves (to avoid leaving fingerprints), the fact that they keep their eyes on the mirror behind the bar, the fact that, after Nick and the cook have been tied up, the gangster who has the shotgun at the service window stations his friend and George out front "like a photographer arranging for a group picture"—all of this before the specific nature of their mission is made clear.

Other observations concerning the technique of the story could be made—the cleverness of composition, the subtlety with which the suspense is maintained in the first scene by the banter of the gangsters, and then is transferred to another level in the second scene. But such observations, though they are worth making, do not answer the first question which, to the reader, usually presents itself, or should be allowed to present itself. That question is: what is the story about?

The importance of giving an early answer to this question is indicated by the fact that a certain kind of reader, upon first acquaintance with the story, is inclined to feel that the story is exhausted in the first scene, and in fact that the first scene itself does not come to focus—does not have a "point." Another kind of reader sees that the first scene, with its lack of resolution, is really being used to "charge" the second scene. He finds his point in Ole Andreson's decision not to try to escape the gangsters—to stop "all that running around." This reader feels that the story should end here. He sees no relevance in the last several pages of the story, and wonders why the author has flattened out his effect. The first reader we may say, feels that "The Killers" is the gangsters' story—a story of action which does not come off. The second and more sophisticated reader interprets it as Andreson's story, though perhaps with some wonder that Andreson's story has been approached so indirectly and is allowed to tail off so irrelevantly. In other words, the reader is inclined to transpose the question, What is the story? into the question, Whose story is it? When he states the question in this way, he confronts the fact that Hemingway has left the story focused not on the gangsters, nor

on Andreson, but on the boys at the lunchroom. Consider the last sentences of the story:

"I'm going to get out of this town," Nick said.
"Yes," said George. "That's a good thing to do."
"I can't stand to think about him waiting in the room and knowing
he's going to get it. It's too damned awful."
"Well," said George, "you better not think about it."

So, of the two boys, it is obviously Nick on whom the impression has
been made. George has managed to come to terms with the situation.
By this line of reasoning, it is Nick's story. And the story is about the
discovery of evil. The theme, in a sense, is the Hamlet theme, or the
theme of Sherwood Anderson's "I Want to Know Why" (p. 335).

This definition of the theme of the story, even if it appears acceptable,
must, of course, be tested against the detailed structure. In evaluating
the story, as well as in understanding it, the skill with which the theme
has been assimilated must be taken into account. For instance, to put a
concrete question: does the last paragraph of the story illuminate for
the reader certain details which had, at their first appearance, seemed
to be merely casual, realistic items? If we take the theme to be the boy's
discovery of evil, several such details do find their fulfillment and meaning. Nick had been bound and gagged by the gangsters, and has been
released by George. To quote: "Nick stood up. He had never had a
towel in his mouth before. 'Say,' he said. 'What the hell?' He was trying
to swagger it off." Being gagged was something you read about in a
thriller and not something which happened to you; and the first effect
is one of excitement, almost pleasurable, certainly an excuse for a manly
pose. (It may be worth noting in this connection that Hemingway uses
the specific word *towel* and not the general word *gag*. It is true that the
word *towel* has a certain sensory advantage over the word *gag*—because
it suggests the coarseness of the fabric and the unpleasant drying effect
on the membranes of the mouth. But this advantage in immediacy is
probably overshadowed by another: the towel is sanctified in the thriller
as the gag, and here that cliché of the thriller has come true.) The way
the whole incident is given—"He had *never* had a towel in his mouth
before"—charges the apparently realistic detail as a pointer to the final
discovery.

Another pointer appears in the gangster's wisecrack about the movies:
"You ought to go to the movies more. The movies are fine for a bright
boy like you." In one sense, of course, the iterated remarks about the

movies, coming just after the gangsters have made their arrangements
in the lunchroom, serve as a kind of indirect exposition: the reader
knows the standard reason and procedure for gang killings. But at
another level, these remarks emphasize the discovery that the unreal
clichés of horror have a reality.

The boy to whom the gangster speaks understands the allusion to
the movies, for he immediately asks: "What are you going to kill Ole
Andreson for? What did he ever do to you?"

"He never had a chance to do anything to us. He never even seen us,"
the gangster replies. The gangster accepts, and even glories a little in,
the terms by which he lives—terms which transcend the small-town
world. He lives, as it were, by a code, which lifts him above questions
of personal likes or personal animosities. This unreal code—unreal because it denies the ordinary personal elements of life—has, like the gag,
suddenly been discovered as real. This unreal and theatrical quality is
reflected in the description of the gangsters as, after leaving the lunchroom, they go out under the arc light and cross the street: "In their tight
overcoats and derby hats they looked like a vaudeville team." It even
permeates their dialogue. The dialogue itself has the sleazy quality of
mechanized gag and wisecrack, a kind of inflexible and stereotyped
banter that is always *a priori* to the situation and overrides the situation.
On this level the comparison to the vaudeville team is a kind of explicit
summary of details which have been presented more indirectly and
dramatically. On another level, the weary and artificial quality of their
wit has a grimmer implication. It is an index to the professional casualness with which they accept a situation which to the boys is shocking.
They are contemptuous and even bored, with the contempt and boredom of the initiated when confronted by callow lay observers. This
code, which has suddenly been transferred from the artificial world
of the thriller and movie into reality, is shocking enough, but even more
shocking to Nick is the fact that Ole Andreson, the hunted man, accepts
the code too. Confronted by the news which Nick brings, he rejects all
the responses which the boy would have considered normal: he will not
call the police; he will not regard the thing as a mere bluff; he will not
leave town. "Couldn't you fix it up some way?" the boy asks. "No. I
got in wrong."

As we observed earlier, for a certain type of reader this is the high
point of the story, and the story should end here. If one is to convince
such a reader that the author is right in proceeding, one is obligated to
answer his question: What is the significance of the rather tame, and

apparently irrelevant, little incident which follows, the conversation with Mrs. Bell? It is sometimes said that Mrs. Bell serves to give a bit of delayed exposition or even to point the story by gaining sympathy for Andreson, who is, to her, "an awfully nice man," not at all like her idea of a pugilist. But this is not enough to satisfy the keen reader, and he is right in refusing to be satisfied with this. Mrs. Bell is, really, the Porter at Hell Gate in *Macbeth*. She is the world of normality, which is shocking now from the very fact that it continues to flow on in its usual course. To her, Ole Andreson is just a nice man, despite the fact that he has been in the ring; he ought to go out and take his walk on such a nice day. She points to his ordinary individuality, which is in contrast to the demands of the mechanical code. Even if the unreal horror of the movie thriller has become real, even if the hunted man lies upstairs on his bed trying to make up his mind to go out, Mrs. Bell is still Mrs. Bell. She is not Mrs. Hirsch. Mrs. Hirsch owns the place, she just looks after it for Mrs. Hirsch. She is Mrs. Bell.

At the door of the rooming house Nick has met Mrs. Bell—normality unconscious of the ironical contrast it presents. Back at the lunchroom, Nick returns to the normal scene, but the normal scene conscious of the impingement of horror. It is the same old lunchroom, with George and the cook going about their business. But they, unlike Mrs. Bell, know what has happened. Yet even they are scarcely deflected from their ordinary routine. George and the cook represent two different levels of response to the situation. The cook, from the first, has wanted no part of it. When he hears Nick's voice, on his return, he says, "I don't even listen to it." And he shuts the door. But George had originally suggested that Nick go see Andreson, telling him, however, "Don't go if you don't want to." After Nick has told his story, George can comment, "It's a hell of a thing," but George, in one sense at least, has accepted the code, too. When Nick says: "I wonder what he did?" George replies, with an echo of the killers' own casualness: "Double-crossed somebody. That's what they kill them for." In other words, the situation is shocking to the cook only in so far as it involves his own safety. George is aware of other implications but can dismiss them. For neither of them, does the situation mean the discovery of evil. But for Nick, it is the discovery, for he has not yet learned to take George's adult advice: "Well, you better not think about it."

To this point the discussion of "The Killers" has been concerned with the structure of the story with regard to the relations among incidents and with regard to the attitudes of the characters. But there remain as important questions such items as the following: What is Hemingway's attitude toward his material? How does this attitude find its expression?

Perhaps the simplest approach to these questions may be through a consideration of the situations and characters which interest Hemingway. These situations are usually violent ones: the hard-drinking and sexually promiscuous world of *The Sun Also Rises;* the chaotic and brutal world of war as in *A Farewell to Arms, For Whom the Bell Tolls,* or "A Way You'll Never Be"; the dangerous and exciting world of the bull ring or the prize ring as in *The Sun Also Rises, Death in the Afternoon,* "The Undefeated," "Fifty Grand"; the world of crime, as in "The Killers," *To Have and to Have Not,* or "The Gambler, the Nun, and the Radio." Hemingway's typical characters are usually tough men, experienced in the hard worlds they inhabit, and apparently insensitive: Lieutenant Henry in *A Farewell to Arms,* the big-game hunter in "The Snows of Kilimanjaro," Robert Jordan in *For Whom the Bell Tolls,* or even Ole Andreson. They are, also, usually defeated men. Out of their practical defeat, however, they have managed to salvage something. And here we come upon Hemingway's basic interest in such situations and such characters. They are not defeated except upon their own terms; some of them have even courted defeat; certainly, they have maintained, even in the practical defeat, an ideal of themselves, formulated or unformulated, by which they have lived. Hemingway's attitude is, in a sense, like that of Robert Louis Stevenson, as Stevenson states it in one of his essays, "Pulvis et Umbra":

"Poor soul, here for so little, cast among so many hardships, filled with desires so incommensurate and so inconsistent, savagely surrounded, savagely descended, irremediably condemned to prey upon his fellow lives: who should have blamed him had he been of a piece with his destiny and a being merely barbarous? And we look and behold him instead filled with imperfect virtues: . . . an ideal of decency, to which he would rise if it were possible; a limit of shame, below which, if it be possible, he will not stoop. . . . Man is indeed marked for failure in his efforts to do right. But where the best consistently miscarry, how tenfold more remarkable that all should continue to strive; and surely we should find it both touching and inspiriting, that in a field from which success is banished, our race should not cease to labor. . . . It matters not where we look, under what climate we observe him, in what stage of society, in what depth of ignorance, burthened with what erroneous morality; by campfires in Assiniboia, the snow powdering his shoulders, the wind plucking his blanket, as he sits, passing the ceremonial calumet and uttering his grave opinions like a Roman senator; in ships at sea, a man inured to hardship and vile pleasures, his brightest hope a fiddle in a tavern and a bedizened trull who sells herself to rob him, and he for all that, simple, innocent, cheerful, kindly like a child, constant to toil, brave to drown, for others; . . . in the brothel, the discard of society, living mainly on strong drink, fed with affronts, a fool, a thief, the comrade of thieves, and even here keeping the point of honor and the touch of pity, often repaying the world's scorn with service, often standing firm upon a scruple, and at a certain cost, rejecting riches;—everywhere some virtue cherished or affected, everywhere some decency of thought and carriage, everywhere the ensign of man's ineffectual goodness! . . . under every circumstance of failure, without hope, without health, without thanks, still obscurely fighting the lost fight of virtue, still clinging, in the brothel or on the scaffold, to some rag of honor, the poor jewel of their souls! They may seek to escape, and yet they cannot; it is not alone their privilege and glory, but their doom, they are condemned to some nobility . . ."

For Stevenson, the world in which this drama is played out is, objectively considered, a violent and meaningless world—"our rotary island loaded with predatory life and more drenched with blood . . . than ever mutinied ship, scuds through space." This is Hemingway's world, too. But its characters, at least those whose story Hemingway cares to tell, make one gallant effort to redeem the incoherence and meaninglessness of this world: they attempt to impose some form upon the disorder of their lives, the technique of the bullfighter or sportsman, the discipline of the soldier, the code of the gangster, which, even though brutal and dehumanizing, has its own ethic. (Ole Andreson is willing to take his medicine without whining. Or the dying Mexican in "The Gambler, the Nun, and the Radio" refuses to squeal, despite the detective's argument: "One can, with honor, denounce one's assailant.") The form is never quite adequate to subdue the world, but the fidelity to it is part of the gallantry of defeat.

It has been said above that the typical Hemingway character is tough and, apparently, insensitive. But only apparently, for the fidelity to a code, to a discipline, may be an index to a sensitivity which allows the characters to see, at moments, their true plight. At times, and usually at times of stress, it is the tough man, for Hemingway, the disciplined man, who actually is aware of pathos or tragedy. The individual toughness (which may be taken to be the private discipline demanded by the

world), may find itself in conflict with some more natural and spontaneous human emotion; in contrast with this the discipline may, even, seem
to be inhuman; but the Hemingway hero, though he is aware of the
claims of this spontaneous human emotion, is afraid to yield to those
claims because he has learned that the only way to hold on to "honor,"
to individuality, to, even, the human order as against the brute chaos of
the world, is to live by his code. This is the irony of the situation in which
the hero finds himself. Hemingway's heroes are aristocrats in the sense
that they are the initiate, and practice a lonely virtue.

Hemingway's heroes utter themselves, not in rant and bombast, but
in terms of ironic understatement. This understatement, stemming from
the contrast between the toughness and the sensitivity, the violence and
the sensitivity, is a constant aspect of Hemingway's method, an aspect
which was happily caught in a cartoon in the *New Yorker* several years
ago. The cartoonist showed a brawny, hairy forearm and a muscled
hand clutching a little rose. The cartoon was entitled "The Soul of
Ernest Hemingway." Just as there is a margin of victory in the defeat of
the Hemingway characters, so there is a little margin of sensibility in
their brutal and violent world. The revelation arises from the most unpromising circumstances and from the most unpromising people—the
little streak of poetry or pathos in "The Pursuit Race," "The Undefeated," "My Old Man," and, let us say, "The Killers."

It has already been pointed out that Ole Andreson fits into this pattern. Andreson won't whimper. He takes his medicine quietly. But Ole
Andreson's story is buried in the larger story, which is focused on Nick.
How does Nick Adams fit into the pattern? Hemingway, as a matter of
fact, is accustomed to treat his basic situation at one or the other of two
levels. There is the story of the person who is already initiated, who
already has adopted his appropriate code, or discipline, in the world
which otherwise he cannot cope with. (One finds examples in Jake and
Brett in *The Sun Also Rises,* Jordan and Pilar in *For Whom the Bell
Tolls,* the bullfighter in "The Undefeated," and many other stories.)
There is also the story of the process of the initiation, the discovery
of evil and disorder, and the first step toward the mastery of the discipline. This is Nick's story. (But the same basic situation occurs in many
other stories by Hemingway, for example, "Up In Michigan," "Indian
Camp," and "The Three-Day Blow.")

It has been observed that the typical Hemingway character is tough
and apparently insensitive. Usually, too, that character is simple. The
impulse which has led Hemingway to the simple character is akin to

that which led a Romantic poet like Wordsworth to the same choice. Wordsworth felt that his unsophisticated peasants or children, who are the characters of so many of his poems, were more honest in their responses than the cultivated man, and therefore more poetic. Instead of Wordsworth's typical peasant we find in Hemingway's work the bullfighter, the soldier, the revolutionist, the sportsman, and the gangster; instead of Wordsworth's children, we find the young men like Nick. There are, of course, differences between the approach of Wordsworth and that of Hemingway, but there is little difference on the point of marginal sensibility.

The main difference between the two writers depends on the difference in their two worlds. Hemingway's world is a more disordered world, and more violent, than the simple and innocent world of Wordsworth. Therefore, the sensibility of Hemingway's characters is in sharper contrast to the nature of his world. This creates an irony which is not found in the work of Wordsworth. Hemingway plays down the sensibility as such, and sheathes it in the code of toughness. Gertrude Stein says of Hemingway: "Hemingway is the shyest and proudest and sweetest-smelling storyteller of my reading." When she refers to his "shyness" she is, apparently, thinking of his use of irony and understatement. The typical character is sensitive, but his sensitivity is never insisted upon; he may be worthy of pity, but he never demands it. The underlying attitude in Hemingway's work may be stated like this: pity is only valid when it is wrung from a man who has been seasoned by experience, and is only earned by a man who never demands it, a man who takes his chances. Therefore, a premium is placed upon the fact of violent experience.

A further question suggests itself. How is Hemingway's style related to his basic fictional concerns? We can notice that in "The Killers," as in many of his other stories, the style is simple even to the point of monotony. The characteristic sentence is simple, or compound; and if compound, there is no implied subtlety in the co-ordination of the clauses. The paragraph structure is, characteristically, based on simple sequence.* First, we can observe that there is an obvious relation between this

* In some of Hemingway's work, especially in the novels, there are examples of a more fluent, lyrical style than is found in "The Killers." But even in such examples, one can observe that the fluency and the lyrical effect is based on the conjunction *and*—that there is no process of subordination but rather a process of sequence in terms of direct perceptions. The lyrical quality of such examples is to be taken as a manifestation of the "marginal sensibility," as can be demonstrated by an analysis of the situations in which the lyrical passages occur.

style and the characters and situations with which the author is concerned: unsophisticated characters and simple, fundamental situations are rendered in an uncomplicated style. But there is another, and more interesting, aspect of the question which involves, not the sensibility of the characters, but the sensibility of the author himself. The short simple rhythms, the succession of co-ordinate clauses, and the general lack of subordination—all suggest a dislocated and ununified world. Hemingway is apparently trying to suggest in his style the direct experience—things as seen and felt, one after another, and not as the mind arranges and analyzes them. A style which involves subordination and complicated shadings of emphasis—a style which tends toward complex sentences with many qualifying clauses and phrases—implies an exercise of critical discrimination—the sifting of experience through the intellect. But Hemingway, apparently, is primarily concerned with giving the immediate impact of experience rather than with analyzing and evaluating it in detail. (We can notice, in this connection, that in his work he rarely indulges in any psychological analysis, and is rarely concerned with the detailed development of a character.) His very style, then, seems to imply that the use of the intellect, with its careful discriminations, may blur the rendering of experience and may falsify it; and this style, in connection with his basic concern for the character of marginal sensibility, may be taken as implying a distrust of the intellect in solving man's basic problems. It is as though he should say: despite the application of the human intellect to the problems of the world, the world is still a disorderly and brutal mess, in which it is hard to find any sure scale of values; therefore, it is well for one to remember the demands of fundamental situations—those involving sex, love, danger, and death, in which the instinctive life is foremost—which are frequently glossed over or falsified by social conventions or sterile intellectuality, and to remember the simple virtues of courage, honesty, fidelity, discipline.

But is all of this a way of saying that Hemingway is really writing innocently, without calculation, crudely? Now, as a matter of fact, his style is a result of calculation, and is not, strictly speaking, spontaneous and naïve at all. His style is, then, a dramatic device, developed because of its appropriateness to the total effect which he intends to give. A writer who was in point of fact uninstructed and spontaneous would probably not be able to achieve the impression of spontaneity and immediacy which is found in Hemingway's best work, the work in which his basic attitude and subject matter can be truly and functionally coordinated.

1. Compare "Tennessee's Partner" and "The Outcasts of Poker Flat" with "The Killers" on the point of "marginal sensibility," especially in connection with the matter of style.

2. Write an interpretation of one of the other stories by Hemingway mentioned in this discussion.

Head by Scopas
EDWARD DONAHOE

WE WALKED for a long time up the steep path which was supposed to lead to the quiet place Alan knew. We had started from Leysin at seven in order to have a full day in the place skiing. Alan expected to do a water color of the Pic Chaussy. Even the dullest Englishmen seem to be able to paint fairly decent water colors. Alan had taught himself to draw during the three years he had been in a clinic at Leysin. His delicate little pictures reminded me of the water colors Jane Austen's sister Cassandra made for *Love and Friendship*. Alan had no business to be painting Alps.

I said I had brought a bottle of Chambertin. "I can't drink much wine because of my face," he said. He had lupus, a tuberculous infection of the skin. The left side of his face was scarred and discolored. The right one was like one of the beautiful heads by Scopas in the Boston Museum. It was always a shock to people in a railway carriage or a restaurant when his left profile was revealed after they had admired his right.

The surface of the snow was broken up into innumerable hard little crystal flakes like rhinestones. We had to put on dark glasses because of the unbearable brightness of the sunlight on the snow. The path was getting steeper and we were very tired under the weight of our skis and rucksacks when we reached the little café. There was no one there. It was too early in the morning for customers. Mme. Veillard had probably gone down to Leysin village to buy provisions and to gossip. I was outdone with her because I had planned to have a warming grog there.

"Well, we can at least stop to put on our skis now," Alan said. "It's level, more or less, from here on." We strapped them on, readjusted our rucksacks, and glided across a long meadow like sailboats. The tips of our skis scattered the hard crystals of snow like sea foam. Our breaths blew white. The left side of Alan's face was bright purple. I tried not to look at it.

"There's the place," he said, pointing to a deep basin of shining snow fringed at the top on all sides by dark fir trees. A deserted chalet was at the bottom, its rotten boards stained black. We went inside and undressed. It is not unusual to ski without clothes at Leysin. The sun is very warm on one's skin. One must be careful, though, not to fall down into the snow. Alan wore a gee-string, but I wanted to be brown all over and said so. Alan climbed to the top of the basin and dropped off into space like a bird. We made figures and faces in the snow and drew intricate patterns with our skis, occasionally falling down like collapsing kites, laughing and shouting in our icy graves.

"We've had enough," Alan said, when it was almost noon. "Let's have some lunch." I poured the wine into aluminum cups. Alan hesitated and took some. "It will warm me up," he said. The black bread and strong cheese were delicious. We ate and drank eagerly and noisily. "If you want a good light you had better begin your water color," I said, after we had sat smoking for an hour or so. We had finished the bottle of Chambertin.

He began to sketch a little more boldly than usual the outline of the mountain far to the north of us above the fir trees. As he mixed his colors I watched him idly, thinking his life unenviable enough. Since childhood he had had the ugly infection on his face. In London, where he lived, he had spent many years trying to be cured. Surgeons there had grafted fresh skin on diseased skin. He had been burned time and again by X rays. The scars from the burning he would never lose. The infection had ceased spreading when he came to Switzerland. His left ear was scarcely touched and his left eye was safe. I refrained from asking him cruel questions: if women ever kissed him, if people minded his sitting down across from them in restaurants, if there was danger of his infecting someone else. It is hard to resist such natural cruelty. Children do not try. He had told me that he had been called Nasty-Face by the boys at his school. After that and worse persecution he had begged to be tutored at home. He was deeply ignorant. He also knew strange, unusual things. At twenty he was virginal. He would be, I supposed, repellent to most women only on account of his infection.

"Do you know my girl?" he asked suddenly. I was startled and confused. It was as if he had guessed what I had been thinking about.

"No, I'm afraid not," I said. "Who is she?"

"Oh she's a jolly girl, pretty as the devil. She's Swiss. You've never seen her around Leysin, I suppose." He laughed aloud to himself. Clearly he wanted the pleasure of talking about her.

"Do you like her very much?" I asked. Immediately I regretted the silly question. I was not interested in knowing whether he liked his girl or not.

"Like her? I say, I *love* her!" He jabbed his brush violently into a mound of Indian Lake. I was silent. He looked up at me surprised and almost displeased that I did not say something.

"That's very nice," I said weakly. "She must be charming."

"She damn well is. She wants to marry me, too. I wrote mother about it. Her father is a patient at L'Aiglon. His family are here to be near him, so she has a dull time. They're from Geneva."

"I've never met anyone from Geneva."

"Would you like to meet Hedwige?"

"Is that her name? Of course. The two of you might have dinner with me tomorrow night." I was suddenly caught with his own enthusiasm.

"She can't go out unchaperoned." He looked at me, waiting.

"Well, I don't want her mother, thank you," I said. "You've got those clouds a little too heavy. They seem solider than your mountain."

"You know," he said, ignoring my criticism of his picture, "I wish I could have an affair with a girl before I marry Hedwige. I'd be more experienced and sure of myself."

"What about Hedwige herself?" I laughed at my daring. Alan was with the Victorians about women. They were only good or bad.

"Oh, she wouldn't."

Some crows were pecking at the crumbs we had scattered. They were very hungry and not at all frightened.

"Have you ever said anything to her about it?" I ventured.

"No, but she wouldn't. She's going to be my wife, you know. She loves me like anything." He laughed aloud to himself again.

"How can you tell? Does she show she loves you in some particular way? I mean, does she kiss you?"

"Oh yes," he said eagerly. "She doesn't seem to mind my face a bit —and that's something, you know. She writes me wonderful letters every day, too. She was going to the university when her father became ill. She writes frightfully well. I have one of her letters in my 'breeks' in the chalet. Shall I read it to you?"

"If you like."

He was unused to wine. The Chambertin had released him from his usual restraint. He stepped away from the easel and ran over to the chalet to get the letter. He came out reading it to himself. Then he smiled and shook his head. "I think this one's too personal, after all. She wouldn't like to let anyone see it."

I was unable to put aside my sudden curiosity. "Please let me read it. I won't tell anybody. Please let me," I pleaded.

He folded the letter and put it into the envelope. I leaped toward him, caught him round the waist, and we tumbled into the snow, laughing. I got the letter away from him and ran into the chalet, bolting the door on the inside. He pounded his fists against it.

The letter was in French. "My dear Alan," I hastily translated, "you did not come to see me last night, and I had to go to bed without seeing your beautiful face. That made me very restless and sad. I must see your face every day. So I lay awake for hours thinking of it, very lovely like a marble head by some Greek sculptor, which had been dug up by the careless assistant of an archaeologist, who scraped the left cheek with his spade and broke away the warm, luminous surface, spoiling the patina forever. I am in love with you, Alan, because you are English and not Swiss. But, more than that, I am in love with you because of your beautiful Greek fragment of a face . . ."

I unbolted the door. He had walked away and would not turn around when I called.*

INTERPRETATION

1. The theme of this story may seem to be a very simple one. Why has the author felt it necessary to approach it so indirectly?

2. Is the detail of the skiing trip justified? How?

* From *Space;* by permission of the author; copyright, 1934.

3. One can easily see the advantages to be gained by making the "reve-lation" come in terms of the girl's letter. Could one say that the structural problem of the story is basically that of arranging matters so that the showing of the deeply personal letter to the narrator shall seem natural and credible and so that what the letter itself says shall seem credible and convincing?

The Fly

KATHERINE MANSFIELD

"Y'ARE very snug in here," piped old Mr. Woodifield, and he peered out of the great, green leather armchair by his friend, the boss's desk, as a baby peers out of its pram. His talk was over; it was time for him to be off. But he did not want to go. Since he had retired, since his . . . stroke, the wife and the girls kept him boxed up in the house every day of the week except Tuesday. On Tuesday he was dressed up and brushed and allowed to cut back to the City for the day. Though what he did there the wife and girls couldn't imagine. Made a nuisance of himself to his friends, they supposed. . . . Well, perhaps so. All the same, we cling to our last pleasures as the tree clings to its last leaves. So there sat old Woodifield, smoking a cigar and staring almost greedily at the boss, who rolled in his office chair, stout, rosy, five years older than he, and still going strong, still at the helm. It did one good to see him.

Wistfully, admiringly, the old voice added, "It's snug in here, upon my word!"

"Yes, it's comfortable enough," agreed the boss, and he flipped *The Financial Times* with a paper knife. As a matter of fact he was proud of his room; he liked to have it admired, especially by old Woodifield. It gave him a feeling of deep, solid satisfaction to be planted there in the midst of it in full view of that frail old figure in the muffler.

"I've had it done up lately," he explained, as he had explained for the past—how many?—weeks. "'New carpet," and he pointed to the bright red carpet with a pattern of large white rings. "New furniture," and he nodded towards the massive bookcase and the table with legs like twisted treacle. "Electric heating!" He waved almost exultantly towards the five transparent, pearly sausages glowing so softly in the tilted copper pan.

But he did not draw old Woodifield's attention to the photograph over the table of a grave-looking boy in uniform standing in one of those spectral photographers' parks with photographers' storm clouds behind him. It was not new. It had been there for over six years.

"There was something I wanted to tell you," said old Woodifield, and his eyes grew dim remembering. "Now what was it? I had it in mind when I started out this morning." His hands began to tremble, and patches of red showed above his beard.

Poor old chap, he's on his last pins, thought the boss. And, feeling kindly, he winked at the old man, and said jokingly, "I tell you what. I've got a little drop of something here that'll do you good before you go out into the cold again. It's beautiful stuff. It wouldn't hurt a child." He took a key off his watch-chain, unlocked a cupboard below his desk, and drew forth a dark, squat bottle. "That's the medicine," said he. "And the man from whom I got it told me on the strict Q.T. it came from the cellars at Windsor Castle."

Old Woodifield's mouth fell open at the sight. He couldn't have looked more surprised if the boss had produced a rabbit.   .

"It's whisky, ain't it?" he piped, feebly.

The boss turned the bottle and lovingly showed him the label. Whisky it was.

"D'you know," said he, peering up at the boss wonderingly, "they won't let me touch it at home." And he looked as though he was going to cry.

"Ah, that's where we know a bit more than the ladies," cried the boss, swooping across for two tumblers that stood on the table with the water bottle, and pouring a generous finger into each. "Drink it down. It'll do you good. And don't put any water with it. It's sacrilege to tamper with stuff like this. Ah!" He tossed off his, pulled out his handkerchief, hastily wiped his mustaches, and cocked an eye at old Woodifield, who was rolling his in his chaps.

The old man swallowed, was silent a moment, and then said faintly, "It's nutty!"

But it warmed him; it crept into his chill old brain—he remembered.

"That was it," he said, heaving himself out of his chair. "I thought you'd like to know. The girls were in Belgium last week having a look at poor Reggie's grave, and they happened to come across your boy's. They are quite near each other, it seems."

Old Woodifield paused, but the boss made no reply. Only a quiver of his eyelids showed that he heard.

"The girls were delighted with the way the place is kept," piped the old voice. "Beautifully looked after. Couldn't be better if they were at home. You've not been across, have yer?"

"No, no!" For various reasons the boss had not been across.

"There's miles of it," quavered old Woodifield, "and it's all as neat as a garden. Flowers growing on all the graves. Nice broad paths." It was plain from his voice how much he liked a nice broad path.

The pause came again. Then the old man brightened wonderfully.

"D'you know what the hotel made the girls pay for a pot of jam?" he piped. "Ten francs! Robbery, I call it. It was a little pot, so Gertrude says, no bigger than a half-crown. And she hadn't taken more than a spoonful when they charged her ten francs. Gertrude brought the pot away with her to teach 'em a lesson. Quite right, too; it's trading on our feelings. They think because we're over there having a look around we're ready to pay anything. That's what it is." And he turned towards the door.

"Quite right, quite right!" cried the boss, though what was quite right he hadn't the least idea. He came round by his desk, followed the shuffling footsteps to the door, and saw the old fellow out. Woodifield was gone.

For a long moment the boss stayed, staring at nothing, while the gray-haired office messenger, watching him, dodged in and out of his cubbyhole like a dog that expects to be taken for a run: "I'll see nobody for half an hour, Macey," said the boss. "Understand? Nobody at all."

"Very good, sir."

The door shut, the firm, heavy steps recrossed the bright carpet, the fat body plumped down in the spring chair, and leaning forward, the boss covered his face with his hands. He wanted, he intended, he had arranged to weep. . . .

It had been a terrible shock to him when old Woodifield sprang that remark upon him about the boy's grave. It was exactly as though the earth had opened and he had seen the boy lying there with Woodifield's girls staring down at him. For it was strange. Although over six years had passed away, the boss never thought of the boy except as lying unchanged, unblemished in his uniform, asleep for ever. "My son!" groaned the boss. But no tears came yet. In the past, in the first months and even years after the boy's death, he had only to say those words to be overcome by such grief that nothing short of a violent fit of weeping could relieve him. Time, he had declared then, he had told everybody, could make no difference. Other men perhaps might recover, might live their loss down, but not he. How was it possible? His boy was an only son. Ever since his birth the boss had worked at building up this business for him; it had no other meaning if it was not for the boy. Life itself had come to have no other meaning. How on earth could he have slaved, denied himself, kept going all these years without the promise for ever before him of the boy's stepping into his shoes and carrying on where he left off?

And that promise had been so near being fulfilled. The boy had been in the office learning the ropes for a year before the war. Every morning they had started off together; they had come back by the same train. And what congratulations he had received as the boy's father! No wonder; he had taken to it marvelously. As to his popularity with the staff, every man jack of them down to old Macey couldn't make enough of the boy. And he wasn't in the least spoiled. No, he was just his bright, natural self, with the right word for everybody, with that boyish look and his habit of saying, "Simply splendid!"

But all that was over and done with as though it never had been. The day had come when Macey had handed him the telegram that brought the whole place crashing about his head. "Deeply regret to inform you . . ." And he had left the office a broken man, with his life in ruins.

Six years ago, six years . . . How quickly time passed! It might have happened yesterday. The boss took his hands from his face; he was puzzled. Something seemed to be wrong with him. He wasn't feeling as he wanted to feel. He decided to get up and have a look at the boy's photograph. But it wasn't a favorite photograph of his; the expression was unnatural. It was cold, even stern-looking. The boy had never looked like that.

At that moment the boss noticed that a fly had fallen into his broad inkpot, and was trying feebly but desperately to clamber out again. Help! help! said those struggling legs. But the sides of the inkpot were wet and slippery; it fell back again and began to swim. The boss took up a pen, picked the fly out of the ink, and shook it on to a piece of blotting paper. For a fraction of a second it lay still on the dark patch that oozed round it. Then the front legs waved, took hold, and, pulling its small sodden body up it began the immense task of cleaning the ink from its wings. Over and under, over and under, went a leg along a wing, as the stone goes over and under the scythe. Then there was a pause, while the fly, seeming to stand on the tips of its toes, tried to expand first one wing and then the other. It succeeded at last, and, sitting down, it began, like a minute cat, to clean its face. Now one could imagine that the little front legs rubbed against each other lightly, joyfully. The horrible danger was over; it had escaped; it was ready for life again.

But just then the boss had an idea. He plunged his pen back into the ink, leaned his thick wrist on the blotting paper, and as the fly tried its wings down came a great heavy blot. What would it make of that? What indeed! The little beggar seemed absolutely cowed, stunned, and afraid to move because of what would happen next. But then, as if painfully, it dragged itself forward. The front legs waved, caught hold, and, more slowly this time, the task began from the beginning.

"He's a plucky little devil," thought the boss, and he felt a real admiration for the fly's courage. That was the way to tackle things; that was the right spirit. Never say die; it was only a question of . . . But the fly had again finished its laborious task, and the boss had just time to refill his pen, to shake fair and square on the new-cleaned body yet another dark drop. What about it this time? A painful moment of suspense followed. But behold, the front legs were again waving; the boss felt a rush of relief. He leaned over the fly and said to it tenderly, "You artful little b. . . ." And he actually had the brilliant notion of breathing on it to help the drying process. All the same, there was something timid and weak about its efforts now, and the boss decided that this time should be the last, as he dipped the pen into the inkpot.

It was. The last blot fell on the soaked blotting paper, and the draggled fly lay in it and did not stir. The back legs were stuck to the body; the front legs were not to be seen.

"Come on," said the boss. "Look sharp!" And he stirred it with his pen—in vain. Nothing happened or was likely to happen. The fly was dead.

The boss lifted the corpse on the end of the paper knife and flung it into the wastepaper basket, but such a grinding feeling of wretchedness seized him that he felt positively frightened. He started forward and pressed the bell for Macey.

"Bring me some fresh blotting paper," he said, sternly, "and look sharp about it." And while the old dog padded away he fell to wondering what it was he had been thinking about before. What was it? It was . . . He took out his handkerchief and passed it inside his collar. For the life of him he could not remember.*

INTERPRETATION

1. Before attempting to define the theme of this story one should consider several preliminary questions. (*a*) It is obvious that the function of old Woodifield is to provide information—to serve as a device for exposition—and to focus attention on the problem of the boss's relation to the dead son. But other functions are served by the introduction of this character, functions which involve the very meaning of the story. What are they? (*b*) What purpose is served beyond the purpose of mere exposition by the cutback following Woodifield's departure? Is the main conflict of the story presented here? The boss has been accustomed to give way to his grief, and has expected to give way to it now, but he cannot weep. Why? (*c*) It is obvious that the introduction of the incident of the fly is used to indicate the boss's distraction from his grief, from his intention to weep, but does the incident have a further function? Can the struggling fly be regarded as a symbol? If so, of what?

2. The boss had felt that time would never dull his grief. Relate this fact to the mention of new carpet and new furniture in the office, to the general atmosphere of well-being in the office of the firm, and to the

* From *The Dove's Nest;* by permission of and special arrangement with Alfred A. Knopf, Inc., authorized publishers.

boss's attitude of pity and patronage toward the broken old employee of the firm. The boss's interest in the fly's struggle to maintain its life, to survive somehow, and his final testing of the fly's strength, a test which kills the fly and leaves the boss confused and ashamed, is intended to tell the reader something about the boss's own situation. What is that "something"?

3. What, then, is the theme of the story? Does the end of the story simply mean that the boss has ceased to be sentimental? Has he gained something, or has he lost something at the end? Or has he done both?

4. In the analysis of the story "War," by Pirandello, the question is raised as to when the son of the patriotic father actually "dies"—dies, that is, for the father. Discuss the present story with the same consideration in mind.

I Want to Know Why

SHERWOOD ANDERSON

WE GOT UP at four in the morning, that first day in the east. On the evening before we had climbed off a freight train at the edge of town, and with the true instinct of Kentucky boys had found our way across town and to the racetrack and the stables at once. Then we knew we were all right. Hanley Turner right away found a nigger we knew. It was Bildad Johnson who in the winter works at Ed Becker's livery barn in our home town, Beckersville. Bildad is a good cook as almost all our niggers are and of course he, like everyone in our part of Kentucky who is anyone at all, likes the horses. In the spring Bildad begins to scratch around. A nigger from our country can flatter and wheedle anyone into letting him do most anything he wants. Bildad wheedles the stable men and the trainers from the horse farms in our country around Lexington. The trainers come into town in the evening to stand around and talk and maybe get into a poker game. Bildad gets in with them. He is always doing little favors and telling about things to eat, chicken browned in a pan, and how is the best way to cook sweet potatoes and corn bread. It makes your mouth water to hear him.

When the racing season comes on and the horses go to the races and there is all the talk on the streets in the evenings about the new colts, and everyone says when they are going over to Lexington or

to the spring meeting at Churchill Downs or to Latonia, and the horse-
men that have been down to New Orleans or maybe at the winter
meeting at Havana in Cuba come home to spend a week before they
start out again, at such a time when everything talked about in Beckersville is just horses and nothing else and the outfits start out and horse
racing is in every breath of air you breathe, Bildad shows up with a
job as cook for some outfit. Often when I think about it, his always
going all season to the races and working in the livery barn in the
winter where horses are and where men like to come and talk about
horses, I wish I was a nigger. It's a foolish thing to say, but that's
the way I am about being around horses, just crazy. I can't help it.

Well, I must tell you about what we did and let you in on what
I'm talking about. Four of us boys from Beckersville, all whites and
sons of men who live in Beckersville regular, made up our minds we
were going to the races, not just to Lexington or Louisville, I don't
mean, but to the big eastern track we were always hearing our Beckersville men talk about, to Saratoga. We were all pretty young then.
I was just turned fifteen and I was the oldest of the four. It was my
scheme. I admit that and I talked the others into trying it. There was
Hanley Turner and Henry Rieback and Tom Tumberton and myself. It had thirty-seven dollars I had earned during the winter working nights and Saturdays in Enoch Myer's grocery. Henry Rieback
had eleven dollars and the others, Hanley and Tom, had only a dollar
or two each. We fixed it all up and laid low until the Kentucky spring
meetings were over and some of our men, the sportiest ones, the ones
we envied the most, had cut out—then we cut out too.

I won't tell you the trouble we had beating our way on freights and
all. We went through Cleveland and Buffalo and other cities and saw
Niagara Falls. We bought things there, souvenirs and spoons and cards
and shells with pictures of the Falls on them for our sisters and
mothers, but thought we had better not send any of the things home.
We didn't want to put the folks on our trail and maybe be nabbed.

We got into Saratoga as I said at night and went to the track.
Bildad fed us up. He showed us a place to sleep in hay over a shed
and promised to keep still. Niggers are all right about things like that.
They won't squeal on you. Often a white man you might meet, when
you had run away from home like that, might appear to be all right

and give you a quarter or a half dollar or something, and then go right and give you away. White men will do that, but not a nigger. You can trust them. They are squarer with kids. I don't know why.

At the Saratoga meeting that year there were a lot of men from home. Dave Williams and Arthur Mulford and Jerry Myers and others. Then there was a lot from Louisville and Lexington Henry Rieback knew but I didn't. They were professional gamblers and Henry Rieback's father is one too. He is what is called a sheet writer and goes away most of the year to tracks. In the winter when he is home in Beckersville he don't stay there much but goes away to cities and deals faro. He is a nice man and generous, is always sending Henry presents, a bicycle and a gold watch and a boy scout suit of clothes and things like that.

My own father is a lawyer. He's all right, but don't make much money and can't buy me things and anyway I'm getting so old now I don't expect it. He never said nothing to me against Henry, but Hanley Turner and Tom Tumberton's fathers did. They said to their boys that money so come by is no good and they didn't want their boys brought up to hear gamblers' talk and be thinking about such things and maybe embrace them.

That's all right and I guess the men know what they are talking about, but I don't see what it's got to do with Henry or horses either. That's what I'm writing this story about. I'm puzzled. I'm getting to be a man and want to think straight and be O.K., and there's something I saw at the race meeting at the eastern track I can't figure out.

I can't help it, I'm crazy about thoroughbred horses. I've always been that way. When I was ten years old and saw I was growing to be big and couldn't be a rider I was so sorry I nearly died. Harry Hellinfinger in Beckersville, whose father is Postmaster, is grown up and too lazy to work, but likes to stand around in the street and get up jokes on boys like sending them to a hardware store for a gimlet to bore square holes and other jokes like that. He played one on me. He told me that if I would eat a half a cigar I would be stunted and not grow any more and maybe could be a rider. I did it. When father wasn't looking I took a cigar out of his pocket and gagged it down some way. It made me awful sick and the doctor had to be sent for, and then it did no good. I kept right on growing. It

was a joke. When I told what I had done and why most fathers
would have whipped me but mine didn't.

Well, I didn't get stunted and didn't die. It serves Harry Hellinfinger right. Then I made up my mind I would like to be a stable
boy, but had to give that up too. Mostly niggers do that work and I
knew father wouldn't let me go into it. No use to ask him.

If you've never been crazy about thoroughbreds it's because you've
never been around where they are much and don't know any better.
They're beautiful. There isn't anything so lovely and clean and full of
spunk and honest and everything as some racehorses. On the big
horse farms that are all around our town Beckersville there are tracks
and the horses run in the early morning. More than a thousand times
I've got out of bed before daylight and walked two or three miles to
the tracks. Mother wouldn't of let me go but father always says, "Let
him alone." So I got some bread out of the bread box and some butter
and jam, gobbled it and lit out.

At the tracks you sit on the fence with men, whites and niggers,
and they chew tobacco and talk, and then the colts are brought out.
It's early and the grass is covered with shiny dew and in another field
a man is plowing and they are frying things in a shed where the
track niggers sleep, and you know how a nigger can giggle and laugh
and say things that make you laugh. A white man can't do it and some
niggers can't but a track nigger can every time.

And so the colts are brought out and some are just galloped by
stable boys, but almost every morning on a big track owned by a
rich man who lives maybe in New York, there are always, nearly
every morning, a few colts and some of the old racehorses and geldings
and mares that are cut loose.

It brings a lump up into my throat when a horse runs. I don't
mean all horses but some. I can pick them nearly every time. It's in
my blood like in the blood of race-track niggers and trainers. Even
when they just go slop-jogging along with a little nigger on their
backs I can tell a winner. If my throat hurts and it's hard for me to
swallow, that's him. He'll run like Sam Hill when you let him out.
If he don't win every time it'll be a wonder and because they've got
him in a pocket behind another or he was pulled or got off bad at

the post or something. If I wanted to be a gambler like Henry Rieback's father I could get rich. I know I could and Henry says so too.
All I would have to do is to wait 'til that hurt comes when I see a
horse and then bet every cent. That's what I would do if I wanted
to be a gambler, but I don't.

When you're at the tracks in the morning—not the race tracks but
the training tracks around Beckersville—you don't see a horse, the
kind I've been talking about, very often, but it's nice anyway. Any
thoroughbred, that is sired right and out of a good mare and trained
by a man that knows how, can run. If he couldn't what would he
be there for and not pulling a plow?

Well, out of the stables they come and the boys are on their backs
and it's lovely to be there. You hunch down on top of the fence and
itch inside you. Over in the sheds the niggers giggle and sing. Bacon
is being fried and coffee made. Everything smells lovely. Nothing
smells better than coffee and manure and horses and niggers and
bacon frying and pipes being smoked out of doors on a morning like
that. It just gets you, that's what it does.

But about Saratoga. We was there six days and not a soul from
home seen us and everything came off just as we wanted it to, fine
weather and horses and races and all. We beat our way home and
Bildad gave us a basket with fried chicken and bread and other eat-
ables in, and I had eighteen dollars when we got back to Beckersville.
Mother jawed and cried but Pop didn't say much. I told everything
we done except one thing. I did and saw that alone. That's what I'm
writing about. It got me upset. I think about it at night. Here it is.

At Saratoga we laid up nights in the hay in the shed Bildad had
showed us and ate with the niggers early and at night when the
race people had all gone away. The men from home stayed mostly in
the grandstand and betting field, and didn't come out around the
places where the horses are kept except to the paddocks just before a
race when the horses are saddled. At Saratoga they don't have paddocks under an open shed as at Lexington and Churchill Downs
and other tracks down in our country, but saddle the horses right out
in an open place under trees on a lawn as smooth and nice as Banker
Bohon's front yard here in Beckersville. It's lovely. The horses are

sweaty and nervous and shine and the men come out and smoke cigars and look at them and the trainers are there and the owners, and your heart thumps so you can hardly breathe.

Then the bugle blows for post and the boys that ride come running out with their silk clothes on and you run to get a place by the fence with the niggers.

I always am wanting to be a trainer or owner, and at the risk of being seen and caught and sent home I went to the paddocks before every race. The other boys didn't but I did.

We got to Saratoga on a Friday and on Wednesday the next week the big Mullford Handicap was to be run. Middlestride was in it and Sunstreak. The weather was fine and the track fast. I couldn't sleep the night before.

What had happened was that both these horses are the kind it makes my throat hurt to see. Middlestride is long and looks awkward and is a gelding. He belongs to Joe Thompson, a little owner from home who only has a half-dozen horses. The Mullford Handicap is for a mile and Middlestride can't untrack fast. He goes away slow and is always way back at the half, then he begins to run and if the race is a mile and a quarter he'll just eat up everything and get there.

Sunstreak is different. He is a stallion and nervous and belongs on the biggest farm we've got in our country, the Van Riddle place that belongs to Mr. Van Riddle of New York. Sunstreak is like a girl you think about sometimes but never see. He is hard all over and lovely too. When you look at his head you want to kiss him. He is trained by Jerry Tillford who knows me and has been good to me lots of times, lets me walk into a horse's stall to look at him close and other things. There isn't anything as sweet as that horse. He stands at the post quiet and not letting on, but he is just burning up inside. Then when the barrier goes up he is off like his name, Sunstreak. It makes you ache to see him. It hurts you. He just lays down and runs like a bird dog. There can't anything I ever see run like him except Middlestride when he gets untracked and stretches himself.

Gee! I ached to see that race and those two horses run, ached and dreaded it too. I didn't want to see either of our horses beaten. We had never sent a pair like that to the races before. Old men in Beckersville said so and the niggers said so. It was a fact.

Before the race I went over to the paddocks to see. I looked a last look at Middlestride, who isn't such a much standing in a paddock that way, then I went to see Sunstreak.

It was his day. I knew when I see him. I forgot all about being seen myself and walked right up. All the men from Beckersville were there and no one noticed me except Jerry Tillford. He saw me and something happened. I'll tell you about that.

I was standing looking at that horse and aching. In some way, I can't tell how, I knew just how Sunstreak felt inside. He was quiet and letting the niggers rub his legs and Mr. Van Riddle himself put the saddle on, but he was just a raging torrent inside. He was like the water in the river at Niagara Falls just before it goes plunk down. That horse wasn't thinking about running. He don't have to think about that. He was just thinking about holding himself back 'til the time for the running came. I knew that. I could just in a way see right inside him. He was going to do some awful running and I knew it. He wasn't bragging or letting on much or prancing or making a fuss, but just waiting. I knew it and Jerry Tillford his trainer knew. I looked up and then that man and I looked into each other's eyes. Something happened to me. I guess I loved the man as much as I did the horse because he knew what I knew. Seemed to me there wasn't anything in the world but that man and the horse and me. I cried and Jerry Tillford had a shine in his eyes. Then I came away to the fence to wait for the race. The horse was better than me, more steadier, and now I know better than Jerry. He was the quietest and he had to do the running.

Sunstreak ran first of course and he busted the world's record for a mile. I've seen that if I never see anything more. Everything came out just as I expected. Middlestride got left at the post and was way back and closed up to be second, just as I knew he would. He'll get a world's record too some day. They can't skin the Beckersville country on horses.

I watched the race calm because I knew what would happen. I was sure. Hanley Turner and Henry Rieback and Tom Tumberton were all more excited than me.

A funny thing had happened to me. I was thinking about Jerry Tillford the trainer and how happy he was all through the race. I liked him that afternoon even more than I ever liked my own father. I almost forgot the horses thinking that way about him. It was because of what I had seen in his eyes as he stood in the paddocks beside Sunstreak before the race started. I knew he had been watching and working with Sunstreak since the horse was a baby colt, had taught him to run and be patient and when to let himself out and not to quit, never. I knew that for him it was like a mother seeing her child do something brave or wonderful. It was the first time I ever felt for a man like that.

After the race that night I cut out from Tom and Hanley and Henry. I wanted to be by myself and I wanted to be near Jerry Tillford if I could work it. Here is what happened.

The track in Saratoga is near the edge of town. It is all polished up and trees around, the evergreen kind, and grass and everything painted and nice. If you go past the track you get to a hard road made of asphalt for automobiles, and if you go along this for a few miles there is a road turns off to a little rummy-looking farmhouse set in a yard.

That night after the race I went along that road because I had seen Jerry and some other men go that way in an automobile. I didn't expect to find them. I walked for a ways and then sat down by a fence to think. It was the direction they went in. I wanted to be as near Jerry as I could. I felt close to him. Pretty soon I went up the side road—I don't know why—and came to the rummy farmhouse. I was just lonesome to see Jerry, like wanting to see your father at night when you are a young kid. Just then an automobile came along and turned in. Jerry was in it and Henry Rieback's father, and Arthur Bedford from home, and Dave Williams and two other men I didn't know. They got out of the car and went into the house, all but Henry Rieback's father who quarreled with them and said he wouldn't go. It was only about nine o'clock, but they were all drunk and the rummy-looking farmhouse was a place for bad women to stay in. That's what it was. I crept up along a fence and looked through a window and saw.

It's what give me the fantods. I can't make it out. The women in the house were all ugly mean-looking women, not nice to look at or be near. They were homely too, except one who was tall and looked a little like the gelding Middlestride, but not clean like him, but with a hard ugly mouth. She had red hair. I saw everything plain. I got up by an old rosebush by an open window and looked. The women had on loose dresses and sat around in chairs. The men came in and some sat on the women's laps. The place smelled rotten and there was rotten talk, the kind a kid hears around a livery stable in a town like Beckersville in the winter but don't ever expect to hear talked when there are women around. It was rotten. A nigger wouldn't go into such a place.

I looked at Jerry Tillford. I've told you how I had been feeling about him on account of his knowing what was going on inside of Sunstreak in the minute before he went to the post for the race in which he made a world's record.

Jerry bragged in that bad-woman house as I know Sunstreak wouldn't never have bragged. He said that he made that horse, that it was him that won the race and made the record. He lied and bragged like a fool. I never heard such silly talk.

And then, what do you suppose he did! He looked at the woman in there, the one that was lean and hard-mouthed and looked a little like the gelding Middlestride, but not clean like him, and his eyes began to shine just as they did when he looked at me and at Sunstreak in the paddocks at the track in the afternoon. I stood there by the window—gee!—but I wished I hadn't gone away from the tracks, but had stayed with the boys and the niggers and the horses. The tall rotten-looking woman was between us just as Sunstreak was in the paddocks in the afternoon.

Then, all of a sudden, I began to hate that man. I wanted to scream and rush in the room and kill him. I never had such a feeling before. I was so mad clean through that I cried and my fists were doubled up so my fingernails cut my hands.

And Jerry's eyes kept shining and he waved back and forth, and then he went and kissed that woman and I crept away and went back to the tracks and to bed and didn't sleep hardly any, and then next day I got the other kids to start home with me and never told them anything I seen.

I been thinking about it ever since. I can't make it out. Spring has come again and I'm nearly sixteen and go to the tracks mornings same as always, and I see Sunstreak and Middlestride and a new colt named Strident I'll bet will lay them all out, but no one thinks so but me and two or three niggers.

But things are different. At the tracks the air don't taste as good or smell as good. It's because a man like Jerry Tillford, who knows what he does, could see a horse like Sunstreak run, and kiss a woman like that the same day. I can't make it out. Darn him, what did he want to do like that for? I keep thinking about it and it spoils looking at horses and smelling things and hearing niggers laugh and everything. Sometimes I'm so mad about it I want to fight someone. It gives me the fantods. What did he do it for? I want to know why.*

INTERPRETATION

This story, like "The Killers," by Hemingway, is a story of the "initiation." That is, the hero—a boy, as in "The Killers"—discovers something about the nature of evil, and tries to find some way of coming to terms with his discovery. Perhaps the best way to define the "discovery" is to trace the stages by which it is arrived at in the story.

The story is a first-person account of what happens to a boy who runs away to the races at Saratoga. But the boy has a special motive in telling the story. The incident which he narrates raises a problem which he finds difficult to cope with. He does not tell us this in so many words as he begins his account, but as the story develops we get hints as to the nature of the problem, long before it is specified at the climax. These hints are not merely important as a means of providing mechanical preparation for the problem. They do accomplish this, but they also, more importantly, accomplish two other things. First, they suggest the nature of the boy to whom the final incident comes with such impact. To some boys this incident would have been almost meaningless; therefore, the story must provide some dramatic probability for the effect on this particular boy. The boy in his first-person narration can give us the details of his experience, but he cannot tell us in so many words what he himself is like; that, too, must be conveyed by hints which the reader can interpret. Second, the hints, arising from many different circumstances, imply that the final problem is an all-pervasive one and is not to be associated merely with the incident at the climax.

The boy starts off in boy fashion by trying to tell us something about

* From *The Triumph of the Egg;* by permission of Eleanor Anderson.

himself, where he lives, how he likes horses, how he wishes he were a Negro so he could be around horses all the time, how Negroes are "squarer" with kids than white men are, how he can't understand how the father of his friend, Henry Rieback, is "a nice man and generous," even though he is a gambler. These details seem merely casual, but we suddenly discover that to the boy they are not casual. They have a bearing on his problem. "That's all right and I guess the men know what they are talking about," he says in commenting on the fact that some families don't want their sons to associate with Henry Rieback because his father is a gambler or don't permit them to hang around the horses because there is gambling at the tracks. But he goes on to say, "I don't see what it's got to do with Henry or with horses either. That's what I'm writing this story about. I'm puzzled. I'm getting to be a man and want to think straight and be O.K."

This pronouncement comes with a little dramatic shock after the apparently casual description of himself and of his home town. How do these details about Negroes and horses and Henry Rieback and gambling have a bearing on thinking straight and being O.K.? We see that the boy has begun to question some of the accepted values and codes of the society in which he lives. (Is the boy's attitude simply one of unthinking rebellion, or are his questions real questions?) He feels that the Negroes, who hold an inferior position in the community in which he lives, have certain points of superiority over the white people; the Negroes love the horses, while many of the white people see the horses only as something associated with the vice of gambling, and the Negroes are, in a sense, more honest, they are "squarer with kids." He feels that the community is unfair in condemning Henry Rieback's father, who, even though he is a gambler, is a "nice man and generous," and is even more unfair in condemning Henry simply because his father is not acceptable. And, furthermore, he feels that something is wrong with people who cannot love horses simply because gambling goes on at race tracks. All of this means that he is beginning to understand that ordinarily accepted standards of inferiority and superiority, of right and wrong, of good and bad, of ugliness and beauty, may really work out unjustly when they are applied by a sort of rule of thumb to particular cases. He is puzzled, because this private discovery is in contradiction to the things he has been taught. So he says; "I guess the men know what they are talking about, but I don't see what it's got to do with Henry or with horses either."

We see, at this point in the story, that the Negroes, the Rieback boy, and the horses are all involved in the problem which puzzles the boy. At first glance, it may seem strange that human beings and horses are bracketed together in his mind. But then the boy begins to develop more fully for us exactly what the horses mean to him. It is not merely the excitement of the race track which attracts him. It is something about the horses themselves. "They're beautiful," he says. And he continues: "There isn't anything so lovely and clean and full of spunk and honest and everything as some racehorses." If we examine this sentence, we see that all of the qualities which he admires in the horses, except the first one, are qualities which are specifically human, which have to do with human character—cleanliness, courage, honesty, and "everything." He is reading the human traits into the horses, and he cannot understand why other people cannot see and admire those same traits just as he cannot see why other people cannot give credit to the Negro for being warm-hearted and square with kids or to Henry Rieback's father for being nice and generous.

From this point, which may be said to conclude the preparatory and expository part of the story, the narrative moves rather rapidly to the scene in which the boy finds Sunstreak and the trainer in the paddock. This scene sums up in dramatic form all that the boy has previously said about his feeling for horses. Again, his admiration for the horse is cast in terms which are essentially human. The horse doesn't brag. The horse is "better" than the boy, "steadier." It is implied that the horse is courageous, confident, and ready to do to the utmost what he has to do, but he will do it for nothing, win or lose.

The boy simply "knows" this as a sort of mystical revelation. Here is something which is fine and beautiful and which is beyond perplexing questions. The horse, for him, stands for all that is most valuable and admirable in life. Jerry Tillford, the boy feels, also knows this. In fact, at the moment, because Jerry Tillford does know it, the boy feels that Jerry shares these same qualities with the horse.

After the race has been won by Sunstreak, the boy feels impelled to stay as close to Jerry Tillford as possible. "I liked him that afternoon," the boy says, "even more than I ever liked my own father." In other words, because he has shared the mystical revelation with Jerry Tillford, he finds a tie which is even stronger than the tie of family affection. That evening, he follows Jerry, not even expecting to find him; he is filled with the exaltation which, he is sure, Jerry still shares with him. But in the scene at the "rummy farmhouse," he discovers another Jerry. This Jerry "lied and bragged like a fool," and we see the implied contrast to the horse, which is "honest" and does not "brag." We see another contrast. This scene is filthy and ugly and rotten, whereas the thoroughbreds had attracted the boy because they are "so lovely and clean and full of spunk." But these contrasts, we learn, are merely preliminary contrasts to the key contrast in the scene. Jerry approaches the woman who "looked a little like the gelding Middlestride, but not clean like him." The scene is set as a parallel to the scene in the paddock: "The tall rotten-looking woman was between us just as Sunstreak was in the paddocks in the afternoon." But now, facing the rotten-looking woman, Jerry's eyes have the same gleam which they had had in the afternoon when he had faced Sunstreak. The horror and disgust which the boy feels is emphasized by the very parallelism of the scenes.

The horror does not come from the fact that the boy discovers that evil exists in the world. He knows about bad women, he has heard rotten talk, he understands that there are good and bad people in the world. His discovery is that the good and evil can be so intimately allied— can exist in the same person. Jerry Tillford, who had been capable of sharing the exaltation which the boy felt in the paddock, is also capable of the experience in the rummy farmhouse. Indeed, Jerry enters fully into that world and is at home there.

This discovery comes as a great shock to the boy, and, in a sense, is a surprise turn to the story. But upon reflection we see that it has been prepared for in two ways: first in regard to the boy's psychology, and second, in regard to the structure of the story.

Although the discovery that moral definitions are complicated comes, in the special incident, as a shock to the boy, nevertheless he has been moving toward that discovery through his questioning of the easy, conventional definitions which society had given him. The boy has wanted to "think straight and be O.K." Though Negroes are social outcasts, he sees that they have certain points, even moral points, of superiority. Mr. Rieback, though a gambler, is a "nice" man, generous to his son. Though gambling may be an evil, the horses, which are gambled on, are "lovely and clean and full of spunk and honest." To sum up, there has been a logic in the boy's experience, though a logic of which he has been largely unaware.

How has the preparation been made in terms of the structure of the story? * The basic device used by the author to point up the contrast in

---

* Naturally the items involved in the boy's psychological development are also involved in the structure of the story, but in so far as these items operate merely in terms of the boy's personal psychology, we may permissibly, as a matter of convenience, distinguish them from the others.

the rummy farmhouse scene is the symbolism of the horse. Constantly, and for the boy unconsciously, the horse becomes a measure of human values. For example, Sunstreak "is like a girl you think about sometimes but never see." The woman that Jerry meets in the farmhouse "looks" a little like the gelding Middlestride but not clean like him, and with a hard ugly mouth. (The phrase "hard mouth" works here perhaps in a double sense: a hard mouth, as applied to a human being, tells us something about character, and as applied to a horse, it tells us that the animal is refractory and stubborn, not like the trained thoroughbred. Furthermore, the fact that the woman is compared to a gelding may be significant: a gelding is sterile, and the "love" found in the rummy farmhouse is sterile, too.)

We have seen that the horse symbolism has pointed to the scene in the farmhouse, and has provided certain preparatory items in the course of the story. But what is the full meaning of this symbolism? To answer this question, however, we must take into consideration the last two paragraphs of the story, which follow the actual scene in the farmhouse.

The boy says that he still goes to the track, and enjoys being there, "but things are different." The incident in the farmhouse, now long past, continues to color his attitude and "spoils looking at horses and smelling things and hearing niggers laugh and everything" which he had once enjoyed. It spoils everything, he says, "because a man like Jerry Tillford, who knows what he does, could see a horse like Sunstreak run, and kiss a woman like that the same day." At first glance this seems to be merely a summary of the meaning of the scene in the farmhouse, but on closer inspection we may see that it adds a further interpretation of the scene. For example, the phrase, "who knows what he does," is important. What is the difference in moral terms between a horse and a man? The man is responsible, and the horse is not: the man "knows what he does."

The boy, we have seen, has taken the horse to be the very embodiment of the virtues which he admires most. But virtue is human. The finely bred racehorse cannot do other than be "spunky," "honest," and "brave." He is bred that way. With man, however, virtue is a matter of knowledge and choice. A deed is not virtuous in itself; it is only virtuous in terms of a particular man's motivation and awareness. In other words, the horse (nature) is not capable of evil or of goodness, which depend upon human choice. This explains why nature—"looking at horses and smelling things," and the like—has been tainted for the boy. He can no longer lose himself in the things which merely seem good to him. The horse is no longer a satisfactory symbol for the things he admires.

But the symbol continues to have an ironical significance. Man, be-cause he is capable of choice—because he "knows" what he does—be-cause he is capable of being better than the brute, becomes, when he fails to exercise his capacity, something worse than the brute. We see this implied in the scene in the farmhouse, when the ugly, hard-mouthed woman is compared to Middlestride. A brute is always innocent, but man, because of his capacity for choice, is always either better or worse than the brute. This ironical use of the beast as a symbol is not a new one. We find it, for example, in Gulliver's adventures among the Houyhnhnms and Yahoos in Swift's *Gulliver's Travels*.* The Houyh-nhnms, the noble horses, which live clean, orderly, "reasonable" lives, are contrasted with filthy, degenerate "men," the Yahoos, who are far worse than beasts.

In the beginning of this analysis it was said that this story is, like Hemingway's "The Killers," the story of an "initiation." The boy dis-covers something about the nature of evil. Not that evil exists, for he had know for a long time that there are good and bad people—that is, he was acquainted with the ordinary conventional definitions. But he discovers that good and bad are very intimately wedded in the very nature of a man, and, perhaps more important still, that it is man's capacity for choice which makes good and evil meaningful.

Having said this, having extracted what may seem to be a moral "message," one should remind himself that the "message" is, as such, not the story. The story may be said to be the dramatization of the dis-covery. Now the message is something of which everyone is aware; it is a platitude. But the platitude ceases to be a platitude, it is revitalized and becomes meaningful again, when it is shown to be operating in terms of experience.

It is obvious that in this story, which is related by a first-person nar-rator, Anderson has attempted to use a *style* (see Glossary) which is appropriate to that narrator. At least two instances seem to be violations of the appropriateness. The first of these occurs in the first paragraph: ". . . and with the true instinct of Kentucky boys had found our way across town and to the racetrack and the stables at once." The second occurs in the sixth paragraph: ". . . and they didn't want their boys brought up to hear gamblers' talk and be thinking about such things

---

* Swift's use of the horse symbol is much more complicated than is Anderson's, and it is certainly not to be understood that Anderson derives his symbol from that of Swift.

and maybe embrace them." In the opinion of the present editors one of these instances is a definite lapse from the dramatic appropriateness of the style; that is, one cannot readily imagine a boy of this sort putting the matter this way. The other instance, in our opinion, can be defended. Consider the two passages in this light and ascertain what case may be made for this view.

A Shore for the Sinking

THOMAS THOMPSON

RASCOE WAS DRIVING slowly, but before he could decipher the peeling street sign, he had almost passed Grant Avenue. He cramped his wheel and the back of his car slid around the corner. Stopping, he looked back to make certain. These streets out here all looked alike, he told himself as he started forward again, slowly, with the heavy realization that he had about arrived at the place he was in no hurry to reach.

Grant Avenue was a shadeless, downhill street—a blind street. At its end rose a huge gas holder bulking over the rows of exposed bungalows like a drum over children's blocks. Here resided the poorest of the white collars with his five rooms of frail privacy, a garage for his car and a spot of yard for his children.

It was the noon hour, and the glare of the July sun had penetrated and become a part of everything. This was a job that had been rankling in Rascoe's mind for weeks. In defense of his purpose his mind darted to Veal.

Six months he had carried the chiseler and not a dime. The fellow had even stopped promising; he had stopped looking for work. One of that bag-eyed, say-nothing sort that put his own value on himself and sat at his window defying the public to get more than a hundred and twenty a month satisfaction out of him. Small wonder he got the sack. Too long a public employee—that was the trouble. Press him and he would lift the corner of his mouth and show his side teeth, snarling: "Polotics, polotics!" And that was the end of it. You couldn't bully him or budge him. The man hadn't the steam, but born in him were the notions of one of these communist fellows in the East. A gone-to-bed communist—that was what he was!

In front of the house stood the deputy's car, but there was no sign of a van or anything to haul their stuff away. . . . Well, this was silly sitting here. He gave the house a quick glance of distaste. It was one of the several monuments to his business foresight. In '28 he had invested some surplus earnings—oil royalties—in short-term loans secured by city property that would always be good. A few years later, when H.O.L.C. came along, he had an opportunity to unload for bonds that were selling at eighty-one, but at that time he had a mind of his own, and now he had a dozen two-thousand-dollar houses, and H.O.L.C.'s were selling around 104. He despised the pettiness of this rent business. Fifteen here, eighteen there, once a month and twice a month. It was an endless business and it had become a sore spot with him; the more so, because all of his real-estate-owning friends had been at him with their advice: Their warning about not turning soft and the little song they chanted at him about Taxes, Insurance, and Depreciation.

Rascoe's hand reached for the door handle. There was little danger of his turning soft. He had been working up to this too long. This was as good a day as any for an eviction.

In the living room window hung a sign that said:

PIANO LESSONS

AND

TAP DANCING

Thinking of Veal, Rascoe gave a mirthless little laugh, the traces of which deepened into a frown. He was reminded of Veal's family that he would have to face—a wife and a daughter the same as he had himself. He had never seen them because he had made a point of catching Veal away from his hole. But the time had come, and here he was, and as Budge Crawford said: Taxes, Insurance, and Depreciation.

With this blithe little phrase lilting through his head he started up to the porch feeling nearly heartless, determined to be detached, warily incurious as to what was to become of them.

They were having their lunch, and it was not Veal that answered the door but his wife.

"Come in, Mr. Rascoe," she said pleasantly in a good voice, "we are just finishing our dinner."

The deputy was sitting in the only easy chair in the front room. His thumb was tucked under his gun belt. He nodded at Rascoe and shifted his toothpick. Bereft of his rehearsed attitude, Rascoe felt stunned and guilty. It seemed somehow ironically natural that the fat old chiseler would have captured himself a fine woman. She was gracious—perhaps kindly—her house was immaculate, but the remarkable thing was that living with Veal had not destroyed the spirit she so obviously had. You felt the imprint of her personality all over the room: the bright little pictures, the cool dish of nasturtiums, the odor of the coffee——

But nothing was packed and that fool deputy had not said a word. Somehow Rascoe had a hopeful picture of him brandishing the eviction papers under Veal's nose. Veal raised his bright shoe-button eyes from his plate and looked at Rascoe.

"Hydo," he said, chewing, like a fat old squirrel, Rascoe thought.

The prospect of being evicted did not seem to alter his appetite. In a way Rascoe envied him: no imagination, enough thick complacency to keep his mental fears fatted down.

Mrs. Veal passed the corn bread. She called to the daughter in the kitchen and said something quietly to Veal who grunted his reply. Rascoe did not hear what was said, did not want to—but about the woman's tone there was an echo, a forgotten quality of faith-for-the-sake-of-faith that had been lost in the women he knew.

The daughter—she was downright pretty—came in with the dessert. It was some sort of light crusted pie. She flashed a glance at Rascoe and hurried around to her father's elbow. "Daddy, here is your pie. Can't I bring you another cup of coffee?" she asked in a sprightly voice hovering over him like some bright bird.

Rascoe thought wryly of his own family. The two of them—his wife and daughter—seemed to be in some sort of pledged conspiracy to extort everything they could from him, to see that he never shirked in living up to his reputation as a good provider. At the same time, it never seemed to occur to them that they hadn't a perfectly legitimate right to criticize and be shocked at his method of doing it. Only this morning Winifred had said in her cool really disinterested voice:

"Joe, you're not going to actually throw them out, are you?"

"For cat sake, Winifred! What do you think that office I keep down town is, an eleemosynary institution?"

"An eleemosynary institution," repeated Kay after him, "that's what Daddy always says."

"Oh, be a sport, Joe," Winifred said, putting on that voice that used to reach him so easily. "This is not the oil business."

"Yes, be a sport, Daddy."

It was a joke the way Winifred could scheme around to defend her emotional life. . . . Well, he thought, looking hard at the deputy, the fellow would have to do the talking. He gave him a harder look— harder and more inquiring.

Finally the fellow spoke up, rising bulkily and adjusting his gun belt. "These folks know a boy that's got a truck. He's goin' to haul their stuff off for them."

Rascoe nodded, relieved. There was nothing to do but wait. The daughter brought Veal his pipe, and while the women washed the dishes, Veal and the deputy sat smoking, not saying a word. Rascoe's eyes, wandering about the room, rested on a handsome old cherry piano —a relic of better days. Rascoe's mind shunned the thought of better days. It was simpler just to consider them poor pay and be done with it.

Mrs. Veal came in with a smile—a strained smile, he guessed.

"Keep your seat, Mr. Rascoe. What part of town do you live in?"

Leave it to the women to make conversation under any circumstances. Better watch out.

"Adam's Park."

"Really. I used to teach music at Adam's Park High School. You know, you have to have your master's to teach in high school now."

Someone stepped up on the porch. Rascoe looked around, but it was not the boy with the truck. It was a neighbor woman squinting into the darkened interior.

"Come in, Mrs. Wyatt," said Mrs. Veal's voice.

The woman stepped inside saying, "Mr. Wyatt is home now for dinner. Him and Mr. Harper and Mr. Albright will be over to help Mr. Veal load as soon as the boy comes."

"That's so good of you, Mrs. Wyatt."

"Nothin', nothin' a-tall. You know, Minnie, the little thing, she's quite upset about your leavin'. She says it won't seem natural, her not comin' over here to her piano lessons."

"Bless her little heart. When we get settled, I want her to start them again. She has real talent, Mrs. Wyatt."

"Well, we could never afforded payin' lessons. The men folks will be over when the boy comes."

The woman was unimpressive, but when her watery blue eyes looked him up and down, Rascoe flinched to his toes. Naturally, Veal's wife was the favorite of the neighborhood! Compared to this sort of thing the oil business was a clean high-class way of making a living. You didn't take the roof off a man's head. You didn't move his family out on the street. At least, you didn't see yourself doing it. But what if he did let the fellow stay on a while? It would be only a brief respite; he was definitely down, and this would be a situation that would have to be faced sooner or later. Moreover, there was the restraining picture of his friends. It would tickle Budge Crawford to death to see him turn soft. What a damned idiot he was. Taxes, Insurance, and—

A fruit company truck came to a fast stop behind Rascoe's car. A boy, whom Rascoe recognized as one of last year's high-school football stars, leaped lightly out of the cab, bursting with energy and muscle. He jumped on the back of the truck and tossed an empty banana crate on to the yard, littering it with paper lining, straw, and two blackened banana stalks. Snapping his fingers and swinging his arms, he came up to the house. The daughter's small feet twinkled across the floor to meet him.

"Hy, Mary," he said, grinning at the family and sweeping his eyes past Rascoe for something to put his hands on.

At first Rascoe was reassured to see someone strutting around with so much energy and confidence, but it was soon apparent that he didn't know how to take a hold and do a thing. He regarded it as a lark, and Rascoe could hear him saying: "Hey, boss, I've got to move my girl's family. How about the truck at noon?" When the other men came Mrs. Veal put him to work outside where he could do no harm.

The neighbor men all swept their eyes past Rascoe as the boy had done. It was the "working man" look; he had seen a lot of it around the oil fields and you did well not to shove at the barrier. Finding that he was invariably in the way, Rascoe went outside and sat on the porch rail. The deputy, however, laughed and joked, working right along with the others. He was accepted.

"Hey, there, Mrs. Veal, don't let that law carry those dishes. You know the story about the bull in the china closet."

"Pipe down, you. Lady, what about this dishpan? There's a hole rusted in the bottom of it."

"Oh, daddy can fix that," said the daughter over her shoulder.

"Yes, Mr. Veal can fix that with his soldering kit."

As for Veal, who puttered around doing little or nothing, the men seemed not to resent his incompetence. They seemed hardly conscious of his presence. It was not he that Rascoe was putting out; it was his wife and daughter.

What made them stick by a man like that? What made them! It couldn't be the misshapen thing hiding in that thick rind of fat, that— It must be the memory of what he had been. No—perhaps an idea of what he should be. Women were damned fools.

Almost too soon Rascoe found himself standing in a house empty of furniture. There was only a broom and a waxing mop left. The daughter flitted between the truck and the bedroom where her mother was packing a few things in a battered suit case. Rascoe could not keep his eyes from her trim ankles and feet twinkling across the floor. It was she who taught the tap dancing. Twice the pep of his own daughter. Alert gray eyes and she hadn't a wheedling or pouty thing in her. Would his own family stick by him on a spot like this? Well, they would darned well have to, but he had a sneaking notion that they would do it whining. Winifred hadn't the guts. He had heard her and her cool-voiced bridge-playing friends talking it over. It was their figures, their hands, their afternoon naps, and the things they were used to, my dear. He was sick of the breed. Here was another kind and whether it was circumstances or God that made them that way, he didn't care. And it was they he was throwing out!

The men were going back to their homes. "No, thank you," Mrs. Veal said, declining further offers of assistance, "everything will be fine now. Good-by, and thank you. Good-by."

She came into the house. With alarm Rascoe watched her take the broom and begin to sweep the floor—the already clean floor.

"Mrs. Veal. Don't do that!"

"I beg your pardon."

"The floors, I mean. They look great. Never mind them."

"Mr. Rascoe, we couldn't think of leaving them this way. They were beautiful when we moved in—except for a few spots of grease where the stove was. There were just a few, but grease is grease. Mrs. Rascoe will tell you that, or does she do her own cooking? Mr. Veal took sandpaper and tried to cut it out, but the stain was too deep. If you'll just step outside, we'll have your house clean for you in five minutes."

As he stepped on to the porch the girl slipped past him. She had rags over her shoes so as not to scar the darned floor.

Suddenly a hot film rushed over his eyes. He heard Budge Crawford's hoarse laugh—"Rascoe, you've gone soft. Wait until the first of the year. Taxes, Insurance, Depreciation. You damned fool—"

Rascoe threw open the screen.

"Mrs. Veal," he said panic-stricken, "I've changed my mind."

"What do you mean, Mr. Rascoe?"

"I don't want you to move. You can tutor my daughter in music—teach her tap dancing."

The corners of her mouth quivered. Then she gave a little laugh. "I'm sorry, Mr. Rascoe. We've made our plans, and Mr. Veal doesn't like living so close to the gas holder. Mary, run to your father and get the key."

Rascoe had known it was no good as soon as he spoke. He should have propositioned Veal. Veal would have accepted calmly—calmly, and sat down on his fat tail.

The daughter brought the key and Rascoe put his hand out for it. She stood there looking at him with her red lower lip turned out. She held the key by the end of a string.

When she dropped it, Rascoe jerked as though he had caught a mouse.

"Thanks very much," she said in her sprightly cutting voice.

When the deputy had gone and when they had all piled into the cab of the truck, Rascoe locked his house. Why, he had acted green as a school boy. Getting in his car, he started back to town glad to forget what he had learned.*

INTERPRETATION

1. This story ends with the statement: ". . . he started back to town glad to forget what he had learned." What Rascoe, the hero, has learned we are not told in so many words. But that "what" is the central idea which the author has attempted to dramatize in the story. The chief problem of interpretation, then, is to define this central idea, this "what," and to see how it is embodied in the story.

In this connection, one might ask what is the attitude toward the eviction taken by the following characters: (a) Veal, (b) Veal's wife and daughter, (c) the deputy, (d) the football star who brings the truck, (e) Rascoe's wife and daughter. Can it be said that each of these characters has a definite and secure attitude toward the eviction, an attitude which allows his emotions and his intellectual picture of the situation to fit neatly together? (This does not mean, of course, that each of these characters has the same attitude.)

In contrast with these characters, Rascoe confronts a problem concerning his own attitude. (a) Does he feel guilty because he is doing an inhuman thing? (b) Does he feel guilty because his uneasiness itself is a mark of "softness" for which his business friends will laugh at him? (c) Does he feel guilty because he participates in a bad system? (d) Does he recognize that his offer to Mrs. Veal at the last minute is merely a sentimental gesture; that is, an attempt to spare his own feelings? (e) Can it be said that Rascoe is, finally, the only character in the story who has to face up to the real issues involved in the situation—the real theme of the story?

2. Why can it be said that the wife and daughter of Rascoe are viciously sentimental? Why can it be said of Rascoe that he is not fundamentally a sentimentalist even though, at the end of the story, he makes a sentimental offer? On the other hand, had Rascoe's offer been accepted, and had the author attempted to make us feel that, somehow, the offer made everything "right," would the story not have been marred by sentimentality, because such a treatment would have dodged the real issues involved in the situation?

3. In one sense, as no doubt the student will have discovered, the present story involves a conflict between a system—in this case, a socio-

* Copyright, 1938, *The Southern Review;* by permission of the author.

economic system—and the individual, with his personal attachments, personal sympathies, personal ambitions, and the like. In this connection, compare this story with such other stories as "The Man Who Would Be King," p. 63, and "War," p. 171. Two other stories, not in this book, which offer special opportunities for studying related problems are "The Gentleman from San Francisco," by Ivan Bunin, and *"La Mère Sauvage,"* by Maupassant. Write an interpretation of one of these stories, and compare it with "A Shore for the Sinking."

SECTION V

Special Problems

THE "special problems" dealt with here are in no sense new. The basic problems that have to do with the organization of fiction have been discussed, in one connection or other, in the earlier sections of this book, and some of the more special problems have been discussed there as well. But the stories in Section V have been chosen with a view to affording the student instances of such problems as style, atmosphere, indirection and irony, suggestion, tone, symbolism, and the like.

Tallow Ball
GUY DE MAUPASSANT

FOR SEVERAL days in succession fragments of a defeated army had passed through the town. They were mere disorganized bands, not disciplined forces. The men wore long, dirty beards and tattered uniforms; they advanced in listless fashion, without a flag, without a leader. All seemed exhausted, worn out, incapable of thought or resolve, marching onward merely by force of habit, and dropping to the ground with fatigue the moment they halted. One saw, in particular, many enlisted men, peaceful citizens, men who lived quietly on their income, bending beneath the weight of their rifles; and little active volunteers, easily frightened but full of enthusiasm, as eager to attack as they were ready to take to flight; and amid these, a sprinkling of red-breeched soldiers, the pitiful remnant of a division cut down in a great battle; somber artillerymen, side by side with nondescript foot soldiers; and, here and there, the gleaming helmet of a heavy-footed dragoon who had difficulty in keeping up with the quicker pace of the soldiers of the line.

359

Legions of irregulars with high-sounding names—"Avengers of Defeat," "Citizens of the Tomb," "Brethren in Death"—passed in their turn, looking like banditti.

Their leaders, former drapers or grain merchants, or tallow- or soap-chandlers—warriors by force of circumstances, officers by reason of their mustachios or their money—covered with weapons, flannel, and gold lace, spoke in an impressive manner, discussed plans of campaign, and behaved as though they alone bore the fortunes of dying France on their braggart shoulders; though, in truth, they frequently were afraid of their own men—scoundrels often brave beyond measure, but pillagers and debauchees.

Rumor had it that the Prussians were about to enter Rouen.

The members of the National Guard, who for the past two months had been reconnoitering with the utmost caution in the neighboring woods, occasionally shooting their own sentinels, and making ready for fight whenever a rabbit rustled in the undergrowth, had now returned to their homes. Their arms, their uniforms, all the death-dealing paraphernalia with which they had terrified all the milestones along the highroad for eight miles round, had suddenly and marvelously disappeared.

The last of the French soldiers had just crossed the Seine on their way to Pont-Audemer, through Saint-Sever and Bourg-Achard, and in their rear the vanquished general, powerless to do aught with the forlorn remnants of his army, himself dismayed at the final overthrow of a nation accustomed to victory and disastrously beaten despite its legendary bravery, walked between two orderlies.

Then a profound calm, a shuddering, silent dread, settled on the city. Many a round-paunched citizen, emasculated by years devoted to business, anxiously awaited the conquerors, trembling lest his roasting jacks or kitchen knives should be looked upon as weapons.

Life seemed to have stopped short; the shops were shut, the streets deserted. Now and then an inhabitant, awed by the silence, glided swiftly by in the shadow of the walls. The anguish of suspense made men even desire the arrival of the enemy.

In the afternoon of the day following the departure of the French troops, a number of uhlans, coming no one knew whence, passed rapidly through the town. A little later on, a black mass descended St.

Catherine's Hill, while two other invading bodies appeared respectively on the Darnetal and the Boisguillaume roads. The advance
guards of the three corps arrived at precisely the same moment at the
Square of the Hôtel de Ville, and the German army poured through
all the adjacent streets, its battalions making the pavement ring with
their firm, measured tread.

Orders shouted in an unknown, guttural tongue rose to the windows of the seemingly dead, deserted houses; while behind the fast-
closed shutters eager eyes peered forth at the victors—masters now of
the city, its fortunes, and its lives, by "right of war." The inhabitants, in
their darkened rooms, were possessed by that terror which follows in
the wake of cataclysms, of deadly upheavals of the earth, against
which all human skill and strength are vain. For the same thing happens whenever the established order of things is upset, when security
no longer exists, when all those rights usually protected by the law
of man or of Nature are at the mercy of unreasoning, savage force.
The earthquake crushing a whole nation under falling roofs; the flood
let loose and engulfing in its swirling depths the corpses of drowned
peasants, along with dead oxen and beams torn from shattered houses;
or the army, covered with glory, murdering those who defended themselves, making prisoners of the rest, pillaging in the name of the
Sword, and giving thanks to God to the thunder of cannon—all these
are appalling scourges, which destroy all belief in eternal justice, all
that confidence we have been taught to feel in the protection of
Heaven and the reason of man.

Small detachments of soldiers knocked at each door, and then disappeared within the houses; for the vanquished saw they would have
to be civil to their conquerors.

At the end of a short time, once the first terror had subsided, calm
was again restored. In many houses the Prussian officer ate at the
same table with the family. He was often well-bred, and, out of politeness, expressed sympathy with France and repugnance at being compelled to take part in the war. This sentiment was received with
gratitude; besides, his protection might be needful some day or other.
By the exercise of tact the number of men quartered in one's house
might be reduced; and why should one provoke the hostility of a
person on whom one's whole welfare depended? Such conduct would

savor less of bravery than of foolhardiness. And foolhardiness is no longer a failing of the citizens of Rouen as it was in the days when their city earned renown by its heroic defense. Last of all—final argument based on the national politeness—the folk of Rouen said to one another that it was only right to be civil in one's own house, provided there was no public exhibition of familiarity with the foreigner. Out of doors, therefore, citizen and soldier did not know each other; but in the house both chatted freely, and each evening the German remained a little longer warming himself at the hospitable hearth.

Even the town itself resumed by degrees its ordinary aspect. The French seldom walked abroad, but the streets swarmed with Prussian soldiers. Moreover, the officers of the Blue Hussars, who arrogantly dragged their instruments of death along the pavements, seemed to hold the simple townsmen in but little more contempt than did the French cavalry officers who had drunk at the same cafés the year before.

But there was something in the air, a something strange and subtle, an intolerable foreign atmosphere like a penetrating odor—the odor of invasion. It permeated dwellings and places of public resort, changed the taste of food, made one imagine one's self in far distant lands, amid dangerous, barbaric tribes.

The conquerors exacted money, much money. The inhabitants paid what was asked; they were rich. But, the wealthier a Norman tradesman becomes, the more he suffers at having to part with anything that belongs to him, at having to see any portion of his substance pass into the hands of another.

Nevertheless, within six or seven miles of the town, along the course of the river as it flows onward to Croisset, Dieppedalle, and Biessart, boatmen and fishermen often hauled to the surface of the water the body of a German, bloated in his uniform, killed by a blow from knife or club, his head crushed by a stone, or perchance pushed from some bridge into the stream below. The mud of the riverbed swallowed up these obscure acts of vengeance—savage, yet legitimate; these unrecorded deeds of bravery; these silent attacks fraught with greater danger than battles fought in broad day, and surrounded, moreover, with no halo of romance. For hatred of the foreigner ever arms a few intrepid souls, ready to die for an idea.

At last, as the invaders, though subjecting the town to the strictest discipline, had not committed any of the deeds of horror with which they had been credited while on their triumphal march, the people grew bolder, and the necessities of business again animated the breasts of the local merchants. Some of these had important commercial interests at Havre—occupied at present by the French army—and wished to attempt to reach that port by overland route to Dieppe, taking the boat from there.

Through the influence of the German officers whose acquaintance they had made, they obtained a permit to leave town from the general in command.

A large four-horse coach having, therefore, been engaged for the journey, and ten passengers having given in their names to the proprietor, they decided to start on a certain Tuesday morning before daybreak, to avoid attracting a crowd.

The ground had been frozen hard for some time past, and about three o'clock on Monday afternoon large black clouds from the north shed their burden of snow uninterruptedly all through that evening and night.

At half past four in the morning the travelers met in the courtyard of the Hôtel de Normandie, where they were to take their seats in the coach.

They were still half asleep, and shivering with cold under their wraps. They could see one another but indistinctly in the darkness, and the mountain of heavy winter wraps in which each was swathed made them look like a gathering of obese priests in their long cassocks. But two men recognized each other, a third accosted them, and the three began to talk. "I am bringing my wife," said one. "So am I." "And I, too." The first speaker added: "We shall not return to Rouen, and if the Prussians approach Havre we will cross to England." All three, it turned out, had made the same plans, being of similar disposition and temperament.

Still the horses were not harnessed. A small lantern carried by a stable boy emerged now and then from one dark doorway to disappear immediately in another. The stamping of horses' hoofs, deadened by the dung and straw of the stable, was heard from time to time, and from inside the building issued a man's voice, talking to the ani-

mals and swearing at them. A faint tinkle of bells showed that the
harness was being got ready; this tinkle soon developed into a continuous jingling, louder or softer according to the movements of the
horse, sometimes stopping altogether, then breaking out in a sudden
peal accompanied by a pawing of the ground by an iron-shod hoof.

The door suddenly closed. All noise ceased. The frozen townsmen
were silent; they remained motionless, stiff with cold.

A thick curtain of glistening white flakes fell ceaselessly to the
ground; it obliterated all outlines, enveloped all objects in an icy mantle of foam; nothing was to be heard throughout the length and
breadth of the silent, winter-bound city save the vague, nameless rustle
of falling snow—a sensation rather than a sound—the gentle mingling
of light atoms which seemed to fill all space, to cover the whole world.

The man reappeared with his lantern, leading by a rope a melancholy-
looking horse, evidently led out against his inclination. The hostler
placed him beside the pole, fastened the traces, and spent some time in
walking round him to make sure that the harness was all right; for
he could use only one hand, the other being engaged in holding the
lantern. As he was about to fetch the second horse he noticed the
motionless group of travelers, already white with snow, and said to
them: "Why don't you get inside the coach? You'd be under shelter,
at least."

This did not seem to have occurred to them, and they at once took
his advice. The three men seated their wives at the far end of the
coach, then got in themselves; lastly the other vague, snow-shrouded
forms clambered to the remaining places without a word.

The floor was covered with straw, into which the feet sank. The
ladies at the far end, having brought with them little copper foot-
warmers heated by means of a kind of chemical fuel, proceeded to light
these, and spent some time in expatiating in low tones on their advantages, saying over and over again things which they had all known
for a long time.

At last, six horses instead of four having been harnessed to the diligence, on account of the heavy roads, a voice outside asked: "Is everyone there?" To which a voice from the interior replied: "Yes," and
they set out.

The vehicle moved slowly, slowly, at a snail's pace; the wheels sank into the snow; the entire body of the coach creaked and groaned; the horses slipped, puffed, steamed, and the coachman's long whip cracked incessantly, flying hither and thither, coiling up, then flinging out its length like a slender serpent, as it lashed some rounded flank, which instantly grew tense as it strained in further effort.

But the day grew apace. Those light flakes which one traveler, a native of Rouen, had compared to a rain of cotton fell no longer. A murky light filtered through dark, heavy clouds, which made the country more dazzlingly white by contrast, a whiteness broken sometimes by a row of tall trees spangled with hoarfrost, or by a cottage roof hooded in snow.

Within the coach the passengers eyed one another curiously in the dim light of dawn.

Right at the back, in the best seats of all, Monsieur and Madame Loiseau, wholesale wine merchants of the Rue Grand-Pont, slumbered opposite each other. Formerly clerk to a merchant who had failed in business, Loiseau had bought his master's interest, and made a fortune for himself. He sold very bad wine at a very low price to the retail dealers in the country, and had the reputation, among his friends and acquaintances, of being a shrewd rascal, a true Norman, full of quips and wiles. So well established was his character as a cheat that, in the mouths of the citizens of Rouen, the very name of Loiseau became a byword for sharp practice.

Above and beyond this, Loiseau was noted for his practical jokes of every description—his tricks, good- or ill-natured; and no one could mention his name without adding at once: "He's an extraordinary man—Loiseau." He was undersized and pot-bellied, had a florid face with grayish whiskers.

His wife—tall, strong, determined, with a loud voice and decided manner—represented the spirit of order and arithmetic in the business house which Loiseau enlivened by his jovial activity.

Beside them, dignified in bearing, belonging to a superior caste, sat Monsieur Carré-Lamadon, a man of considerable importance, a king in the cotton trade, proprietor of three spinning mills, officer of the Legion of Honor, and member of the General Council. During the whole time the Empire was in the ascendancy he remained the chief of the well-disposed Opposition, merely in order to command a higher value for his devotion when he should rally to the cause which he meanwhile opposed with "courteous weapons," to use his own expression.

Madame Carré-Lamadon, much younger than her husband, was the consolation of all the officers of good family quartered at Rouen. Pretty, slender, graceful, she sat opposite her husband, curled up in her furs, and gazing mournfully at the sorry interior of the coach.

Her neighbors, the Count and Countess Hubert de Bréville, bore one of the noblest and most ancient names in Normandy. The count, a nobleman advanced in years and of aristocratic bearing, strove to enhance, by every artifice of the toilet, his natural resemblance to King Henry IV, who, according to a legend of which the family were inordinately proud, had been the favored lover of a Bréville lady, and father of her child—the frail one's husband having, in recognition of this fact, been made a count and governor of a province.

A colleague of Monsieur Carré-Lamadon in the General Council, Count Hubert represented the Orleanist party in his department. The story of his marriage with the daughter of a small shipowner at Nantes had always remained more or less a mystery. But as the countess had an air of unmistakable breeding, entertained faultlessly, and was even supposed to have been loved by a son of Louis-Philippe, the nobility vied with one another in doing her honor, and her drawing room remained the most select in the whole countryside—the only one which retained the old spirit of gallantry, and to which access was not easy.

The fortune of the Brévilles, all in real estate, amounted, it was said, to five hundred thousand francs a year.

These six people occupied the farther end of the coach, and represented Society—with an income—the strong, established Society of good people with religion and principle.

It happened by chance that all the women were seated on the same side; and the countess had, moreover, as neighbors two nuns, who spent the time in fingering their long rosaries and murmuring paternosters and aves. One of them was old, and so deeply pitted with smallpox that she looked for all the world as if she had received a charge of shot in the face. The other, of sickly appearance, had a pretty but wasted countenance, and a narrow, consumptive chest, sapped by that devouring faith which is the making of martyrs and visionaries.

A man and woman, sitting opposite the two nuns, attracted all eyes.

The man—a well-known character—was Cornudet, the democrat, the terror of all respectable people. For the past twenty years his big red beard had been on terms of intimate acquaintance with the tankards of all the republican cafés. With the help of his comrades and brethren he had dissipated a respectable fortune left him by his father, an old-established confectioner, and he now impatiently awaited the Republic, that he might at last be rewarded with the post he had earned by his revolutionary orgies. On the fourth of September—possibly as the result of a practical joke—he was led to believe that he had been appointed prefect; but when he attempted to take up the duties of the position the clerks in charge of the office refused to recognize his authority, and he was compelled in consequence to retire. A good sort of fellow in other respects, inoffensive and obliging, he had thrown himself zealously in to the work of making an organized defense of the town. He had had pits dug in the level country, young forest trees felled, and traps set on all the roads; then at the approach of the enemy, thoroughly satisfied with his preparations, he had hastily returned to the town. He thought he might now do more good at Havre, where new intrenchments would soon be necessary.

The woman, who belonged to the courtesan class, was celebrated for an *embonpoint* unusual for her age, which had earned for her the sobriquet of "Boule de Suif" (Tallow Ball). Short and round, fat as a pig, with puffy fingers constricted at the joints, looking like rows of short sausages; with a shiny, tightly stretched skin and an enormous bust filling out the bodice of her dress, she was yet attractive and much sought after, owing to her fresh and pleasing appearance. Her face was like a crimson apple, a peony-bud just bursting into bloom; she had two magnificent dark eyes, fringed with thick, heavy lashes, which cast a shadow into their depths; her mouth was small, ripe, kissable, and was furnished with the tiniest of white teeth.

As soon as she was recognized the respectable matrons of the party began to whisper among themselves, and the words "hussy" and "public scandal" were uttered so loudly that Boule de Suif raised her head. She forthwith cast such a challenging, bold look at her neighbors that a sudden silence fell on the company, and all lowered their eyes, with the exception of Loiseau, who watched her with evident interest.

But conversation was soon resumed among the three ladies, whom the presence of this girl had suddenly drawn together in the bonds of friendship—one might almost say in those of intimacy. They decided that they ought to combine, as it were, in their dignity as wives in the face of this shameless hussy; for legitimized love always despises its easy-going brother.

The three men, also, brought together by a certain conservative instinct awakened by the presence of Cornudet, spoke of money matters in a tone expressive of contempt for the poor. Count Hubert related the losses he had sustained at the hands of the Prussians, spoke of the cattle which had been stolen from him, the crops which had been ruined, with the easy manner of a nobleman who was also a tenfold millionaire, and whom such reverses would scarcely inconvenience for a single year. Monsieur Carré-Lamadon, a man of wide experience in the cotton industry, had taken care to send six hundred thousand francs to England as provision against the rainy day he was always anticipating. As for Loiseau, he had managed to sell to the French commissariat department all the wines he had in stock, so that the state now owed him a considerable sum, which he hoped to receive at Havre.

And all three eyed one another in friendly, well-disposed fashion. Although of varying social status, they were united in the brotherhood of money—in that vast freemasonry made up of those who possess, who can jingle gold whenever they choose to put their hands into their breeches pockets.

The coach went along so slowly that at ten o'clock in the morning it had not covered twelve miles. Three times the men of the party got out and climbed the hills on foot. The passengers were becoming uneasy, for they had counted on lunching at Tôtes, and it seemed now as if they would hardly arrive there before nightfall. Everyone was eagerly looking out for an inn by the roadside, when, suddenly, the coach foundered in a snowdrift, and it took two hours to extricate it.

As appetites increased, their spirits fell; no inn, no wine shop could be discovered, the approach of the Prussians and the transit of the starving French troops having frightened away all business.

The men sought food in the farmhouses beside the road, but could not find so much as a crust of bread; for the suspicious peasant invariably hid his stores for fear of being pillaged by the soldiers, who, being entirely without food, would take violent possession of everything they found.

About one o'clock Loiseau announced that he positively had a big hollow in his stomach. They had all been suffering in the same way for some time, and the increasing gnawings of hunger had put an end to all conversation.

Now and then someone yawned, another followed his example, and each in turn, according to his character, breeding and social position, yawned either quietly or noisily, placing his hand before the gaping void whence issued breath condensed into vapor.

Several times Boule de Suif stooped, as if searching for something under her petticoats. She would hesitate a moment, look at her neighbors, and then quietly sit upright again. All faces were pale and drawn. Loiseau declared he would give a thousand francs for a knuckle of ham. His wife made an involuntary and quickly checked gesture of protest. It always hurt her to hear of money being squandered, and she could not even understand jokes on such a subject.

"As a matter of fact, I don't feel well," said the count. "Why did I not think of bringing provisions?" Each one reproached himself in similar fashion.

Cornudet, however, had a bottle of rum, which he offered to his neighbors. They all coldly refused except Loiseau, who took a sip, and returned the bottle with thanks, saying: "That's good stuff; it warms one up, and cheats the appetite." The alcohol put him in good humor, and he proposed they should do as the sailors did in the song: eat the fattest of the passengers. This indirect allusion to Boule de Suif shocked the respectable members of the party. No one replied; only Cornudet smiled. The two good sisters had ceased to mumble their rosary, and, with hands enfolded in their wide sleeves, sat motionless, their eyes steadfastly cast down, doubtless offering up as a sacrifice to Heaven the suffering it had sent them.

At last, at three o'clock, as they were in the midst of an apparently limitless plain, with not a single village in sight, Boule de Suif stooped quickly, and drew from underneath the seat a large basket covered with a white napkin.

From this she extracted first of all a small earthenware plate and a silver drinking cup, then an enormous dish containing two whole chickens cut into joints and imbedded in jelly. The basket was seen to contain other good things: pies, fruit, dainties of all sorts—provisions, in fine, for a three days' journey, rendering their owner independent of wayside inns. The necks of four bottles protruded from among the food. She took a chicken wing, and began to eat it daintily, together with one of those rolls called in Normandy "régence."

All looks were directed toward her. An odor of food filled the air, causing nostrils to dilate, mouths to water, and jaws to contract painfully. The scorn of the ladies for this disreputable female grew positively ferocious; they would have liked to kill her, or throw her and her drinking cup, her basket, and her provisions out of the coach into the snow of the road below.

But Loiseau's gaze was fixed greedily on the dish of chicken. He said:

"Well, well, this lady had more forethought than the rest of us. Some people think of everything."

She looked up at him.

"Would you like some, sir? It is hard to go on fasting all day."

He bowed.

"Upon my soul, I can't refuse; I cannot hold out another minute. All is fair in war time, is it not, madame?" And, casting a glance on those around, he added:

"At times like this it is very pleasant to meet with obliging people."

He spread a newspaper over his knees to avoid soiling his trousers, and, with a pocketknife he always carried, helped himself to a chicken leg coated with jelly, which he thereupon proceeded to devour.

Then Boule de Suif, in low, humble tones, invited the nuns to partake of her repast. They both accepted the offer unhesitatingly, and after a few stammered words of thanks began to eat quickly, without raising their eyes. Neither did Cornudet refuse his neighbor's offer, and, in combination with the nuns, a sort of table was formed by opening out the newspaper over the four pairs of knees.

Mouths kept opening and shutting, ferociously masticating and devouring the food. Loiseau, in his corner, was hard at work, and in low tones urged his wife to follow his example. She held out for a long time, but overstrained Nature gave way at last. Her husband, assuming his politest manner, asked their "charming companion" if he might be allowed to offer Madame Loiseau a small helping.

"Why, certainly, sir," she replied, with an amiable smile, holding out the dish.

When the first bottle of claret was opened some embarrassment was caused by the fact that there was only one drinking cup, but this was passed from one to another, after being wiped. Cornudet alone, doubtless in a spirit of gallantry, raised to his own lips that part of the rim which was still moist from those of his fair neighbor.

Then, surrounded by people who were eating, and well-nigh suffocated by the odor of food, the Count and Countess de Bréville and Monsieur and Madame Carré-Lamadon endured that hateful form of torture which has perpetuated the name of Tantalus. All at once the manufacturer's young wife heaved a sigh which made everyone turn and look at her; she was white as the snow without; her eyes closed, her head fell forward; she had fainted. Her husband, beside himself, implored the help of his neighbors. No one seemed to know what to do until the elder of the two nuns, raising the patient's head, placed Boule de Suif's drinking cup to her lips, and made her swallow a few drops of wine. The pretty invalid moved, opened her eyes, smiled, and declared in a feeble voice that she was all right again. But, to prevent a recurrence of the catastrophe, the nun made her drink a cupful of claret, adding: "It's just hunger—that's what is wrong with you."

Then Boule de Suif, blushing and embarrassed, stammered, looking at the four passengers who were still fasting:

"*Mon Dieu,* if I might offer these ladies and gentlemen—"

She stopped short, fearing a snub. But Loiseau continued:

"Hang it all, in such a case as this we are all brothers and sisters and ought to assist each other. Come, come, ladies, don't stand on ceremony, for goodness' sake! Do we even know whether we shall find a house in which to pass the night? At our present rate of going we shan't be at Tôtes till midday tomorrow."

They hesitated, no one daring to be the first to accept. But the count settled the question. He turned toward the abashed girl, and in his most distinguished manner said:

"We accept gratefully, madame."

As usual, it was only the first step that cost. This Rubicon once crossed, they set to work with a will. The basket was nearly emptied. It still contained a *paté de foie gras,* a lark pie, a piece of smoked tongue, Crassane pears, Pont-Léveque gingerbread, fancy cakes, and a cup full of pickled gherkins and onions—Boule de Suif, like all women, being very fond of indigestible things.

They could not eat this girl's provisions without speaking to her. So they began to talk, stiffly at first; then, as she seemed by no means forward, with greater freedom. Mesdames de Bréville and Carré-Lamadon, who were accomplished women of the world, were gracious and tactful. The countess especially displayed that amiable condescension characteristic of great ladies whom no contact with baser mortals can sully, and was absolutely charming. But the sturdy Madame Loiseau, who had the soul of a gendarme, continued morose, speaking little and eating much.

Conversation naturally turned on the war. Terrible stories were told about the Prussians, deeds of bravery were recounted of the French; and all these people who were fleeing themselves were ready to pay homage to the courage of their compatriots. Personal experiences soon followed, and Boule de Suif related with genuine emotion, and with that warmth of language not uncommon in women of her class and temperament, how it came about that she had left Rouen.

"I thought at first that I should be able to stay," she said. "My house was well stocked with provisions, and it seemed better to put up with feeding a few soldiers than to banish myself goodness knows where. But when I saw these Prussians it was too much for me! My blood boiled with rage; I wept the whole day for very shame. Oh, if only I had been a man! I looked at them from my window—the fat swine, with their pointed helmets!—and my maid held my hands to keep me from throwing my furniture down on them. Then some of them were quartered on me; I flew at the throat of the first one who entered. They are just as easy to strangle as other men! And I'd have been the death of that one if I hadn't been dragged away from him by my hair. I had to hide after that. And as soon as I could get an opportunity I left the place, and here I am."

She was warmly congratulated. She rose in the estimation of her companions, who had not been so brave; and Cornudet listened to her with the approving and benevolent smile of an apostle, the smile a priest might wear in listening to a devotee praising God; for long-bearded democrats of his type have a monopoly of patriotism, just as priests have a monopoly of religion. He held forth in turn, with dogmatic self-assurance, in the style of the proclamations daily pasted on the walls of the town, winding up with a specimen of stump oratory in which he reviled "that besotted fool of a Louis-Napoleon."

But Boule de Suif was indignant, for she was an ardent Bonapartist. She turned as red as a cherry, and stammered in her wrath: "I'd just like to have seen you in his place—you and your sort! There would have been a nice mix-up. Oh, yes! It was you who betrayed that man. It would be impossible to live in France if we were governed by such rascals as you!"

Cornudet, unmoved by this tirade, still smiled a superior, contemptuous smile; and one felt that high words were impending, when the count interposed, and, not without difficulty, succeeded in calming the exasperated woman, saying that all sincere opinions ought to be respected. But the countess and the manufacturer's wife, imbued with the unreasoning hatred of the upper classes for the Republic, and instinct, moreover, with the affection felt by all women for the pomp and circumstance of despotic government, were drawn, in spite of themselves, toward this dignified young woman, whose opinions coincided so closely with their own.

The basket was empty. The ten people had finished its contents without difficulty amid general regret that it did not hold more. Conversation went on a little longer, though it flagged somewhat after the passengers had finished eating.

Night fell, the darkness grew deeper and deeper, and the cold made Boule de Suif shiver, in spite of her plumpness. So Madame de Bréville offered her her footwarmer, the fuel of which had been several times renewed since the morning, and she accepted the offer at once, for her feet were icy cold. Mesdames Carré-Lamadon and Loiseau gave theirs to the nuns.

The driver lighted his lanterns. They cast a bright gleam on a cloud of vapor which hovered over the sweating flanks of the horses, and on the roadside snow, which seemed to unroll as they went along in the changing light of the lamps.

All was now indistinguishable in the coach; but suddenly a movement occurred in the corner occupied by Boule de Suif and Cornudet; and Loiseau, peering into the gloom, fancied he saw the big, bearded democrat move hastily to one side, as if he had received a well-directed, though noiseless, blow in the dark.

Tiny lights glimmered ahead. It was Tôtes. The coach had been on the road eleven hours, which, with the three hours allotted the horses in four periods for feeding and breathing, made fourteen. It entered the town, and stopped before the Hôtel du Commerce.

The coach door opened; a well-known noise made all the travelers start; it was the clanging of a scabbard on the pavement; then a voice called out something in German.·

Although the coach had come to a standstill, no one got out; it looked as if they were afraid of being murdered the moment they left their seats. Thereupon the driver appeared, holding in his hand one of his lanterns, which cast a sudden glow on the interior of the coach, lighting up the double row of startled faces, mouths agape, and eyes wide open in surprise and terror.

Beside the driver stood in the full light a German officer, a tall young man, fair and slender, tightly encased in his uniform like a woman in her corset, his flat shiny cap, tilted to one side of his head, making him look like an English hotel runner. His exaggerated mustache, long and straight and tapering to a point at either end in a single blond hair that could hardly be seen, seemed to weigh down the corners of his mouth and give a droop to his lips.

In Alsatian French he requested the travelers to alight, saying stiffly: "Kindly get down, ladies and gentlemen."

The two nuns were the first to obey, manifesting the docility of holy women accustomed to submission on every occasion. Next appeared the count and countess, followed by the manufacturer and his wife, after whom came Loiseau, pushing his larger and better half before him.

"Good-day, sir," he said to the officer as he put his foot to the ground, acting on an impulse born of prudence rather than of politeness. The other, insolent like all in authority, merely stared without replying.

Boule de Suif and Cornudet, though near the door, were the last to alight, grave and dignified before the enemy. The stout girl tried to control herself and appear calm; the democrat stroked his long russet beard with a somewhat trembling hand. Both strove to maintain their dignity, knowing well that at such a time each individual is always looked upon as more or less typical of his nation; and, also, resenting the complaisant attitude of their companions, Boule de Suif tried to wear a bolder front than her neighbors, the virtuous women, while he, feeling that it was incumbent on him to set a good example, kept up the attitude of resistance which he had first assumed when he undertook to mine the highroads round Rouen.

They entered the spacious kitchen of the inn, and the German, having demanded the passports signed by the general in command, in which were mentioned the name, description and profession of each traveler, inspected them all minutely, comparing their appearance with the written particulars.

Then he said brusquely: "All right," and turned on his heel.

They breathed freely. All were still hungry; so supper was ordered. Half an hour was required for its preparation, and while two servants were apparently engaged in getting it ready the travelers went to look at their rooms. These all opened off a long corridor, at the end of which was a glazed door with a number on it.

They were just about to take their seats at table when the innkeeper appeared in person. He was a former horse-dealer—a large, asthmatic individual, always wheezing, coughing, and clearing his throat. Follenvie was his patronymic.

He called:

"Mademoiselle Elisabeth Rousset?"

Boule de Suif started, and turned round.

"That is my name."

"Mademoiselle, the Prussian officer wishes to speak to you immediately."

"To me?"

"Yes; if you are Mademoiselle Elisabeth Rousset."

She hesitated, reflected a moment, and then declared roundly:

"That may be; but I'm not going."

They moved restlessly around her; everyone wondered and speculated as to the cause of this order. The count approached:

"You are wrong, madame, for your refusal may bring trouble not only on yourself, but also on all your companions. It never pays to resist those in authority. Your compliance with this request cannot possibly be fraught with any danger; it has probably been made because some formality or other was forgotten."

All added their voices to that of the count; Boule de Suif was begged, urged, lectured, and at last convinced; everyone was afraid of the complications which might result from headstrong action on her part. She said finally:

"I am doing it for your sakes, remember that!"

The countess took her hand.

"And we are grateful to you."

She left the room. All waited for her return before commencing the meal. Each was distressed that he or she had not been sent for rather than this impulsive, quick-tempered girl, and each mentally rehearsed platitudes in case of being summoned also.

But at the end of ten minutes she reappeared, breathing hard, crimson with indignation.

"Oh! the scoundrel! the scoundrel!" she stammered.

All were anxious to know what had happened; but she declined to enlighten them, and when the count pressed the point, she silenced him with much dignity, saying:

"No; the matter has nothing to do with you, and I cannot speak of it."

Then they took their places round a high soup tureen, from which issued an odor of cabbage. In spite of this coincidence, the supper was cheerful. The cider was good; the Loiseaus and the nuns drank it from motives of economy. The others ordered wine; Cornudet demanded beer. He had his own fashion of uncorking the bottle and making the beer foam, gazing at it as he inclined his glass and then raised it to a position between the lamp and his eye that he might judge of its color. When he drank, his great beard, which matched the color of his favorite beverage, seemed to tremble with affection; his eyes positively squinted in the endeavor not to lose sight of the beloved glass, and he looked for all the world as if he were fulfilling the only function for which he was born. He seemed to have established in his mind an affinity between the two great passions of his life—pale ale and revolution—and assuredly he could not taste the one without dreaming of the other.

Monsieur and Madame Follenvie dined at the end of the table. The man, wheezing like a broken-down locomotive, was too short-winded to talk when he was eating. But the wife was not silent a moment; she told how the Prussians had impressed her on their arrival, what they did, what they said; execrating them in the first place because they cost her money, and in the second because she had two sons in the army. She addressed herself principally to the countess, flattered at the opportunity of talking to a lady of quality.

Then she lowered her voice, and began to broach delicate subjects. Her husband interrupted her from time to time, saying:

"You would do well to hold your tongue, Madame Follenvie."

But she took no notice of him, and went on:

"Yes, madame, these Germans do nothing but eat potatoes and pork, and then pork and potatoes. And don't imagine for a moment that they are clean! No, indeed! And if only you saw them drilling for hours, indeed for days, together; they all collect in a field, then they do nothing but march backward and forward, and wheel this way and that. If only they would cultivate the land, or remain at home and work on their highroads! Really, madame, these soldiers are of no earthly use! Poor people have to feed and keep them, only in order that they may learn how to kill! True, I am only an old woman with no education, but when I see them wearing themselves out marching about from morning till night, I say to myself: When there are people who make discoveries that are of use to people, why should others take so much trouble to do harm? Really, now, isn't it a terrible thing to kill people, whether they are Prussians, or English, or Poles, or French? If we revenge ourselves on anyone who injures us we do wrong, and are punished for it; but when our sons are shot down like partridges, that is all right, and decorations are given to the man who kills the most. No, indeed, I shall never be able to understand it."

Cornudet raised his voice:

"War is a barbarous proceeding when we attack a peaceful neighbor, but it is a sacred duty when undertaken in defense of one's country."

The old woman looked down:

"Yes; it's another matter when one acts in self-defense; but would it not be better to kill all the kings, seeing that they make war just to amuse themselves?"

Cornudet's eyes kindled.

"Bravo, citizens!" he said.

Monsieur Carré-Lamadon was reflecting profoundly. Although an ardent admirer of great generals, the peasant woman's sturdy common sense made him reflect on the wealth which might accrue to a country by the employment of so many idle hands now maintained at a great expense, of so much unproductive force, if they were employed in those great industrial enterprises which it will take centuries to complete.

But Loiseau, leaving his seat, went over to the innkeeper and began chatting in a low voice. The big man chuckled, coughed, sputtered; his enormous carcass shook with merriment at the pleasantries of the other; and he ended by buying six casks of claret from Loiseau to be delivered in spring, after the departure of the Prussians.

The moment supper was over everyone went to bed, worn out with fatigue.

But Loiseau, who had been making his observations on the sly, sent his wife to bed, and amused himself by placing first his ear, and then his eye, to the bedroom keyhole, in order to discover what he called "the mysteries of the corridor."

At the end of about an hour he heard a rustling, peeped out quickly, and caught sight of Boule de Suif, looking more rotund than ever in a dressing gown of blue cashmere trimmed with white lace. She held a candle in her hand, and directed her steps to the numbered door at the end of the corridor. But one of the side doors was partly opened, and when, at the end of a few minutes, she returned, Cornudet, in his shirt sleeves, followed her. They spoke in low tones, then stopped short. Boule de Suif seemed to be stoutly denying him admission to her room. Unfortunately, Loiseau could not at first hear what they said; but toward the end of the conversation they raised their voices, and he caught a few words. Cornudet was loudly insistent.

"How silly you are! What does it matter to you?" he said.

She seemed indignant, and replied:

"No, my good man, there are times when one does not do that sort of thing; besides, in this place it would be shameful."

Apparently he did not understand, and asked the reason. Then she lost her temper and her caution, and, raising her voice still higher, said:

"Why? Can't you understand why? When there are Prussians in the house! Perhaps even in the very next room!"

He was silent. The patriotic shame of this wanton, who would not suffer herself to be caressed in the neighborhood of the enemy, must have roused his dormant dignity, for after bestowing on her a simple kiss he crept softly back to his room. Loiseau, much edified, capered round the bedroom before taking his place beside his slumbering spouse.

Then silence reigned throughout the house. But soon there arose from some remote part—it might easily have been either cellar or attic —a stertorous, monotonous, regular snoring, a dull, prolonged rumbling, varied by tremors like those of a boiler under pressure of steam. Monsieur Follenvie had gone to sleep.

As they had decided on starting at eight o'clock the next morning, everyone was in the kitchen at that hour; but the coach, its roof covered with snow, stood by itself in the middle of the yard, without either horses or driver. They sought the latter in the stables, coach-houses and barns—but in vain. So the men of the party resolved to scour the country for him, and sallied forth. They found themselves in the square, with the church at the farther side, and to right and left low-roofed houses where there were some Prussian soldiers. The first soldier they saw was peeling potatoes. The second, farther on, was washing out a barber's shop. Another, bearded to the eyes, was fondling a crying infant, and dandling it on his knees to quiet it; and the stout peasant women, whose menfolk were for the most part at the war, were, by means of signs, telling their obedient conquerors what work they were to do: chop wood, prepare soup, grind coffee; one of them even was doing the washing for his hostess, an infirm old grandmother.

The count, astonished at what he saw, questioned the beadle who was coming out of the presbytery. The old man answered:

"Oh, those men are not at all a bad sort; they are not Prussians, I am told; they come from somewhere farther off, I don't exactly know where. And they have all left wives and children behind them; they are not fond of war either, you may be sure! I am sure they are mourning for the men where they come from, just as we do here; and the war causes them just as much unhappiness as it does us. As a matter of fact, things are not so very bad here just now, because the soldiers do no harm, and work just as if they were in their own homes. You see, sir, poor folk always help one another; it is the great ones of this world who make war."

Cornudet, indignant at the friendly understanding established between conquerors and conquered, withdrew, preferring to shut himself up in the inn.

"They are repeopling the country," jested Loiseau.

"They are undoing the harm they have done," said Monsieur Carré-Lamadon gravely.

But they could not find the coach driver. At last he was discovered in the village café, fraternizing cordially with the officer's orderly.

"Were you not told to harness the horses at eight o'clock?" demanded the count.

"Oh, yes; but I've had different orders since."

"What orders?"

"Not to harness at all."

"Who gave you such orders?"

"Why, the Prussian officer."

"But why?"

"I don't know. Go and ask him. I am forbidden to harness the horses, so I don't harness them—that's all."

"Did he tell you so himself?"

"No, sir; the innkeeper gave me the order from him."

"When?"

"Last evening, just as I was going to bed."

The three men returned in a very uneasy frame of mind.

They asked for Monsieur Follenvie, but the servant replied that on account of his asthma he never got up before ten o'clock. They were strictly forbidden to rouse him earlier, except in case of fire.

They wished to see the officer, but that also was impossible, although he lodged in the inn. Monsieur Follenvie alone was authorized to interview him on civil matters. So they waited. The women returned to their rooms, and occupied themselves with trivial matters.

Cornudet settled down beside the tall kitchen fireplace, before a blazing fire. He had a small table and a jug of beer placed beside him, and he smoked his pipe—a pipe which enjoyed among democrats a consideration almost equal to his own, as though it had served its country in serving Cornudet. It was a fine meerschaum, admirably colored to a black the shade of its owner's teeth, but sweet-smelling, gracefully curved, at home in its master's hand, and completing his physiognomy. And Cornudet sat motionless, his eyes fixed now on the dancing flames, now on the froth which crowned his beer; and after each draught he passed his long, thin fingers with an air of satisfaction through his long, greasy hair, as he sucked the foam from his mustache.

Loiseau, under pretense of stretching his legs, went out to see if he could sell wine to the country dealers. The count and the manufacturer began to talk politics. They forecast the future of France. One believed in the Orleans dynasty, the other in an unknown savior—a hero who should rise up in the last extremity: a Du Guesclin, perhaps a Joan of Arc? or another Napoleon the First? Ah! if only the Prince Imperial were not so young! Cornudet, listening to them, smiled like a man who holds the keys of destiny in his hands. His pipe perfumed the whole kitchen.

As the clock struck ten, Monsieur Follenvie appeared. He was immediately surrounded and questioned, but could only repeat, three or four times in succession, and without variation, the words:

"The officer said to me, just like this: 'Monsieur Follenvie, you will forbid them to harness up the coach for those travelers tomorrow. They are not to start without an order from me. You hear? That is sufficient.'"

Then they asked to see the officer. The count sent him his card, on which Monsieur Carré-Lamadon also inscribed his name and titles. The Prussian sent word that the two men would be admitted to see him after his luncheon—that is to say, about one o'clock.

The ladies reappeared, and they all ate a little, in spite of their anxiety. Boule de Suif appeared ill and very much worried.

They were finishing their coffee when the orderly came to fetch the gentlemen.

Loiseau joined the other two; but when they tried to get Cornudet to accompany them, by way of adding greater solemnity to the occasion, he declared proudly that he would never have anything to do with the Germans, and, resuming his seat in the chimney corner, he called for another jug of beer.

The three men went upstairs, and were ushered into the best room in the inn, where the officer received them lolling at his ease in an armchair, his feet on the mantelpiece, smoking a long porcelain pipe, and enveloped in a gorgeous dressing gown, doubtless stolen from the deserted dwelling of some citizen destitute of taste in dress. He neither rose, greeted them, nor even glanced in their direction. He afforded a fine example of that insolence of bearing which seems natural to the victorious soldier.

After the lapse of a few moments he said in his halting French:

"What do you want?"

"We wish to start on our journey," said the count.

"No."

"May I ask the reason of your refusal?"

"Because I don't choose."

"I would respectfully call your attention, monsieur, to the fact that your general in command gave us a permit to proceed to Dieppe; and I do not think we have done anything to deserve this harshness at your hands."

"I don't choose—that's all. You may go."

They bowed, and retired.

The afternoon was wretched. They could not understand the caprice of this German, and the strangest ideas came into their heads. They all congregated in the kitchen, and talked the subject to death, imagining all kinds of unlikely things. Perhaps they were to be kept as hostages—but for what reason? or to be extradited as prisoners of war? or possibly they were to be held for ransom? They were panic-stricken at this last supposition. The richest among them were the most alarmed, seeing themselves forced to empty bags of gold into the insolent soldier's hands in order to buy back their lives. They racked their brains for plausible lies whereby they might conceal the fact that they were rich, and pass themselves off as poor—very poor. Loiseau took off his watch-chain, and put it in his pocket. The approach of night increased their apprehension. The lamp was lighted, and as it wanted yet two hours to dinner Madame Loiseau proposed a game of *trente et un*. It would distract their thoughts. The rest agreed, and Cornudet himself joined the party, first putting out his pipe for politeness' sake.

The count shuffled the cards—dealt, and Boule de Suif had thirty-one to start with; soon the interest of the game assuaged the anxiety of the players. But Cornudet noticed that Loiseau and his wife were in league to cheat.

They were about to sit down to dinner when Monsieur Follenvie appeared, and in his grating voice announced:

"The Prussian officer sends to ask Mademoiselle Elisabeth Rousset if she has changed her mind yet."

Boule de Suif stood still, pale as death. Then, suddenly turning crimson with anger, she gasped out:

"Kindly tell that scoundrel, that cur, that carrion of a Prussian, that I will never consent—you understand?—never, never, never!"

The fat innkeeper left the room. Then Boule de Suif was surrounded, questioned, entreated on all sides to reveal the mystery of her visit to the officer. She refused at first; but her wrath soon got the better of her.

"What does he want? He wants to make me his mistress!" she cried.

No one was shocked at the word, so great was the general indignation. Cornudet broke his jug as he banged it down on the table. A loud outcry arose against this base soldier. All were furious. They drew together in common resistance against the foe, as if some part of the sacrifice exacted of Boule de Suif had been demanded of each. The count declared, with supreme disgust, that those people behaved like ancient barbarians. The women, above all, manifested a lively and tender sympathy for Boule de Suif. The nuns, who appeared only at meals, cast down their eyes, and said nothing.

They dined, however, as soon as the first indignant outburst had subsided; but they spoke little, and thought much.

The ladies went to bed early; and the men, having lighted their pipes, proposed a game of écarté, in which Monsieur Follenvie was invited to join, the travelers hoping to question him skillfully as to the best means of vanquishing the officer's obduracy. But he thought of nothing but his cards, would listen to nothing, reply to nothing, and repeated, time after time: "Attend to the game, gentlemen! attend to the game!" So absorbed was his attention that he even forgot to expectorate. The consequence was that his chest gave forth rumbling sounds like those of an organ. His wheezing lungs struck every note of the asthmatic scale, from deep, hollow tones to a shrill, hoarse piping resembling that of a young cock trying to crow.

He refused to go to bed when his wife, overcome with sleep, came to fetch him. So she went off alone, for she was an early bird, always up with the sun; while he was as addicted to late hours, ever ready to spend the night with friends. He merely said: "Put my eggnog by the fire," and went on with the game. When the other men saw that nothing was to be got out of him they declared it was time to retire, and each sought his bed.

They rose fairly early the next morning, with a vague hope of being allowed to start, a greater desire than ever to do so, and a terror at having to spend another day in this wretched little inn.

Alas! the horses remained in the stable, the driver was invisible. They spent their time, for want of something better to do, in wandering round the coach.

Luncheon was a gloomy affair; and there was a general coolness toward Boule de Suif, for night, which brings counsel, had somewhat modified the judgment of her companions. In the cold light of the morning they almost bore a grudge against the girl for not having secretly sought out the Prussian, that the rest of the party might receive a joyful surprise when they awoke. What more simple? Besides, who would have been the wiser? She might have saved appearances by telling the officer that she had taken pity on their distress. Such a step would be of so little consequence to her.

But no one as yet confessed to such thoughts.

In the afternoon, seeing that they were all bored to death, the count proposed a walk in the neighborhood of the village. Each one wrapped himself up well, and the little party set out, leaving behind only Cornudet, who preferred to sit over the fire, and the two nuns, who were in the habit of spending their day in the church or at the presbytery.

The cold, which grew more intense each day, almost froze the noses and ears of the pedestrians, their feet began to pain them so that each step was a penance, and when they reached the open country it looked so mournful and depressing in its limitless mantle of white that they all hastily retraced their steps, with bodies benumbed and hearts heavy.

The four women walked in front, and the three men followed a little in their rear.

Loiseau, who saw perfectly well how matters stood, asked suddenly "if that trollop were going to keep them waiting much longer in this God-forsaken spot." The count, always courteous, replied that they could not exact so painful a sacrifice from any woman, and that the first move must come from herself. Monsieur Carré-Lamadon remarked that if the French, as they talked of doing, made a counter-attack by way of Dieppe, their encounter with the enemy must inevitably take place at Tôtes. This reflection made the other two anxious.

"Supposing we escape on foot?" said Loiseau.

The count shrugged his shoulders.

"How can you think of such a thing, in this snow? And with our wives? Besides, we should be pursued at once, overtaken in ten minutes, and brought back as prisoners at the mercy of the soldiery."

This was true enough; they were silent.

The ladies talked of dress, but a certain constraint seemed to prevail among them.

Suddenly, at the end of the street, the officer appeared. His tall, wasplike, uniformed figure was outlined against the snow which bounded the horizon, and he walked, knees apart, with that motion peculiar to soldiers, who are always anxious not to soil their carefully polished boots.

He bowed as he passed the ladies, then glanced scornfully at the men, who had sufficient dignity not to raise their hats, though Loiseau made a movement to do so.

Boule de Suif flushed crimson to the ears, and the three married women felt unutterably humiliated at being met thus by the soldier in company with the girl whom he had treated with such scant ceremony.

Then they began to talk about him, his figure, and his face. Madame Carré-Lamadon, who had known many officers and judged them as a connoisseur, thought him not at all bad looking; she even regretted that he was not a Frenchman, because in that case he would have made a very handsome hussar, with whom all the women would assuredly have fallen in love.

When they were once more within doors they did not know what to do with themselves. Sharp words even were exchanged apropos of the merest trifles. The silent dinner was quickly over, and each one went to bed early in the hope of sleeping, and thus killing time.

They came down next morning with tired faces and irritable tempers; the women scarcely spoke to Boule de Suif.

A church bell summoned the faithful to a baptism. Boule de Suif had a child being brought up by peasants at Yvetot. She did not see him once a year, and never thought of him; but the idea of the child who was about to be baptized induced a sudden wave of tenderness for her own, and she insisted on being present at the ceremony.

As soon as she had gone out, the rest of the company looked at one another and then drew their chairs together; for they realized that they must decide on some course of action. Loiseau had an inspiration: he proposed that they should ask the officer to detain Boule de Suif only, and to let the rest depart on their way.

Monsieur Follenvie was intrusted with this commission, but he returned to them almost immediately. The German, who knew human nature, had shown him the door. He intended to keep all the travelers until his condition had been complied with.

Whereupon Madame Loiseau's vulgar temperament broke bounds. "We're not going to die of old age here!" she cried. "Since it's that vixen's trade to behave so with men I don't see that she has any right to refuse one more than another. I may as well tell you she took any lovers she could get at Rouen—even coachmen! Yes, indeed, madame —the coachman at the prefecture! I know it for a fact, for he buys his wine of us. And now that it is a question of getting us out of a difficulty she puts on virtuous airs, the drab! For my part, I think this officer has behaved very well. Why, there were three others of us, any one of whom he would undoubtedly have preferred. But no, he contents himself with the girl who is common property. He respects married women. Just think. He is master here. He had only to say: 'I wish it!' and he might have taken us by force, with the help of his soldiers."

The two other women shuddered; the eyes of pretty Madame Carré-

Lamadon glistened, and she grew pale, as if the officer were indeed in the act of laying violent hands on her.

The men, who had been discussing the subject among themselves, drew near. Loiseau, in a state of furious resentment, was for delivering up "that miserable woman," bound hand and foot, into the enemy's power. But the count, descended from three generations of ambassadors, and endowed, moreover, with the lineaments of a diplomat, was in favor of more tactful measures.

"We must persuade her," he said.

Then they laid their plans.

The women drew together; they lowered their voices, and the discussion became general, each giving his or her opinion. But the conversation was not in the least coarse. The ladies, in particular, were adepts at delicate phrases and charming subtleties of expression to describe the most improper things. A stranger would have understood none of their allusions, so guarded was the language they employed. But, seeing that the thin veneer of modesty with which every woman of the world is furnished goes but a very little way below the surface, they began rather to enjoy this unedifying episode and at bottom were hugely delighted—feeling themselves in their element, furthering the schemes of lawless love with the gusto of a gourmand cook who prepares supper for another.

Their gayety returned of itself, so amusing at last did the whole business seem to them. The count uttered several rather *risqué* witticisms, but so tactfully were they said that his audience could not help smiling. Loiseau in turn made some considerably broader jokes, but no one took offense; and the thought expressed with such brutal directness by his wife was uppermost in the minds of all: "Since it's the girl's trade, why should she refuse this man more than another?" Dainty Madame Carré-Lamadon seemed to think even that in Boule de Suif's place she would be less inclined to refuse him than another.

The blockade was as carefully arranged as if they were investing a fortress. Each agreed on the role which he or she was to play, the arguments to be used, the maneuvers to be executed. They decided on the plan of campaign, the stratagems they were to employ, and the surprise attacks which were to reduce this human citadel and force it to receive the enemy within its walls.

But Cornudet remained apart from the rest, taking no share in the plot.

So absorbed was the attention of all that Boule de Suif's entrance was almost unnoticed. But the count whispered a gentle "Hush!" which made the others look up. She was there. They suddenly stopped talking, and a vague embarrassment prevented them for a few moments from addressing her. But the countess, more practiced than the others in the wiles of the drawing room, asked her:

"Was the baptism interesting?"

The girl, still under the stress of emotion, told what she had seen and heard, described the faces, the attitudes of those present, and even the appearance of the church. She concluded with the words:

"It does one good to pray sometimes."

Until lunch time the ladies contented themselves with being pleasant to her, so as to increase her confidence and make her amenable to their advice.

As soon as they took their seats at table the attack began. First they opened a vague conversation on the subject of self-sacrifice. Ancient examples were quoted: Judith and Holofernes; then, irrationally enough, Lucrece and Sextus; Cleopatra and the hostile generals whom she reduced to abject slavery by a surrender of her charms. Next was recounted an extraordinary story, born of the imagination of these ignorant millionaires, which told how the matrons of Rome seduced Hannibal, his lieutenants, and all his mercenaries at Capua. They held up to admiration all those women who from time to time have arrested the victorious progress of conquerors, made of their bodies a field of battle, a means of ruling, a weapon; who have vanquished by their heroic caresses hideous or detested beings, and sacrificed their chastity to vengeance and devotion.

All was said with due restraint and regard for propriety, the effect heightened now and then by an outburst of forced enthusiasm calculated to excite emulation.

A listener would have thought at last that the one role of woman on earth was a perpetual sacrifice of her person, a continual abandonment of herself to the caprices of a hostile soldiery.

The two nuns seemed to hear nothing, and to be lost in thought. Boule de Suif also was silent.

During the whole afternoon she was left to her reflections. But instead of calling her *madame* as they had done hitherto, her companions addressed her simply as *mademoiselle,* without exactly knowing why, but as if desirous of making her descend a step in the esteem she had won, and forcing her to realize her degraded position.

Just as soup was served, Monsieur Follenvie reappeared, repeating his phrase of the evening before:

"The Prussian officer sends to ask if Mademoiselle Elisabeth Rousset has changed her mind."

Boule de Suif answered briefly:

"No, monsieur."

But at dinner the coalition weakened. Loiseau made three unfortunate remarks. Each was cudgeling his brains for further examples of self-sacrifice, and could find none, when the countess, possibly without ulterior motive, and moved simply by a vague desire to do homage to religion, began to question the elder of the two nuns on the most striking facts in the lives of the saints. Now, it fell out that many of these had committed acts which would be crimes in our eyes, but the Church readily pardons such deeds when they are accomplished for the glory of God or the good of mankind. This was a powerful argument, and the countess made the most of it. Then, whether by reason of a tacit understanding, a thinly veiled act of complaisance such as those who wear the ecclesiastical habit excel in, or whether merely as the result of sheer stupidity—a stupidity admirably adapted to further their designs—the old nun rendered formidable aid to the conspirators. They had thought her timid; she proved herself bold, talkative, bigoted. She was not troubled by the ins and outs of casuistry; her doctrines were as iron bars; her faith knew no doubt; her conscience no scruples. She looked on Abraham's sacrifice as natural enough, for she herself would not have hesitated to kill both father and mother if she had received a divine order to that effect; and nothing, in her opinion, could displease our Lord, provided the motive were praiseworthy. The countess, putting to good use the consecrated authority of her unexpected ally, led her on to make a lengthy and edifying paraphrase of that axiom enunciated by a certain school of moralists: "The end justifies the means."

"Then, sister," she asked, "you think God accepts all methods, and pardons the act when the motive is pure?"

"Undoubtedly, madame. An action reprehensible in itself often derives merit from the thought which inspires it."

And in this wise they talked on, fathoming the wishes of God, predicting His judgments, describing Him as interested in matters which assuredly concern Him but little.

All was said with the utmost care and discretion, but every word uttered by the holy woman in her nun's garb weakened the indignant resistance of the courtesan. Then the conversation drifted somewhat, and the nun began to talk of the convents of her order, of her Superior, of herself, and of her fragile little neighbor, Sister St. Nicephore. They had been sent for from Havre to nurse the hundreds of soldiers who were in hospitals, stricken with smallpox. She described these wretched invalids and their malady. And, while they themselves were detained on their way by the caprices of the Prussian officer, scores of Frenchmen might be dying, whom they would otherwise have saved! For the nursing of soldiers was the old nun's specialty; she had been in the Crimea, in Italy, in Austria; and as she told the story of her campaigns she revealed herself as one of those holy sisters of the fife and drum who seemed designed by nature to follow camps, to snatch the wounded from amid the strife of battle, and to quell with a word, more effectually than any general, the rough and insubordinate troopers—a masterful woman, her seamed and pitted face itself an image of the devastations of war.

No one spoke when she had finished for fear of spoiling the excellent effect of her words.

As soon as the meal was over the travelers retired to their rooms, whence they emerged the following day at a late hour of the morning.

Luncheon passed off quietly. The seed sown the preceding evening was being given time to germinate and bring forth fruit.

In the afternoon the countess proposed a walk; then the count, as had been arranged beforehand, took Boule de Suif's arm, and walked with her at some distance behind the rest.

He began talking to her in that familiar, paternal, slightly contemp-

tuous tone which men of his class adopt in speaking to women like her,
calling her "my dear child," and talking down to her from the height
of his exalted social position and stainless reputation. He came straight
to the point.

"So you prefer to leave us here, exposed like yourself to all the violence which would follow on a repulse of the Prussian troops, rather
than consent to surrender yourself, as you have done so many times
in your life?"

The girl did not reply.

He tried kindness, argument, sentiment. He still bore himself as
count, even while adopting, when desirable, an attitude of gallantry,
and making pretty—nay, even tender—speeches. He exalted the service
she would render them, spoke of their gratitude; then, suddenly, using
the familiar "thou":

"And you know, my dear, he could boast then of having made a
conquest of a pretty girl such as he won't often find in his own
country."

Boule de Suif did not answer, and joined the rest of the party.

As soon as they returned she went to her room, and was seen no
more. The general anxiety was at its height. What would she do? If
she still resisted, how awkward for them all!

The dinner hour struck; they waited for her in vain. At last Monsieur Follenvie entered, announcing that Mademoiselle Rousset was
not well, and that they might sit down to table. They all pricked up
their ears. The count drew near the innkeeper, and whispered:

"Is it all right?"

"Yes."

Out of regard for propriety he said nothing to his companions, but
merely nodded slightly toward them. A great sigh of relief went up
from all breasts; every face was lighted up with joy.

"By Gad!" shouted Loiseau. "I'll stand champagne all round if
there's any to be found in this place." And great was Madame Loiseau's
dismay when the proprietor came back with four bottles in his hands.
They had all suddenly become talkative and merry; a lively joy filled
all hearts. The count seemed to perceive for the first time that Madame
Carré-Lamadon was charming; the manufacturer paid compliments
to the countess. The conversation was animated, sprightly, witty, and,

although many of the jokes were in the worst possible taste, all the company were amused by them, and none offended—indignation being dependent, like other emotions, on surroundings. And the mental atmosphere had gradually become filled with gross imaginings and unclean thoughts.

At dessert even the women indulged in discreetly worded allusions. Their glances were full of meaning; they had drunk much. The count, who even in his moments of relaxation preserved a dignified demeanor, hit on a much-appreciated comparison of the condition of things with the termination of a winter spent in the icy solitude of the North Pole and the joy of shipwrecked mariners who at last perceive a southward track opening out before their eyes.

Loiseau, fairly in his element, rose to his feet, holding aloft a glass of champagne.

"I drink to our deliverance!" he shouted.

All stood up, and greeted the toast with acclamation. Even the two good sisters yielded to the solicitations of the ladies, and consented to moisten their lips with the foaming wine, which they had never before tasted. They declared it was like effervescent lemonade, but with a pleasanter flavor.

"It is a pity," said Loiseau, "that we have no piano; we might have had a quadrille."

Cornudet had not spoken a word or made a movement; he seemed plunged in serious thought, and now and then tugged furiously at his great beard, as if trying to add still further to its length. At last, toward midnight, when they were about to separate, Loiseau, whose gait was far from steady, suddenly slapped him on the back, saying thickly:

"You're not jolly tonight; why are you so silent, old man?"

Cornudet threw back his head, cast one swift and scornful glance over the assemblage, and answered:

"I tell you all, you have done an infamous thing!"

He rose, reached the door, and repeating: "Infamous!" disappeared.

A chill fell on all. Loiseau himself looked foolish and disconcerted for a moment, but soon recovered his aplomb, and, writhing with laughter, exclaimed:

"Really, you are all too green for anything!"

Pressed for an explanation, he related the "mysteries of the corridor," whereat his listeners were hugely amused. The ladies could hardly contain their delight. The count and Monsieur Carré-Lamadon laughed till they cried. They could scarcely believe their ears.

"What! you are sure? He wanted—"

"I tell you I saw it with my own eyes."

"And she refused?"

"And she refused!"

"Because the Prussian was in the next room!"

"Surely you are mistaken?"

"I swear I'm telling you the truth."

The count was choking with laughter. The manufacturer held his sides. Loiseau continued:

"So you may well imagine he doesn't think this evening's business at all amusing."

And all three began to laugh again, choking, coughing, almost ill with merriment.

Then they separated. But Madame Loiseau, who was nothing if not spiteful, remarked to her husband as they were on the way to bed that "that stuck-up little minx of a Carré-Lamadon had laughed on the wrong side of her mouth all the evening."

"You know," she said, "when women run after uniforms it's all the same to them whether the men who wear them are French or Prussian. It's perfectly sickening!"

The next morning the snow showed dazzling white under a clear winter sun. The coach, ready at last, waited before the door; while a flock of white pigeons, with pink eyes spotted in the centers with black, puffed out their white feathers and walked sedately between the legs of the six horses, picking at the steaming manure.

The driver, wrapped in his sheepskin coat, was smoking a pipe on the box, and all the passengers, radiant with delight at their approaching departure, were putting up provisions for the remainder of the journey.

They were waiting only for Boule de Suif. At last she appeared.

She seemed rather shamefaced and embarrassed, and advanced with timid step toward her companions, who with one accord turned aside as if they had not seen her. The count, with much dignity, took his wife by the arm, and removed her from the unclean contact.

The girl stood still, stupefied with astonishment; then, plucking up courage, accosted the manufacturer's wife with a humble "Good-morning, madame," to which the other replied merely with a slight and insolent nod, accompanied by a look of outraged virtue. Every-one suddenly appeared extremely busy, and kept as far from Boule de Suif as if her skirts had been infected with some deadly disease. Then they hurried to the coach, followed by the despised courtesan, who, arriving last of all, silently took the place she had occupied during the first part of the journey.

The rest seemed neither to see nor to know her—all save Madame Loiseau, who, glancing contemptuously in her direction, remarked, half aloud, to her husband:

"What a mercy I am not sitting beside that creature!"

The lumbering vehicle started on its way, and the journey began afresh.

At first no one spoke. Boule de Suif dared not even raise her eyes. She felt at once indignant with her neighbors, and humiliated at hav-ing yielded to the Prussian into whose arms they had so hypocritically cast her.

But the countess, turning toward Madame Carré-Lamadon, soon broke the painful silence:

"I think you know Madame d'Etrelles?"

"Yes; she is a friend of mine."

"Such a charming woman!"

"Delightful! Exceptionally talented, and an artist to the fingertips. She sings marvelously and draws to perfection."

The manufacturer was chatting with the count, and amid the clatter of the windowpanes a word of their conversation was now and then distinguishable: "Shares—maturity—premium—time limit."

Loiseau, who had abstracted from the inn the time-worn pack of cards, thick with the grease of five years' contact with half-wiped-off tables, started a game of bézique with his wife.

The good sisters, taking up simultaneously the long rosaries hanging from their waists, made the sign of the cross, and began to mutter in unison interminable prayers, their lips moving ever more and more swiftly, as if they sought which should outdistance the other in the race of orisons; from time to time they kissed a medal, and crossed themselves anew, then resumed their rapid and unintelligible murmur.

Cornudet sat still, lost in thought.

At the end of three hours Loiseau gathered up the cards, and re-marked that he was hungry.

His wife thereupon produced a parcel tied with string, from which she extracted a piece of cold veal. This she cut into neat, thin slices, and both began to eat.

"We may as well do the same," said the countess. The rest agreed, and she unpacked the provisions which had been prepared for herself, the count, and the Carré-Lamadons. In one of those oval dishes, the lids of which are decorated with an earthenware hare, by way of showing that a game pie lies within, was a succulent delicacy consist-ing of the brown flesh of the game, larded with streaks of bacon and flavored with other meats chopped fine. A solid wedge of Gruyère cheese, which had been wrapped in a newspaper, bore the imprint: "Items of News," on its rich, oily surface.

The two good sisters brought to light a hunk of sausage smelling strongly of garlic; and Cornudet, plunging both hands at once into the capacious pockets of his loose overcoat, produced from one four hard-boiled eggs and from the other a crust of bread. He removed the shells, threw them into the straw beneath his feet, and began to devour the eggs, letting morsels of the bright yellow yolk fall in his mighty beard, where they looked like stars.

Boule de Suif, in the haste and confusion of her departure, had not thought of anything, and, stifling with rage, she watched all these people placidly eating. At first, ill-suppressed wrath shook her whole person, and she opened her lips to shriek the truth at them, to over-whelm them with a volley of insults; but she could not utter a word, so choked was she with indignation.

No one looked at her, no one thought of her. She felt herself swal-lowed up in the scorn of these virtuous creatures, who had first sacri-ficed, then rejected her as a thing useless and unclean. Then she re-membered her big basket full of the good things they had so greedily devoured: the two chickens coated in jelly, the pies, the pears, the four bottles of claret; and her fury broke forth like a cord that is over-strained, and she was on the verge of tears. She made terrible efforts at self-control, drew herself up, swallowed the sobs which choked her;

but the tears rose nevertheless, shone at the brink of her eyelids, and soon two heavy drops coursed slowly down her cheeks. Others followed more quickly, like water filtering from a rock, and fell, one after another, on her rounded bosom. She sat upright, with a fixed expression, her face pale and rigid, hoping desperately that no one saw her give way.

But the countess noticed that she was weeping, and with a sign drew her husband's attention to the fact. He shrugged his shoulders, as if to say: "Well, what of it? It's not my fault." Madame Loiseau chuckled triumphantly, and murmured:

"She's weeping for shame."

The two nuns had betaken themselves once more to their prayers, first wrapping the remainder of their sausage in paper.

Then Cornudet, who was digesting his eggs, stretched his long legs under the opposite seat, threw himself back, folded his arms, smiled like a man who had just thought of a good joke, and began to whistle the *Marseillaise*.

The faces of his neighbors clouded; the popular air evidently did not find favor with them; they grew nervous and irritable, and seemed ready to howl as a dog does at the sound of a barrel organ. Cornudet saw the discomfort he was creating, and whistled the louder; sometimes he even hummed the words:

> *Amour sacré de la patrie,*
> *Conduis, soutiens, nos bras vengeurs,*
> *Liberté, liberté chérie,*
> *Combats avec tes défenseurs!*

The coach progressed more swiftly, the snow being harder now; and all the way to Dieppe, during the long, dreary hours of the journey, first in the gathering dusk, then in the thick darkness, raising his voice above the rumbling of the vehicle, Cornudet continued with fierce obstinacy his vengeful and monotonous whistling, forcing his weary and exasperated hearers to follow the song from end to end, to recall every word of every line, as each was repeated over and over again with untiring persistency.

And Boule de Suif still wept, and sometimes a sob she could not restrain was heard in the darkness between two verses of the song.

INTERPRETATION

The basic irony in this story is so obvious that it may be easy for the reader to conclude that the story is really oversimple and that the author is, consequently, engaged in overwriting, straining a great deal to extract all the irony he can from a rather simple contrast. But the story is more complicated than that, and it is easy enough to make out a case for its relative length. But the fundamental ironic contrast offers a proper place from which to start.

The basic irony, of course, involves the contrast between the patriotism of the disrespectable girl and the coldness and insincerity of the various "respectable" people who are associated with her. She is generous—with her food, for example; she is warm-bloodedly patriotic—not calculatingly so, as are some of her neighbors; she even has a sense of honor, poor though it may be by the world's standards, yet one to which she honestly tries to adhere. Measured against these virtues, the respectable representatives of society come off very badly. They are selfish, self-centered, preoccupied with their own comfort and their own interests, and worst of all, when their comfort demands it, they conspire to strip the girl even of the only kind of honor and self-respect which she possesses.

Thus far, the irony involved in the basic situation is related to that in the parable of the Good Samaritan: virtue is found to reside in the despised man, not in the professedly good men. But we need not press the resemblance. It represents only one aspect of Maupassant's general interest in this situation. That larger interest is revealed in his selection of the people with whom Tallow Ball is associated: the wine merchant and his wife, the rich cotton manufacturer and his wife, the Count and Countess de Bréville, the "democrat" Cornudet, and the two nuns. In his selection of the travelers, the author has taken care to represent church and state, trade and aristocracy, various types of wealth and social prestige. Indeed, the three couples represent the *petite bourgeoisie,* the *haute bourgeoisie,* and the aristocracy itself. Together they stand for Society, as Maupassant puts it, "the strong, established Society of good people with religion and principle." These are the people who have the greatest stake, one would feel, in the Society which is under attack. And Cornudet himself, though ostensibly a foe of this Society, a revolutionist who awaits the advent of the Republic, is a part of it as well. He wants the Republic to come about in order "that he might at last be rewarded with the post he had earned by his revolutionary orgies." The

nuns represent, of course, the institution which is supposed to give
the state its fundamental principles. But all of Tallow Ball's companions in practice represent institutional interests and all of them tend to
act in terms of their special codes. Even Cornudet himself, though a
revolutionary democrat, behaves as a respectable revolutionary democrat
should behave. Only Tallow Ball, the woman of the streets, has no system to dictate her feelings; and, untrammeled by any system, she can act
directly and warmly as a human being. She likes to be liked. She is really
happy to share her dinner with the travelers. She really hates the enemy.
He impresses her as being brutal and dirty. She really loves her country
with something of the simple and direct love of a child: for her, her
country does not mean the preservation of certain powers, or of certain
institutions with which her own selfish well-being is tied up.

We have already alluded to the possibility that such an irony might
easily seem too bitter and direct. It should be noticed that Maupassant is
careful not to overplay it by making Tallow Ball too good or heroic.
She becomes no Joan of Arc in the story. She is roly-poly, though childishly pretty; she is simple. She is characterized by no special delicacy
or sensitiveness. She is what she is, and Maupassant does not attempt to
make us believe that she is better than she is. When the journey is over,
Tallow Ball will resume her vocation, which of course it has not occurred to her to abandon, and perhaps she will not even resent very
much what the rest of the travelers have done to her. The story, as we
have indicated, attempts no glorification of the girl. Rather, as we have
seen, it is basically satirical. But in what is the irony centered? Observing
the classes and types which are measured unfavorably against Tallow
Ball, we might easily come to the conclusion, not that the irony was too
simple and bitter, but that the irony had no center at all: that it was a
"free" irony which refers to no central standards against which the
imperfections of the characters are to be measured, but was merely irresponsible, gratuitously slurring at any type or class or institution which
came within its range. Certainly, it would not be too difficult for the
casual reader to conclude that the story is an attack on aristocracy as
such, or on pretensions to decency in general, or on patriotism "as the
last refuge of a scoundrel," or on religion. It is true that the story operates to deflate the more conventional pretensions to religion, patriotism,
honor, and the like. But the irony is not irresponsible. Indeed, the irony
is possible at all only as the threadbare honor of Tallow Ball exposes by
comparison the respectable people's pretensions to honor. If we take the

story as attacking religion, patriotism, or honor, we are missing the point.

It has already been pointed out that Maupassant is interested in the codes, the patterns of manners and of morals, by which men live. The relations of all the travelers to the street girl focus on this point. She brings up sharply the whole matter of their own respectability and their own selfish interests. Ironically, because she has no reputation to protect, she can and does act unselfishly. Maupassant seems to be implying that the process of institutionalizing, the process of codifying, the process of applying labels of good and bad to various actions, in itself introduces an impure element. At any rate, throughout this story, the simple and perhaps foolishly childish patriotism and generosity of the prostitute is juxtaposed with the pharisaical, self-regarding, self-conscious actions of her companions. But we shall distort the story if we conclude that Maupassant takes the essentially romantic view that impulsive warm-hearted actions are in themselves inherently good, and that all codes are by their very nature evil. Maupassant here is no more a romantic anarchist than he is an irresponsible cynic, though to the tender-minded he may seem cynical. Instead, the story as a whole makes a judgment upon society, a judgment which is shrewd and tough-minded, which is alive to the complexities of the situation, and which relates them to a coherent center. There is the central irony of situation, it is true, but the whole story is an orchestration of ironies, and it is through the various ironies that the author indicates the various qualifications of his attitude.

What, for instance, is the author's attitude toward Cornudet? It is Cornudet, for example, who alone of the group reproaches the group for what it has done: "He rose, reached the door, and repeating: 'Infamous!' disappeared." Moreover it is Cornudet who at the end of the story whistles the "Marseillaise" as a sort of bitter commentary on the patriotism which the group has shown, and as a sort of ironical tribute to the sacrifice which poor Tallow Ball has made. He even hums the words to increase his companions' exasperation. But Cornudet does not try to console Tallow Ball as she weeps in the coach, nor does he offer her one of the four hard-boiled eggs which he has brought with him. He does not become the heroic spokesman for the prostitute. Or, to take another example, the women in the party are not necessarily wicked and cruel women. In a sense, it is thoroughly natural that they should be unable to see why Tallow Ball should make an exception of the Prussian, when after all she is a prostitute. Maupassant has not presented us with an unbelievably virtuous prostitute, or put her in company with incredibly cruel and wicked companions. Instead, by an act of special insight into a credible situation, he has indicated the callousness in ordinary "good people" and a kind of honor in "bad people." But his special instrument for giving shadings of judgment, for indicating indirectly his own interpretations and judgments, is irony. It is through his irony that the exact measure and pressure of the insight is given.

1. What is the importance of the description of the retreating army and the invaded countryside with which the author introduces the story proper? What is the *tone* (see Glossary) of this description; that is, how is the attitude of the author toward his material reflected in the way in which he treats it?

2. What is the function of the scene in which Tallow Ball describes the baptism which she has witnessed?

3. Balzac, in his "Christ in Flanders," selects his boatload of characters with an eye to their representative value much as Maupassant in this story chooses the passengers in the coach so as to get a cross section of society. Compare the two stories: as to theme; as to tone. How much of the "parable" quality resides in "The Tallow Ball" in spite of the ironic commentary which overlays it?

4. Compare this story with "Tennessee's Partner" and with "The Killers" as to theme.

A Rose for Emily
WILLIAM FAULKNER

I

WHEN Miss Emily Grierson died, our whole town went to her funeral: the men through a sort of respectful affection for a fallen monument, the women mostly out of curiosity to see the inside of her house, which no one save an old manservant—a combined gardener and cook—had seen in at least ten years.

It was a big, squarish frame house that had once been white, decorated with cupolas and spires and scrolled balconies in the heavily lightsome style of the seventies, set on what had once been our most select street. But garages and cotton gins had encroached and obliterated even the august names of that neighborhood; only Miss Emily's house was left, lifting its stubborn and coquettish decay above the cotton wagons and the gasoline pumps—an eyesore among eyesores. And now Miss Emily had gone to join the representatives of those august names where they lay in the cedar-bemused cemetery among the ranked and anonymous graves of Union and Confederate soldiers who fell at the battle of Jefferson.

Alive, Miss Emily had been a tradition, a duty, and a care; a sort of hereditary obligation upon the town, dating from that day in 1894 when Colonel Sartoris, the mayor—he who fathered the edict that no Negro woman should appear on the streets without an apron—remitted her taxes, the dispensation dating from the death of her father on into perpetuity. Not that Miss Emily would have accepted charity. Colonel Sartoris invented an involved tale to the effect that Miss Emily's father had loaned money to the town, which the town, as a matter of business, preferred this way of repaying. Only a man of Colonel Sartoris' generation and thought could have invented it, and only a woman could have believed it.

When the next generation, with its more modern ideas, became mayors and aldermen, this arrangement created some little dissatisfaction. On the first of the year they mailed her a tax notice. February came, and there was no reply. They wrote her a formal letter, asking her to call at the sheriff's office at her convenience. A week later the mayor wrote her himself, offering to call or to send his car for her, and received in reply a note on paper of an archaic shape, in a thin, flowing calligraphy in faded ink, to the effect that she no longer went out at all. The tax notice was also enclosed, without comment.

They called a special meeting of the Board of Aldermen. A deputation waited upon her, knocked at the door through which no visitor had passed since she ceased giving china-painting lessons eight or ten years earlier. They were admitted by the old Negro into a dim hall from which a stairway mounted into still more shadow. It smelled of dust and disuse—a close, dank smell. The Negro led them into the parlor. It was furnished in heavy, leather-covered furniture. When the Negro opened the blinds of one window, they could see that the leather was cracked; and when they sat down, a faint dust rose sluggishly about their thighs, spinning with slow motes in the single sun-ray. On a tarnished gilt easel before the fireplace stood a crayon portrait of Miss Emily's father.

They rose when she entered—a small, fat woman in black, with a thin gold chain descending to her waist and vanishing into her belt, leaning on an ebony cane with a tarnished gold head. Her skeleton was small and spare; perhaps that was why what would have been merely plumpness in another was obesity in her. She looked bloated, like a body long submerged in motionless water, and of that pallid hue. Her eyes, lost in the fatty ridges of her face, looked like two small pieces of coal pressed into a lump of dough as they moved from one face to another while the visitors stated their errand.

She did not ask them to sit. She just stood in the door and listened quietly until the spokesman came to a stumbling halt. Then they could hear the invisible watch ticking at the end of the gold chain.

Her voice was dry and cold. "I have no taxes in Jefferson. Colonel Sartoris explained it to me. Perhaps one of you can gain access to the city records and satisfy yourselves."

"But we have. We are the city authorities, Miss Emily. Didn't you get a notice from the sheriff, signed by him?"

"I received a paper, yes," Miss Emily said. "Perhaps he considers himself the sheriff. . . . I have no taxes in Jefferson."

"But there is nothing on the books to show that, you see. We must go by the—"

"See Colonel Sartoris. I have no taxes in Jefferson."

"But, Miss Emily—"

"See Colonel Sartoris." (Colonel Sartoris had been dead almost ten years.) "I have no taxes in Jefferson. Tobe!" The Negro appeared. "Show these gentlemen out."

II

So she vanquished them, horse and foot, just as she had vanquished their fathers thirty years before about the smell. That was two years after her father's death and a short time after her sweetheart—the one we believed would marry her—had deserted her. After her father's death she went out very little; after her sweetheart went away, people hardly saw her at all. A few of the ladies had the temerity to call, but were not received, and the only sign of life about the place was the

Negro man—a young man then—going in and out with a market basket.

"Just as if a man—any man—could keep a kitchen properly," the ladies said; so they were not surprised when the smell developed. It was another link between the gross, teeming world and the high and mighty Griersons.

A neighbor, a woman, complained to the mayor, Judge Stevens, eighty years old.

"But what will you have me do about it, madam?" he said.

"Why, send her word to stop it," the woman said. "Isn't there a law?"

"I'm sure that won't be necessary," Judge Stevens said. "It's probably just a snake or a rat that nigger of hers killed in the yard. I'll speak to him about it."

The next day he received two more complaints, one from a man who came in diffident deprecation. "We really must do something about it, Judge. I'd be the last one in the world to bother Miss Emily, but we've got to do something." That night the Board of Aldermen met—three graybeards and one younger man, a member of the rising generation.

"It's simple enough," he said. "Send her word to have her place cleaned up. Give her a certain time to do it in, and if she don't . . ."

"Dammit, sir," Judge Stevens said, "will you accuse a lady to her face of smelling bad?"

So the next night, after midnight, four men crossed Miss Emily's lawn and slunk about the house like burglars, sniffing along the base of the brickwork and at the cellar openings while one of them performed a regular sowing motion with his hand out of a sack slung from his shoulder. They broke open the cellar door and sprinkled lime there, and in all the outbuildings. As they recrossed the lawn, a window that had been dark was lighted and Miss Emily sat in it, the light behind her, and her upright torso motionless as that of an idol. They crept quietly across the lawn and into the shadow of the locusts that lined the street. After a week or two the smell went away.

That was when people had begun to feel really sorry for her. People in our town, rmembering how old lady Wyatt, her great-aunt, had gone completely crazy at last, believed that the Griersons held them-

selves a little too high for what they really were. None of the young
men were quite good enough for Miss Emily and such. We had long
thought of them as a tableau; Miss Emily a slender figure in white in
the background, her father a spraddled silhouette in the foreground,
his back to her and clutching a horsewhip, the two of them framed
by the back-flung front door. So when she got to be thirty and was
still single, we were not pleased exactly, but vindicated; even with
insanity in the family she wouldn't have turned down all of her
chances if they had really materialized.

When her father died, it got about that the house was all that was
left to her; and in a way, people were glad. At last they could pity
Miss Emily. Being left alone, and a pauper, she had become human-
ized. Now she too would know the old thrill and the old despair of a
penny more or less.

The day after his death all the ladies prepared to call at the house
and offer condolence and aid, as is our custom. Miss Emily met them
at the door, dressed as usual and with no trace of grief on her face.
She told them that her father was not dead. She did that for three
days, with the ministers calling on her, and the doctors, trying to
persuade her to let them dispose of the body. Just as they were about
to resort to law and force, she broke down, and they buried her father
quickly.

We did not say she was crazy then. We believed she had to do that.
We remembered all the young men her father had driven away, and
we knew that with nothing left, she would have to cling to that which
had robbed her, as people will.

III

She was sick for a long time. When we saw her again, her hair was
cut short, making her look like a girl, with a vague resemblance to
those angels in colored church windows—sort of tragic and serene.

The town had just let the contracts for paving the sidewalks, and
in the summer after her father's death they began the work. The
construction company came with niggers and mules and machinery,
and a foreman named Homer Barron, a Yankee—a big, dark, ready
man, with a big voice and eyes lighter than his face. The little boys
would follow in groups to hear him cuss the niggers, and the niggers

singing in time to the rise and fall of picks. Pretty soon he knew everybody in town. Whenever you heard a lot of laughing anywhere about the square, Homer Barron would be in the center of the group. Presently we began to see him and Miss Emily on Sunday afternoons driving in the yellow-wheeled buggy and the matched team of bays from the livery stable.

At first we were glad that Miss Emily would have an interest, because the ladies all said, "Of course a Grierson would not think seriously of a Northerner, a day laborer." But there were still others, older people, who said that even grief could not cause a real lady to forget *noblesse oblige*—without calling it *noblesse oblige*. They just said, "Poor Emily. Her kinsfolk should come to her." She had some kin in Alabama; but years ago her father had fallen out with them over the estate of old lady Wyatt, the crazy woman, and there was no communication between the two families. They had not even been represented at the funeral.

And as soon as the old people said, "Poor Emily," the whispering began. "Do you suppose it's really so?" they said to one another. "Of course it is. What else could . . ." This behind their hands; rustling of craned silk and satin behind jalousies closed upon the sun of Sunday afternoon as the thin, swift clop-clop-clop of the matched team passed: "Poor Emily."

She carried her head high enough—even when we believed that she was fallen. It was as if she demanded more than ever the recognition of her dignity as the last Grierson; as if it had wanted that touch of earthiness to reaffirm her imperviousness. Like when she bought the rat poison, the arsenic. That was over a year after they had begun to say "Poor Emily," and while the two female cousins were visiting her.

"I want some poison," she said to the druggist. She was over thirty then, still a slight woman, though thinner than usual, with cold, haughty black eyes in a face the flesh of which was strained across the temples and about the eyesockets as you imagine a lighthouse-keeper's face ought to look. "I want some poison," she said.

"Yes, Miss Emily. What kind? For rats and such? I'd recom—"

"I want the best you have. I don't care what kind."

The druggist named several. "They'll kill anything up to an elephant. But what you want is—"

"Arsenic," Miss Emily said. "Is that a good one?"

"Is . . . arsenic? Yes, ma'am. But what you want—"

"I want arsenic."

The druggist looked down at her. She looked back at him, erect, her face like a strained flag. "Why, of course," the druggist said. "If that's what you want. But the law requires you to tell what you are going to use it for."

Miss Emily just stared at him, her head tilted back in order to look him eye for eye, until he looked away and went and got the arsenic and wrapped it up. The Negro delivery boy brought her the package; the druggist didn't come back. When she opened the package at home there was written on the box, under the skull and bones: "For rats."

IV

So the next day we all said, "She will kill herself"; and we said it would be the best thing. When she had first begun to be seen with Homer Barron, we had said, "She will marry him." Then we said, "She will persuade him yet," because Homer himself had remarked— he liked men, and it was known that he drank with the younger men in the Elk's Club—that he was not a marrying man. Later we said, "Poor Emily," behind the jalousies as they passed on Sunday after- noon in the glittering buggy, Miss Emily with her head high and Homer Barron with his hat cocked and a cigar in his teeth, reins and whip in a yellow glove.

Then some of the ladies began to say that it was a disgrace to the town and a bad example to the young people. The men did not want to interfere, but at last the ladies forced the Baptist minister—Miss Emily's people were Episcopal—to call upon her. He would never divulge what happened during that interview, but he refused to go back again. The next Sunday they again drove about the streets, and the following day the minister's wife wrote to Miss Emily's relations in Alabama.

So she had blood-kin under her roof again and we sat back to watch developments. At first nothing happened. Then we were sure that they were to be married. We learned that Miss Emily had been to the jeweler's and ordered a man's toilet set in silver, with the letters H.B.

on each piece. Two days later we learned that she had bought a complete outfit of men's clothing, including a nightshirt, and we said, "They are married." We were really glad. We were glad because the two female cousins were even more Grierson than Miss Emily had ever been.

So we were not surprised when Homer Barron—the streets had been finished some time since—was gone. We were a little disappointed that there was not a public blowing-off, but we believed that he had gone on to prepare for Miss Emily's coming, or to give her a chance to get rid of the cousins. (By that time it was a cabal, and we were all Miss Emily's allies to help circumvent the cousins.) Sure enough, after another week they departed. And, as we had expected all along, within three days Homer Barron was back in town. A neighbor saw the Negro man admit him at the kitchen door at dusk one evening.

And that was the last we saw of Homer Barron. And of Miss Emily for some time. The Negro man went in and out with the market basket, but the front door remained closed. Now and then we would see her at a window for a moment, as the men did that night when they sprinkled the lime, but for almost six months she did not appear on the streets. Then we knew that this was to be expected too; as if that quality of her father which had thwarted her woman's life so many times had been too virulent and too furious to die.

When we next saw Miss Emily, she had grown fat and her hair was turning gray. During the next few years it grew grayer and grayer until it attained an even pepper-and-salt iron-gray, when it ceased turning. Up to the day of her death at seventy-four it was still that vigorous iron-gray, like the hair of an active man.

From that time on her front door remained closed, save for a period of six or seven years, when she was about forty, during which she gave lessons in china-painting. She fitted up a studio in one of the downstairs rooms, where the daughters and granddaughters of Colonel Sartoris' contemporaries were sent to her with the same regularity and in the same spirit that they were sent on Sundays with a twenty-five cent piece for the collection plate. Meanwhile her taxes had been remitted.

Then the newer generation became the backbone and the spirit of the town, and the painting pupils grew up and fell away and did not send their children to her with boxes of color and tedious brushes and pictures cut from the ladies' magazines. The front door closed upon the last one and remained closed for good. When the town got free postal delivery Miss Emily alone refused to let them fasten the metal numbers above her door and attach a mailbox to it. She would not listen to them.

Daily, monthly, yearly we watched the Negro grow grayer and more stooped, going in and out with the market basket. Each December we sent her a tax notice, which would be returned by the post office a week later, unclaimed. Now and then we would see her in one of the downstairs windows—she had evidently shut up the top floor of the house—like the carven torso of an idol in a niche, looking or not looking at us, we could never tell which. Thus she passed from generation to generation—dear, inescapable, impervious, tranquil, and perverse.

And so she died. Fell ill in the house filled with dust and shadows, with only a doddering Negro man to wait on her. We did not even know she was sick; we had long since given up trying to get any information from the Negro. He talked to no one, probably not even to her, for his voice had grown harsh and rusty, as if from disuse.

She died in one of the downstairs rooms, in a heavy walnut bed with a curtain, her gray head propped on a pillow yellow and moldy with age and lack of sunlight.

V

The Negro met the first of the ladies at the front door and let them in, with their hushed, sibilant voices and their quick, curious glances, and then he disappeared. He walked right through the house and out the back and was not seen again.

The two female cousins came at once. They held the funeral on the second day, with the town coming to look at Miss Emily beneath a mass of bought flowers, with the crayon face of her father musing profoundly above the bier and the ladies sibilant and macabre; and the very old men—some in their brushed Confederate uniforms—on the porch and the lawn, talking of Miss Emily as if she had been a contemporary of theirs, believing that they had danced with her and courted her perhaps, confusing time with its mathematical progression, as the old do, to whom all the past is not a diminishing road, but, instead, a huge meadow which no winter ever quite touches, divided from them now by the narrow bottleneck of the most recent decade of years.

Already we knew that there was one room in that region above stairs which no one had seen in forty years, and which would have to be forced. They waited until Miss Emily was decently in the ground before they opened it.

The violence of breaking down the door seemed to fill this room with pervading dust. A thin, acrid pall as of the tomb seemed to lie everywhere upon this room decked and furnished as for a bridal: upon the valance curtains of faded rose color, upon the rose-shaded lights, upon the dressing table, upon the delicate array of crystal and the man's toilet things backed with tarnished silver, silver so tarnished that the monogram was obscured. Among them lay a collar and tie, as if they had just been removed, which, lifted, left upon the surface a pale crescent in the dust. Upon a chair hung the suit, carefully folded; beneath it the two mute shoes and the discarded socks.

The man himself lay in the bed.

For a long while we just stood there, looking down at the profound and fleshless grin. The body had apparently once lain in the attitude of an embrace, but now the long sleep that outlasts love, that conquers even the grimace of love, had cuckolded him. What was left of him, rotted beneath what was left of the nightshirt, had become inextricable from the bed in which he lay; and upon him and upon the pillow beside him lay that even coating of the patient and biding dust.

Then we noticed that in the second pillow was the indentation of a head. One of us lifted something from it, and leaning forward, that faint and invisible dust dry and acrid in the nostrils, we saw a long strand of iron-gray hair.*

INTERPRETATION

This story, like Poe's "The Fall of the House of Usher," is a story of horror. In both stories we have a decaying mansion in which the protaganist, shut away from the world, grows into something monstrous, and becomes as divorced from the human as some fungus grow-

* From *These Thirteen;* reprinted by permission of Random House.

ing in the dark on a damp wall. Roderick Usher and Miss Emily Grier-son remain in voluntary isolation (or perhaps fettered by some inner compulsion) away from the bustle and dust and sunshine of the human world of normal affairs. As we have seen, Poe closes his story with a melodramatic gesture in which the house falls into the lake, carrying with it its dead master. The ending of Faulkner's story is not so spectac-ular, but what is found in the upstairs room gives perhaps a sense of more penetrating and gruesome horror than ever Poe has achieved.

It has been indicated that, in the case of Poe, the sense of horror has been conjured up for its own sake. Is this true of Faulkner's story? If it is not, then why has he contrived to insert so much of the monstrous into the story? In other words, does the horror contribute to the theme of Faulkner's story? Is the horror meaningful?

In order to answer this question, we shall have to examine rather care-fully some of the items earlier in the story. In the first place, why does Miss Emily commit her monstrous act? Is she supplied with a proper motivation—a matter which we concluded was handled rather weakly in "The Fall of the House of Usher." Faulkner has been rather careful to prepare for his *dénouement* (see Glossary). Miss Emily, it becomes obvious fairly early in the story, is one of those persons for whom the distinction between reality and illusion has blurred out. For example, she refuses to admit that she owes any taxes. When the mayor protests, she does not recognize him as mayor. Instead, she refers the committee to Colonel Sartoris, who, as the reader is told, has been dead for nearly ten years. For Miss Emily, apparently, Colonel Sartoris is still alive. Most specific preparation of all, when her father dies, she denies to the townspeople for three days that he is dead: "Just as they were about to resort to law and force, she broke down, and they buried her father quickly."

Miss Emily is obviously a pathological case. The narrator indicates plainly enough that people felt that she was crazy. All of this explana-tion prepares us for what Miss Emily does in order to hold her lover— the dead lover is in one sense still alive for her—the realms of reality and appearance merge. But having said this, we have got no nearer to justi-fying the story: for, if Faulkner is merely interested in relating a case history of abnormal psychology, the story lacks meaning and justifica-tion as a story. His interest in this case is as "clinical" as is the interest of Poe in Roderick Usher. If the story is to be justified, there must be what may be called a moral significance, a meaning in moral terms— not merely psychological terms.

Incidentally, it is very easy to misread the story as merely a horrible case history, presented in order to titillate the reader. Faulkner has been frequently judged to be doing nothing more than this in his work.

The lapse of the distinction between illusion and reality, between life and death, is important, therefore, as helping supply the motivation for the story, but a definition of this in itself is not a complete definition of the author's intention. We shall have to go behind it if we are to understand what Faulkner is about.

Suppose we approach the motivation again in these terms: what is Miss Emily like? What are the mainsprings of her character? What causes the distinction between illusion and reality to blur out for her? She is obviously a woman of tremendous firmness of will. In the matter of the taxes, crazed though she is, she is never at a loss. She is utterly composed. She dominates the rather frightened committee of officers who see her. In the matter of her purchase of the poison, she completely overawes the clerk. She makes no pretenses. She refuses to tell him what she wants the poison for. And yet this firmness of will and this iron pride have not kept her from being thwarted and hurt. Her father has run off the young men who came to call upon her, and for the man who tells the story, Miss Emily and her father form a tableau: "Miss Emily a slender figure in white in the background, her father a spraddled silhouette in the foreground, his back to her and clutching a horsewhip, the two of them framed by the back-flung front door." Whether the picture is a remembered scene, or merely a symbolical construct, this is the picture which remains in the storyteller's mind.

We have indicated that her pride is connected with her contempt for public opinion. This comes to the fore, of course, when she rides around about the town with the foreman whom everybody believes is beneath her. And it is her proud refusal to admit an external set of codes, or conventions, or other wills which contradict her own will, which makes her capable at the end of keeping her lover from going away. Confronted with his jilting her, she tries to override not only his will and the opinion of other people, but the laws of death and decay themselves.

But this, still, hardly gives the meaning of the story. For in all that has been said thus far, we are still merely accounting for a psychological aberration—we are still merely dealing with a case history in abnormal psychology. In order to make a case for the story as "meaningful," we shall have to tie Miss Emily's thoughts and actions back into the normal life of the community, and establish some sort of relationship between them. And just here one pervasive element in the narration suggests a clue. The story is told by one of the townspeople. And in it, as a constant factor, is the reference to what the community thought of Miss Emily. Continually through the story it is what "we" said, and then what "we" did, and what seemed true to "us," and so on. The narrator puts the matter even more sharply still. He says, in the course of the story, that to the community Miss Emily seemed "dear, inescapable, impervious, tranquil, and perverse." Each of the adjectives is important and meaningful. In a sense, Miss Emily because of her very fact of isolation and perversity belongs to the whole community. She is even something treasured by it. Ironically, because of Emily's perversion of an aristocratic independence of mores and because of her contempt for "what people say," her life is public, even communal. And various phrases used by the narrator underline this view of her position. For example, her face looks "as you imagine a lighthouse-keeper's face ought to look," like the face of a person who lives in the kind of isolation imposed on a lighthouse-keeper, who looks out into the blackness and whose light serves a public function. Or, again, after her father's death, she becomes very ill, and when she appears after the illness, she has "a vague resemblance to those angels in colored church windows—sort of tragic and serene." Whatever we make of these descriptions, certainly the author is trying to suggest a kind of calm and dignity which is supermundane, unearthly, or "over-earthly," such as an angel might possess.

Miss Emily, then, is a combination of idol and scapegoat for the community. On the one hand, the community feels admiration for Miss Emily—she represents something in the past of the community which the community is proud of. They feel a sort of awe of her, as is illustrated by the behavior of the mayor and the committee in her presence. On the other hand, her queerness, the fact that she cannot compete with them in their ordinary life, the fact that she is hopelessly out of touch with the modern world—all of these things make them feel superior to her, and also to that past which she represents. It is, then, Miss Emily's complete detachment which gives her actions their special meaning for the community.

Miss Emily, since she is the conscious aristocrat, since she is consciously "better" than other people, since she is above and outside their canons of behavior, can, at the same time, be worse than other people; and she *is* worse, horribly so. She is worse than other people, but at the same time, as the narrator implies, she remains somehow admirable. This raises a fundamental question: why is this true?

Perhaps the horrible and the admirable aspects of Miss Emily's final deed arise from the same basic fact of her character: she insists on meeting the world on her own terms. She never cringes, she never begs for sympathy, she refuses to shrink into an amiable old maid, she never accepts the community's ordinary judgments or values. This independence of spirit and pride can, and does in her case, twist the individual into a sort of monster, but, at the same time, this refusal to accept the herd values carries with it a dignity and courage. The community senses this, as we gather from the fact that the community carries out the decencies of the funeral before breaking in the door of the upper room. There is, as it were, a kind of secret understanding that she has won her right of privacy, until she herself has entered history. Furthermore, despite the fact that, as the narrator says, "already we knew that there was one room in that region above stairs which no one had seen in forty years, and which would have to be forced," her funeral is something of a state occasion, with "the very old men—some in their brushed Confederate uniforms—on the porch and the lawn, talking of Miss Emily as if she had been a contemporary of theirs, believing that they had danced with her and courted her perhaps . . ." In other words, the community accepts her into its honored history. All of this works as a kind of tacit recognition of Miss Emily's triumph of will. The community, we are told earlier, had wanted to pity Miss Emily when she had lost her money, just as they had wanted to commiserate over her when they believed that she had actually become a fallen woman, but she had triumphed over their pity and commiseration and condemnation, just as she had triumphed over all their other attitudes.

But, as we have indicated earlier, it may be said that Miss Emily is mad. This may be true, but there are two things to consider in this connection. First, one must consider the special terms which her "madness" takes. Her madness is simply a development of her pride and her refusal to submit to ordinary standards of behavior. So, because of this fact, her "madness" is meaningful after all. It involves issues which in themselves are really important and have to do with the world of conscious moral choice. Second, the community interprets her "madness" as meaningful. They admire her, even if they are disappointed by her refusals to let herself be pitied, and the narrator, who is a spokesman for the community, recognizes the last grim revelation as an instance of her having carried her own values to their ultimate conclusion. She would marry the common laborer, Homer Barron, let the community think what it would. She would not be jilted. And she would hold him as a lover. But it would all be on her own terms. She remains completely dominant, and contemptuous of the day-to-day world.

It has been suggested by many critics that tragedy implies a hero who is completely himself, who insists on meeting the world on his own terms, who wants something so intensely, or lives so intensely, that he cannot accept any compromise. It cannot be maintained that this story is comparable to any of the great tragedies, such as *Hamlet* or *King Lear,* but it can be pointed out that this story, in its own way, involves some of the same basic elements. Certainly, Miss Emily's pride, isolation, and independence remind one of factors in the character of the typical tragic hero. And it can be pointed out that, just as the horror of her deed lies outside the ordinary life of the community, so the magnificence of her independence lies outside their ordinary virtues.

1. Why is it significant that Miss Emily chooses for her lover a man who is scornfully regarded by the community as a "Northerner, a day laborer"?

2. Compare Miss Emily's servant with the servants in "The Fall of the House of Usher." Which characterization is the more effective?

3. Look back at "R.M.S. *Titanic,*" "Old Red," "The Birthmark," and "The Killers," in the light of their general symbolic significance. Can it be argued that the present story, like them, has a more general significance—that it is a symbolic commentary on our society?

Araby

JAMES JOYCE

NORTH RICHMOND STREET, being blind, was a quiet street except at the hour when the Christian Brothers' School set the boys free. An uninhabited house of two stories stood at the blind end, detached from its neighbors in a square ground. The other houses of the street, conscious of decent lives within them, gazed at one another with brown imperturbable faces.

The former tenant of our house, a priest, had died in the back drawing room. Air, musty from having been long enclosed, hung in all the rooms, and the waste room behind the kitchen was littered with old useless papers. Among these I found a few paper-covered books, the pages of which were curled and damp: *The Abbot,* by Walter

Scott, *The Devout Communicant,* and *The Memoirs of Vidocq.* I liked the last best because its leaves were yellow. The wild garden behind the house contained a central apple tree and a few straggling bushes under one of which I found the late tenant's rusty bicycle pump. He had been a very charitable priest; in his will he had left all his money to institutions and the furniture of his house to his sister.

When the short days of winter came dusk fell before we had well eaten our dinners. When we met in the street the houses had grown somber. The space of sky above us was the color of ever-changing violet and towards it the lamps of the street lifted their feeble lanterns. The cold air stung us and we played till our bodies glowed. Our shouts echoed in the silent street. The career of our play brought us through the dark muddy lanes behind the houses where we ran the gauntlet of the rough tribes from the cottages, to the back doors of the dark dripping gardens where odors arose from the ashpits, to the dark odorous stables where a coachman smoothed and combed the horse or shook music from the buckled harness. When we returned to the street, light from the kitchen windows had filled the areas. If my uncle was seen turning the corner we hid in the shadow until we had seen him safely housed. Or if Mangan's sister came out on the doorstep to call her brother in to his tea we watched her from our shadow peer up and down the street. We waited to see whether she would remain or go in and, if she remained, we left our shadow and walked up to Mangan's steps resignedly. She was waiting for us, her figure defined by the light from the half-opened door. Her brother always teased her before he obeyed and I stood by the railings looking at her. Her dress swung as she moved her body and the soft rope of her hair tossed from side to side.

Every morning I lay on the floor in the front parlor watching her door. The blind was pulled down to within an inch of the sash so that I could not be seen. When she came out on the doorstep my heart leaped. I ran to the hall, seized my books and followed her. I kept her brown figure always in my eye and, when we came near the point at which our ways diverged, I quickened my pace and passed her. This happened morning after morning. I had never spoken to her, except for a few casual words, and yet her name was like a summons to all my foolish blood.

Her image accompanied me even in places the most hostile to romance. On Saturday evenings when my aunt went marketing I had to go to carry some of the parcels. We walked through the flaring streets, jostled by drunken men and bargaining women, amid the curses of laborers, the shrill litanies of shop boys who stood on guard by the barrels of pigs' cheeks, the nasal chanting of street singers, who sang a *come-all-you* about O'Donovan Rossa, or a ballad about the troubles in our native land. These noises converged in a single sensation of life for me: I imagined that I bore my chalice safely through a throng of foes. Her name sprang to my lips at moments in strange prayers and praises which I myself did not understand. My eyes were often full of tears (I could not tell why) and at times a flood from my heart seemed to pour itself out into my bosom. I thought little of the future. I did not know whether I would ever speak to her or not or, if I spoke to her, how I could tell her of my confused adoration. But my body was like a harp and her words and gestures were like fingers running upon the wires.

One evening I went into the back drawing room in which the priest had died. It was a dark rainy evening and there was no sound in the house. Through one of the broken panes I heard the rain impinge upon the earth, the fine incessant needles of water playing in the sodden beds. Some distant lamp or lighted window gleamed below me. I was thankful that I could see so little. All my senses seemed to desire to veil themselves and, feeling that I was about to slip from them, I pressed the palms of my hands together until they trembled, murmuring: *"O love! O love!"* many times.

At last she spoke to me. When she addressed the first words to me I was so confused that I did not know what to answer. She asked me was I going to *Araby*. I forgot whether I answered yes or no. It would be a splendid bazaar, she said; she would love to go.

"And why can't you?" I asked.

While she spoke she turned a silver bracelet round and round her wrist. She could not go, she said, because there would be a retreat that week in her convent. Her brother and two other boys were fighting for their caps and I was alone at the railings. She held one of the spikes, bowing her head towards me. The light from the lamp opposite our door caught the white curve of her neck, lit up her hair that rested there and, falling, lit up the hand upon the railing. It fell over one side of her dress and caught the white border of a petticoat, just visible as she stood at ease.

"It's well for you," she said.

"If I go," I said, "I will bring you something."

What innumerable follies laid waste my waking and sleeping thoughts after that evening! I wished to annihilate the tedious intervening days. I chafed against the work of school. At night in my bedroom and by day in the classroom her image came between me and the page I strove to read. The syllables of the word *Araby* were called to me through the silence in which my soul luxuriated and cast an Eastern enchantment over me. I asked for leave to go to the bazaar on Saturday night. My aunt was surprised and hoped it was not some Freemason affair. I answered few questions in class. I watched my master's face pass from amiability to sternness; he hoped I was not beginning to idle. I could not call my wandering thoughts together. I had hardly any patience with the serious work of life which, now that it stood between me and my desire, seemed to me child's play, ugly monotonous child's play.

On Saturday morning I reminded my uncle that I wished to go to the bazaar in the evening. He was fussing at the hall stand, looking for the hat brush, and answered me curtly:

"Yes, boy, I know."

As he was in the hall I could not go into the front parlor and lie at the window. I left the house in bad humor and walked slowly towards the school. The air was pitilessly raw and already my heart misgave me.

When I came home to dinner my uncle had not yet been home. Still it was early. I sat staring at the clock for some time and, when its ticking began to irritate me, I left the room. I mounted the staircase and gained the upper part of the house. The high cold empty gloomy rooms liberated me and I went from room to room singing. From the front window I saw my companions playing below in the street. Their cries reached me weakened and indistinct and, leaning my forehead against the cool glass, I looked over at the dark house where she lived. I may have stood there for an hour, seeing nothing but the brown-clad figure cast by my imagination, touched discreetly by the lamplight at the curved neck, at the hand upon the railings and at the border below the dress.

When I came downstairs again I found Mrs. Mercer sitting at the fire. She was an old garrulous woman, a pawnbroker's widow, who collected used stamps for some pious purpose. I had to endure the gossip of the tea table. The meal was prolonged beyond an hour and still my uncle did not come. Mrs. Mercer stood up to go: she was sorry she couldn't wait any longer, but it was after eight o'clock and she did not like to be out late, as the night air was bad for her. When she had gone I began to walk up and down the room, clenching my fists. My aunt said:

"I'm afraid you may put off your bazaar for this night of Our Lord."

At nine o'clock I heard my uncle's latchkey in the hall door. I heard him talking to himself and heard the hall stand rocking when it had received the weight of his overcoat. I could interpret these signs. When he was midway through his dinner I asked him to give me the money to go to the bazaar. He had forgotten.

"The people are in bed and after their first sleep now," he said.

I did not smile. My aunt said to him energetically:

"Can't you give him the money and let him go? You've kept him late enough as it is."

My uncle said he was very sorry he had forgotten. He said he believed in the old saying: "All work and no play makes Jack a dull boy." He asked me where I was going and, when I had told him a second time he asked me did I know *The Arab's Farewell to His Steed*. When I left the kitchen he was about to recite the opening lines of the piece to my aunt.

I held a florin tightly in my hand as I strode down Buckingham Street towards the station. The sight of the streets thronged with buyers and glaring with gas recalled to me the purpose of my journey. I took my seat in a third-class carriage of a deserted train. After an intolerable delay the train moved out of the station slowly. It crept onward among ruinous houses and over the twinkling river. At Westland Row Station a crowd of people pressed to the carriage doors; but the porters moved them back, saying that it was a special train for the bazaar. I remained alone in the bare carriage. In a few minutes the train drew up beside an improvised wooden platform. I passed out on to the road and saw by the lighted dial of a clock that it was ten minutes to ten. In front of me was a large building which displayed the magical name.

I could not find any sixpenny entrance and, fearing that the bazaar would be closed, I passed in quickly through a turnstile, handing a shilling to a weary-looking man. I found myself in a big hall girdled at half its height by a gallery. Nearly all the stalls were closed and the greater part of the hall was in darkness. I recognized a silence like that which pervades a church after a service. I walked into the center of the bazaar timidly. A few people were gathered about the stalls which were still open. Before a curtain, over which the words *Café Chantant* were written in colored lamps, two men were counting money on a salver. I listened to the fall of the coins.

Remembering with difficulty why I had come I went over to one of stalls and examined porcelain vases and flowered tea sets. At the door of the stall a young lady was talking and laughing with two young gentlemen. I remarked their English accents and listened vaguely to their conversation.

"O, I never said such a thing!"

"O, but you did!"

"O, but I didn't!"

"Didn't she say that?"

"Yes. I heard her."

"O, there's a . . . fib!"

Observing me, the young lady came over and asked me did I wish to buy anything. The tone of her voice was not encouraging; she seemed to have spoken to me out of a sense of duty. I looked humbly at the great jars that stood like eastern guards at either side of the dark entrance to the stall and murmured:

"No, thank you."

The young lady changed the position of one of the vases and went back to the two young men. They began to talk of the same subject. Once or twice the young lady glanced at me over her shoulder.

I lingered before her stall, though I knew my stay was useless, to make my interest in her wares seem the more real. Then I turned away slowly and walked down the middle of the bazaar. I allowed the two pennies to fall against the sixpence in my pocket. I heard a voice call from one end of the gallery that the light was out. The upper part of the hall was now completely dark.

Gazing up into the darkness I saw myself as a creature driven and derided by vanity; and my eyes burned with anguish and anger.*

INTERPRETATION

On what may be called the simplest level this is a story of a boy's disappointment. The description of the street in which he lives, the information about the dead priest and the priest's abandoned belongings, the relations with the aunt and uncle—all of these items, which occupy so much space, seem to come very naturally into the story. That is, they may be justified individually in the story on realistic grounds. But when one considers the fact that such material constitutes the bulk of the story, one is led to observe that, if such items *merely* serve as "setting" and atmosphere (see Glossary), the story is obviously overloaded with nonfunctional material. Obviously, for any reader except the most casual, these items do have a function. If we find in what way these apparently irrelevant items in "Araby" are related to each other and to the disappointment of the boy, we shall have defined the theme of the story.

What, then, is the relation of the boy's disappointment to such matters as the belongings of the dead priest, the fact that he stands apart talking to the girl while his friends are quarreling over the cap, the gossip over the tea table, the uncle's lateness, and so on? One thing that is immediately suggested by the mention of these things is the boy's growing sense of isolation, the lack of sympathy between him and his friends, teachers, and family. He says, "I imagined that I bore my chalice safely through a throng of foes." For instance, when the uncle is standing in the hall, the boy could not go into the front parlor and lie at the window; or at school his ordinary occupations began to seem "ugly monotonous child's play." But this sense of isolation has, also, moments which are almost triumphant, as for example, is implied when the porters at the station wave the crowds back, "saying that it was a special train for the bazaar" and was not for them. The boy is left alone in the bare carriage, but he is going to "Araby," which name involves, as it were, the notion of the romantic and exotic fulfillment. The metaphor of the chalice implies the same kind of precious secret triumph. It is not only the ordinary surrounding world, however, from which he is

* From *Dubliners;* by permission of the Viking Press, Inc., New York.

cruelly or triumphantly isolated. He is also isolated from the girl herself. He talks to her only once, and then is so confused that he does not know how to answer her. But the present which he hopes to bring her from Araby would somehow serve as a means of communicating his feelings to her, a symbol for their relationship in the midst of the inimical world.

In the last scene at the bazaar, there is a systematic, though subtle, preparation for the final realization on the part of the boy. There is the "improvised wooden platform" in contrast with the "magical name" displayed above the building. Inside, most of the stalls are closed. The young lady and young men who talk together are important in the preparation. They pay the boy no mind, except in so far as the young lady is compelled by her position as clerk to ask him what he wants. But her tone is not "encouraging." She, too, belongs to the inimical world. But she, also, belongs to a world into which he is trying to penetrate: she and her admirers are on terms of easy intimacy—an intimacy in contrast to his relation to Mangan's sister. It is an exotic, rich world into which he cannot penetrate: he can only look "humbly at the great jars that stood like eastern guards at either side of the dark entrance to the stall. . . ." But, ironically, the young lady and her admirers, far from realizing that they are on holy, guarded ground, indulge in a trivial, easy banter, which seems to defile and cheapen the secret world from which the boy is barred. How do we know this? It is not stated, but the contrast between the conversation of the young lady and her admirers, and the tone of the sentence quoted just above indicates such an interpretation.

This scene, then, helps to point up and particularize the general sense of isolation suggested by the earlier descriptive materials, and thereby to prepare for the last sentence of the story, in which, under the sudden darkness of the cheap and barnlike bazaar, the boy sees himself as "a creature driven and derided by vanity," while his eyes burn with anguish and anger.

We have seen how the apparently casual incidents and items of description do function in the story to build up the boy's sense of intolerable isolation. But this is only part of the function of this material. The careful reader will have noticed how many references, direct or indirect, there are to religion and the ritual of the church. The atmosphere of the story is saturated with such references. We have the dead priest, the Christian Brothers' School, the aunt's hope that the bazaar is not "some Freemason affair," her remark when the uncle has been delayed, to "this night of Our Lord." These references are all obvious enough. At one level, these references merely indicate the type of community in which the impressionable boy is growing up. But there are other, less obvious, references, which relate more intimately to the boy's experience. Even the cries of the shop boys for him are "shrill litanies." He imagines that he bears a "chalice safely through a throng of foes." When he is alone the name of Mangan's sister springs to his lips "in strange prayers and praises." For this reason, when he speaks of his "confused adoration," we see that the love of the girl takes on, for him, something of the nature of a mystic, religious experience. The use of the very word *confused* hints of the fact that romantic love and religious love are mixed up in his mind.

It has been said that the boy is isolated from a world which seems ignorant of, and even hostile to, the experience of his love. In a sense he knows that his aunt and uncle are good and kind, but they do not understand him. He had once found satisfaction in the society of his companions and in his school work, but he has become impatient with both. But there is also a sense in which he accepts his isolation and is even proud of it. The world not only does not understand his secret but would cheapen and contaminate it. The metaphor of the chalice borne through a throng of foes, supported as it is by the body of the story, suggests a sort of consecration like that of the religious devotee. The implications of the references to religion, then, help define the boy's attitude and indicate why, for him, so much is staked upon the journey to the bazaar. It is interesting to note, therefore, that the first overt indication of his disillusionment and disappointment is expressed in a metaphor involving a church: "Nearly all the stalls were closed and the greater part of the hall was in darkness. I recognized a silence like that which pervades a church after a service. . . . Two men were counting money on a salver. I listened to the fall of the coins." So, it would seem, here we have the idea that the contamination of the world has invaded the very temple of love. (The question may arise as to whether this is not reading too much into the passage. Perhaps it is. But whatever interpretation is to be made of the particular incident, it is by just such suggestion and implication that closely wrought stories, such as this one, are controlled by the author and embody their fundamental meaning.)

Is this a sentimental story? It is about an adolescent love affair, about "calf love," a subject which usually is not to be taken seriously and is often the cause of amusement. The boy of the story is obviously investing casual incidents with a meaning which they do not deserve; and himself admits, in the end, that he has fallen into self-deception. How does the author avoid the charge that he has taken the matter over-seriously?

The answer to this question would involve a consideration of the point of view from which the story is told. It is told by the hero him-self, but after a long lapse of time, after he has reached maturity. This fact, it is true, is not stated in the story, but the style itself is not that of an adolescent boy. It is a formal and complicated style, rich, as has already been observed, in subtle implications. In other words, the man is looking back upon the boy, detachedly and judicially. For instance, the boy, in the throes of the experience, would never have said of him-self: "I had never spoken to her, except for a few casual words, and yet her name was like a summons to all my foolish blood." The man knows, as it were, that the behavior of the boy was, in a sense, foolish. The emotions of the boy are confused, but the person telling the story, the boy grown up, is not confused. He has unraveled the confusion long after, knows that it existed and why it existed.

If the man has unraveled the confusions of the boy, why is the event still significant to him? Is he merely dwelling on the pathos of adolescent experience? It seems, rather, that he sees in the event, as he looks back on it, a kind of parable of a problem which has run through later ex-perience. The discrepancy between the real and the ideal scarcely exists for the child, but it is a constant problem, in all sorts of terms, for the adult. This story is about a boy's first confrontation of that problem—that is, about his growing up. The man may have made adjustments to this problem, and may have worked out certain provisional solu-tions, but, looking back, he still recognizes it as a problem, and an im-portant one. The sense of isolation and disillusion which, in the boy's experience, may seem to spring from a trivial situation, becomes not less, but more aggravated and fundamental in the adult's experience. So, the story is not merely an account of a stage in the process of grow-ing up—it does not merely represent a clinical interest in the psychology of growing up—but is a symbolic rendering of a central conflict in mature experience.

1. What does the boy have in common with the dead priest? Suppose that the dead man had been a shopkeeper, a lawyer, or anyone else who did not "carry a chalice." Would that have made any difference in the story?

2. Children are supposed to have more imagination than adults. What has happened when, for the boy, his previous occupations seem to be "ugly monotonous child's play"?

3. Compare and contrast the situation in this story with that in "I Want to Know Why"; with that in "The Face."

The Kiss

ANTON CHEKHOV

ON THE TWENTIETH of May, at eight o'clock in the evening, six batteries of the N Artillery Brigade arrived at the village of Miestetchki to spend the night, before going to their camp.

The confusion was at its height—some officers at the guns, others in the church square with the quartermaster—when a civilian upon a remarkable horse rode from the rear of the church. The small cob with well-shaped neck wobbled along, all the time dancing on its legs as if someone were whipping them. Reaching the officers, the rider doffed his cap with ceremony and said—

"His Excellency, General von Rabbek, requests the honor of the officers' company at tea in his house near-by. . . ."

The horse shook its head, danced, and wobbled backwards; its rider again took off his cap, and turning around disappeared behind the church.

"The devil!" the general exclaimed, the officers dispersing to their quarters. "We are almost asleep, yet along comes this von Rabbek with his tea! That tea! I remember it!"

The officers of the six batteries had vivid recollections of a past invitation. During recent maneuvers they had been asked, with their Cossack comrades, to tea at the house of a local country gentleman, a Count, retired from military service; and this hearty old Count overwhelmed them with attentions, fed them like gourmands, poured vodka into them and made them stay the night. All this, of course, was fine. The trouble was that the old soldier entertained his guests too well. He kept them up till daybreak while he poured forth tales of past adventures and pointed out valuable paintings, engravings, arms, and letters from celebrated men. And the tired officers listened, perforce, until he ended, only to find out then the time for sleep had gone.

Was von Rabbek another old Count? It might easily be. But there was no neglecting his invitation. The officers washed and dressed, and set out for von Rabbek's house. At the church square they learnt that they must descend the hill to the river, and follow the bank till they reached the general's gardens, where they would find a path direct to the house. Or, if they chose to go uphill, they would reach the general's barns half a *verst* from Miestetchki. It was this route they chose.

"But who is this von Rabbek?" asked one. "The man who commanded the N Cavalry Division at Plevna?"

"No, that was not von Rabbek, but simply Rabbe—without the von."

"What glorious weather!"

At the first barn they came to, two roads diverged; one ran straight forward and faded in the dusk; the other, turning to the right, led to the general's house. As the officers drew near they talked less loudly. To right and to left stretched rows of red-roofed brick barns, in aspect heavy and morose as the barracks of provincial towns. In front gleamed the lighted windows of von Rabbek's house.

"A good omen, gentlemen!" cried a young officer. "Our setter runs in advance. There is game ahead!"

On the face of Lieutenant Lobuitko, the tall stout officer referred to, there was not one trace of hair though he was twenty-five years old. He was famed among comrades for the instinct which told him of the presence of women in the neighborhood. On hearing his comrade's remark, he turned his head and said—

"Yes. There are women there. My instinct tells me."

A handsome, well-preserved man of sixty, in mufti, came to the hall door to greet his guests. It was von Rabbek. As he pressed their hands, he explained that though he was delighted to see them, he must beg pardon for not asking them to spend the night; as guests he already had his two sisters, their children, his brother, and several neighbors—in fact, he had not one spare room. And though he shook their hands and apologized and smiled, it was plain that he was not half as glad to see them as was last year's Count, and that he had invited them merely because good manners demanded it. The officers climbing the soft-carpeted steps and listening to their host understood this perfectly well; and realized that they carried into the house an atmosphere of intrusion and alarm. Would any man—they asked themselves—who had gathered his two sisters and their children, his brother and his neighbors, to celebrate, no doubt, some family festival, find pleasure in the invasion of nineteen officers whom he had never seen before?

A tall elderly lady, with a good figure, and a long face with black eyebrows, who resembled closely the ex-Empress Eugénie, greeted them at the drawing-room door. Smiling courteously and with dignity, she affirmed that she was delighted to see the officers, and only regretted that she could not ask them to stay the night. But the courteous, dignified smile disappeared when she turned away, and it was quite plain that she had seen many officers in her day, that they caused not the slightest interest, and that she had invited them merely because an invitation was dictated by good breeding and by her position in the world.

In a big dining room, at a big table, sat ten men and women, drinking tea. Behind them, veiled in cigar smoke, stood several young men, among them one, red-whiskered and extremely thin, who spoke English loudly with a lisp. Through an open door the officers saw into a brightly lighted room with blue wallpaper.

"You are too many to introduce singly, gentlemen!" said the general loudly, with affected joviality. "Make one another's acquaintance, please—without formalities!"

The visitors, some with serious, even severe faces, some smiling constrainedly, all with a feeling of awkwardness, bowed, and took their seats at the table. Most awkward of all felt Staff-Captain Riabovitch, a short, round-shouldered, spectacled officer, whiskered like a lynx. While his brother officers looked serious or smiled constrainedly, his face, his lynx whiskers, and his spectacles seemed to explain: "I am the most timid, modest, undistinguished officer in the whole brigade." For some time after he took his seat at the table he could not fix his attention on any single thing. Faces, dresses, the cut-glass cognac bottles, the steaming tumblers, the molded cornices—all merged in a single, overwhelming sentiment which caused him intense fright and made him wish to hide his head. Like an inexperienced lecturer he saw everything before him, but could distinguish nothing, and was in fact the victim of what men of science diagnose as "psychical blindness."

But, slowly conquering his diffidence, Riabovitch began to distinguish and observe. As became a man both timid and unsocial, he remarked first of all the amazing temerity of his new friends. Von Rabbek, his wife, two elderly ladies, a girl in lilac, and the red-whiskered youth (who, it appeared, was a young von Rabbek) sat down among the officers as unconcernedly as if they had held rehearsals, and at once plunged into various heated arguments in which they soon involved their guests. That artillerists have a much better time than cavalrymen or infantrymen was proved conclusively by the lilac girl, while von Rabbek and the elderly ladies affirmed the converse. The conversation became desultory. Riabovitch listened to the lilac girl fiercely debating themes she knew nothing about and took no interest in, and watched the insincere smiles which appeared on and disappeared from her face.

While the von Rabbek family with amazing strategy inveigled their guests into the dispute, they kept their eyes on every glass and mouth. Had everyone tea, was it sweet enough, why didn't one eat biscuits, was another fond of cognac? And the longer Riabovitch listened and looked, the more pleased he was with this disingenuous, disciplined family.

After tea the guests repaired to the drawing room. Instinct had not cheated Lobuitko. The room was packed with young women and girls, and ere a minute had passed the setter-lieutenant stood beside a very young, fair-haired girl in black, and, bending down as if resting on an invisible sword, shrugged his shoulders coquettishly. He was uttering, no doubt, most unentertaining nonsense, for the fair girl looked indulgently at his sated face, and exclaimed indifferently, "Indeed!" And this indifferent "Indeed!" might have quickly convinced the setter that he was on a wrong scent.

Music began. As the notes of a mournful valse throbbed out of the open window, through the heads of all flashed the feeling that outside that window it was springtime, a night of May. The air was odorous of young poplar leaves, of roses and lilacs—and the valse and the spring were sincere. Riabovitch, with valse and cognac mingling tipsily in his head, gazed at the window with a smile; then began to follow the movements of the women; and it seemed that the smell of roses, poplars, and lilacs came not from the gardens outside, but from the women's faces and dresses.

They began to dance. Young von Rabbek valsed twice round the room with a very thin girl; and Lobuitko, slipping on the parqueted floor, went up to the girl in lilac, and was granted a dance. But Riabovitch stood near the door with the wallflowers, and looked silently on. Amazed at the daring of men who in sight of a crowd could take unknown women by the waist, he tried in vain to picture himself doing the same. A time had been when he envied his comrades their courage and dash, suffered from painful heart-searchings, and was hurt by the knowledge that he was timid, round-shouldered, and undistinguished, that he had lynx whiskers, and that his waist was much too long. But with years he had grown reconciled to his own insignificance, and now looking at the dancers and loud talkers, he felt no envy, but only mournful emotions.

At the first quadrille von Rabbek junior approached and invited two nondancing officers to a game of billiards. The three left the room; and Riabovitch, who stood idle, and felt impelled to join in the general movement, followed. They passed the dining room, traversed a narrow glazed corridor and a room where three sleepy footmen jumped from a sofa with a start; and after walking, it seemed, through a whole houseful of rooms, entered a small billiard room.

Von Rabbek and the two officers began their game. Riabovitch, whose only game was cards, stood near the table and looked indifferently on, as the players, with unbuttoned coats, wielded their cues, moved about, joked, and shouted obscure technical terms. Riabovitch was ignored, save when one of the players jostled him or nudged him with the cue, and turning towards him said briefly, "Pardon!" so that before the game was over he was thoroughly bored, and, impressed by a sense of his superfluity, resolved to return to the drawing room and turned away.

It was on the way back that his adventure took place. Before he had gone far he saw that he had missed his way. He remembered distinctly the room with the three sleepy footmen; and after passing through five or six rooms entirely vacant, he saw his mistake. Retracing his steps, he turned to the left, and found himself in an almost dark room which he had not seen before; and after hesitating a minute, he boldly opened the first door he saw, and found himself in complete darkness. Through a chink of the door in front peered a bright light; from afar throbbed the dullest music of a mournful mazurka. Here, as in the drawing room, the windows were open wide, and the smell of poplars, lilacs, and roses flooded the air.

Riabovitch paused in irresolution. For a moment all was still. Then came the sound of hasty footsteps; then, without any warning of what was to come, a dress rustled, a woman's breathless voice whispered "At last!" and two soft, scented, unmistakably womanly arms met round his neck, a warm cheek impinged on his, and he received a sounding kiss. But hardly had the kiss echoed through the silence when the unknown shrieked loudly, and fled away—as it seemed to Riabovitch—in disgust. Riabovitch himself nearly screamed, and rushed headlong towards the bright beam in the door chink.

As he entered the drawing room his heart beat violently, and his hands trembled so perceptibly that he clasped them behind his back. His first emotion was shame, as if everyone in the room already knew that he had just been embraced and kissed. He retired into his shell, and looked fearfully around. But finding that hosts and guests were calmly dancing or talking, he regained courage, and surrendered himself to sensations experienced for the first time in life. The unexampled had happened. His neck, fresh from the embrace of two soft, scented arms, seemed anointed with oil; near his left mustache, where the kiss had fallen, trembled a slight, delightful chill, as from peppermint drops; and from head to foot he was soaked in new and extraordinary sensations, which continued to grow and grow.

He felt that he must dance, talk, run into the garden, laugh unrestrainedly. He forgot altogether that he was round-shouldered, undistinguished, lynx-whiskered, that he had an "indefinite exterior"—a description from the lips of a woman he had happened to overhear. As Madame von Rabbek passed him he smiled so broadly and graciously that she came up and looked at him questioningly.

"What a charming house you have!" he said, straightening his spectacles.

And Madame von Rabbek smiled back, said that the house still belonged to her father, and asked were his parents still alive, how long he had been in the Army, and why he was so thin. After hearing his answers she departed. But though the conversation was over, he continued to smile benevolently, and think what charming people were his new acquaintances.

At supper Riabovitch ate and drank mechanically what was put before him, heard not a word of the conversation, and devoted all his powers to the unraveling of his mysterious, romantic adventure. What was the explanation? It was plain that one of the girls, he reasoned, had arranged a meeting in the dark room, and after waiting some time in vain had, in her nervous tension, mistaken Riabovitch for her hero. The mistake was likely enough, for on entering the dark room Riabovitch had stopped irresolutely as if he, too, were waiting for someone. So far the mystery was explained.

"But which of them was it?" he asked, searching the women's faces. She certainly was young, for old women do not indulge in such romances. Secondly, she was not a servant. That was proved unmistakably by the rustle of her dress, the scent, the voice. . . .

When at first he looked at the girl in lilac she pleased him; she had pretty shoulders and arms, a clever face, a charming voice. Riabovitch piously prayed that it was she. But, smiling insincerely, she wrinkled her long nose, and that at once gave her an elderly air. So Riabovitch turned his eyes on the blonde in black. The blonde was younger, simpler, sincerer; she had charming kiss-curls, and drank from her tumbler with inexpressible grace. Riabovitch hoped it was she—but soon he noticed that her face was flat, and bent his eyes on her neighbor.

"It is a hopeless puzzle," he reflected. "If you take the arms and shoulders of the lilac girl, add the blonde's curls, and the eyes of the girl on Lobuitko's left, then—"

He composed a portrait of all these charms, and had a clear vision of the girl who had kissed him. But she was nowhere to be seen.

Supper over, the visitors, sated and tipsy, bade their entertainers good-by. Both host and hostess apologized for not asking them to spend the night.

"I am very glad, gentlemen!" said the general, and this time seemed to speak sincerely, no doubt because speeding the parting guest is a kindlier office than welcoming him unwelcomed. "I am very glad indeed! I hope you will visit me on your way back. Without ceremony, please! Which way will you go? Up the hill? No, go down the hill and through the garden. That way is shorter."

The officers took his advice. After the noise and glaring illumination within doors, the garden seemed dark and still. Until they reached the wicket gate all kept silence. Merry, half tipsy, and content, as they were, the night's obscurity and stillness inspired pensive thought. Through their brains, as through Riabovitch's, sped probably the same question: "Will the time ever come when I, like von Rabbek, shall have a big house, a family, a garden, the chance of being gracious—even insincerely—to others, of making them sated, tipsy, and content?"

But once the garden lay behind them, all spoke at once, and burst into causeless laughter. The path they followed led straight to the river, and then ran beside it, winding around bushes, ravines, and overhanging willow trees. The track was barely visible; the other bank was lost entirely in gloom. Sometimes the black water imaged stars, and this was the only indication of the river's speed. From beyond it sighed a drowsy snipe, and beside them in a bush, heedless of the crowd, a nightingale chanted loudly. The officers gathered in a group, and swayed the bush, but the nightingale continued his song.

"I like his cheek!" they echoed admiringly. "He doesn't care a *kopek!* The old rogue!"

Near their journey's end the path turned up the hill, and joined the road not far from the church enclosure; and there the officers, breathless from climbing, sat on the grass and smoked. Across the river gleamed a dull red light, and for want of a subject they argued the problem, whether it was a bonfire, a window light, or something else. Riabovitch looked also at the light, and felt that it smiled and winked at him as if it knew about the kiss.

On reaching home, he undressed without delay, and lay upon his bed. He shared the cabin with Lobuitko and a Lieutenant Merzliakoff, a staid, silent little man, by repute highly cultivated, who took with him everywhere *The Messenger of Europe,* and read it eternally. Lobuitko undressed, tramped impatiently from corner to corner, and sent his servant for beer. Merzliakoff lay down, balanced the candle on his pillow, and hid his head behind *The Messenger of Europe.*

"Where is she now?" muttered Riabovitch, looking at the soot-blacked ceiling.

His neck still seemed anointed with oil, near his mouth still trembled the speck of peppermint chill. Through his brain twinkled successively the shoulders and arms of the lilac girl, the kiss-curls and honest eyes of the girl in black, the waists, dresses, brooches. But though he tried his best to fix these vagrant images, they glimmered, winked, and dissolved; and as they faded finally into the vast black curtain which hangs before the closed eyes of all men, he began to hear hurried footsteps, the rustle of petticoats, the sound of a kiss. A strong, causeless joy possessed him. But as he surrendered himself to this joy, Lobuitko's servant returned with the news that no beer was obtainable. The lieutenant resumed his impatient march up and down the room.

"The fellow's an idiot," he exclaimed, stopping first near Riabovitch and then near Merzliakoff. "Only the worst numbskull and blockhead can't get beer! *Canaille!*"

"Everyone knows there's no beer here," said Merzliakoff, without lifting his eyes from *The Messenger of Europe.*

"You believe that!" exclaimed Lobuitko. "Lord in heaven, drop me on the moon, and in five minutes I'll find both beer and women! I will find them myself! Call me a rascal if I don't!"

He dressed slowly, silently lighted a cigarette, and went out.

"Rabbek, Grabbek, Labbek," he muttered, stopping in the hall. "I won't go alone, devil take me! Riabovitch, come for a walk! What?"

As he got no answer, he returned, undressed slowly, and lay down. Merzliakoff sighed, dropped *The Messenger of Europe,* and put out the light. "Well?" muttered Lobuitko, puffing his cigarette in the dark.

Riabovitch pulled the bedclothes up to his chin, curled himself into a roll, and strained his imagination to join the twinkling images into one coherent whole. But the vision fled him. He soon fell asleep, and his last impression was that he had been caressed and gladdened, that into his life had crept something strange, and indeed ridiculous, but uncommonly good and radiant. And this thought did not forsake him even in his dreams.

When he awoke the feeling of anointment and peppermint chill were gone. But joy, as on the night before, filled every vein. He looked entranced at the windowpanes gilded by the rising sun, and listened to the noises outside. Someone spoke loudly under the very window. It was Lebedietsky, commander of his battery, who had just overtaken the brigade. He was talking to the sergeant-major, loudly, owing to lack of practice in soft speech.

"And what next?" he roared.

"During yesterday's shoeing, your honor, *Golubtchik* was pricked. The *feldscher* ordered clay and vinegar. And last night, your honor, mechanic Artemieff was drunk, and the lieutenant ordered him to be put on the limber of the reserve gun carriage."

The sergeant-major added that Karpoff had forgotten the tent pegs and the new lanyards for the friction tubes, and that the officers had spent the evening at General von Rabbek's. But here at the window appeared Lebedietsky's red-bearded face. He blinked his short-sighted eyes at the drowsy men in bed, and greeted them.

"Is everything all right?"

"The saddle wheeler galled his withers with the new yoke," answered Lobuitko.

The commander sighed, mused a moment, and shouted—

"I am thinking of calling on Alexandra Yegorovna. I want to see her. Good-by! I will catch you up before night."

Fifteen minutes later the brigade resumed its march. As he passed von Rabbek's barns, Riabovitch turned his head and looked at the house. The Venetian blinds were down; evidently all still slept. And among them slept she—she who had kissed him but a few hours before. He tried to visualize her asleep. He projected the bedroom window opened wide with green branches peering in, the freshness of the morning air, the smell of poplars, lilacs, and roses, the bed, a chair, the dress which rustled last night, a pair of tiny slippers, a ticking watch on the table—all these came to him clearly with every detail. But the features, the kind, sleepy smile—all, in short, that was essential and characteristic—fled his imagination as quicksilver flees the hand. When he had covered half a *verst* he again turned back. The yellow church, the house, gardens, and river were bathed in light. Imaging an azure sky, the green-banked river specked with silver sunshine flakes was inexpressibly fair; and, looking at Miestetchki for the last time, Riabovitch felt sad, as if parting forever with something very near and dear.

By the road before him stretched familiar, uninteresting scenes; to the right and left, fields of young rye and buckwheat with hopping rooks; in front, dust and the napes of human necks; behind, the same dust and faces. Ahead of the column marched four soldiers with swords—that was the advance guard. Next came the bandsmen. Advance guard and bandsmen, like mutes in a funeral procession, ignored the regulation intervals and marched too far ahead. Riabovitch, with the first gun of Battery No. 5, could see four batteries ahead.

To a layman, the long, lumbering march of an artillery brigade is novel, interesting, inexplicable. It is hard to understand why a single gun needs so many men; why so many, such strangely harnessed horses are needed to drag it. But to Riabovitch, a master of all these things, it was profoundly dull. He had learned years ago why a solid sergeant-major rides beside the officer in front of each battery; why the sergeant-major is called the *unosni,* and why the drivers of leaders and wheelers ride behind him. Riabovitch knew why the near horses are called saddle horses, and why the off horses are called led horses— and all of this was uninteresting beyond words. On one of the wheelers rode a soldier still covered with yesterday's dust, and with a cumbersome, ridiculous guard on his right leg. But Riabovitch, knowing the use of this leg guard, found it in no way ridiculous. The drivers, mechanically and with occasional cries, flourished their whips. The guns in themselves were unimpressive. The limbers were packed with tarpaulin-covered sacks of oats; and the guns themselves, hung round with teapots and satchels, looked like harmless animals, guarded for some obscure reason by men and horses. In the lee of the gun tramped six gunners, swinging their arms, and behind each gun came more *unosniye,* leaders, wheelers; and yet more guns, each as ugly and uninspiring as the one in front. And as every one of the six batteries in the brigade had four guns, the procession stretched along the road at least half a *verst.* It ended with a wagon train, with which, its head bent in thought, walked the donkey Magar, brought from Turkey by a battery commander.

Dead to his surroundings, Riabovitch marched onward, looking at the napes ahead or at the faces behind. Had it not been for last night's event, he would have been half asleep. But now he was absorbed in novel, entrancing thoughts. When the brigade set out that morning he had tried to argue that the kiss had no significance save as a trivial though mysterious adventure; that it was without real import; and that to think of it seriously was to behave himself absurdly. But logic soon flew away and surrendered him to his vivid imaginings. At times he saw himself in von Rabbek's dining room, *tête-à-tête* with a composite being, formed of the girl in lilac and the blonde in black. At times he closed his eyes, and pictured himself with a different, this time quite an unknown, girl of cloudy feature; he spoke to her, caressed her, bent over her shoulders; he imagined war and parting . . . then reunion, the first supper together, children . . .

"To the brakes!" rang the command as they topped the brow of each hill.

Riabovitch also cried "To the brakes!" and each time dreaded that the cry would break the magic spell, and recall him to realities.

They passed a big country house. Riabovitch looked across the fence into the garden, and saw a long path, straight as a ruler, carpeted with yellow sand, and shaded by young birches. In an ecstasy of enchantment, he pictured little feminine feet treading the yellow sand; and, in a flash, imagination restored the woman who had kissed him, the woman he had visualized after supper the night before. The image settled in his brain and never afterward forsook him.

The spell reigned until midday, when a loud command came from the rear of the column.

"Attention! Eyes right! Officers!"

In a *calèche* drawn by a pair of white horses appeared the general of the brigade. He stopped at the second battery, and called out something which no one understood. Up galloped several officers, among them Riabovitch.

"Well, how goes it?" The general blinked his red eyes, and continued, "Are there any sick?"

Hearing the answer, the little skinny general mused a moment, turned to an officer, and said—

"The driver of your third-gun wheeler has taken off his leg guard and hung it on the limber. *Canaille!* Punish him!"

Then raising his eyes to Riabovitch, he added—
"And in your battery, I think, the harness is too loose."

Having made several other equally tiresome remarks, he looked at Lobuitko, and laughed.

"Why do you look so downcast, Lieutenant Lobuitko? You are sighing for Madame Lopukhoff, eh? Gentlemen, he is pining for Madame Lopukhoff!"

Madame Lopukhoff was a tall, stout lady, long past forty. Being partial to big women, regardless of age, the general ascribed the same taste to his subordinates. The officers smiled respectfully; and the general, pleased that he had said something caustic and laughable, touched the coachman's back and saluted. The *calèche* whirled away.

"All this, though it seems to me impossible and unearthly, is in reality very commonplace," thought Riabovitch, watching the clouds of dust raised by the general's carriage. "It is an everyday event, and within everyone's experience. . . . This old general, for instance, must have loved in his day; he is married now, and has children. Captain Wachter is also married, and his wife loves him, though he has an ugly red neck and no waist. . . . Salmanoff is coarse, and a typical Tartar, but he has had a romance ending in marriage. . . . I, like the rest, must go through it all sooner or later."

And the thought that he was an ordinary man, and that his life was ordinary, rejoiced and consoled him. He boldly visualized *her* and his happiness, and let his imagination run mad.

Towards evening the brigade ended its march. While the other officers sprawled in their tents, Riabovitch, Merzliakoff, and Lobuitko sat round a packing case and supped. Merzliakoff ate slowly, and, resting *The Messenger of Europe* on his knees, read on steadily. Lobuitko, chattering without cease, poured beer into his glass. But Riabovitch, whose head was dizzy from uninterrupted daydreams, ate in silence. When he had drunk three glasses he felt tipsy and weak; and an overmastering impulse forced him to relate his adventure to his comrades.

"A most extraordinary thing happened to me at von Rabbek's," he began, doing his best to speak in an indifferent, ironical tone. "I was on my way, you understand, from the billiard room . . ."

And he attempted to give a very detailed history of the kiss. But in a minute he had told the whole story. In that minute he had exhausted every detail; and it seemed to him terrible that the story required such a short time. It ought, he felt, to have lasted all the night. As he finished, Lobuitko, who as a liar himself believed in no one, laughed incredulously. Merzliakoff frowned, and, with his eyes still glued to *The Messenger of Europe,* said indifferently—

"God knows who it was! She threw herself on your neck, you say, and didn't cry out! Some lunatic, I expect!"

"It must have been a lunatic," agreed Riabovitch.

"I, too, have had adventures of that kind," began Lobuitko, making a frightened face. "I was on my way to Kovno. I traveled second-class. The carriage was packed, and I couldn't sleep. So I gave the guard a *rouble,* and he took my bag, and put me in a *coupé.* I lay down, and pulled my rug over me. It was pitch dark, you understand. Suddenly I felt someone tapping my shoulder and breathing in my face. I stretched out my hand, and felt an elbow. Then I opened my eyes. Imagine! A woman! Coal-black eyes, lips red as good coral, nostrils breathing passion, breasts—buffers!"

"Draw it mild!" interrupted Merzliakoff in his quiet voice. "I can believe about the breasts, but if it was pitch dark how could you see the lips?"

By laughing at Merzliakoff's lack of understanding, Lobuitko tried to shuffle out of the dilemma. The story annoyed Riabovitch. He rose from the box, lay on his bed, and swore that he would never again take anyone into his confidence.

Life in camp passed without event. The days flew by, each like the one before. But on every one of these days Riabovitch felt, thought, and acted as a man in love. When at daybreak his servant brought him cold water, and poured it over his head, it flashed at once into his half-awakened brain that something good and warm and caressing had crept into his life.

At night when his comrades talked of love and of women, he drew in his chair, and his face was the face of an old soldier who talks of battles in which he has taken part. And when the rowdy officers, led by setter Lobuitko, made Don Juanesque raids upon the neighboring "suburb," Riabovitch, though he accompanied them, was morose and conscience-struck, and mentally asked *her* forgiveness. In free hours and sleepless nights, when his brain was obsessed by memories of childhood, of his father, his mother, of everything akin and dear, he remembered always Miestetchki, the dancing horse, von Rabbek, von Rabbek's wife, so like the ex-Empress Eugénie, the dark room, the chink in the door.

On the thirty-first of August he left camp, this time not with the whole brigade but with only two batteries. As an exile returning to his native land, he was agitated and enthralled by daydreams. He longed passionately for the queer-looking horse, the church, the insincere von Rabbeks, the dark room; and that internal voice which so often cheats the lovelorn whispered an assurance that he should see *her* again. But doubt tortured him. How should he meet her? What must he say? Would she have forgotten the kiss? If it came to the worst—he consoled himself—if he never saw her again, he might walk once more through the dark room, and remember. . . .

Towards evening the white barns and well-known church rose on the horizon. Riabovitch's heart beat wildly. He ignored the remark of an officer who rode by, he forgot the whole world, and he gazed greedily at the river glimmering afar, at the green roofs, at the dovecote, over which fluttered birds dyed golden by the setting sun.

As he rode towards the church, and heard again the quartermaster's raucous voice, he expected every second a horseman to appear from behind the fence and invite the officers to tea. . . . But the quartermaster ended his harangue, the officers hastened to the village, and no horseman appeared.

"When Rabbek hears from the peasants that we are back he will send for us," thought Riabovitch. And so assured was he of this, that when he entered the hut he failed to understand why his comrades had lighted a candle, and why the servants were preparing the samovar.

A painful agitation oppressed him. He lay on his bed. A moment later he rose to look for the horseman. But no horseman was in sight. Again he lay down; again he rose; and this time, impelled by restlessness, went into the street and walked towards the church. The square was dark and deserted. On the hill stood three silent soldiers. When they saw Riabovitch they started and saluted, and he, returning their salute, began to descend the well-remembered path.

Beyond the stream, in a sky stained with purple, the moon slowly rose. Two chattering peasant women walked in a kitchen garden and pulled cabbage leaves; behind them their log cabins stood out black against the sky. The river bank was as it had been in May; the bushes were the same; things differed only in that the nightingale no longer sang, that it smelt no longer of poplars and young grass.

When he reached von Rabbek's garden Riabovitch peered through the wicket gate. Silence and darkness reigned. Save only the white birch trunks and patches of pathway, the whole garden merged in a black, impenetrable shade. Riabovitch listened greedily, and gazed intent. For a quarter of an hour he loitered; then hearing no sound, and seeing no light, he walked wearily towards home.

He went down to the river. In front rose the general's bathing box; and white towels hung on the rail of the bridge. He climbed on to the bridge and stood still; then, for no reason whatever, touched a towel. It was clammy and cold. He looked down at the river which sped past swiftly, murmuring almost inaudibly against the bathing-box piles. Near the left bank glowed the moon's ruddy reflection, overrun by ripples which stretched it, tore it in two, and, it seemed, would sweep it away as twigs and shavings are swept.

"How stupid! How stupid!" thought Riabovitch, watching the hurrying ripples. "How stupid everything is!"

Now that hope was dead, the history of the kiss, his impatience, his ardor, his vague aspirations and disillusion appeared in a clear light. It no longer seemed strange that the general's horseman had not come, and that he would never again see *her* who had kissed him by accident instead of another. On the contrary, he felt, it would be strange if he did ever see her again. . . .

The water flew past him, whither and why no one knew. It had flown past in May; it had sped a stream into a great river; a river, into the sea; it had floated on high in mist and fallen again in rain; it might be, the water of May was again speeding past under Riabovitch's eyes. For what purpose? Why?

And the whole world—life itself—seemed to Riabovitch an inscrutable, aimless mystification. . . . Raising his eyes from the stream and gazing at the sky, he recalled how Fate in the shape of an unknown woman had once caressed him; he recalled his summer fantasies and images—and his whole life seemed to him unnaturally thin and color-less and wretched. . . .

When he reached the cabin his comrades had disappeared. His servant informed him that all had set out to visit "General Fonrabb-kin," who had sent a horseman to bring them. . . . For a moment Riabovitch's heart thrilled with joy. But that joy he extinguished. He cast himself upon his bed, and wroth with his evil fate, as if he wished to spite it, ignored the invitation.

INTERPRETATION

1. In this story a trivial event is made to effect a psychological re-sult all out of proportion to its own importance. Does Chekhov succeed in making credible to us the effect of the kiss on Riabovitch? In con-sidering the problem, take into account the following items: (a) Che-khov is careful to define and emphasize the habitual timidity of Riabo-vitch. (b) The author has Riabovitch admit to himself that what has crept into his life, though "uncommonly good and radiant," is some-thing which is "strange, and indeed ridiculous." Moreover, the next morning Riabovitch "had tried to argue that the kiss had no significance save as a trivial though mysterious adventure; that it was without real import; and that to think of it seriously was to behave himself absurdly." (c) Riabovitch tries to tell his companions about the adventure, and so has borne in upon him, in a sense at least, how little there is to tell, and how pointless the little incident seems to others.

2. If Riabovitch had been able to identify the girl who had kissed him, would the incident have had the same effect? As it is, he imagines a girl who possesses the most attractive features of each of the girls in the ballroom, and thus has "a clear vision of the girl who had kissed him. But she was nowhere to be seen." Does this passage throw any light on the nature of the psychological change wrought on him by the kiss?

3. At the end of the story, why does not Riabovitch avail himself of the invitation when he returns to his cabin?

4. Make a detailed comparison of this story with "Araby." In what sense are the two stories alike in their endings? In their general themes? Account for the differences in methods.

In the Penal Colony

FRANZ KAFKA

(*Translated by Eugene Jolas*)

"IT'S A curious machine," said the officer to the explorer, and despite the fact that he was well acquainted with the apparatus, he nevertheless looked at it with a certain admiration, as it were. It was apparently merely out of courtesy that the explorer had accepted the invitation of the commanding officer to attend the execution of a private soldier condemned for disobedience and insulting a superior officer. Nor did there appear to be great interest in this execution in the penal colony. At any rate, here in the deep, sandy little valley shut in on every side by naked slopes, there were present, beside the officer and the explorer, only the condemned man—an obtuse, wide-mouthed fellow, with neglected face and hair—and a soldier acting as guard. The latter held the heavy chain to which were attached the little chains that fettered the offender's ankles and wrists as well as his neck, and which were themselves linked together by connecting chains. As a matter of fact, however, the condemned man looked so doglike and submissive, one had the impression that he might be allowed to run freely about the slopes, and that, when the execution was about to begin, one would have only to whistle for him to come right back.

The explorer had little thought for the apparatus and started walking up and down behind the condemned man with almost visible indifference. Meanwhile, the officer began the final preparations, now crawling beneath the machine, which was built deep in the ground, now climbing a ladder in order to inspect the upper parts. These were tasks which could easily have been left to a mechanic, but the officer performed them with great zeal, either because he was a special advocate of this apparatus, or because for other reasons the work could not be entrusted to anyone else. "Now everything's ready," he finally called out and climbed down the ladder. He was exceedingly fatigued, breathing with his mouth wide open, and had stuck two dainty lady's handkerchiefs under the collar of his uniform. "These uniforms are much too heavy for the tropics," commented the explorer instead of making inquiries about the machine, as the officer had expected him to do. "Certainly," said the officer, washing his hands, stained with oil and grease, in a pail of water that stood ready near-by, "but they are the symbols of home, and we don't want to lose our homeland." "But take a look at this machine," he added immediately, as he dried his hands with a towel, pointing at the same time to the apparatus. "Up till now, it still had to be worked by hand; now it works entirely alone." The explorer nodded and followed the officer. The latter, wanting to safeguard himself against all eventualities, said: "Of course disturbances do occur; I hope there will be none today, yet we must always reckon with one. For the apparatus has to run for twelve consecutive hours. But if there should be any disturbances, they will only be insignificant ones, and they will be repaired at once."

"Don't you want to sit down?" he finally asked, and choosing a wicker chair from a heap of others, he offered it to the explorer, who could not refuse. He was now sitting on the edge of a pit, into which he cast a fugitive glance. It was not very deep. On one side of the pit the turned-up earth had been heaped into a wall: on the other side stood the machine. "I don't know," said the officer, "if the commanding officer has already explained the apparatus to you." The explorer made a vague gesture of the hand; the officer asked nothing better, for now he could explain the apparatus himself. "This machine," he said, grasping the crankshaft, on which he was leaning, "is an invention of our former commanding officer. I collaborated with him in the early experiments and took part in all the stages of the work up till the end. But credit for the invention belongs to him alone. Have you ever heard of our former commander? No? Well, I'm not exaggerating when I say that the organizing of the entire penal colony is his work. We who were his friends knew already, at the time of his death, that the organization of the colony was so complete in itself, that his successor, even though he were to have a thousand new ideas in his head, would not be able to change anything for many years to come, at least. What we foresaw has come about: the new commander has had to recognize this. It's too bad you did not know the former commander. But"—here the officer interrupted himself, "here I am gabbling away, and his apparatus is standing right here before us. It consists, as you see, of three parts. In the course of time, each of these parts has come to be designated by certain folk names, as it were. The lower one is called the 'bed,' the upper one the 'draughtsman,' and the middle one hanging up there is called the 'harrow.'" "The harrow?" asked the explorer. He had not been listening with undivided attention; the sun was much too tightly ensnared in the shadowless valley; it was hard to concentrate one's thoughts. The officer seemed to him all the more admirable, therefore, as he explained his cause so zealously, in his tight dress uniform, heavy with epaulets and hung with gold braid. Moreover, as he spoke he was busying himself with a screwdriver, tightening a screw here and there. The soldier seemed to be in a state of mind similar to that of the explorer. He had tied the condemned man's chain around both his wrists and was now leaning with one hand on his gun, his head drooping from the nape of his neck, indifferent to everything. The explorer was not surprised by this, for the officer was speaking French and certainly neither the soldier nor the condemned man understood French. It was, therefore, all the more striking that the condemned man should nevertheless have made an effort to follow the explanations of the officer. With a kind of sleepy perseverance he continued to direct his glance where the officer happened to be pointing. When the latter was now interrupted by a question from the explorer, he, too, looked, as did the officer, at the explorer.

"Yes, harrow," said the officer. "It's a suitable name. The needles are arranged as in a harrow and the whole thing is worked like a harrow, although always on the same spot, and much more artistically. You'll understand it right away, anyhow. The condemned man is laid here on the bed.—But I shall first of all describe the apparatus, and after that, I'll get the operation itself under way. You will then be able to follow more easily. Also, there is a cog-wheel in the draughtsman which has gotten too worn down; it makes a creaking noise when it runs so that a person can hardly understand what is being said. Spare parts are hard to get here, too, unfortunately.—Well, then, as I said, here's the bed. It is entirely covered with a layer of cotton, the purpose of which you will learn later on. The condemned man is laid on this cotton, belly down and naked, of course; these straps for the hands, these for the feet, these for the throat, so as to fasten him tight. Here, at the head of the bed where, as I said, the man first lies on his face, there is this little ball of felt, which can be easily adjusted so that it goes right into the man's mouth. Its purpose is to prevent his screaming and biting his tongue. Of course, the man must take hold of the ball of felt since, otherwise, his neck would be broken by the throat-straps." "Is this cotton?" asked the explorer, bending forward. "Why certainly," said the officer smiling, "just feel it yourself." He seized the explorer's hand and guided it across the bed. "It's a specially prepared cotton, that's why it looks so unfamiliar; I'll have something to say about its purpose later on." The explorer was already won over a little in favor of the apparatus; he put his hands over his eyes as a protection against the sun and looked up at it. It was a large structure. The bed and the draughtsman were of equal dimensions and looked like two dark chests. The draughtsman was placed about two meters above the bed; both were connected at the corners by four brass poles which almost gave forth rays in the sunlight. The harrow was hanging between the chests, on a steel band.

The officer had hardly noticed the explorer's earlier indifference; he became aware, however, that his interest was now awakening; he therefore interrupted his explanations to give the explorer time for undisturbed contemplation. The condemned man imitated the explorer; since he could not place his hand over his eyes, he blinked directly upward.

"So the man lies down," said the explorer, and he leaned back in his armchair, crossing his legs.

"Yes," said the officer, pushing his cap back a little and passing his hand over his hot face, "now listen! Both the bed and the draughtsman have their own electric batteries; the bed needs one for itself, the draughtsman one for the harrow. As soon as the man has been strapped down, the bed is put in motion. It quivers simultaneously from side to side, as well as up and down, in tiny, very rapid vibrations. You will probably have seen similar machines in hospitals; only, in the case of our bed, all the motions are very precisely calculated; for they have to be painstakingly accorded to the motions of the harrow. But the execution proper of the sentence is left to this harrow."

"What is the sentence, anyway?" asked the explorer. "So you don't know that, either?" said the officer with astonishment, biting his lips. "Please excuse me; if my explanations are perhaps a bit disjointed, I sincerely beg your pardon. For these explanations were formerly given by the commanding officer; the new commander, however, has shunned this duty of rank; but that he should have failed to enlighten such an important visitor"—the explorer sought to wave away the mark of honor with both hands, but the officer insisted on the expression—"such an important visitor, about the form of our sentence, is another innovation which—," he had a curse on his lips, but restrained himself and said: "I was not informed, it is not my fault. As a matter of fact, I am the best qualified to explain our ways of judging, for I carry here"—he tapped his breast pocket—"the original drawings on the subject, made by the former commander."

"Drawings made by the commander himself?" asked the explorer. "Did he combine everything in his own person? Was he a soldier, a judge, a builder, a chemist, a draughtsman, all in one?"

"Surely," said the officer, nodding his head with a fixed, meditative expression. Then he examined his hands: they did not seem to him to be clean enough to touch the drawings; so he went to the pail and washed them once more. Then he took out a small leather brief case. "Our sentence does not sound severe," he said. "The law which the condemned man broke is written on his body with the harrow. For instance, this offender"—the officer pointed to the condemned man—"will have inscribed on his body: 'HONOR YOUR SUPERIOR.' "

The explorer gave a fleeting glance at the man; when the officer pointed towards him, he hung his head and seemed to be concentrating all his powers of hearing, on finding out something. But the motions of his tightly pressed, puffy lips showed clearly that he could understand nothing. The explorer had wanted to ask various questions but at the sight of the man he only asked: "Does he know his sentence?" "No," the officer said, and wanted to go right ahead with his explanations. But the explorer interrupted him: "So he does not know his sentence?" "No," said the officer again, and he hesitated a moment, as if demanding further justification of his question from the explorer. "It would be useless to announce it to him," he said, "he'll learn it anyway, on his own body." The explorer was inclined to remain silent, when he felt the condemned man's gaze upon him; it seemed to be asking if he could approve of the procedure described. So the explorer, who had already leaned back, bent forward once more and asked: "But he certainly must know that he has been condemned, doesn't he?" "He doesn't know that either," said the officer, smiling at the explorer, as if expecting further strange disclosures. "Well, then," said the explorer, passing his hand over his forehead, "so this man still does not know how his defense was undertaken?" "He had no opportunity of defending himself," said the officer, and looked to one side, as if he were talking to himself and did not want to embarrass the explorer by telling these things which seemed to him self-evident. "But he must surely have had a chance to defend himself?" said the explorer, rising from the armchair.

The officer realized that he was in danger of being held up for some time in his explanation of the apparatus. So he walked over to the explorer, took his arm, pointed towards the condemned man who, seeing that interest was so obviously directed his way, now stood at attention, while the guard drew the chain tighter. "The situation is as follows," said the officer. "I was appointed judge in the penal colony, despite my youth. For I was assistant to the former commander in all punitive matters and I am the one who knows the machine best. The principle on which I base my decisions is this: There is never any doubt about the guilt! Other courts cannot follow this principle, for they consist of many heads and also have still higher courts over them. Such is not the case here, or at least it was not the case with our former commander. To be sure, the new commander has already shown an inclination to meddle with my decisions, but I have always succeeded so far in warding him off, and I shall continue to do so.—You wanted an explanation of this case: it is as simple as all of them. The captain notified us this morning that this man, who had been assigned to his personal service and who slept in front of his door, had fallen asleep while on duty. For it is his duty to get up each time the hour strikes and salute before the captain's door. This is certainly not a difficult duty, but it is a necessary one, for he must be alert while on guard as well as while serving his superior. Last night the captain wanted to see if the servant was doing his duty. He opened the door at two o'clock sharp and found him asleep in a crouching position. He took his riding whip and lashed the man across the face. Now, instead of getting up and asking forgiveness, the man seized his superior by the legs, shook him, and shouted: 'Throw that whip away, or I'll eat you up.' These are the facts. The captain came to me an hour ago. I wrote down his statement and added the sentence immediately. Then I ordered the man to be put in chains. That was all very simple. If I had called the man first and questioned him, it would have only resulted in confusion. He would have lied;

then, if I had succeeded in contradicting the first lies, he would have replaced these with new ones, and so forth. But now I've got hold of him, and I'll not let him go.—Is everything clear now? But time passes, the execution should have begun, and I am not yet through with the explanation of the apparatus." He forced the explorer back into his armchair, went back over to the machine and began: "As you see, this harrow corresponds to the form of a human being; here is the harrow for the upper part of the body, here are the harrows for the legs. For the head, this little burin alone is designated. Have I made myself clear?" He bent amiably towards the explorer, prepared to give the most exhaustive explanations.

The explorer looked at the harrow with wrinkled forehead. The information about the court proceedings had not satisfied him. After all, he was forced to tell himself, this was a penal colony; special measures were necessary here, and they were obliged to proceed according to military regulations up to the very last detail. Besides, he placed some hope in the new commander, who obviously intended to introduce—slowly, to be sure—a new procedure which could not penetrate the limited mind of this officer. This train of thought led the explorer to ask: "Is the commander going to attend the execution?" "That's not certain," said the officer, painfully affected by the unmotivated question, and his friendly expression became distorted. "That's exactly why we have to hurry," he continued. "I shall even have to cut my explanations short, as much as I regret to do so. But then I might add further explanations tomorrow, when the apparatus will have been cleaned again—the fact that it gets so dirty is its only defect. So now I'll give you only the most essential facts.—When the man lies on the bed and it has been made to vibrate, the harrow is lowered onto the body. Of itself it assumes a position that permits the sharp points just barely to touch the body; once it is in place, this steel cord tautens at once into a rod. And then the play begins. The uninitiated notice no external difference in the penalties. The harrow appears to be working uniformly. Tremblingly it sticks its points into the body, which has begun to tremble too, because of the bed. To make it possible for everyone to verify the execution of the sentence, the harrow was made of glass. A few technical difficulties had to be surmounted in order to fasten the needles into it, but we finally succeeded after many attempts. We simply spared no pains. And now everyone can watch the progress of the writing on the body through the glass. Would you mind coming nearer to look at the needles?"

Slowly the explorer arose, walked over and bent over the harrow. "You can see," said the officer, "two kinds of needles in different arrangements. Each long one has a short one next to it. For the long one writes and the short one sprays water in order to wash off the blood, and so keep the writing always clear. The bloody water is then conducted into little drains and finally flows into this principal drain which has an overflow pipe leading into the ditch." The officer pointed out the exact direction which the blood-water had to take. As he held both hands to the mouth of the overflow pipe in order to best illustrate his point, the explorer lifted his head and, groping behind him, was about to return to his seat. At that moment he saw to his horror that the condemned man, like himself, had acted on the invitation of the officer to inspect closely the construction of the harrow. He had dragged the drowsy guard a little way forward with his chain, and was also bending over the glass. He could be seen looking with uncertain eyes for the thing the two gentlemen had just been examining but, because he lacked the explanation, he was not successful. He bent first to one side, then to the other. Again and again his eye roved over the glass. The explorer wanted to push him back, for what he was doing was probably punishable. But the officer held the explorer back with one hand, took a clod of earth from the ditch with the other and threw it at the guard. The latter lifted his eyes suddenly, saw what the condemned man had dared do, let his gun drop and, digging his heels into the ground, he wrenched the condemned man back so that he fell right over. The guard looked down at the man as he writhed and clanked his chains. "Stand him up straight!" the officer shouted, for he noticed that the explorer's attention was far too diverted by the offender. What's more, the explorer was bending across the harrow, without bothering about it, intent only on finding out what was going to happen to the condemned man. "Handle him carefully," the officer shouted again. He ran around the apparatus, seized the condemned man, whose feet kept slipping from under him, by the shoulders and stood him upright, with the help of the guard.

"Now I know everything," said the explorer when the officer came back to him again. "Except the most important part," said the latter and grasping the explorer by the arm, he pointed upward; "There, in the draughtsman is the clockwork that determines the motions of the harrow, and this clockwork is regulated according to the drawing called for by the sentence. I still use the sketches made by the former commanding officer. Here they are,"—he pulled a few sheets out of his leather brief case—"but unfortunately I cannot let you take them in your hand, for they are my most precious possession. Please sit down, I'll show them to you from this distance, so that you may see everything well." He showed him the first page. The explorer would have liked to say a word of approval, but he only saw labyrinthine lines that frequently crossed and recrossed each other and covered the paper so densely that one could recognize only with difficulty the white spaces in between. "Please read this," said the officer. "I can't," said the explorer. "Why, it's perfectly clear," said the officer. "It's undoubtedly very artistic," said the explorer evasively, "but I cannot decipher it." "Of course," said the officer laughing, as he put the brief case away, "it's not fine penmanship for schoolchildren. You have to pore over it for a long while. In the end, you too would certainly make it out. Naturally it can't be ordinary handwriting, for it is not supposed to kill at once, but within an average space of twelve hours; the turning point being calculated for the sixth hour. The writing proper has to be surrounded by many, many embellishments; the real writing only encircles the body in a narrow girdle; the rest of the body is intended for decorative effects. Can you now understand the value of the work of the harrow, and of the entire machine? Just look at this!" He jumped onto the ladder, turned a wheel and called down: "Look out! step aside!" Everything began to move. If the wheel had not creaked, it would have been wonderful. As if surprised by this disturbing wheel, the officer threatened it with his fist; then, excusing himself, stretched his arms out towards the explorer and hurriedly climbed down in order to observe the action of the apparatus from below. Something was still out of order which he alone noticed. He climbed up again, grasped the inner part of the draughtsman with both hands and then, in order to get down quickly, instead of using the ladder, slid down one of the rods. To make himself understood above the noise, he shouted as loudly as possible into the ear of the explorer: "Do you understand what's happening now? The harrow is beginning to write: when it has finished the first inscription on the man's back, the layer of cotton begins to furl up and rolls the body slowly over on its side so as to present a fresh surface to the harrow. In the meantime, the wound-written parts take their place on the cotton, which stops the bleeding at once, by means of a special preparation, and makes further deepening of the writing possible. Just here, the spikes on the edge of the harrow tear the cotton from the wounds, as the body is turned over again, hurl it into the ditch, and the harrow starts working again. Thus it writes more and more deeply during the whole twelve hours. The first six hours the condemned man lives about as before, he only suffers pain. After two hours the piece of felt is removed, for the man hasn't the strength to scream any more. Here, at the head end, we put warm rice porridge into this electrically heated tray, from which the man, if he cares to, can eat whatever he can lap up with his tongue. None of them ever misses this opportunity. I know really of none, and my experience is great. Only around the sixth hour does he lose his pleasure in eating. Then I usually kneel down here and observe the following phenomenon. Rarely does the man swallow the last morsel. All he does is to turn it about in his mouth and spit it out into the ditch. I have to stoop over then; otherwise I would catch it in the face. But around the sixth hour how quiet the man becomes! Even the dullest begins to understand. It starts around the eyes. From here it spreads out. It's a sight which could tempt you to lie down under the harrow with him. But nothing further happens, the man is just beginning to decipher the writing, and he purses his lips as if listening. You have seen that it is not easy to decipher the writing with the eye; but our man deciphers it with his wounds. Of course, that means a lot of work; he needs six hours to accomplish it. Then the harrow spears him clean through and hurls him into the ditch, where he plumps down into the bloody water and cotton. The tribunal is ended and we, the soldier and I, shovel him under."

The explorer had bent his ear to the officer and, with his hands in his coat pockets, observed the work of the machine. The condemned man was also observing it but without comprehension. He leaned over a little to follow the oscillating needles, when the guard, at a sign from the officer, slashed his shirt and trousers from behind with a knife so that they fell down off him. The man tried to seize the falling garments in order to cover his nakedness, but the soldier lifted him into the air and shook the last shreds from him. The officer brought the machine to a standstill and in the silence that now reigned the condemned man was placed under the harrow. The chains were undone and straps fastened in their place. Just at first it seemed almost to spell relief for the condemned man. Then the harrow settled down a bit lower, for he was a thin man. When the points touched him, a shudder ran over his skin; while the guard was busy with his right hand, he reached out blindly with his left; but it was towards where the explorer was standing. Uninterruptedly the officer kept looking at the explorer from the side, as if trying to read on his face the impression that the execution, which he had explained to him at least superficially, was making on him.

The strap intended for the wrist broke; the guard had probably pulled on it too hard. The guard showed him the broken bit of strap and the officer was obliged to help. Turning his face toward the explorer, he walked over to the guard and said: "This machine is quite complicated; here and there something is bound to tear or break; but one should not for this reason allow oneself to be misled as to one's general judgment. As a matter of fact, a substitute for the strap may be had promptly; I am going to use a chain, only the delicacy of the vibration of the right arm will in that case of course be reduced." And as he attached the chain, he added: "The means at my disposal for the upkeep of the machine are very limited now. Under the former commander there existed a fund intended only for this purpose, to which I had free access. There was also a warehouse here in which all kinds of spare parts were kept. I confess I was almost wasteful with them, I mean formerly, not now, as the new commander—to whom everything is only a pretext for combating old institutions—asserts. Now he administers the Machine Fund himself, and whenever I send for a new strap the broken one is required as proof, the new one takes ten days to arrive, then it's of poor quality and not worth much. But in the meantime how am I to make the machine go without straps? Nobody bothers about that!"

The explorer reflected: It is always a delicate matter to intervene effectively in other people's affairs. He was neither a citizen of the penal colony nor a citizen of the state to which it belonged. If he wanted to condemn the execution, or even to prevent it, they could say to him: You are a foreigner, be silent. To this he would not be able to reply other than to add that as far as this matter was concerned, he didn't understand it himself, for he was traveling with the sole intention of observing and certainly not with that of changing foreign court procedures. But here, however, the situation appeared to be very tempting. There was no doubt about the injustice of the proceedings and the inhumanity of the execution. Nobody would assume that the explorer had any personal interest in the matter, for the condemned man was a stranger to him. They were not compatriots, nor was he at all a man who invited pity. The explorer himself had recommendations from high officials, he had been received with great courtesy, and the fact that he had been asked to the execution seemed even to indicate that they might desire his opinion concerning this procedure. This was all the more likely in fact since the commanding officer, as he had just heard distinctly, was not a partisan of this procedure and maintained an almost hostile attitude towards the officer.

At that moment, the explorer heard a cry of rage from the officer. Not without difficulty, he had just succeeded in shoving the felt gag into the mouth of the offender, when the latter closed his eyes in an irresistible nausea and vomited. Hurriedly the officer wrenched him away from the gag and tried to turn his head towards the ditch; but it was too late, the slop was already running all over the machine. "All this is the commander's fault!" the officer cried and shook the brass rods in front without rhyme or reason. "They're getting my machine as filthy as a stable." His hands shaking, he showed the explorer what had happened. "Haven't I tried for hours to make the commander understand that no meals should be given for a day before the execution? But the new, lenient tendency disagrees. The ladies of the commander's family stuff the man's mouth with sweets before he is led away. All his life he has fed on stinking fish, and now he has to eat candy! But it certainly would be possible, I wouldn't object—why on earth don't they get a new felt gag, as I have urged for the last three months? How can anyone take into his mouth, without loathing, a gag on which more than a hundred dying men have sucked and bitten?"

The condemned man had laid his head back and looked very peaceful, the guard was busy cleaning the machine with the condemned man's shirt. The officer walked towards the explorer, who took a step backwards in some sort of premonition, but the officer took his hand

and drew him to one side. "I want to say a few words to you in confidence," he said, "may I?" "Certainly," said the explorer, and listened, his eyes lowered.

"This procedure and this execution, which you now have the opportunity to admire, no longer have any open adherents in our colony at present. I am their only advocate, as well as the only advocate of the old commander's legacy. I am no longer able to consider further improvements of the procedure; I exhaust all my strength trying to preserve what already exists. During the old commander's lifetime, the colony was filled with his adherents; I possess some of his strength of conviction, but I entirely lack his power; in consequence, the adherents have slipped away. There are still a good many, but nobody admits it. If you go to the tea house today, that is on an execution day, and listen around a bit, you will perhaps hear only ambiguous utterances. These people are all adherents, but they are quite useless to me under the present commander with his present views. And now I ask you: Shall such a lifework as this"—here he pointed to the machine—"be allowed to perish just because of this commander and the women in his family who influence him? Can we allow this? Even though one is only on our island for a few days, as a stranger? But there is no time to lose, there is something afoot to undermine my jurisdiction; discussions are already taking place in the commander's office to which I am not summoned. Even your visit today seems to me to be characteristic of the entire situation; they are cowards, so they send you, a stranger, ahead of them.—How different the executions were in the old days! Already, a day before the execution, the entire valley was overcrowded with people; they all came just to watch; early in the morning the commander appeared with his ladies; a flourish of trumpets awakened the entire encampment; I made the announcement that everything was ready; the society people—no high official was allowed to be absent —took their places around the machine; this heap of wicker chairs is a miserable relic of those times. The machine was freshly painted and shone brightly, I used new spare parts for almost every execution. Before hundreds of eyes—all the spectators stood on tip-toe as far back as those slopes over there—the condemned man was laid under the harrow by the commander himself. What a common soldier is allowed to do today, was then my task, as presiding judge, and I felt honored by it. And now the execution began! Not a single discord disturbed the work of the machine. Many stopped looking, even, and just lay there in the sand with their eyes closed. Everybody realized: Justice is now being done. In the stillness only the sighing of the condemned man, muffled by the felt, could be heard. Today the machine no longer succeeds in wringing from the condemned man a sigh that is sufficiently loud for the felt not to stifle it. In those days, however, the writing needles dripped a corrosive liquid which we are not allowed to use today. Well, then came the sixth hour! It was impossible to grant all the petitions to be allowed to witness the spectacle from close by. The commander in his wisdom gave orders that the children should be considered first; of course I was always allowed to stand close by on account of my position; many's the time I used to crouch there with a small child in each arm. How we all absorbed the expression of transfiguration from the man's tortured face, how we lifted our cheeks into the glow of this justice, finally achieved and already fading! What times those were, comrade!" The officer had evidently forgotten who it was standing before him; he had embraced the explorer and laid his head on his shoulder. The latter was greatly embarrassed and looked impatiently beyond the officer. The guard had finished the cleaning job and was now pouring rice porridge from a can into the tray. The condemned man, who seemed to have almost completely recovered, no sooner noticed this than he began to clack with his tongue for the porridge. The guard kept shoving him away, for the porridge was undoubtedly intended for a later moment, but it was nevertheless unseemly for him to put his dirty hands in the tray and eat out of it in front of the ravenous offender.

The officer quickly pulled himself together. "I was not really trying to touch your emotions," he said. "I know it is impossible to make those times comprehensible today. Besides, the machine still works and can speak for itself. It speaks for itself, even when it is standing all alone in this valley. And in the end, the corpse still falls with an unbelievably gentle flying motion into the ditch, even though there are no longer hundreds to gather around the ditch like flies, as there used to be. At that time we had to put up a strong railing around the ditch, but that has been torn down long ago."

The explorer looked aimlessly about him, wanting to keep his face from the officer. The latter, thinking he was looking at the barrenness of the valley, seized his hands and walked around him in order to catch his glance: "Do you see the shame of it?" he said.

But the explorer remained silent. For a little while the officer left him alone; with outspread legs and his hands on his hips, he stood still, looking at the ground. Then he smiled encouragingly at the explorer and said: "I was standing near-by yesterday, when the commander gave you the invitation. I heard it. I know the commander. I understood at once what he had in mind with that invitation. Although his power would be sufficient to take measures against me, he does not yet dare do so; but he wants to expose me to your judgment, as being that of a distinguished foreigner. He has made a careful calculation; this is your second day on the island, you did not know the old commander and his thought processes, you are prejudiced by the European point of view, you are perhaps, on principle, an opponent of capital punishment in general, and of such a machinelike type of execution in particular; furthermore you see how the execution takes place, without public sympathy, sadly, on a machine that is already somewhat damaged; now would it not be easily possible—this is what the commander thinks—that you should not approve of my procedure? And if you did not approve of it, would you not keep silent about it—I am still speaking from the commander's point of view—for you certainly have complete confidence in your own much tried convictions? You have surely seen and learned to appreciate the different peculiarities of many peoples; therefore you will in all probability not speak out with all your might against the procedure as you would, perhaps, do in your own country. But that isn't at all necessary for the commander. A haphazard, merely an incautious, word suffices. It need not in any way correspond to your convictions, if only it appears to meet with his wishes. I am sure he will question you with all the cunning he possesses. And the ladies will sit around in a circle, all ears. You'll probably say: 'In our country the court proceedings are different,' or, 'In our country the accused is examined before judgment is pronounced,' or, 'In our country there are other penalties than the death penalty,' or, 'In our country there have been no tortures since the Middle Ages.' These are all observations that are as right as they appear self-evident to you; innocent observations that do not touch my procedure. But how will the commander take them? I can see him now, our friend the commander, as he pushes his chair aside and hurries to the balcony, I can see his ladies flocking after him, I can hear his voice—the ladies call it a thunder voice—as he says: 'A great occidental researcher designated to examine court proceedings in many countries, has just announced that our procedure in accordance with old customs is an inhuman one. After this judgment, pronounced by such a distinguished man, it is of course no longer possible for me to tolerate this method. Beginning today, I therefore issue the following order—and so forth.' You want to protest, you did not really say what he announces you did, you did not call my method inhuman; on the contrary, in your innermost thoughts you regard it as the most human and most worthy of humanity; you also admire this mechanism—but it is too late; you can't even reach the balcony, which is already crowded with ladies; you try to attract attention, you try to shout, but a lady's hand holds your mouth shut—and I, and the old commander's work, are lost."

The explorer had to suppress a smile; so the task he had regarded as being so difficult was really as easy as that. He said evasively, "You overestimate my influence; the commander has read my letter of introduction; he knows that I am no connoisseur of court proceedings. If I were to express an opinion, it would be the opinion of a private individual, of no more importance than that of anyone else, and certainly much less important than that of the commander who, unless I am mistaken, has very extensive powers in this penal colony. If his opinion concerning this procedure is such a positive one as you believe, then, I am afraid that its end is indeed here, without there being any need of my modest co-operation."

Did the officer understand this? No, he did not yet understand. He shook his head vigorously and threw a brief glance back at the condemned man and the soldier, who was startled and let go of the rice. The officer came quite near the explorer, and without looking at him directly but at something or other on his coat, said more softly than before: "You don't know the commander; you are, as it were, under no obligations—if you'll pardon my expression—to him, or to us all. Believe me, your influence cannot be too highly estimated. I was indeed delighted when I heard that you were to attend the execution alone. This order of the commander was aimed at me, but now I am

going to turn it to my own advantage. Uninfluenced by false insinua-
tions and contemptuous looks—which would have been inevitable with
a larger attendance at the execution—you have listened to my explanations, you have seen the machine and are now about to witness the
execution. Surely your judgment is already formed; should there still
be a few uncertainties in your mind, the sight of the execution will do
away with them. And now I make this plea to you: help me with the
commander!"

The explorer did not allow him to continue. "But how could I do
that?" he cried. "That's quite impossible. I am as powerless to help you
as to hinder you."

"You certainly can," said the officer. The explorer noticed somewhat
anxiously that the officer's fists were clenched. "You certainly can," he
repeated, still more insistently. "I have a plan that must succeed. You
believe your influence is insufficient. I know it is sufficient. But allowing that you're right, isn't it necessary then to try everything, even what
may possibly fail, in order to maintain this procedure? So listen to my
plan. In order to carry it out, it is above all necessary for you to be as
reticent as possible concerning your judgment of this procedure in the
colony today. Unless someone questions you directly, you must by no
means say anything; your utterances should be brief and vague; people
should notice that it becomes increasingly difficult for you to talk about
it, that you are acrimonious, that you practically have to burst into
invective, were you to talk openly. I don't ask you to lie, in any sense;
you should give only the briefest answers, such as: 'Yes, I've seen the
execution,' or, 'Yes, I've heard all the explanations.' Only that, no
more. Of course there is sufficient cause for the acrimony people should
notice in you, even though it does not correspond to the commander's
viewpoint. Of course he will misunderstand completely and give it his
own interpretation. That is the basis of my plan. Tomorrow an important meeting of all the higher administrative officers will take place
under the chairmanship of the commander at headquarters. The commander naturally knows how to make a spectacle out of these sessions.
A gallery has been built which is always occupied by spectators. I am
obliged to attend these consultations, but I am loath to do so. In any
case, you will certainly be invited to this meeting; if you will follow
my plan today, the invitation will become an urgent request. Should

you not be invited, however, for some undiscoverable reason, you must ask for an invitation; you will get it then without any doubt. So to-morrow you're seated with the ladies in the commander's box. He reassures himself frequently, by looking upward, that you are there. After disposing of diverse indifferent and ludicrous subjects, calcu-lated solely to interest the spectators,—mostly about port constructions, eternally about port constructions—the court procedure also comes up for discussion. If this point should not occur to the commander, or rather not early enough, I'll see to it that it does. I'll stand up and make a report of today's execution. Quite brief, only a report. Such a report is not customary, but I make it nevertheless. The commander thanks me, as always, with a friendly smile; and then he cannot restrain him-self, he sees his chance: 'A report of today's execution has just been made,' he will say, or something similar to this. 'I'd only like to add to this report that this particular execution was attended by the great scholar, whose visit—an exceptional honor for our colony—you all know about. Our session today also takes on an added significance as a re-sult of his presence. Let us now question this great scholar as to his opinion of this execution, carried out in accordance with early customs, as well as of the procedure that led up to it.' Naturally, applause throughout the house, and general approval; I am the loudest. The commander makes a bow before you and says: 'Then I put the ques-tion in the name of everyone present.' And now you step up to the balustrade. Lay your hands on it, so that they are visible to everybody, otherwise the ladies will take hold of them and dally with your fingers. —And now, finally, comes a word from you. I don't know how I shall stand the tension of the hours until that moment. You must place no limit on your speech, blare forth the truth; lean over the balustrade, bellow your opinion, yes, bellow it, at the commander, your unshakable opinion! But maybe you don't want to do this, maybe it does not corre-spond to your character; in your country people act differently in such situations; this too is all right; this too is quite sufficient; don't get up at all, say only a few words, whisper them so that they may be heard by the officials below you, that'll do. You needn't even mention the small attendance at the execution, the creaking wheel, the broken strap, the repulsive felt gag; no, I'll take care of everything else. And believe me, if my speech doesn't chase him from the hall, it'll force him to his knees, so that he will have to acknowledge: I bow down before you, old commander!—That's my plan; won't you help me to carry it out? But of course you will; what's more, you must." And the officer seized the explorer by both arms and looked into his face, breathing heavily. He had shouted the last sentences so loudly that even the guard and the condemned man became attentive; although they understood nothing, they stopped eating and looked towards the explorer, chewing the while.

The explorer had no doubt from the very beginning as to the answer he would have to give. He had experienced too much in his life to vacillate now; at bottom he was an honest man, and he was not afraid. Nevertheless, he hesitated, just the time of a breath, at the sight of the soldier and the condemned man. But finally he said what he had to say: "No." The officer blinked several times and did not take his eyes off him. "Do you want an explanation?" asked the explorer. The officer nodded silently. "I am opposed to this procedure," the explorer then said. "Before you even took me into your confidence—I'll not abuse this confidence, of course, under any circumstances—I had already considered whether I would be justified in taking steps against this procedure, and whether there would be the slightest prospect of success in case I did so. It was clear to me to whom I should have to turn first: to the commander, of course. You have made it still clearer, but without having strengthened my resolution; on the contrary, your honest conviction moves me, even though it could never influence me."

The officer remained silent, turned to the machine and, seizing one of the brass rods, leaned slightly backwards to look up at the draughtsman, as if to check whether or not everything was in order. The guard and the condemned man seemed to have become friends; the condemned man was making signs to the guard, despite the fact that the tight straps which bound him made this difficult: the soldier bent over towards him; the condemned man whispered something to him and the soldier nodded.

The explorer followed the officer: "You don't know yet what I am going to do," he said. "Of course, I shall give my opinion about the procedure to the commander, not at the meeting, however, but tête-à-

tête; nor shall I stay here long enough to be drawn into any meeting: I am going away early tomorrow morning, or at least I'll board ship then."

It seemed as though the officer had been listening. "So the procedure did not convince you," he said to himself, and smiled as an old man smiles at a child's nonsense, withholding his own real musings behind the smile.

"Then the time has come," he said finally, and looked suddenly at the explorer, his eyes shining with a certain challenge, a certain appeal for co-operation. "Time for what?" the explorer asked anxiously, but received no answer.

"You're free," said the officer to the condemned man in the latter's own language. At first the condemned man did not believe it. "You're free now," the officer said. The face of the condemned man showed signs of life for the first time. Was this the truth? Or was it only a passing whim on the part of the officer? Had the foreign explorer obtained pardon for him? Which was it? His face seemed to ask these questions. But not for long. Whatever it might be, if he could, he really wanted to be free, and he began to shake himself as much as the harrow permitted.

"You're breaking my straps," the officer shouted. "Keep quiet, we'll unfasten them for you." And with the help of the guard, to whom he had made a sign, he got to work. The condemned man chuckled gently to himself, saying nothing; he turned his face first to the left towards the officer, then to the right towards the guard; not forgetting the explorer.

"Pull him out," the officer ordered the guard. To do this, they were obliged to move with a certain caution, on account of the harrow. The condemned man, due to his impatience, already had a few slight lacerations on his back.

From this moment on, however, the officer hardly bothered about him any more. He walked over to the explorer, took out again his small leather brief case, rummaged through it, finally found the paper he was looking for and showed it to the explorer. "Read this," he said. "I can't," said the explorer. "I told you before I can't read those pages." "But take a good look at the page anyway," said the officer, stepping to the explorer's side to read with him. When this did not help, either, in order to facilitate the explorer's reading, he ran his little finger across the page, well above it, as if the paper must not be touched under any condition. The explorer made an effort, in order to be agreeable to the officer at least in this, but it was impossible. Now the officer began to spell out the writing, then he read it once more connectedly. "It says: 'BE JUST!'—Now you can read it," he said. The explorer bent so low over the paper that the officer drew it back, fearing he might touch it; actually the explorer said nothing more, but it was clear that he still had not been able to read it. "It says: 'BE JUST!'" the officer repeated. "That may be so," said the explorer, "I believe that's what it says." "All right then," said the officer, at least partially satisfied, and he climbed the ladder still holding the page; with great caution he laid it on the draughtsman, and then began apparently to rearrange the entire mechanism; it was a very tedious job, for the wheels in question must have been very tiny; sometimes his head disappeared completely in the draughtsman, he was obliged to examine the wheelwork so closely.

The explorer continued to follow the work from below, his neck grew stiff, his eyes began to smart from the sunlight-flooded sky. The guard and the condemned man were now occupied only with each other. With the point of his bayonet, the guard lifted up the condemned man's shirt and trousers which were lying in the ditch. The shirt was frightfully dirty, and the condemned man washed it in the water-pail. Both had to laugh aloud when the condemned man put the shirt and trousers on, for both garments had been slashed in two behind. Perhaps the offender thought it his duty to entertain the guard; in his slit clothes he made circles around the guard, who was crouching on the ground, laughing and beating his knees. Nevertheless they restrained themselves somewhat, out of respect for the presence of the two gentlemen.

When the officer had finally finished up above, he smilingly surveyed the whole in all its parts once more, banged shut the cover of the draughtsman, which until now had been open, climbed down and looked first into the ditch, then at the condemned man; noticed with satisfaction that the latter had recovered his garments, walked towards the pail to wash his hands, recognized too late the repulsive filth in it, became saddened at the fact that now he could not wash his hands, at last dipped his fingers in the sand—this substitute did not suffice but he had to accommodate himself—then rose and began to unbutton the coat of his uniform. At this, the two lady's handkerchiefs which he had stuck in his collar fell into his hands. "Here, take your handkerchiefs," he said, and threw them towards the condemned man. In explanation he said to the explorer: "Gifts from the ladies."

In spite of the evident hurry with which he took off his coat and then undressed completely, he nevertheless handled each garment very carefully. He even let his fingers run over the silver cord on his tunic and shook one of the tassels straight. Yet it was little in keeping with this carefulness that, as soon as he had finished handling a garment, he immediately threw it into the ditch, with an angry gesture. The last thing that remained was his smallsword and belt. He drew the sword from its scabbard, broke it, then gathered everything together—the pieces of the sword, the scabbard and the belt—and threw them away so violently that they clinked together in the ditch.

Now he stood there naked. The explorer bit his lips and said nothing. To be sure, he knew what was going to happen, yet he had no right to prevent the officer from doing anything. If the court procedure to which the officer was so attached really was about to be abolished—possibly as a consequence of the action which the explorer had felt obliged to take—then the officer was acting entirely rightly; the explorer would not have acted differently in his place.

The guard and the condemned man understood nothing at first; in the beginning, they did not even look on. The condemned man was overjoyed at having got back his pocket handkerchiefs, but he was not allowed to enjoy them very long, for the soldier snatched them away from him with a quick, unpredictable gesture. The condemned man now tried once more to pull the handkerchiefs from the soldier's belt, into which the latter had carefully put them, but the soldier was on his guard. So they struggled, half in jest. Only when the officer was completely naked did they pay any attention to him. The condemned man especially seemed to be seized with a foreboding of some great change. What had happened to him, was now happening to the officer. It might even go on to the very end. Most likely, the foreign explorer had given the order for it. So this was revenge. Without himself having suffered to the end, he was nevertheless avenged to the end.

A broad, noiseless laughter appeared now on his face, and remained there.

The officer turned towards the machine. If it had already been clear before that he understood the machine well, it was now almost horrifying to see the way he took charge of it, and the way it obeyed him. He had hardly brought his hand near the harrow when it rose and sank several times until it had reached the right position to receive him; he took hold of the bed by the edge only, and it started to vibrate right away; the ball of felt came toward his mouth. One saw that the officer did not really want to take it, but his hesitancy lasted just a moment, he submitted at once and took it in his mouth. Everything was ready, only the straps were still hanging down at the sides, but they were obviously unnecessary, as the officer did not need to be strapped in. Then the condemned man noticed the hanging straps; in his opinion the execution would not be complete unless the straps were tightly fastened; he waved excitedly to the guard and both of them ran to buckle the officer in. The latter had already stretched out one foot in order to push the crank that was to start the draughtsman going; then he saw that the two men had come near him. He drew his foot back and let himself be strapped in. Now, however, he was no longer able to reach the crank; neither the guard nor the condemned man would be able to find it, and the explorer was determined not to make a move. This was not necessary; hardly had the straps been fastened, when the machine began to work; the bed trembled, the needles danced on the skin, the harrow swung up and down. The explorer had been staring at it quite a while before he remembered that a wheel in the draughtsman should have made a creaking noise; yet all was silent, not the slightest hum was to be heard.

Because of this silent action the machine ceased to be the focus of attention. The explorer looked over towards the soldier and the condemned man. The latter was the more lively of the two, everything about the machine interested him; first he would bend down, then he would stretch himself, holding his index finger constantly extended to point out something to the guard. The explorer felt uncomfortable. He was determined to remain there till the end, but he could not have borne the sight of the two men very long. "Go home," he said. The soldier would, perhaps, have been ready to go, but the condemned man considered the order as a sort of punishment. He begged and implored with clasped hands to be allowed to stay, and when the explorer, shaking his head, refused to give in, he even went on his knees. The explorer saw that orders were of no avail here and he was about to go over and drive the two of them away. At that moment he heard a noise up in the draughtsman. He looked up. Could that one cogwheel be giving trouble? But it was something else. Slowly the cover of the draughtsman rose and then fell wide open. The teeth of a cogwheel began to show, then rose up; soon the whole wheel appeared; it was as if some great force were pressing the draughtsman together so that there was no room left for this wheel; it kept rotating till it reached the edge of the draughtsman, fell down, reeled upright a bit in the sand, then lay there. But already another one rose up above, followed by many more, big ones, little ones, and others that could hardly be told apart; the same thing happened to them all, one kept thinking that the draughtsman must surely be emptied by now, when a new, particularly numerous lot appeared, rose up, fell down, reeled in the sand and lay there. At the sight of this occurrence the condemned man forgot all about the explorer's orders; the cogwheels completely fascinated him; he kept trying to seize one of them, at the same time urging the soldier to help him; but he withdrew his hand in fright, for another cogwheel always followed at once, and this, at least at first when it would come rolling towards him, frightened him.

The explorer, however, was very disturbed; the machine was evidently going to pieces; its quiet action was a delusion; he had the feeling that he would have to care for the officer now, since the latter was no longer able to care for himself. But while the dropping of the cogwheels had claimed his entire attention, he had neglected to watch the rest of the machine; now, however, when the last cogwheel had left the draughtsman, he bent over the harrow, only to have a fresh, more annoying surprise. The harrow was not writing, it was just sticking the body, nor was the bed rolling it but just lifting it, trembling, up to the needles. The explorer wanted to interfere and, if possible, bring the whole thing to a stop, for this was not the torture the officer had wanted to arrive at, this was outright murder. He stretched out his hands. But at that moment the harrow was already beginning to rise sideways with the impaled body, the way it usually did only at the twelfth hour. Blood was flowing in a hundred streams, unmixed with water, for the little water pipes had also failed this time. And now the last thing failed too, the body did not release itself from the long needles, but, bleeding profusely, hung over the ditch without falling into it. The harrow was ready to fall back into its usual position, but, as if it had noticed itself that it was not yet freed of its burden, it remained suspended above the ditch. "Why don't you help?" the explorer shouted over to the guard and the condemned man, as he, himself, seized the officer's feet. He tried to hold the feet down on his side and the other two were to take hold of the officer's head from the other side, so that he might be slowly lifted off the needles. But the two could not make up their minds to join him; the condemned man practically turned away; the explorer had to go over to them and force them to come over near the officer's head. Just here he saw the face of the corpse, almost against his will. It was as it had been in life; no sign of the promised redemption was to be detected; that which all the others had found in the machine, the officer had not found; his lips were tightly pressed together, his eyes were open, and had an expression of life; their look was calm and convinced; the point of the big iron prong pierced his forehead.

When the explorer reached the first houses of the colony, with the soldier and the condemned man behind him, the soldier pointed at one house and said, "That's the tea house."

On the ground floor of one house there was a deep, low, cavernous room with smoke stained walls and ceiling. On the street side it was wide open. Although the tea house differed little from the other houses in the colony, which were all very run-down, with the exception of the palatial structures that housed headquarters, it nevertheless gave the impression to the explorer of an historic memory, and he felt the power of other days. He walked nearer and, followed by his companions, he passed between the unoccupied tables standing on the street before the tea house, and inhaled the cool, musty air which came from the inside. "The old man's buried here," said the soldier. "The priest refused him a place in the cemetery. At first they were undecided as to where to bury him, but they finally buried him here. I'm sure the officer did not tell you anything about it, for that was the thing he was most ashamed of. He even tried a few times to disinter the old man at night, but he was always chased away." "Where is the grave?" asked the explorer, who found it hard to believe the guard. Both the guard and the condemned man immediately dashed ahead of him and with outstretched hands pointed to the spot where the grave was to be found. They led the explorer straight to the back wall where customers were sitting at a few of the tables. They were probably longshoremen, sturdy looking men with short, glossy, full black beards. All of them were coatless, their shirts torn; they were poor humble folk. As the explorer approached, several of them rose, flattened themselves up against the wall and looked in his direction. "He's a foreigner," was the whisper that went about the explorer; "he wants to see the grave." They shoved one of the tables aside, underneath which there really was a tombstone. It was a simple slab, low enough to be hidden under the table. On it was an inscription in quite small letters, to read which the explorer was obliged to kneel down. It read: "HERE LIES THE OLD COMMANDER. HIS ADHERENTS, WHO MAY NO LONGER BEAR A NAME, HAVE DUG THIS GRAVE FOR HIM AND ERECTED THIS STONE. THERE EXISTS A PROPHECY TO THE EFFECT THAT, AFTER A CERTAIN NUMBER OF YEARS, THE COMMANDER WILL RISE FROM THE DEAD AND LEAD THEM OUT OF THIS HOUSE TO THE RECONQUEST OF THE COLONY. BELIEVE AND WAIT!" When he had finished reading, the explorer rose and saw the men standing about him and smiling as if they had read the inscription with him, had found it ridiculous and were calling upon him to join in their viewpoint. The explorer acted as though he had noticed nothing, distributed a few coins among them, waited until the table had been shoved back over the grave, then left the tea house and walked towards the port.

The guard and the condemned man had come across acquaintances in the tea house who detained them. But they must have torn themselves away soon after, for the explorer was no further than the middle of the long stairway leading to the boats, when they came running after him. They probably wanted to force the explorer at the last moment to take them along. While the explorer was negotiating with a sailor down below for his crossing to the liner, the two men rushed down the steps, silently, for they did not dare cry out. But when they arrived below, the explorer was already in the boat and the sailor was just about to shove off. They might still have been able to jump into the boat, but the explorer picked up a heavy, knotted towrope from the floor, threatened them with it, and thus prevented them from jumping.*

INTERPRETATION

After reading only a little of "In the Penal Colony," one realizes that this story is not intended to be a realistic account of events which, though imagined by the author, are to be judged by ordinary notions of probability. Instead, it is a fantasy. The strangeness of the situation—an execution to be performed by one soldier and a high officer in the vacant valley, the unusual behavior of the condemned man and the soldier, the mysterious nature of the machine—is an indication that we are dealing with fantasy, just as we are in Hawthorne's "The Birthmark," or Poe's "The Fall of the House of Usher."

But are we to take the story to be merely fantastic, a parade of strangeness for the sake of strangeness? Would the presentation of the marvelous merely because it was marvelous constitute a piece of fiction? Do we not, rather, expect that the unrealistic and fantastic elements in such a piece of fiction as "In the Penal Colony" shall have some bearing, finally, on real human experience? That is, in so far as fantasy appears in fiction we expect it to have some meaning. The violation of our ordinary notions of probability, which is characteristic of fantasy, seems to promise an imaginative escape from ordinary experience, but in the end we discover that the intention of the creator of the fantasy is not to provide us with an escape from our ordinary experience but to provide us with an interpretation of our experience, to illuminate our experience. In other words, fantasy as a type of fiction differs from other types of fiction merely in method and not in its basic intention.

The specific method employed by "In the Penal Colony" is allegorical. In an allegory, one finds a surface narrative the items of which—characters, objects, and events—stand for ideas and relations among ideas. That is, in so far as the allegory is strictly maintained, there is a point-to-point equating of the surface narrative with the background meaning. This method of communicating meaning is essentially different from that of ordinary realistic fiction. For instance, in "The Lament" the persons do not stand for ideas and events do not indicate relationships among ideas. The old man does not stand for grief, for example, but is simply himself, an old man who is suffering from grief and loneliness. The meaning of the story, then, does not come from

* By permission of *The Partisan Review*, publishers in the United States; copyright, 1941.

our grasp of particular concepts and relations as exemplified, item by item, in the narrative, but as a result of the total story: in so far as the character and situation of the old man work on our imagination, we become aware of the unthinking callousness of the world, and our comprehension of, and our sympathy for, the lonely and outcast are awakened. That is, we arrive at the meaning of a realistic story much as we arrive at the meaning of an event in real life.

This leads to a second distinction between allegory and realistic fiction. In realistic fiction, we are convinced by the logic of character and event, by our notion of probability. But in allegory the principle of organization does not finally depend upon the logic in the surface narrative, but upon the logic of the relationships among the ideas represented. (Of course, the surface narrative may be more or less realistic, and in so far as it is realistic it possesses an independent logic.) In fact, in allegorical fantasy, the more or less complete abandonment of probability in the surface narrative indicates that the dependence is placed upon the logic of the background. For example, in "The Birthmark" we do not judge Aylmer's attempt to remove the little mark of the hand from his wife's cheek by standards of psychological realism; by such standards, Aylmer's obsession would amount to madness. We are concerned, rather, with the meaning of the event in terms of the pattern of ideas behind the surface narrative (p. 105), and judge the event in terms of the logic of that background meaning.

We have said that in so far as an allegory is strictly maintained there is a point-to-point equating of the items of the surface narrative with ideas and relationships among ideas in the background. But there are degrees of strictness in allegorical practice. The method in "The Birthmark" is not so strict as that in "In the Penal Colony." If "The Birthmark" were an absolute allegory we should find every item, say the instruments used by Aylmer in his experiment, to have a specific equivalent in the background of ideas. But that is scarcely the case, and we have what might be termed allegorical lags—elements of the surface narrative which do not find specific equivalents in the background of ideas.

"In the Penal Colony," as we have said, is stricter in its allegory than "The Birthmark" and is at the same time more difficult of interpretation. "In the Penal Colony," as interpreted by one critic, Austin Warren,* is an allegory concerning the state of religion in the modern world.

* "An Exegetical Note on 'In the Penal Colony,'" *The Southern Review*, vii, 2, pp. 363–365.

We know that the characteristic beliefs of the modern world are primarily founded on science. Science is concerned with the realm of the natural and not with the realm of the supernatural. Its assumption is that the events of the world are in accord with natural laws, and that by the use of his reason man may become acquainted with natural law and can, in so far as his knowledge of that law is perfect, predict the course of nature. It pictures a completely rational world, in which there is no place for the irrational, the miraculous, the supernatural. It assumes that miraculous and supernatural manifestations would, if man's scientific knowledge were adequate, be seen to be merely natural phenomena. Associated with this belief in science is the belief in progress: as man learns more his control of nature increases and he can improve his world. That is, perfect knowledge, in the scientific sense, would bring perfect control of nature, including human nature. And associated with this purely natural or secular view of the world we find the belief in humanitarianism. Pain is the great evil, according to such a belief, and the conquest of pain becomes the greatest good. Furthermore, the idea of natural law as applied in human affairs leads to an emphasis on the idea of determinism—people are good or bad as a result of heredity and environment and not as a matter of responsible moral choice. Over against these beliefs which are characteristic of modernism as it is popularly understood are the traditional religious beliefs: that there is a supernatural realm, that God's will is finally inscrutable and that man must have faith, that the salvation of the soul is the greatest good, and that men are free moral agents. According to Austin Warren's interpretation, "In the Penal Colony" is an allegory of the conflict between these two sets of beliefs:

"The earth is a penal colony, and we are all under sentence of judgment for sin. There was once a very elaborate machine, of scholastic theology, for the pronouncement of sentence, and an elaborate ecclesiastic system for its administration. Now it is in the process of disappearance: the Old Commander (God) has died, though there is a legend, which you can believe or not, that He will come again. Meanwhile the 'machine' seems antiquated and inhuman to ladies, who are sentimental about criminals, and to the new governor, who is a humanitarian.

"The two interlocutors are an old official, still faithful to the inventor of the machine, and an explorer: the former a survivor from the old theology, a member of the saving remnant of believers in God and sin;

the latter is a naturalist, a scientist who shares the humanitarian views of his secularist generation but who, as a social scientist, is capable of intellectual curiosity and a suspension of judgment. When he sees that the old officer is willing to testify to his faith by martyrdom, by taking his own place in the machine (which only a moral-professional law requires), he respects him for his loyalty to his code, and 'would not have acted differently in his place': Scientist and theologian have in common a respect for law, an adherence to professional duty over personal comfort, and a willingness to see life as it painfully is.

"Important is the setting of the machine's draughtsman. The first victim suffers under 'Honor your Superior,' the moral law which he has broken: this is a law appropriate to his caste of servant. For his own use, the old officer adjusts the legend to 'Be just.' Has he violated this injunction? Not consciously; but a judge of his fellowmen should be 'just' and no mortal man can be: 'none is Good save God': the old officer can be sure that, whatever his intentions, he has been unjust in the sight of Justice.

"At the end of the story, the explorer has become converted to the doctrine of the machine: he excludes from his boat those who wish to escape from the penal island. 'Converted' is too strong: if really converted, he would stay on the island—at least if the machine still operated. But at least he makes no report to the new commander; and he takes the Prophecy of Return seriously: when the men about him ridicule the inscription, he does not join in their laughter: the Prophecy may be true. Like Pilate, he refuses to judge; he finds no fault in the just manipulators of the machine.

"In its tone, the story is a matter-of-fact description of an elaborate method of punishment, no longer believed in by the 'enlightened,' kept going a little longer by the devotion of an old man who doesn't understand it very well and can't repair it. Narration is from the point of view of, through the eyes of, the explorer, who is shocked by what he sees and yet who, unlike the present management of the penal colony, can understand the possible use of the machine in what is, after all, a penal colony; and who becomes increasingly sympathetic as he sees that the operator of the machine believes in it for himself as well as for others. But it is essential to Kafka's purpose that there shall be no suppression of the difficulties in accepting the gospel of the machine: it is cruel; it makes errors; it is costly to keep up; people have ceased to believe in it; its inventor has died, and it is generally thought ridiculous to credit the pious legend that he will come again. 'My ways are not your ways, neither my thoughts as your thoughts,' saith the Lord. . . . Kafka, fearful of softening religion, wants to present it in all its rigor, its repellence to the flesh—in its irrationality and inscrutability and uncertainty, too. We must put up with the professional pride and the pedantry of the old officer: religionists are always forgetting ends in absorption with means, taking human (and impious) pride in the details of their theological and ecclesiastical systems. Nothing is simple, nothing unmixed. We never get reality straight, but always . . . through a veil of illusion. If we are determined to be scrupulously positivistic and 'accept no illusion,' then we shall have to content ourselves with no more than statistics: we shan't find reality."

If Mr. Warren's interpretation of "In the Penal Colony" is acceptable, then one sees that the allegory of the story is strict rather than loose— that most of the details of the surface narrative have specific parallels at the level of ideas. One sees also that here we have a contrast between the fantastic surface—which cannot be judged in terms of the logic of actual experience—and the represented argument—which can be judged in terms of actual experience. That is, the argument in the background is a possible view of the subject under discussion, and is held by many intelligent people. There is an ironical contrast between the fantastic way of representing the ideas and the ideas themselves which are not fantastic, which are one way of interpreting an actual situation; in other words, the fantasy may, ironically, be logical after all.

A similar irony is indicated in the contrast between the fantastic events and the style in which they are narrated. The style is a rather bare, factual style—the style of a person who is trying to be scrupulously accurate and does not wish to color the truth by indulging in any literary and rhetorical devices. It implies that the narrator is willing to let the case rest on the facts alone. It does not try, we might say, to provoke the reader to horror or sympathy, as does the style of, for example, "The Fall of the House of Usher." This contrast between the fantastic events and setting and the particular style * is commented on by Mr. Warren: "Its [the story's] powerful effect is indeed produced by its complete absence of fantasy in detail: The story offers, by its method, the sense of a fact which you can interpret as you like, of which you can make what you will: I'm telling you, as a sober scientist, what I

---

* A similar contrast between the fantasy of the surface narrative and the style in which it is rendered may be observed in Jonathan Swift's *Gulliver's Travels* and John Bunyan's *Pilgrim's Progress*.

saw." The style, then, has a dramatic function, in connection with the total story, just as it does in "The Killers" or "I Want to Know Why" or any other successful piece of fiction. It here indicates a fusion, an interpenetration, of the fantastic and realistic elements of experience, an idea which is to be associated with the basic meaning of the story.

1. In the light of Mr. Austin Warren's interpretation, what is one to make of such a passage as the following: " 'These uniforms are much too heavy for the tropics,' commented the explorer. . . . 'Certainly,' said the officer, washing his hands, stained with oil and grease, in a pail of water that stood near-by, 'but they are the symbols of home, and we don't want to lose our homeland.' " One might approach the problem in this way: If the penal colony is the world, then what is the "home-land"? Is this a contrast between time and eternity, the natural and the supernatural realms, with the implication that man's true "home" is not in the natural world of time? In that case, what about the "uni-forms" which are not comfortable by the standards of the penal colony? Is there any significance in the pail of water?

2. What is represented by the original drawings of the machine made by the Old Commander?

3. What interpretation could you make of the strange expression which, according to the old officer, always comes over the victim's face toward the end? Why does it not appear on the face of the officer him-self when he is in the machine?

4. What distinction is made between the attitude of the explorer, whom we may take to be a figure representing the "true" scientist, and the attitude of the new commander and the ordinary inhabitants of the penal colony? Develop the hints on this point which are given in Mr. Warren's analysis.

Old Mr. Marblehall

EUDORA WELTY

OLD MR. MARBLEHALL never did anything, never got married until he was sixty. You can see him out taking a walk. Watch and you'll see how preciously old people come to think they are made— the way they walk, like conspirators, bent over a little, filled with pro-tection. They stand long on the corners but more impatiently than any-one, as if they expected traffic to take notice of them, rear up the horses and throw on the brakes, so they can go where they want to go. That's

Mr. Marblehall. He has short white bangs, and a bit of snapdragon in his lapel. He walks with a big polished stick, a present. That's what people think of him. Everybody says to his face, "So well preserved!" Behind his back they say cheerfully, "One foot in the grave." He has on his thick, beautiful, glowing coat—tweed, but he looks as gratified as an animal in its own tingling fur. You see, even in summer he wears it, because he is cold all the time. He looks quaintly secretive and prepared for anything, out walking very luxuriously on Catherine Street.

His wife, back at home in the parlor standing up to think, is a large, elongated old woman with electric-looking hair and curly lips. She has spent her life trying to escape from the parlorlike jaws of self-consciousness. Her late marriage has set in upon her nerves like a retriever nosing and puffing through old dead leaves out in the woods. When she walks around the room she looks remote and nebulous, out on the fringe of habitation, and rather as if she must have been cruelly trained—otherwise she couldn't do actual, immediate things, like answering the telephone or putting on a hat. But she has gone further than you'd think: into club work. Surrounded by other more suitably exclaiming women, she belongs to the Daughters of the American Revolution and the United Daughters of the Confederacy, attending teas. Her long, disquieted figure towering in the candlelight of other women's houses looks like something accidental. Any occasion, and she dresses her hair like a unicorn horn. She even sings, and is requested to sing. She even writes some of the songs she sings ("O Trees in the Evening"). She has a voice that dizzies other ladies like an organ note, and amuses men like a halloo down the well. It's full of a hollow wind and echo, winding out through the wavery hope of her mouth. Do people know of her perpetual amazement? Back in safety she wonders, her untidy head trembles in the domestic dark. She remembers how everyone in Natchez will suddenly grow quiet around her. Old Mrs. Marblehall, Mr. Marblehall's wife: she even goes out in the rain, which Southern women despise above everything, in big neat biscuit-colored galoshes, for which she "ordered off." She is only looking around—servile, undelighted, sleepy, expensive, tortured Mrs. Marblehall, pinning her mind with a pin to her husband's diet. She wants to tempt him, she tells him. What would he like best, that he can have?

There is Mr. Marblehall's ancestral home. It's not so wonderfully large—it has only four columns—but you always look toward it, the way you always glance into tunnels and see nothing. The river is after it now, and the little back garden has assuredly crumbled away, but the box maze is there on the edge like a trap, to confound the Mississippi River. Deep in the red wall waits the front door—it weighs such a lot, it is perfectly solid, all one piece, black mahogany. . . . And you see—one of *them* is always going in it. There is a knocker shaped like a gasping fish on the door. You have every reason in the world to imagine the inside is dark, with old things about. There's many a big, deathly looking tapestry, wrinkling and thin, many a sofa shaped like an S. Brocades as tall as the wicked queens in Italian tales stand gathered before the windows. Everything is draped and hooded and shaded, of course, unaffectionate but close. Such rosy lamps! The only sound would be a breath against the prisms, a stirring of the chandelier. It's like old eyelids, the house with one of its shutters, in careful working order, slowly opening outward. Then the little son softly comes and stares out like a kitten, with button nose and pointed ears and little fuzz of silky hair running along the top of his head.

The son is the worst of all. Mr. and Mrs. Marblehall had a child! When both of them were terribly old, they had this little, amazing, fascinating son. You can see how people are taken aback, how they jerk and throw up their hands every time they so much as think about it. At least, Mr. Marblehall sees them. He thinks Natchez people do nothing themselves, and really, most of them have done or could do the same thing. This son is six years old now. Close up, he has a monkey look, a very penetrating look. He has very sparse Japanese hair, tiny little pearly teeth, long little wilted fingers. Every day he is slowly and expensively dressed and taken to the Catholic school. He looks quietly and maliciously absurd, out walking with old Mr. Marblehall or old Mrs. Marblehall, placing his small booted foot on a little green worm, while they stop and wait on him. Everybody passing by thinks that he looks quite as if he thinks his parents had him just to show they could. You see, it becomes complicated, full of vindictiveness.

But now, as Mr. Marblehall walks as briskly as possible toward the river where there is sun, you have to merge him back into his proper blur, into the little party-giving town he lives in. Why look twice at him? There has been an old Mr. Marblehall in Natchez ever since the first one arrived back in 1818—with a theatrical presentation of Otway's *Venice,* ending with *A Laughable Combat between Two Blind Fiddlers*—an actor! Mr. Marblehall isn't so important. His name is on the list, he is forgiven, but nobody gives a hoot about any old Mr. Marblehall. He could die, for all they care; some people even say, "Oh, is he still alive?" Mr. Marblehall walks and walks, and now and then he is driven in his ancient fringed carriage with the candle burners like empty eyes in front. And yes, he is supposed to travel for his health. But why consider his absence? There isn't any other place besides Natchez, and even if there were, it would hardly be likely to change Mr. Marblehall if it were brought up against him. Big fingers could pick him up off the Esplanade and take him through the air, his old legs still measuredly walking in a dangle, and set him down where he could continue that same old Natchez stroll of his in the East or the West or Kingdom Come. What difference could anything make now about old Mr. Marblehall—so late? A week or two would go by in Natchez and then there would be Mr. Marblehall, walking down Catherine Street again, still exactly in the same degree alive and old.

People naturally get bored. They say, "Well, he waited till he was sixty years old to marry, and what did he want to marry for?" as though what he did were the excuse for their boredom and their lack of concern. Even the thought of his having a stroke right in front of one of the Pilgrimage houses during Pilgrimage Week makes them only sigh, as if to say it's nobody's fault but his own if he wants to be so insultingly and precariously well-preserved. He ought to have a little black boy to follow around after him. Oh, his precious old health, which never had reason to be so inspiring! Mr. Marblehall has a formal, reproachful look as he stands on the corners arranging himself to go out into the traffic to cross the streets. It's as if he's thinking of shaking his stick and saying, "Well, look! I've done it, don't you see?" But really, nobody pays much attention to his look. He is just like other people to them. He could have easily danced with a troupe of angels in Paradise every night, and they wouldn't have guessed. Nobody is likely to find out that he is leading a double life.

The funny thing is he just recently began to lead this double life. He waited until he was sixty years old. Isn't he crazy? Before that, he'd never done anything. He didn't know what to do. Everything was for all the world like his first party. He stood about, and looked in his father's books, and long ago he went to France, but he didn't like it.

Drive out any of these streets in and under the hills and you find yourself lost. You see those scores of little galleried houses nearly alike. See the yellowing China trees at the eaves, the round flower beds in the front yards, like bites in the grass, listen to the screen doors whining, the ice wagons dragging by, the twittering noises of children. Nobody ever looks to see who is living in a house like that. These people come out themselves and sprinkle the hose over the street at this time of day to settle the dust, and after they sit on the porch, they go back into the house, and you hear the radio for the next two hours. It seems to mourn and cry for them. They go to bed early.

Well, old Mr. Marblehall can easily be seen standing beside a row of zinnias growing down the walk in front of that little house, bending over, easy, easy, so as not to strain anything, to stare at the flowers. Of course he planted them! They are covered with brown—each petal is a little heart-shaped pocket of dust. They don't have any smell, you know. It's twilight, all amplified with locusts screaming; nobody could see anything. Just what Mr. Marblehall is bending over the zinnias for is a mystery, any way you look at it. But there he is, quite visible, alive and old, leading his double life.

There's his other wife, standing on the night-stained porch by a potted fern, screaming things to a neighbor. This wife is really worse than the other one. She is more solid, fatter, shorter, and while not so ugly, funnier looking. She looks like funny furniture—an unornamented stairpost in one of these little houses, with her small monotonous round stupid head—or sometimes like a woodcut of a Bavarian witch, forefinger pointing, with scratches in the air all around her. But she's so static she scarcely moves, from her thick shoulders down past her cylindered brown dress to her short, stubby house slippers. She stands still and screams to the neighbors.

This wife thinks Mr. Marblehall's name is Mr. Bird. She says, "I declare I told Mr. Bird to go to bed, and look at him! I don't understand him!" All her devotion is combustible and goes up in despair. This wife tells everything she knows. Later, after she tells the neighbors, she will tell Mr. Marblehall. Cymbal-breasted, she fills the house with wifely complaints. She calls, "After I get Mr. Bird to bed, what does he do then? He lies there stretched out with his clothes on and don't have one word to say. Know what he does?"

And she goes on, while her husband bends over the zinnias, to tell what Mr. Marblehall (or Mr. Bird) does in bed. She does tell the truth. He reads *Terror Tales* and *Astonishing Stories*. She can't see anything to them: they scare her to death. These stories are about horrible and fantastic things happening to nude women and scientists. In one of them, when the characters open bureau drawers, they find a woman's leg with a stocking and garter on. Mrs. Bird had to shut the magazine. "The glutinous shadows," these stories say, "the red-eyed, muttering old crone," "the moonlight on her thigh," "an ancient cult of sun worshipers," "an altar suspiciously stained. . . ." Mr. Marblehall doesn't feel as terrified as all that, but he reads on and on. He is killing time. It is richness without taste, like some holiday food. The clock gets a fruity bursting tick, to get through midnight—then leisurely, leisurely on. When time is passing it's like a bug in his ear. And then Mr. Bird—he doesn't even want a shade on the light, this wife moans respectably. He reads under a bulb. She can tell you how he goes straight through a stack of magazines. "He might just as well not have a family," she always ends, unjustly, and rolls back into the house as if she had been on a little wheel all this time.

But the worst of them all is the other little boy. Another little boy just like the first one. He wanders around the bungalow full of tiny little schemes and jokes. He has lost his front tooth, and in this way he looks slightly different from Mr. Marblehall's other little boy—more shocking. Otherwise, you couldn't tell them apart if you wanted to. They both have that look of cunning little jugglers, violently small under some spotlight beam, preoccupied and silent, amusing themselves. Both of the children will go into sudden fits and tantrums that frighten their mothers and Mr. Marblehall to death. Then they can get anything they want. But this little boy, the one who's lost the tooth, is the smarter. For a long time he supposed that his mother was totally solid, down to her thick separated ankles. But when she stands there on the porch screaming to the neighbors, she reminds him of those flares that charm him so, that they leave burning in the street at night—the dark solid ball, then, tonguelike, the wicked, yellow, continuous, enslaving blaze on the stem. He knows what his father thinks.

Perhaps one day, while Mr. Marblehall is standing there gently bent over the zinnias, this little boy is going to write on a fence, "Papa leads a double life." He finds out things you wouldn't find out. He is a monkey.

You see, one night he is going to follow Mr. Marblehall (or Mr. Bird) out of the house. Mr. Marblehall has said as usual that he is leaving for one of his health trips. He is one of those correct old gentlemen who are still going to the wells and drinking the waters—exactly like his father, the late old Mr. Marblehall. But why does he leave on foot? This will occur to the little boy.

So he will follow his father. He will follow him all the way across town. He will see the shining river come winding around. He will see the house where Mr. Marblehall turns in at the wrought-iron gate. He will see a big speechless woman come out and lead him in by the heavy door. He will not miss those rosy lamps beyond the many-folded draperies at the windows. He will run around the fountains and around the japonica trees, past the stone figure of the pigtailed courtier mounted on the goat, down to the back of the house. From there he can look far up at the strange upstairs rooms. In one window the other wife will be standing like a giant, in a long-sleeved gathered nightgown, combing her electric hair and breaking it off each time in the comb. From the next window the other little boy will look out secretly into the night, and see him—or not see him. That would be an interesting thing, a moment of strange telepathies. (Mr. Marblehall can imagine it.) Then in the corner room there will suddenly be turned on the bright, naked light. Aha! Father!

Mr. Marblehall's little boy will easily climb a tree there and peep through the window. There, under a stark shadeless bulb, on a great four-poster with carved griffins, will be Mr. Marblehall, reading *Terror Tales,* stretched out and motionless.

Then everything will come out.

At first, nobody will believe it.

Or maybe the policeman will say, "Stop! How dare you!"

Maybe, better than that, Mr. Marblehall himself will confess his duplicity—how he has led two totally different lives, with completely different families, two sons instead of one. What an astonishing, unbelievable, electrifying confession that would be, and how his two wives would topple over, how his sons would cringe! To say nothing of most men aged sixty-six. So thinks self-consoling Mr. Marblehall.

You will think, what if nothing ever happens? What if there is no climax, even to this amazing life? Suppose old Mr. Marblehall simply remains alive, getting older by the minute, shuttling, still secretly, back and forth?

Nobody cares. Not an inhabitant of Natchez, Mississippi, cares if he is deceived by old Mr. Marblehall. Neither does anyone care that Mr. Marblehall has finally caught on, he thinks, to what people are supposed to do. This is it: they endure something inwardly—for a time secretly; they establish a past, a memory; thus they store up life. He has done this; most remarkably, he has even multiplied his life by deception; and plunging deeper and deeper he speculates upon some glorious finish, a great explosion of revelations . . . the future.

But he still has to kill time, and get through the clocking nights. Otherwise he dreams that he is a great blazing butterfly stitching up a net; which doesn't make sense.

Old Mr. Marblehall! He may have years ahead yet in which to wake up bolt upright in the bed under the naked bulb, his heart thumping, his old eyes watering and wild, imagining that if people knew about his double life, they'd die.*

INTERPRETATION

This story, like "In the Penal Colony," is not strictly realistic, but here the element of fantasy is constantly interwoven with elements of realism. In the early stages of the story, in fact, the element of fantasy does not emerge at all—we simply have the portrait of old Mr. Marblehall given in terms which would be acceptable in an ordinary story. But the fantastic element in this story is not employed for purposes of allegory. Rather, this is a kind of fable, in which, though the fantasy has a meaning, the meaning is not conveyed by any system of point-to-point equating of items of the surface narrative with ideas, as in strict allegory.

One may get at the meaning of "Old Mr. Marblehall" by comparing it with "The Poor Relation's Story." Both stories deal with a character who in the world's eyes is one thing but in his own is quite another. Mr. Marblehall's appearance to society is unprepossessing and unimportant; and Mr. Marblehall is acutely aware that this is so. But his secret, inner life is something else again, and how people will be shocked when they discover what it is! (Mr. Marblehall evidently lives this over in anticipation: "From the next window the other little boy will look out secretly into the night, and see him—or not see him. . . . Then in the corner room there will suddenly be turned on the bright, naked light. Aha! Father!" Or he imagines that a policeman will say: "Stop! How dare you!" Or better than that, "Mr. Marblehall himself will confess his duplicity. . . . What an astonishing, unbelievable, electrifying confession that would be. . . . So thinks self-consoling Mr. Marblehall.")

Write an interpretation of the story which will take account of the following items:

1. What is Mr. Marblehall's character? Why does the author apply the adjective "self-consoling" to him? What is the importance of the reference to *Terror Tales* and *Astonishing Stories?* How does the last sentence of the story sum up his character?

2. What is the significance of the fact that the two wives are in so many ways the antitheses of each other, one silent and the other talkative, one tall and the other short, and so on? In this connection consider the descriptions of the two houses and of the two little boys.

3. Are there any grounds for concluding that the second wife and second son are merely figments of Mr. Marblehall's imagination—Mr. Marblehall's "castle in the air" as it were?

4. Is there any resemblance between Mr. Marblehall and Roderick Usher of Poe's story?

5. Obviously in this story the tone is extremely important. Try to define it. In other words, what is the author's attitude toward Mr. Marblehall—one of pity, of amusement, of patronizing banter, of good-natured but ironical indulgence, or what? How is this attitude conveyed by the way in which the story is told?

6. Discuss, in connection with the author's total intention, the significance of the third paragraph from the end of the story, the paragraph beginning, "Nobody cares. Not an inhabitant of Natchez . . ."

7. Read Hawthorne's story, "The Minister's Black Veil," which is readily accessible, and compare the theme and method found there with the theme and method of this story.

Old Mortality

KATHERINE ANNE PORTER

PART ONE: 1885–1902

SHE WAS a spirited-looking young woman, with dark curly hair cropped and parted on the side, a short oval face with straight eyebrows, and a large curved mouth. A round white collar rose from the neck of her tightly buttoned black basque, and round white cuffs set off lazy hands with dimples in them, lying at ease in the folds of her flounced skirt which gathered around to a bustle. She sat thus, forever in the pose of being photographed, a motionless image in her dark walnut frame with silver oak leaves in the corners, her smiling gray eyes following one about the room. It was a reckless indifferent smile, rather disturbing to her nieces Maria and Miranda. Quite often they wondered why every older person who looked at the picture said, "How lovely"; and why everyone who had known her thought her so beautiful and charming.

There was a kind of faded merriment in the background, with its vase of flowers and draped velvet curtains, the kind of vase and the kind of curtains no one would have any more. The clothes were not even romantic looking, but merely most terribly out of fashion, and the whole affair was associated, in the minds of the little girls, with dead things: the smell of Grandmother's medicated cigarettes and her furniture that smelled of beeswax, and her old-fashioned perfume, Orange Flower. The woman in the picture had been Aunt Amy, but she was only a ghost in a frame, a sad, pretty story from old times. She had been beautiful, much loved, unhappy, and she had died young.

Maria and Miranda, aged twelve and eight years, knew they were young, though they felt they had lived a long time. They had lived not only their own years; but their memories, it seemed to them, began years before they were born, in the lives of grown-ups around them, old people above forty, most of them, who had a way of insisting that they too had been young once. It was hard to believe.

Their father was Aunt Amy's brother Harry. She had been his favorite sister. He sometimes glanced at the photograph and said, "It's not very good. Her hair and her smile were her chief beauties, and they aren't shown at all. She was much slimmer than that, too. There were never any fat women in the family, thank God."

When they heard their father say things like that, Maria and Miranda simply wondered, without criticism, what he meant. Their grandmother was thin as a match; the pictures of their mother, long since dead, proved her to have been a candlewick, almost. Dashing young ladies, who turned out to be, to Miranda's astonishment, merely more of Grandmother's grandchildren, like herself, came visiting from school for the holidays, boasting of their eighteen-inch waists. But how did their father account for great-aunt Eliza, who quite squeezed herself through doors, and who, when seated, was one solid pyramidal monument from floor to neck? What about great-aunt Keziah, in Kentucky? Her husband, great-uncle John Jacob, had refused to allow her to ride his good horses after she had achieved two hundred and twenty pounds. "No," said great-uncle John Jacob, "my sentiments of chivalry are not dead in my bosom; but neither is my common sense, to say nothing of charity to our faithful dumb friends. And the greatest of these is charity." It was suggested to great-uncle John Jacob that charity should forbid him to wound great-aunt Keziah's female vanity by such a comment on her figure. "Female vanity will recover," said great-uncle John Jacob, callously, "but what about my horses' backs? And if she had the proper female vanity in the first place, she would never have got into such shape." Well, great-aunt Keziah was famous for her heft, and wasn't she in the family? But something seemed to happen to their father's memory when he thought of the girls he had known in the family of his youth, and he declared steadfastly they had all been, in every generation without exception, as slim as reeds and graceful as sylphs.

This loyalty of their father's in the face of evidence contrary to his ideal had its springs in family feeling, and a love of legend that he shared with the others. They loved to tell stories, romantic and poetic, or comic with a romantic humor; they did not gild the outward circumstance, it was the feeling that mattered. Their hearts and imaginations were captivated by their past, a past in which worldly considerations had played a very minor role. Their stories were almost always love stories against a bright blank heavenly blue sky.

Photographs, portraits by inept painters who meant earnestly to flatter, and the festival garments folded away in dried herbs and camphor were disappointing when the little girls tried to fit them to the living beings created in their minds by the breathing words of their elders. Grandmother, twice a year compelled in her blood by the change of seasons, would sit nearly all of one day beside old trunks and boxes in the lumber room, unfolding layers of garments and small keepsakes; she spread them out on sheets on the floor around her, crying over certain things, nearly always the same things, looking again at pictures in velvet cases, unwrapping locks of hair and dried flowers, crying gently and easily as if tears were the only pleasure she had left.

If Maria and Miranda were very quiet, and touched nothing until it was offered, they might sit by her at these times, or come and go. There was a tacit understanding that her grief was strictly her own, and must not be noticed or mentioned. The little girls examined the objects, one by one, and did not find them, in themselves, impressive. Such dowdy little wreaths and necklaces, some of them made of pearly shells; such moth-eaten bunches of pink ostrich feathers for the hair; such clumsy big breast pins and bracelets of gold and colored enamel; such silly-looking combs, standing up on tall teeth capped with seed pearls and French paste. Miranda, without knowing why, felt melancholy. It seemed such a pity that these faded things, these yellowed long gloves and misshapen satin slippers, these broad ribbons cracking where they were folded, should have been all those vanished girls had to decorate themselves with. And where were they now, those girls, and the boys in the odd-looking collars? The young men seemed even more unreal than the girls, with their high-buttoned coats, their puffy neckties, their waxed mustaches, their waving thick hair combed carefully over their foreheads. Who could have taken them seriously, looking like that?

No, Maria and Miranda found it impossible to sympathize with those young persons, sitting rather stiffly before the camera, hopelessly out of fashion; but they were drawn and held by the mysterious love of the living, who remembered and cherished these dead. The visible remains were nothing; they were dust, perishable as the flesh; the features stamped on paper and metal were nothing, but their living memory enchanted the little girls. They listened, all ears and eager minds, picking here and there among the floating ends of narrative, patching together as well as they could fragments of tales that were like bits of poetry or music, indeed were associated with the poetry they had heard or read, with music, with the theater.

"Tell me again how Aunt Amy went away when she was married." "She ran into the gray cold and stepped into the carriage and turned and smiled with her face as pale as death, and called out 'Good-by, good-by,' and refused her cloak, and said, 'Give me a glass of wine.' And none of us saw her alive again." "Why wouldn't she wear her cloak, Cousin Cora?" "Because she was not in love, my dear." Ruin hath taught me thus to ruminate, that time will come and take my love away. "Was she really beautiful, Uncle Bill?" "As an angel, my child." There were golden-haired angels with long blue pleated skirts dancing around the throne of the Blessed Virgin. None of them resembled Aunt Amy in the least, nor the type of beauty they had been brought up to admire. There were points of beauty by which one was judged severely. First, a beauty must be tall; whatever color the eyes, the hair must be dark, the darker the better; the skin must be pale and smooth. Lightness and swiftness of movement were important points. A beauty must be a good dancer, superb on horseback, with a serene manner, an amiable gaiety tempered with dignity at all hours. Beautiful teeth and hands, of course, and over and above all this, some mysterious crown of enchantment that attracted and held the heart. It was all very exciting and discouraging.

Miranda persisted through her childhood in believing, in spite of her smallness, thinness, her little snubby nose saddled with freckles, her speckled gray eyes and habitual tantrums, that by some miracle she would grow into a tall, cream-colored brunette, like Cousin Isabel; she decided always to wear a trailing white satin gown. Maria, born sensible, had no such illusions. "We are going to take after our Mamma's family," she said. "It's no use, we are. We'll never be beautiful, we'll always have freckles. And *you*," she told Miranda, "haven't even a good disposition."

Miranda admitted both truth and justice in this unkindness, but still secretly believed that she would one day suddenly receive beauty, as by inheritance, riches laid suddenly in her hands through no deserts of her own. She believed for quite a while that she would one day be like Aunt Amy, not as she appeared in the photograph, but as she was remembered by those who had seen her.

When Cousin Isabel came out in her tight black riding habit, sursounded by young men, and mounted gracefully, drawing her horse up and around so that he pranced learnedly on one spot while the other riders sprang to their saddles in the same sedate flurry, Miranda's heart would close with such a keen dart of admiration, envy, vicarious pride it was almost painful, but there would always be an elder present to lay a cooling hand upon her emotions. "She rides almost as well as Amy, doesn't she? But Amy had the pure Spanish style, she could bring out paces in a horse no one else knew he had."

Young namesake Amy, on her way to a dance, would swish through the hall in ruffled white taffeta, glimmering like a moth in the lamplight, carrying her elbows pointed backward stiffly as wings, sliding along as if she were on rollers, in the fashionable walk of her day. She was considered the best dancer at any party, and Maria, sniffing the wave of perfume that followed Amy, would clasp her hands and say, "Oh, I can't *wait* to be grown up." But the elders would agree that the first Amy had been lighter, more smooth and delicate in her waltzing; young Amy would never equal her.

Cousin Molly Parrington, far past her youth—indeed she belonged to the generation before Aunt Amy—was a noted charmer. Men who had known her all her life still gathered about her; now that she was happily widowed for the second time there was no doubt that she would yet marry again. But Amy, said the elders, had the same high spirits and wit without boldness, and you really could not say that Molly had ever been discreet. She dyed her hair, and made jokes about it. She had a way of collecting the men around her in a corner, where she told them stories. She was an unnatural mother to her ugly daughter Eva, an old maid past forty while her mother was still the belle of the ball. "Born when I was fifteen, you remember," Molly would say shamelessly, looking an old beau straight in the eye, both of them remembering that he had been best man at her first wedding when she was past twenty-one. "Everyone said I was like a little girl with her doll."

Eva, shy and chinless, straining her upper lip over two enormous teeth, would sit in corners watching her mother. She looked hungry, her eyes were strained and tired. She wore her mother's old clothes, made over, and taught Latin in a Female Seminary. She believed in votes for women, and had traveled about, making speeches. When her mother was not present, Eva bloomed out a little, danced prettily, smiled, showing all her teeth, and was like a dry little plant set out in a gentle rain. Molly was merry about her ugly duckling. "It's lucky for me my daughter is an old maid. She's not so apt," said Molly naughtily, "to make a grandmother of me." Eva would blush as if she had been slapped.

Eva was a blot, no doubt about it, but the little girls felt she belonged to their everyday world of dull lessons to be learned, stiff shoes to be limbered up, scratchy flannels to be endured in cold weather, measles and disappointed expectations. Their Aunt Amy belonged to the world of poetry. The romance of Uncle Gabriel's long, unrewarded love for her, her early death, was such a story as one found in old books: unworldly books, but true, such as the *Vita Nuova,* the Sonnets of Shakespeare and the Wedding Song of Spenser; and poems by Edgar Allan Poe. "Her tantalized spirit now blandly reposes, Forgetting or never regretting its roses. . . ." Their father read that to them, and said, "He was our greatest poet," and they knew that "our" meant he was Southern. Aunt Amy was real as the pictures in the old Holbein and Dürer books were real. The little girls lay flat on their stomachs and peered into a world of wonder, turning the shabby leaves that fell apart easily, not surprised at the sight of the Mother of God sitting on a hollow log nursing her Child; not doubting either Death or the Devil riding at the stirrups of the grim knight; not questioning the propriety of the stiffly dressed ladies of Sir Thomas More's household, seated in dignity on the floor, or seeming to be. They missed all the dog and pony shows, and lantern-slide entertainments, but their father took them to see *Hamlet,* and *The Taming of the Shrew,* and *Richard the Third,* and a long sad play with Mary, Queen of Scots, in it. Miranda thought the magnificent lady in black velvet was truly the Queen of Scots, and was pained to learn that the real Queen had died long ago, and not at all on the night she, Miranda, had been present.

The little girls loved the theater, that world of personages taller than human beings, who swept upon the scene and invested it with their presences, their more than human voices, their gestures of gods and goddesses ruling a universe. But there was always a voice recalling other and greater occasions. Grandmother in her youth had heard Jenny Lind, and thought that Nellie Melba was much overrated. Father had seen Bernhardt, and Madame Modjeska was no sort of rival. When Paderewski played for the first time in their city, cousins came from all over the state and went from the grandmother's house to hear him. The little girls were left out of this great occasion. They shared the excitement of the going away, and shared the beautiful moment of return, when cousins stood about in groups, with coffee cups and glasses in their hands, talking in low voices, awed and happy. The little girls, struck with the sense of a great event, hung about in their nightgowns and listened, until someone noticed and hustled them away from the sweet nimbus of all that glory. One old gentleman, however, had heard Rubinstein frequently. He could not but feel that Rubinstein had reached the final height of musical interpretation, and, for him, Paderewski had been something of an anticlimax. The little girls heard him muttering on, holding up one hand, patting the air as if he were calling for silence. The others looked at him, and listened, without any disturbance of their grave tender mood. They had never heard Rubinstein; they had, one hour since, heard Paderewski, and why should anyone need to recall the past? Miranda, dragged away, half understanding the old gentleman, hated him. She felt that she too had heard Paderewski.

There was then a life beyond a life in this world, as well as in the next; such episodes confirmed for the little girls the nobility of human feeling, the divinity of man's vision of the unseen, the importance of life and death, the depths of the human heart, the romantic value of tragedy. Cousin Eva, on a certain visit, trying to interest them in the study of Latin, told them the story of John Wilkes Booth, who, handsomely garbed in a long black cloak, had leaped to the stage after assassinating President Lincoln. *"Sic semper tyrannis,"* he had shouted superbly, in spite of his broken leg. The little girls never doubted that it had happened in just that way, and the moral seemed to be that one should always have Latin, or at least a good classical poetry quotation, to depend upon in great or desperate moments. Cousin Eva reminded them that no one, not even a good Southerner, could possibly approve of John Wilkes Booth's deed. It was murder, after all. They were to remember that. But Miranda, used to tragedy in books and in family legends—two great-uncles had committed suicide and a remote ancestress had gone mad for love—decided that, without the murder, there would have been no point to dressing up and leaping to the stage shouting in Latin. So how could she disapprove of the deed? It was a fine story. She knew a distantly related old gentleman who had been devoted to the art of Booth, had seen him in a great many plays, but not, alas, at his greatest moment. Miranda regretted this; it would have been so pleasant to have the assassination of Lincoln in the family.

Uncle Gabriel, who had loved Aunt Amy so desperately, still lived somewhere, though Miranda and Maria had never seen him. He had gone away, far away, after her death. He still owned racehorses, and ran them at famous tracks all over the country, and Miranda believed there could not possibly be a more brilliant career. He had married again, quite soon, and had written to Grandmother, asking her to accept his new wife as a daughter in place of Amy. Grandmother had written coldly, accepting, inviting them for a visit, but Uncle Gabriel had somehow never brought his bride home. Harry had visited them in New Orleans, and reported that the second wife was a very good-looking well-bred blonde girl who would undoubtedly be a good wife for Gabriel. Still, Uncle Gabriel's heart was broken. Faithfully once a year he wrote a letter to someone of the family, sending money for a wreath for Amy's grave. He had written a poem for her gravestone, and had come home, leaving his second wife in Atlanta, to see that it was carved properly. He could never account for having written this poem; he had certainly never tried to write a single rhyme since leaving school. Yet one day when he had been thinking about Amy, the verse occurred to him, out of the air. Maria and Miranda had seen it, printed in gold on a mourning card. Uncle Gabriel had sent a great number of them to be handed around among the family.

> *She lives again who suffered life,*
> *Then suffered death, and now set free*
> *A singing angel, she forgets*
> *The griefs of old mortality.*

"Did she really sing?" Maria asked her father.

"Now what has that to do with it?" he asked. "It's a poem."

"I think it's very pretty," said Miranda, impressed. Uncle Gabriel was second cousin to her father and Aunt Amy. It brought poetry very near.

"Not so bad for tombstone poetry," said their father, "but it should be better."

Uncle Gabriel had waited five years to marry Aunt Amy. She had been ill, her chest was weak; she was engaged twice to other young men and broke her engagements for no reason; and she laughed at the advice of older and kinder-hearted persons who thought it very capricious of her not to return the devotion of such a handsome and romantic young man as Gabriel, her second cousin, too; it was not as if she would be marrying a stranger. Her coldness was said to have driven Gabriel to a wild life and even to drinking. His grandfather was wealthy and Gabriel was his favorite; they had quarreled over the racehorses, and Gabriel had shouted, "By God, I must have *something*." As if he had not everything already: youth, health, good looks, the prospect of riches, and a devoted family circle. His grandfather pointed out to him that he was little better than an ingrate, and showed signs of being a wastrel as well. Gabriel said, "You had racehorses, and made a good thing of them." "I never depended upon them for a livelihood, sir," said his grandfather.

Gabriel wrote letters about this and many other things to Amy from Saratoga and from Kentucky and from New Orleans, sending her presents, and flowers packed in ice, and telegrams. The presents were amusing, such as a huge cage full of small green lovebirds; or, as an ornament for her hair, a full-petaled enameled rose with paste dew-drops, with an enameled butterfly in brilliant colors suspended quivering on a gold wire about it; but the telegrams always frightened her mother, and the flowers, after a journey by train and then by stage into the country, were much the worse for wear. He would send roses when the rose garden at home was in full bloom. Amy could not help smiling over it, though her mother insisted it was touching and sweet of Gabriel. It must prove to Amy that she was always in his thoughts.

"That's no place for me," said Amy, but she had a way of speaking, a tone of voice, which made it impossible to discover what she meant by what she said. It was possible always that she might be serious. And she would not answer questions.

"Amy's wedding dress," said the grandmother, unfurling an immense cloak of dove-colored cut velvet, spreading beside it a silvery-gray water-silk frock, and a small gray velvet toque with a dark red breast of feathers. Cousin Isabel, the beauty, sat with her. They talked to each other, and Miranda could listen if she chose.

"She would not wear white, nor a veil," said Grandmother. "I couldn't oppose her, for I had said my daughters should each have exactly the wedding dress they wanted. But Amy surprised me. 'Now what would I look like in white satin?' she asked. It's true she was pale, but she would have been angelic in it, and all of us told her so. 'I shall wear mourning if I like,' she said, 'it is *my* funeral, you know.' I reminded her that Lou and your mother had worn white with veils and it would please me to have my daughters all alike in that. Amy said, 'Lou and Isabel are not like me,' but I could not persuade her to explain what she meant. One day when she was ill she said, 'Mammy, I'm not long for this world,' but not as if she meant it. I told her, 'You might live as long as anyone, if only you will be sensible.' 'That's the whole trouble,' said Amy. 'I feel sorry for Gabriel,' she told me. 'He doesn't know what he's asking for.'

"I tried to tell her once more," said the grandmother, "that marriage and children would cure her of everything. 'All women of our family are delicate when they are young,' I said. 'Why, when I was your age no one expected me to live a year. It was called greensickness, and everybody knew there was only one cure.' 'If I live for a hundred years and turn green as grass,' said Amy, 'I still shan't want to marry Gabriel.' So I told her very seriously that if she truly felt that way she must never do it, and Gabriel must be told once for all, and sent away. He would get over it. 'I have told him, and I have sent him away,' said Amy. 'He just doesn't listen.' We both laughed at that, and I told her young girls found a hundred ways to deny they wished to be married, and a thousand more to test their power over men, but that she had more than enough of that, and now it was time for her to be entirely sincere and make her decision. As for me," said the grandmother, "I wished with all my heart to marry your grandfather, and if he had not asked me, I should have asked him most certainly. Amy insisted that she could not imagine wanting to marry anybody. She would be, she said, a nice old maid like Eva Parrington. For even then it was pretty plain that Eva was an old maid, born. Harry said, 'Oh, Eva—Eva has no chin, that's her trouble. If you had no chin, Amy, you'd be in the same fix as Eva, no doubt.' Your Uncle Bill would say, 'When women haven't anything else, they'll take a vote for consolation. A pretty thin bedfellow,' said your Uncle Bill. 'What I really need is a good dancing partner to guide me through life,' said Amy, 'that's the match I'm looking for.' It was no good trying to talk to her."

Her brothers remembered her tenderly as a sensible girl. After listening to their comments on her character and ways, Maria decided that they considered her sensible because she asked their advice about her appearance when she was going out to dance. If they found fault in any way, she would change her dress or her hair until they were pleased, and say, "You are an angel not to let your poor sister go out looking like a freak." But she would not listen to her father, nor to Gabriel. If Gabriel praised the frock she was wearing, she was apt to disappear and come back in another. He loved her long black hair, and once, lifting it up from her pillow when she was ill, said, "I love your hair, Amy, the most beautiful hair in the world." When he returned on his next visit, he found her with her hair cropped and curled close to her head. He was horrified, as if she had willfully mutilated herself. She would not let it grow again, not even to please her brothers. The photograph hanging on the wall was one she had made at that time to send to Gabriel, who sent it back without a word. This pleased her, and she framed the photograph. There was a thin inky scrawl low in one corner, "To dear brother Harry, who likes my hair cut."

This was a mischievous reference to a very grave scandal. The little girls used to look at their father, and wonder what would have happened if he had really hit the young man he shot at. The young man was believed to have kissed Aunt Amy, when she was not in the least engaged to him. Uncle Gabriel was supposed to have had a duel with the young man, but Father had got there first.

He was a pleasant, everyday sort of father, who held his daughters on his knee if they were prettily dressed and well behaved, and pushed them away if they had not freshly combed hair and nicely scrubbed finger-nails. "Go away, you're disgusting," he would say, in a matter-of-fact voice. He noticed if their stocking seams were crooked. He caused them to brush their teeth with a revolting mixture of prepared chalk, powdered charcoal and salt. When they behaved stupidly he could not endure the sight of them. They understood dimly that all this was for their own future good; and when they were snively with colds, he prescribed delicious hot toddy for them, and saw that it was given them. He was always hoping they might not grow up to be so silly as they seemed to him at any given moment, and he had a disconcerting way of inquiring, "How do you *know?*" when they forgot and made dogmatic statements in his presence. It always came out embarrassingly that they did not know at all, but were repeating something they had heard. This made conversation with him difficult, for he laid traps and they fell into them, but it became important to them that their father should not believe them to be fools. Well, this very father had gone to Mexico once and stayed there for nearly a year, because he had shot at a man with whom Aunt Amy had flirted at a dance. It had been very wrong of him, because he should have challenged the man to a duel, as Uncle Gabriel had done. Instead, he just took a shot at him, and this was the lowest sort of manners. It had caused great disturbance in the whole community and had almost broken up the affair between Aunt Amy and Uncle Gabriel for good. Uncle Gabriel insisted that the young man had kissed Aunt Amy, and Aunt Amy insisted that the young man had merely paid her a compliment on her hair.

During the Mardi Gras holidays there was to be a big gay fancy-dress ball. Harry was going as a bullfighter because his sweetheart, Mariana, had a new black lace mantilla and high comb from Mexico. Maria and Miranda had seen a photograph of their mother in this dress, her lovely face without a trace of coquetry looking gravely out from under a tremendous fall of lace from the peak of the comb, a rose tucked firmly over her ear. Amy copied her costume from a small Dresden-china shepherdess which stood on the mantelpiece in the parlor; a careful copy with ribboned hat, gilded crook, very low-laced bodice, short basket skirts, green slippers and all. She wore it with a black half-mask, but it was no disguise. "You would have known it was Amy at any distance," said Father. Gabriel, six feet three in height as he was, had got himself up to match, and a spectacle he provided in pale blue satin knee breeches and a blond curled wig with a hair ribbon. "He felt a fool, and he looked like one," said Uncle Bill, "and he behaved like one before the evening was over."

Everything went beautifully until the party gathered downstairs to leave for the ball. Amy's father—he must have been born a grandfather, thought Miranda—gave one glance at his daughter, her white ankles shining, bosom deeply exposed, two round spots of paint on her cheeks, and fell into a frenzy of outraged propriety. "It's disgraceful," he pronounced, loudly. "No daughter of mine is going to show herself in such a rig-out. It's bawdy," he thundered. "Bawdy!"

Amy had taken off her mask to smile at him. "Why, Papa," she said very sweetly, "what's wrong with it? Look on the mantelpiece. She's been there all along, and you were never shocked before."

"There's all the difference in the world," said her father, "all the difference, young lady, and you know it. You go upstairs this minute and pin up that waist in front and let down those skirts to a decent length before you leave this house. *And wash your face!*"

"I see nothing wrong with it," said Amy's mother, firmly, "and you shouldn't use such language before innocent young girls." She and Amy sat down with several females of the household to help, and they made short work of the business. In ten minutes Amy returned, face clean, bodice filled in with lace, shepherdess skirt modestly sweeping the carpet behind her.

When Amy appeared from the dressing room for her first dance with Gabriel, the lace was gone from her bodice, her skirts were tucked up more daringly than before, and the spots on her cheeks were like pomegranates. "Now Gabriel, tell me truly, wouldn't it have been a pity to spoil my costume?" Gabriel, delighted that she had asked his opinion, declared it was perfect. They agreed with kindly tolerance that old people were often tiresome, but one need not upset them by open disobedience: their youth was gone, what had they to live for?

Harry, dancing with Mariana who swung a heavy train around her expertly at every turn of the waltz, began to be uneasy about his sister Amy. She was entirely too popular. He saw young men make beelines across the floor, eyes fixed on those white silk ankles. Some of the young men he did not know at all, others he knew too well and could not approve of for his sister Amy. Gabriel, unhappy in his lyric satin and wig, stood about holding his ribboned crook as though it had sprouted thorns. He hardly danced at all with Amy, he did not enjoy dancing with anyone else, and he was having a thoroughly wretched time of it.

There appeared late, alone, got up as Jean Lafitte, a young Creole gentleman who had, two years before, been for a time engaged to Amy. He came straight to her, with the manner of a happy lover, and said, clearly enough for everyone near-by to hear him, "I only came because I knew you were to be here. I only want to dance with you and I shall go again." Amy, with a face of delight, cried out "Raymond!" as if to a lover. She had danced with him four times, and had then disappeared from the floor on his arm.

Harry and Mariana, in conventional disguise of romance, irreproach- ably betrothed, safe in their happiness, were waltzing slowly to their favorite song, the melancholy farewell of the Moorish King on leaving Granada. They sang in whispers to each other, in their uncertain Spanish, a song of love and parting and that sword's point of grief that makes the heart tender towards all other lost and disinherited creatures: Oh, mansion of love, my earthly paradise . . . that I shall see no more . . . whither flies the poor swallow, weary and homeless, seeking for shelter where no shelter is? I too am far from home without the power to fly. . . . Come to my heart, sweet bird, beloved pilgrim, build your nest near my bed, let me listen to your song, and weep for my lost land of joy. . . .

Into this bliss broke Gabriel. He had thrown away his shepherd's crook and he was carrying his wig. He wanted to speak to Harry at once, and before Mariana knew what was happening she was sitting be- side her mother and the two excited young men were gone. Waiting, disturbed and displeased, she smiled at Amy who waltzed past with a young man in Devil costume, including ill-fitting scarlet cloven hoofs. Almost at once, Harry and Gabriel came back, with serious faces, and Harry darted on the dance floor, returning with Amy. The girls and the chaperones were asked to come at once, they must be taken home. It was all mysterious and sudden, and Harry said to Mariana, "I will tell you what is happening, but not now—"

The grandmother remembered of this disgraceful affair only that Gabriel brought Amy home alone and that Harry came in somewhat

later. The other members of the party straggled in at various hours, and
the story came out piecemeal. Amy was silent and, her mother discovered later, burning with fever. "I saw at once that something was
very wrong. 'What has happened, Amy?' 'Oh, Harry goes about shooting at people at a party,' she said, sitting down as if she were exhausted.
'It was on your account, Amy,' said Gabriel. 'Oh, no, it was not,' said
Amy. 'Don't believe him, Mammy.' So I said, 'Now enough of this.
Tell me what happened, Amy.' And Amy said, 'Mammy, this is it.
Raymond came in, and you know I like Raymond, and he is a good
dancer. So we danced together, too much, maybe. We went on the
gallery for a breath of air, and stood there. He said, "How well your
hair looks. I like this new shingled style." ' She glanced at Gabriel. 'And
then another young man came out and said, "I've been looking everywhere. This is our dance, isn't it?" And I went in to dance. And now
it seems that Gabriel went out at once and challenged Raymond to a
duel about something or other, but Harry doesn't wait for that.
Raymond had already gone out to have his horse brought, I suppose
one doesn't duel in fancy dress,' she said, looking at Gabriel, who fairly
shriveled in his blue satin shepherd's costume, 'and Harry simply went
out and shot at him. I don't think that was fair,' said Amy."

Her mother agreed that indeed it was not fair; it was not even decent,
and she could not imagine what her son Harry thought he was doing.
"It isn't much of a way to defend your sister's honor," she said to him
afterward. "I didn't want Gabriel to go fighting duels," said Harry.
"That wouldn't have helped much, either."

Gabriel had stood before Amy, leaning over, asking once more the
question he had apparently been asking her all the way home. "Did he
kiss you, Amy?"

Amy took off her shepherdess hat and pushed her hair back. "Maybe
he did," she answered, "and maybe I wished him to."

"Amy, you must not say such things," said her mother. "Answer
Gabriel's question."

"He hasn't the right to ask it," said Amy, but without anger.

"Do you love him, Amy?" asked Gabriel, the sweat standing out on
his forehead.

"It doesn't matter," answered Amy, leaning back in her chair.

"Oh, it does matter; it matters terribly," said Gabriel. "You must answer me now." He took both of her hands and tried to hold them. She drew her hands away firmly and steadily so that he had to let go.

"Let her alone, Gabriel," said Amy's mother. "You'd better go now. We are all tired. Let's talk about it tomorrow."

She helped Amy to undress, noticing the changed bodice and the shortened skirt. "You shouldn't have done that, Amy. That was not wise of you. It was better the other way."

Amy said, "Mammy, I'm sick of this world. I don't like anything in it. It's so *dull,*" she said, and for a moment she looked as if she might weep. She had never been tearful, even as a child, and her mother was alarmed. It was then she discovered that Amy had fever.

"Gabriel is dull, Mother—he sulks," she said. "I could see him sulking every time I passed. It spoils things," she said. "Oh, I want to go to sleep."

Her mother sat looking at her and wondering how it had happened she had brought such a beautiful child into the world. "Her face," said her mother, "was angelic in sleep."

Some time during that fevered night, the projected duel between Gabriel and Raymond was halted by the offices of friends on both sides. There remained the open question of Harry's impulsive shot, which was not so easily settled. Raymond seemed vindictive about that, it was possible he might choose to make trouble. Harry, taking the advice of Gabriel, his brothers and friends, decided that the best way to avoid further scandal was for him to disappear for a while. This being decided upon, the young men returned about daybreak, saddled Harry's best horse and helped him pack a few things; accompanied by Gabriel and Bill, Harry set out for the border, feeling rather gay and adventurous.

Amy, being wakened by the stirring in the house, found out the plan. Five minutes after they were gone, she came down in her riding dress, had her own horse saddled, and struck out after them. She rode almost every morning; before her parents had time to be uneasy over her prolonged absence, they found her note.

What had threatened to be a tragedy became a rowdy lark. Amy rode to the border, kissed her brother Harry good-by, and rode back again with Bill and Gabriel. It was a three days' journey, and when they arrived Amy had to be lifted from the saddle. She was really ill by now, but in the gayest of humors. Her mother and father had been prepared to be severe with her, but, at sight of her, their feelings changed. They turned on Bill and Gabriel. "Why did you let her do this?" they asked.

"You know we could not stop her," said Gabriel helplessly, "and she did enjoy herself so much!"

Amy laughed. "Mammy, it was splendid, the most delightful trip I ever had. And if I am to be the heroine of this novel, why shouldn't I make the most of it?"

The scandal, Maria and Miranda gathered, had been pretty terrible. Amy simply took to bed and stayed there, and Harry had skipped out blithely to wait until the little affair blew over. The rest of the family had to receive visitors, write letters, go to church, return calls, and bear the whole brunt, as they expressed it. They sat in the twilight of scandal in their little world, holding themselves very rigidly, in a shared tension as if all their nerves began at a common center. This center had received a blow, and family nerves shuddered, even into the farthest reaches of Kentucky. From whence in due time great-great-aunt Sally Rhea addressed a letter to *Mifs Amy Rhea*. In deep brown ink like dried blood, in a spidery hand adept at archaic symbols and abbreviations, great-great-aunt Sally informed Amy that she was fairly convinced that this calamity was only the forerunner of a series shortly to be visited by the Almighty God upon a race already condemned through its own wickedness, a warning that man's time was short, and that they must all prepare for the end of the world. For herself, she had long expected it, she was entirely resigned to the prospect of meeting her Maker; and Amy, no less than her wicked brother Harry, must likewise place herself in God's hands and prepare for the worst. *"Oh, my dear unfortunate young relative,"* twittered great-great-aunt Sally, *"we must in our Extremty join hands and appr before ye Dread Throne of Jdgmnt a United Fmly, if One is Mssg from ye Flock, what will Jesus say?"*

Great-great-aunt Sally's religious career had become comic legend. She had forsaken her Catholic rearing for a young man whose family were Cumberland Presbyterians. Unable to accept their opinions, however, she was converted to the Hard-Shell Baptists, a sect as loathsome to her husband's family as the Catholic could possibly be. She had spent a life of vicious self-indulgent martyrdom to her faith; as Harry commented: "Religion put claws on Aunt Sally and gave her a post to whet

them on." She had outargued, outfought, and outlived her entire generation, but she did not miss them. She bedeviled the second generation
without ceasing, and was beginning hungrily on the third.

Amy, reading this letter, broke into her gay full laugh that always
caused everyone around her to laugh too, even before they knew why,
and her small green lovebirds in their cage turned and eyed her
solemnly. "Imagine drawing a pew in heaven beside Aunt Sally," she
said. "What a prospect."

"Don't laugh too soon," said her father. "Heaven was made to order
for Aunt Sally. She'll be on her own territory there."

"For my sins," said Amy, "I must go to heaven with Aunt Sally."

During the uncomfortable time of Harry's absence, Amy went on
refusing to marry Gabriel. Her mother could hear their voices going
on in their endless colloquy, during many long days. One afternoon
Gabriel came out, looking very sober and discouraged. He stood looking
down at Amy's mother as she sat sewing, and said, "I think it is all over,
I believe now that Amy will never have me." The grandmother always
said afterward, "Never have I pitied anyone as I did poor Gabriel at
that moment. But I told him, very firmly, 'Let her alone, then, she is
ill.' " So Gabriel left, and Amy had no word from him for more than
a month.

The day after Gabriel was gone, Amy rose looking extremely well,
went hunting with her brothers Bill and Stephen, bought a velvet wrap,
had her hair shingled and curled again, and wrote long letters to Harry,
who was having a most enjoyable exile in Mexico City.

After dancing all night three times in one week, she woke one morning in a hemorrhage. She seemed frightened and asked for the doctor,
promising to do whatever he advised. She was quiet for a few days,
reading. She asked for Gabriel. No one knew where he was. "You
should write him a letter; his mother will send it on." "Oh, no," she
said. "I miss him coming in with his sour face. Letters are no good."

Gabriel did come in, only a few days later, with a very sour face and
unpleasant news. His grandfather had died, after a day's illness. On his
deathbed, in the name of God, being of a sound and disposing mind, he
had cut off his favorite grandchild Gabriel with one dollar. "In the
name of God, Amy," said Gabriel, "the old devil has ruined me in one
sentence."

It was the conduct of his immediate family in the matter that had embittered him, he said. They could hardly conceal their satisfaction. They had known and envied Gabriel's quite just, well-founded expectations. Not one of them offered to make any private settlement. No one even thought of repairing this last-minute act of senile vengeance. Privately they blessed their luck. "I have been cut off with a dollar," said Gabriel, "and they are all glad of it. I think they feel somehow that this justifies every criticism they ever made against me. They were right about me all along. I am a worthless poor relation," said Gabriel. "My God, I wish you could see them."

Amy said, "I wonder how you will ever support a wife, now."

Gabriel said, "Oh, it isn't so bad as that. If you would, Amy—"

Amy said, "Gabriel, if we get married now there'll be just time to be in New Orleans for Mardi Gras. If we wait until after Lent, it may be too late."

"Why, Amy," said Gabriel, "how could it ever be too late?"

"You might change your mind," said Amy. "You know how fickle you are."

There were two letters in the grandmother's many packets of letters that Maria and Miranda read after they were grown. One of them was from Amy. It was dated ten days after her marriage.

"Dear Mammy, New Orleans hasn't changed as much as I have since we saw each other last. I am now a staid old married woman, and Gabriel is very devoted and kind. Footlights won a race for us yesterday, she was the favorite, and it was wonderful. I go to the races every day, and our horses are doing splendidly; I had my choice of Erin Go Bragh or Miss Lucy, and I chose Miss Lucy. She is mine now, she runs like a streak. Gabriel says I made a mistake, Erin Go Bragh will stay better. I think Miss Lucy will stay my time.

"We are having a lovely visit. I'm going to put on a domino and take to the streets with Gabriel sometime during Mardi Gras. I'm tired of watching the show from a balcony. Gabriel says it isn't safe. He says he'll take me if I insist, but I doubt it. Mammy, he's very nice. Don't worry about me. I have a beautiful black-and-rose-colored velvet gown for the Proteus Ball. Madame, my new mother-in-law, wanted to know if it wasn't a little dashing. I told her I hoped so or I had been cheated. It is fitted perfectly smooth in the bodice, very low in the shoulders—Papa would not approve—and the skirt is looped with wide silver ribbons between the waist and knees in front, and then it surges around and is looped enormously in the back, with a train just one yard long. I now have an eighteen-inch waist, thanks to Madame Duré. I expect to be so dashing that my mother-in-law will have an attack. She has them quite often. Gabriel sends love. Please take good care of Graylie and Fiddler. I want to ride them again when I come home. We're going to Saratoga, I don't know just when. Give everybody my dear dear love. It rains all the time here, of course. . . .

"P.S. Mammy, as soon as I get a minute to myself, I'm going to be terribly homesick. Good-by, my darling Mammy."

The other was from Amy's nurse, dated six weeks after Amy's marriage.

"I cut off the lock of hair because I was sure you would like to have it. And I do not want you to think I was careless, leaving her medicine where she could get it, the doctor has written and explained. It would not have done her any harm except that her heart was weak. She did not know how much she was taking, often she said to me, one more of those little capsules wouldn't do any harm, and so I told her to be careful and not take anything except what I gave her. She begged me for them sometimes but I would not give her more than the doctor said. I slept during the night because she did not seem to be so sick as all that and the doctor did not order me to sit up with her. Please accept my regrets for your great loss and please do not think that anybody was careless with your dear daughter. She suffered a great deal and now she is at rest. She could not get well but she might have lived longer. Yours respectfully . . ."

The letters and all the strange keepsakes were packed away and forgotten for a great many years. They seemed to have no place in the world.

PART II: 1904

During vacation on their grandmother's farm, Maria and Miranda, who read as naturally and constantly as ponies crop grass, and with much the same kind of pleasure, had by some happy chance laid hold of some forbidden reading matter, brought in and left there with missionary intent, no doubt, by some Protestant cousin. It fell into the right hands if enjoyment had been its end. The reading matter was printed in poor type on spongy paper, and was ornamented with smudgy illustrations all the more exciting to the little girls because they could not make head or tail of them. The stories were about beautiful but unlucky maidens, who for mysterious reasons had been trapped by nuns and priests in dire collusion; they were then "immured" in convents, where they were forced to take the veil—an appalling rite during which the victims shrieked dreadfully—and condemned forever after to most uncomfortable and disorderly existences. They seemed to divide their time between lying chained in dark cells and assisting other nuns to bury throttled infants under stones in moldering rat-infested dungeons.

Immured! It was the word Maria and Miranda had been needing all along to describe their condition at the Convent of the Child Jesus, in New Orleans, where they spent the long winters trying to avoid an education. There were no dungeons at the Child Jesus, and this was only one of numerous marked differences between convent life as Maria and Miranda knew it and the thrilling paper-backed version. It was no good at all trying to fit the stories to life, and they did not even try. They had long since learned to draw the lines between life, which was real and earnest, and the grave was not its goal; poetry, which was true but not real; and stories, or forbidden reading matter, in which things happened as nowhere else, with the most sublime irrelevance and unlikelihood, and one need not turn a hair, because there was not a word of truth in them.

It was true the little girls were hedged and confined, but in a large garden with trees and a grotto; they were locked at night into a long cold dormitory, with all the windows open, and a sister sleeping at either end. Their beds were curtained with muslin, and small night-lamps were so arranged that the sisters could see through the curtains, but the children could not see the sisters. Miranda wondered if they ever slept, or did they sit there all night quietly watching the sleepers through the muslin? She tried to work up a little sinister thrill about this, but she found it impossible to care much what either of the sisters did. They were very dull good-natured women who managed to make the whole dormitory seem dull. All days and all things in the Convent of the Child Jesus were dull, in fact, and Maria and Miranda lived for Saturdays.

No one had even hinted that they should become nuns. On the contrary Miranda felt that the discouraging attitude of Sister Claude and Sister Austin and Sister Ursula towards her expressed ambition to be a nun barely veiled a deeply critical knowledge of her spiritual deficiencies. Still Maria and Miranda had got a fine new word out of their summer reading, and they referred to themselves as "immured." It gave a romantic glint to what was otherwise a very unexciting life for them, except for blessed Saturday afternoons during the racing season.

If the nuns were able to assure the family that the deportment and scholastic achievements of Maria and Miranda were at least passable, some cousin or other always showed up smiling, in holiday mood, to take them to the races, where they were given a dollar each to bet on any horse they chose. There were black Saturdays now and then, when Maria and Miranda sat ready, hats in hand, curly hair plastered down and slicked behind their ears, their stiffly pleated navy-blue skirts spread out around them, waiting with their hearts going down slowly into their high-topped laced-up black shoes. They never put on their hats until the last minute, for somehow it would have been too horrible to have their hats on, when, after all, Cousin Henry and Cousin Isabel, or Uncle George and Aunt Polly, were not coming to take them to the races. When no one appeared, and Saturday came and went a sickening waste, they were then given to understand that it was a punishment for bad marks during the week. They never knew until it was too late to avoid the disappointment. It was very wearing.

One Saturday they were sent down to wait in the visitors' parlor, and there was their father. He had come all the way from Texas to see them. They leaped at sight of him, and then stopped short, suspiciously.

Was he going to take them to the races? If so, they were happy to see him.

"Hello," said Father, kissing their cheeks. "Have you been good girls? Your Uncle Gabriel is running a mare at the Crescent City to-day, so we'll all go and bet on her. Would you like that?"

Maria put on her hat without a word, but Miranda stood and addressed her father sternly. She had suffered many doubts about this day. "*Why* didn't you send word yesterday? I could have been looking forward all this time."

"We didn't know," said Father, in his easiest paternal manner, "that you were going to deserve it. Remember Saturday before last?"

Miranda hung her head and put on her hat, with the round elastic under the chin. She remembered too well. She had, in midweek, given way to despair over her arithmetic and had fallen flat on her face on the classroom floor, refusing to rise until she was carried out. The rest of the week had been a series of novel deprivations, and Saturday a day of mourning; secret mourning, for if one mourned too noisily, it simply meant another bad mark against deportment.

"Never mind," said Father, as if it were the smallest possible matter, "today you're going. Come along now. We've barely time."

These expeditions were all joy, every time, from the moment they stepped into a closed one-horse cab, a treat in itself with its dark, thick upholstery, soaked with strange perfumes and tobacco smoke, until the thrilling moment when they walked into a restaurant under big lights and were given dinner with things to eat they never had at home, much less at the convent. They felt worldly and grown up, each with her glass of water colored pink with claret.

The great crowd was always exciting as if they had never seen it before, with the beautiful, incredibly dressed ladies, all plumes and flowers and paint, and the elegant gentlemen with yellow gloves. The bands played in turn with thundering drums and brasses, and now and then a wild beautiful horse would career around the track with a tiny, monkey-shaped boy on his back, limbering up for his race.

Miranda had a secret personal interest in all this which she knew better than to confide to anyone, even Maria. Least of all to Maria. In ten minutes the whole family would have known. She had lately decided to be a jockey when she grew up. Her father had said one day that she was going to be a little thing all her life, she would never be tall; and this meant, of course, that she would never be a beauty like Aunt Amy, or Cousin Isabel. Her hope of being a beauty died hard, until the notion of being a jockey came suddenly and filled all her thoughts. Quietly, blissfully, at night before she slept, and too often in the daytime when she should have been studying, she planned her career as jockey. It was dim in detail, but brilliant at the right distance. It seemed too silly to be worried about arithmetic at all, when what she needed for her future was to ride better—much better. "You ought to be ashamed of yourself," said Father, after watching her gallop full tilt down the lane at the farm, on Trixie, the mustang mare. "I can see the sun, moon and stars between you and the saddle every jump." Spanish style meant that one sat close to the saddle, and did all kinds of things with the knees and reins. Jockeys bounced lightly, their knees almost level with the horse's back, rising and falling like a rubber ball. Miranda felt she could do that easily. Yes, she would be a jockey, like Tod Sloan, winning every other race at least. Meantime, while she was training, she would keep it a secret, and one day she would ride out, bouncing lightly, with the other jockeys, and win a great race, and surprise everybody, her family most of all.

On that particular Saturday, her idol, the great Tod Sloan, was riding, and he won two races. Miranda longed to bet her dollar on Tod Sloan, but Father said, "Not now, honey. Today you must bet on Uncle Gabriel's horse. Save your dollar for the fourth race, and put it on Miss Lucy. You've got a hundred to one shot. Think if she wins."

Miranda knew well enough that a hundred to one shot was no bet at all. She sulked, the crumpled dollar in her hand grew damp and warm. She could have won three dollars already on Tod Sloan. Maria said virtuously, "It wouldn't be nice not to bet on Uncle Gabriel. That way, we keep the money in the family." Miranda put out her under lip at her sister. Maria was too prissy for words. She wrinkled her nose back at Miranda.

They had just turned their dollar over to the bookmaker for the fourth race when a vast bulging man with a red face and immense tan ragged mustaches fading into gray hailed them from a lower level of the grandstand, over the heads of the crowd, "Hey, there, Harry!" Father said, "Bless my soul, there's Gabriel." He motioned to the man, who came pushing his way heavily up the shallow steps. Maria and Miranda stared, first at him, then at each other. "Can that be our Uncle Gabriel?" their eyes asked. "Is that Aunt Amy's handsome romantic beau? Is that the man who wrote the poem about our Aunt Amy?" Oh, what did grown-up people *mean* when they talked, anyway?

He was a shabby fat man with bloodshot blue eyes, sad beaten eyes, and a big melancholy laugh, like a groan. He towered over them shouting to their father, "Well, for God's sake, Harry, it's been a coon's age. You ought to come out and look 'em over. You look just like yourself, Harry, how are you?"

The band struck up "Over the River" and Uncle Gabriel shouted louder. "Come on, let's get out of this. What are you doing up here with the pikers?"

"Can't," shouted Father. "Brought my little girls. Here they are."

Uncle Gabriel's bleared eyes beamed blindly upon them. "Fine looking set, Harry," he bellowed, "pretty as pictures, how old are they?"

"Ten and fourteen now," said Father; "awkward ages. Nest of vipers," he boasted, "perfect batch of serpent's teeth. Can't do a thing with 'em." He fluffed up Miranda's hair, pretending to tousle it.

"Pretty as pictures," bawled Uncle Gabriel, "but rolled into one they don't come up to Amy, do they?"

"No, they don't," admitted their father at the top of his voice, "but they're only half-baked." *Over the river, over the river,* moaned the band, *my sweetheart's waiting for me.*

"I've got to get back now," yelled Uncle Gabriel. The little girls felt quite deaf and confused. "Got the God-damnedest jockey in the world, Harry, just my luck. Ought to tie him on. Fell off Fiddler yesterday, just plain fell off on his tail— Remember Amy's mare, Miss Lucy? Well, this is her namesake, Miss Lucy IV. None of 'em ever came up to the first one, though. Stay right where you are, I'll be back."

Maria spoke up boldly. "Uncle Gabriel, tell Miss Lucy we're betting on her." Uncle Gabriel bent down and it looked as if there were tears in his swollen eyes. "God bless your sweet heart," he bellowed, "I'll tell her." He plunged down through the crowd again, his fat back bowed slightly in his loose clothes, his thick neck rolling over his collar.

Miranda and Maria, disheartened by the odds, by their first sight of their romantic Uncle Gabriel, whose language was so coarse, sat listlessly without watching, their chances missed, their dollars gone, their hearts sore. They didn't even move until their father leaned over and hauled them up. "Watch your horse," he said, in a quick warning voice, "watch Miss Lucy come home."

They stood up, scrambled to their feet on the bench, every vein in them suddenly beating so violently they could hardly focus their eyes, and saw a thin little mahogany-colored streak flash by the judges' stand, only a neck ahead, but their Miss Lucy, oh, their darling, their lovely —oh, Miss Lucy, their Uncle Gabriel's Miss Lucy, had won, had won. They leaped up and down screaming and clapping their hands, their hats falling back on their shoulders, their hair flying wild. *Whoa, you heifer,* squalled the band with snorting brasses, and the crowd broke into a long roar like the falling of the walls of Jericho.

The little girls sat down, feeling quite dizzy, while their father tried to pull their hats straight, and taking out his handkerchief held it to Miranda's face, saying very gently, "Here, blow your nose," and he dried her eyes while he was about it. He stood up then and shook them out of their daze. He was smiling with deep laughing wrinkles around his eyes, and spoke to them as if they were grown young ladies he was squiring around.

"Let's go out and pay our respects to Miss Lucy," he said. "She's the star of the day."

The horses were coming in, looking as if their hides had been drenched and rubbed with soap, their ribs heaving, their nostrils flaring and closing. The jockeys sat bowed and relaxed, their faces calm, moving a little at the waist with the movement of their horses. Miranda noted this for future use; that was the way you came in from a race, easy and quiet, whether you had won or lost. Miss Lucy came last, and a little handful of winners applauded her and cheered the jockey. He smiled and lifted his whip, his eyes and shriveled brown face perfectly serene. Miss Lucy was bleeding at the nose, two thick red rivulets were stiffening her tender mouth and chin, the round velvet chin that Miranda thought the nicest kind of chin in the world. Her eyes were wild and her knees were trembling, and she snored when she drew her breath.

Miranda stood staring. That was winning, too. Her heart clinched tight; that was winning, for Miss Lucy. So instantly and completely did her heart reject that victory, she did not know when it happened, but she hated it, and was ashamed that she had screamed and shed tears for joy when Miss Lucy, with her bloodied nose and bursting heart, had gone past the judges' stand a neck ahead. She felt empty and sick and held to her father's hand so hard that he shook her off a little impatiently and said, "What is the matter with you? Don't be so fidgety."

Uncle Gabriel was standing there waiting, and he was completely drunk. He watched the mare go in, then leaned against the fence with its whitewashed posts and sobbed openly. "She's got the nosebleed, Harry," he said. "Had it since yesterday. We thought we had her all fixed up. But she did it, all right. She's got a heart like a lion. I'm going to breed her, Harry. Her heart's worth a million dollars, by itself, God bless her." Tears ran over his brick-colored face and into his straggling mustaches. "If anything happens to her now I'll blow my brains out. She's my last hope. She saved my life. I've had a run," he said, groaning into a large handkerchief and mopping his face all over, "I've had a run of luck that would break a brass billy goat. God, Harry, let's go somewhere and have a drink."

"I must get the children back to school first, Gabriel," said their father, taking each by a hand.

"No, no, don't go yet," said Uncle Gabriel desperately. "Wait here a minute, I want to see the vet and take a look at Miss Lucy, and I'll be right back. Don't go, Harry, for God's sake. I want to talk to you a few minutes."

Maria and Miranda, watching Uncle Gabriel's lumbering, unsteady back, were thinking that this was the first time they had ever seen a man that they knew to be drunk. They had seen pictures and read descriptions, and had heard descriptions, so they recognized the symptoms at once. Miranda felt it was an important moment in a great many ways.

"Uncle Gabriel's a drunkard, isn't he?" she asked her father, rather proudly.

"Hush, don't say such things," said Father, with a heavy frown, "or I'll never bring you here again." He looked worried and unhappy, and, above all, undecided. The little girls stood stiff with resentment against such obvious injustice. They loosed their hands from his and moved away coldly, standing together in silence. Their father did not notice, watching the place where Uncle Gabriel had disappeared. In a few minutes he came back, still wiping his face, as if there were cobwebs on it, carrying his big black hat. He waved at them from a short distance, calling out in a cheerful way, "She's going to be all right, Harry. It's stopped now. Lord, this will be good news for Miss Honey. Come on, Harry, let's all go home and tell Miss Honey. She deserves some good news."

Father said, "I'd better take the children back to school first, then we'll go."

"No, no," said Uncle Gabriel, fondly. "I want her to see the girls. She'll be tickled pink to see them, Harry. Bring 'em along."

"Is it another racehorse we're going to see?" whispered Miranda in her sister's ear.

"Don't be silly," said Maria. "It's Uncle Gabriel's second wife."

"Let's find a cab, Harry," said Uncle Gabriel, "and take your little girls out to cheer up Miss Honey. Both of 'em rolled into one look a lot like Amy, I swear they do. I want Miss Honey to see them. She's always liked our family, Harry, though of course she's not what you'd call an expansive kind of woman."

Maria and Miranda sat facing the driver, and Uncle Gabriel squeezed himself in facing them beside their father. The air became at once bitter and sour with his breathing. He looked sad and poor. His necktie was on crooked and his shirt was rumpled. Father said, "You're going to see Uncle Gabriel's second wife, children," exactly as if they had not heard everything; and to Gabriel, "How *is* your wife nowadays? It must be twenty years since I saw her last."

"She's pretty gloomy, and that's a fact," said Uncle Gabriel. "She's been pretty gloomy for years now, and nothing seems to shake her out of it. She never did care for horses, Harry, if you remember; she hasn't been near the track three times since we were married. When I think how Amy wouldn't have missed a race for anything . . . She's very different from Amy, Harry, a very different kind of woman. As fine a woman as ever lived in her own way, but she hates change and moving around, and she just lives in the boy."

"Where is Gabe now?" asked Father.

"Finishing college," said Uncle Gabriel; "a smart boy, but awfully like his mother. Awfully like," he said, in a melancholy way. "She hates being away from him. Just wants to sit down in the same town and wait for him to get through with his education. Well, I'm sorry it can't be done if that's what she wants, but God Almighty— And this last run of luck has about got her down. I hope you'll be able to cheer her up a little, Harry, she needs it."

The little girls sat watching the streets grow duller and dingier and narrower, and at last the shabbier and shabbier white people gave way to dressed-up Negroes, and then to shabby Negroes, and after a long way the cab stopped before a desolate-looking little hotel in Elysian Fields. Their father helped Maria and Miranda out, told the cabman to wait, and they followed Uncle Gabriel through a dirty damp-smelling patio, down a long gas-lighted hall full of a terrible smell, Miranda couldn't decide what it was made of but it had a bitter taste even, and up a long staircase with a ragged carpet. Uncle Gabriel pushed open a door without warning, saying, "Come in, here we are."

A tall pale-faced woman with faded straw-colored hair and pink-rimmed eyelids rose suddenly from a squeaking rocking chair. She wore a stiff blue-and-white-striped shirtwaist and a stiff black skirt of some hard shiny material. Her large knuckled hands rose to her round, neat pompadour at sight of her visitors.

"Honey," said Uncle Gabriel, with large false heartiness, "you'll never guess who's come to see you." He gave her a clumsy hug. Her face did not change and her eyes rested steadily on the three strangers. "Amy's brother Harry, Honey, you remember, don't you?"

"Of course," said Miss Honey, putting out her hand straight as a paddle, "of course I remember you, Harry." She did not smile.

"And Amy's two little nieces," went on Uncle Gabriel, bringing them forward. They put out their hands limply, and Miss Honey gave each one a slight flip and dropped it. "And we've got good news for you," went on Uncle Gabriel, trying to bolster up the painful situation. "Miss Lucy stepped out and showed 'em today, Honey. We're rich again, old girl, cheer up."

Miss Honey turned her long, despairing face towards her visitors. "Sit down," she said with a heavy sigh, seating herself and motioning towards various rickety chairs. There was a big lumpy bed, with a grayish-white counterpane on it, a marble-topped washstand, grayish coarse lace curtains on strings at the two small windows, a small closed fireplace with a hole in it for a stovepipe, and two trunks, standing at odds as if somebody were just moving in, or just moving out. Everything was dingy and soiled and neat and bare; not a pin out of place.

"We'll move to the St. Charles tomorrow," said Uncle Gabriel, as much to Harry as to his wife. "Get your best dresses together, Honey, the long dry spell is over."

Miss Honey's nostrils pinched together and she rocked slightly, with her arms folded. "I've lived in the St. Charles before, and I've lived here before," she said, in a tight deliberate voice, "and this time I'll just stay where I am, thank you. I prefer it to moving back here in three months. I'm settled now, I feel at home here," she told him, glancing at Harry, her pale eyes kindling with blue fire, a stiff white line around her mouth.

The little girls sat trying not to stare, miserably ill at ease. Their grandmother had pronounced Harry's children to be the most unteachable she had ever seen in her long experience with the young; but they had learned by indirection one thing well—nice people did not carry on quarrels before outsiders. Family quarrels were sacred, to be waged privately in fierce hissing whispers, low choked mutters and growls. If they did yell and stamp, it must be behind closed doors and windows. Uncle Gabriel's second wife was hopping mad and she looked ready to fly out at Uncle Gabriel any second, with him sitting there like a hound when someone shakes a whip at him.

"She loathes and despises everybody in this room," thought Miranda, coolly, "and she's afraid we won't know it. She needn't worry, we knew it when we came in." With all her heart she wanted to go, but her father, though his face was a study, made no move. He seemed to be trying to think of something pleasant to say. Maria, feeling guilty, though she couldn't think why, was calculating rapidly, "Why, she's only Uncle Gabriel's second wife, and Uncle Gabriel was only married before to Aunt Amy, why, she's no kin at all, and I'm glad of it." Sitting back easily, she let her hands fall open in her lap; they would be going in a few minutes, undoubtedly, and they need never come back.

Then Father said, "We mustn't be keeping you, we just dropped in for a few minutes. We wanted to see how you are."

Miss Honey said nothing, but she made a little gesture with her hands, from the wrist, as if to say, "Well, you see how I am, and now what next?"

"I must take these young ones back to school," said Father, and Uncle Gabriel said stupidly, "Look, Honey, don't you think they resemble Amy a little? Especially around the eyes, especially Maria, don't you think, Harry?"

Their father glanced at them in turn. "I really couldn't say," he decided, and the little girls saw he was more monstrously embarrassed than ever. He turned to Miss Honey. "I hadn't seen Gabriel for so many years," he said, "we thought of getting out for a talk about old times together. You know how it is."

"Yes, I know," said Miss Honey, rocking a little, and all that she knew gleamed forth in a pallid, unquenchable hatred and bitterness that seemed enough to bring her long body straight up out of the chair in a fury, "I know," and she sat staring at the floor. Her mouth shook and straightened. There was a terrible silence, which was broken when the little girls saw their father rise. They got up, too, and it was all they could do to keep from making a dash for the door.

"I must get the young ones back," said their father. "They've had enough excitement for one day. They each won a hundred dollars on Miss Lucy. It was a good race," he said, in complete wretchedness, as if he simply could not extricate himself from the situation. "Wasn't it, Gabriel?"

"It was a grand race," said Gabriel, brokenly, "a grand race."

Miss Honey stood up and moved a step towards the door. "Do you take them to the races, actually?" she asked, and her lids flickered towards them as if they were loathsome insects, Maria felt.

"If I feel they deserve a little treat, yes," said their father, in an easy tone but with wrinkled brow.

"I had rather, much rather," said Miss Honey clearly, "see my son dead at my feet than hanging around a race track."

The next few moments were rather a blank, but at last they were out of it, going down the stairs, across the patio, with Uncle Gabriel seeing them back into the cab. His face was sagging, the features had fallen as if the flesh had slipped from the bones, and his eyelids were puffed and blue. "Good-by, Harry," he said soberly. "How long you expect to be here?"

"Starting back tomorrow," said Harry. "Just dropped in on a little business and to see how the girls were getting along."

"Well," said Uncle Gabriel, "I may be dropping into your part of the country one of these days. Good-by, children," he said, taking their hands one after the other in his big warm paws. "They're nice children, Harry. I'm glad you won on Miss Lucy," he said to the little girls, tenderly. "Don't spend your money foolishly, now. Well, so long. Harry." As the cab jolted away he stood there fat and sagging, holding up his arm and wagging his hand at them.

"Goodness," said Maria, in her most grown-up manner, taking her hat off and hanging it over her knee, "I'm glad that's over."

"What I want to know is," said Miranda, "is Uncle Gabriel a real drunkard?"

"Oh, hush," said their father, sharply, "I've got the heartburn."

There was a respectful pause, as before a public monument. When their father had the heartburn it was time to lay low. The cab rumbled on, back to clean gay streets, with the lights coming on in the early February darkness, past shimmering shop windows, smooth pavements, on and on, past beautiful old houses set in deep gardens, on, on back to the dark walls with the heavy-topped trees hanging over them. Miranda sat thinking so hard she forgot and spoke out in her thoughtless way: "I've decided I'm not going to be a jockey, after all." She could as usual have bitten her tongue, but as usual it was too late.

Father cheered up and twinkled at her knowingly, as if that didn't surprise him in the least. "Well, well," said he, "so you aren't going to be a jockey! That's very sensible of you. I think that she ought to be a a lion-tamer, don't you, Maria? That's a nice, womanly profession."

Miranda, seeing Maria from the height of her fourteen years suddenly joining with their father to laugh at her, made an instant decision and laughed with them at herself. That was better. Everybody laughed and it was such a relief.

"Where's my hundred dollars?" asked Maria, anxiously.

"It's going in the bank," said their father, "and yours too," he told Miranda. "That is your nest-egg."

"Just so they don't buy my stockings with it," said Miranda, who had long resented the use of her Christmas money by their grandmother. "I've got enough stockings to last me a year."

"I'd like to buy a racehorse," said Maria, "but I know it's not enough." The limitations of wealth oppressed her. "*What* could you buy with a hundred dollars?" she asked fretfully.

"Nothing, nothing at all," said their father, "a hundred dollars is just something you put in the bank."

Maria and Miranda lost interest. They had won a hundred dollars on a horse race once. It was already in the far past. They began to chatter about something else.

The lay sister opened the door on a long cord, from behind the grille; Maria and Miranda walked in silently to their familiar world of shining bare floors and insipid wholesome food and cold-water washing and regular prayers; their world of poverty, chastity and obedience, of early to bed and early to rise, of sharp little rules and tittle-tattle. Resignation was in their childish faces as they held them up to be kissed.

"Be good girls," said their father, in the strange, serious, rather helpless way he always had when he told them good-by. "Write to your daddy, now, nice long letters," he said, holding their arms firmly for a moment before letting go for good. Then he disappeared, and the sister swung the door closed after him.

Maria and Miranda went upstairs to the dormitory to wash their faces and hands and slick down their hair again before supper.

Miranda was hungry. "We didn't have a thing to eat, after all," she grumbled. "Not even a chocolate nut bar. I think that's mean. We didn't even get a quarter to spend," she said.

"Not a living bite," said Maria. "Not a nickel." She poured out cold water into the bowl and rolled up her sleeves.

Another girl about her own age came in and went to a washbowl near another bed. "Where have you been?" she asked. "Did you have a good time?"

"We went to the races, with our father," said Maria, soaping her hands.

"Our uncle's horse won," said Miranda.

"My goodness," said the other girl, vaguely, "that must have been grand."

Maria looked at Miranda, who was rolling up her own sleeves. She tried to feel martyred, but it wouldn't go. "Immured for another week," she said, her eyes sparkling over the edge of her towel.

PART III: 1912

Miranda followed the porter down the stuffy aisle of the sleeping car, where the berths were nearly all made down and the dusty green curtains buttoned, to a seat at the further end. "Now yo' berth's ready any time, Miss," said the porter.

"But I want to sit up awhile," said Miranda. A very thin old lady raised choleric black eyes and fixed upon her a regard of unmixed disapproval. She had two immense front teeth and a receding chin, but she did not lack character. She had piled her luggage around her like a barricade, and she glared at the porter when he picked some of it up to make room for his new passenger. Miranda sat, saying mechanically, "May I?"

"You may, indeed," said the old lady, for she seemed old in spite of a certain brisk, rustling energy. Her taffeta petticoats creaked like hinges every time she stirred. With ferocious sarcasm, after a half second's pause, she added, "You may be so good as to get off my hat!"

Miranda rose instantly in horror, and handed to the old lady a wilted contrivance of black horsehair braid and shattered white poppies. "I'm dreadfully sorry," she stammered, for she had been brought up to treat ferocious old ladies respectfully, and this one seemed capable of spanking her, then and there. "I didn't dream it was your hat."

"And whose hat did you dream it might be?" inquired the old lady, baring her teeth and twirling the hat on a forefinger to restore it.

"I didn't think it was a hat at all," said Miranda with a touch of hysteria.

"Oh, you didn't think it was a hat? Where on earth are your eyes, child?" and she proved the nature and function of the object by placing it on her head at a somewhat tipsy angle, though still it did not much resemble a hat. "Now can you see what it is?"

"Yes, oh yes," said Miranda, with a meekness she hoped was disarming. She ventured to sit again after a careful inspection of the narrow space she was to occupy.

"Well, well," said the old lady, "let's have the porter remove some of these encumbrances," and she stabbed the bell with a lean sharp forefinger. There followed a flurry of rearrangements, during which they both stood in the aisle, the old lady giving a series of impossible directions to the Negro which he bore philosophically while he disposed of the luggage exactly as he had meant to do. Seated again, the old lady asked in a kindly, authoritative tone, "And what might your name be, child?"

At Miranda's answer, she blinked somewhat, unfolded her spectacles, straddled them across her high nose competently, and took a good long look at the face beside her.

"If I'd had my spectacles on," she said, in an astonishingly changed voice, "I might have known. I'm Cousin Eva Parrington," she said, "Cousin Molly Parrington's daughter, remember? I knew you when you were a little girl. You were a lively little girl," she added as if to console her, "and very opinionated. The last thing I heard about you, you were planning to be a tight-rope walker. You were going to play the violin and walk the tight-rope at the same time."

"I must have seen it at the vaudeville show," said Miranda. "I couldn't have invented it. Now I'd like to be an air pilot!"

"I used to go to dances with your father," said Cousin Eva, busy with her own thoughts, "and to big holiday parties at your grandmother's house, long before you were born. Oh, indeed, yes, a long time before."

Miranda remembered several things at once. Aunt Amy had threatened to be an old maid like Eva. Oh, Eva, the trouble with her is she has no chin. Eva has given up, and is teaching Latin in a Female Seminary. Eva's gone out for votes for women, God help her. The nice thing about an ugly daughter is, she's not apt to make me a grandmother. . . . "They didn't do you much good, those parties, dear Cousin Eva," thought Miranda.

"They didn't do me much good, those parties," said Cousin Eva aloud as if she were a mind-reader, and Miranda's head swam for a moment with fear that she had herself spoken aloud. "Or at least, they didn't serve their purpose, for I never got married; but I enjoyed them,

just the same. I had a good time at those parties, even if I wasn't a
belle. And so you are Harry's child, and here I was quarreling with
you. You do remember me, don't you?"

"Yes," said Miranda, and thinking that even if Cousin Eva had been
really an old maid ten years before, still she couldn't be much past
fifty now, and she looked so withered and tired, so famished and sunken
in the cheeks, so *old,* somehow. Across the abyss separating Cousin
Eva from her own youth, Miranda looked with painful premonition.
"Oh, must I ever be like that?"

She said aloud, "Yes, you used to read Latin to me, and tell me not
to bother about the sense, to get the sound in my mind, and it would
come easier later."

"Ah, so I did," said Cousin Eva delighted. "So I did. You don't happen to remember that I once had a beautiful sapphire velvet dress with
a train on it?"

"No, I don't remember that dress," said Miranda.

"It was an old dress of my mother's made over and cut down to
fit," said Eva, "and it wasn't in the least becoming to me, but it was
the only really good dress I ever had, and I remember it as if it were
yesterday. Blue was never my color." She sighed with a humorous
bitterness. The humor seemed momentary, but the bitterness was a
constant state of mind.

Miranda, trying to offer the sympathy of fellow suffering, said, "I
know. I've had Maria's dresses made over for me, and they were never
right. It was dreadful."

"Well," said Cousin Eva, in the tone of one who did not wish to
share her unique disappointments. "How is your father? I always liked
him. He was one of the finest-looking young men I ever saw. Vain, too,
like all his family. He wouldn't ride any but the best horses he could
buy, and I used to say he made them prance and then watched his
own shadow. I used to tell this on him at dinner parties, and he hated
me for it. I feel pretty certain he hated me." An overtone of complacency in Cousin Eva's voice explained better than words that she
had her own method of commanding attention and arousing emotion.
"How *is* your father, I asked you, my dear?"

"I haven't seen him for nearly a year," answered Miranda, quickly,
before Cousin Eva could get ahead again. "I'm going home now to

Uncle Gabriel's funeral; you know, Uncle Gabriel died in Lexington and they have brought him back to be buried beside Aunt Amy."

"So that's how we meet," said Cousin Eva. "Yes, Gabriel drank himself to death at last. I'm going to the funeral, too. I haven't been home since I went to Mother's funeral, it must be, let's see, yes, it will be nine years next July. I'm going to Gabriel's funeral, though. I wouldn't miss that. Poor fellow, what a life he had. Pretty soon, they'll all be gone."

Miranda said, "We're left, Cousin Eva," meaning those of her own generation, the young, and Cousin Eva said, "Pshaw, you'll live forever, and you won't bother to come to our funerals." She didn't seem to think this was a misfortune, but flung the remark from her like a woman accustomed to saying what she thought.

Miranda sat thinking, "Still, I suppose it would be pleasant if I could say something to make her believe that she and all of them would be lamented, but—but—" With a smile which she hoped would be her denial of Cousin Eva's cynicism about the younger generation, she said, "You were right about the Latin, Cousin Eva, your reading did help when I began with it. I still study," she said. "Latin, too."

"And why shouldn't you?" asked Cousin Eva, sharply, adding at once mildly, "I'm glad you are going to use your mind a little, child. Don't let yourself rust away. Your mind outwears all sorts of things you may set your heart upon; you can enjoy it when all other things are taken away." Miranda was chilled by her melancholy. Cousin Eva went on: "In our part of the country, in my time, we were so provincial—a woman didn't dare to think or act for herself. The whole world was a little that way," she said, "but we were the worst, I believe. I suppose you must know how I fought for votes for women when it almost made a pariah of me—I was turned out of my chair at the Seminary, but I'm glad I did it and I would do it again. You young things don't realize. You'll live in a better world because we worked for it."

Miranda knew something of Cousin Eva's career. She said sincerely, "I think it was brave of you, and I'm glad you did it, too. I loved your courage."

"It wasn't just showing off, mind you," said Cousin Eva, rejecting praise, fretfully. "Any fool can be brave. We were working for something we knew was right, and it turned out that we needed a lot of courage for it. That was all. I didn't expect to go to jail, but I went three times, and I'd go three times three more if it were necessary. We aren't voting yet," she said, "but we will be."

Miranda did not venture any answer, but she felt convinced that indeed women would be voting soon if nothing fatal happened to Cousin Eva. There was something in her manner which said such things could be left safely to her. Miranda was dimly fired for the cause herself; it seemed heroic and worth suffering for, but discouraging, too, to those who came after: Cousin Eva so plainly had swept the field clear of opportunity.

They were silent for a few minutes, while Cousin Eva rummaged in her handbag, bringing up odds and ends: peppermint drops, eye drops, a packet of needles, three handkerchiefs, a little bottle of violet perfume, a book of addresses, two buttons, one black, one white, and, finally, a packet of headache powders.

"Bring me a glass of water, will you, my dear?" she asked Miranda. She poured the headache powder on her tongue, swallowed the water, and put two peppermints in her mouth.

"So now they're going to bury Gabriel near Amy," she said after a while, as if her eased headache had started her on a new train of thought. "Miss Honey would like that, poor dear, if she could know. After listening to stories about Amy for twenty-five years, she must lie alone in her grave in Lexington while Gabriel sneaks off to Texas to make his bed with Amy again. It was a kind of life-long infidelity, Miranda, and now an eternal infidelity on top of that. He ought to be ashamed of himself."

"It was Aunt Amy he loved," said Miranda, wondering what Miss Honey could have been like before her long troubles with Uncle Gabriel. "First, anyway."

"Oh, that Amy," said Cousin Eva, her eyes glittering. "Your Aunt Amy was a devil and a mischief-maker, but I loved her dearly. I used to stand up for Amy when her reputation wasn't worth that." Her fingers snapped like castanets. "She used to say to me, in that gay soft way she had, 'Now, Eva, don't go talking votes for women when the lads ask you to dance. Don't recite Latin poems to 'em,' she would say, 'they got sick of that in school. Dance and say nothing, Eva,' she would say, her eyes perfectly devilish, 'and hold your chin up, Eva.' My chin was my weak point, you see. 'You'll never catch a husband if you don't look out,' she would say. Then she would laugh and fly away, and where did she fly to?" demanded Cousin Eva, her sharp eyes pinning Miranda down to the bitter facts of the case. "To scandal and to death, nowhere else."

"She was joking, Cousin Eva," said Miranda, innocently, "and everybody loved her."

"Not everybody, by a long shot," said Cousin Eva in triumph. "She had enemies. If she knew, she pretended she didn't. If she cared, she never said. You couldn't make her quarrel. She was sweet as a honeycomb to everybody. *Everybody*," she added, "that was the trouble. She went through life like a spoiled darling, doing as she pleased and letting other people suffer for it, and pick up the pieces after her. I never believed for one moment," said Cousin Eva, putting her mouth close to Miranda's ear and breathing peppermint hotly into it, "that Amy was an impure woman. Never! But let me tell you, there were plenty who did believe it. There were plenty to pity poor Gabriel for being so completely blinded by her. A great many persons were not surprised when they heard that Gabriel was perfectly miserable all the time, on their honeymoon, in New Orleans. Jealousy. And why not? But I used to say to such persons that, no matter what the appearances were, I had faith in Amy's virtue. Wild, I said, indiscreet, I said, heartless, I said, but *virtuous,* I feel certain. But you could hardly blame anyone for being mystified. The way she rose up suddenly from death's door to marry Gabriel Breaux, after refusing him and treating him like a dog for years, looked odd, to say the least. To say the very least," she added, after a moment, "odd is a mild word for it. And there was something very mysterious about her death, only six weeks after marriage."

Miranda roused herself. She felt she knew this part of the story and could set Cousin Eva right about one thing. "She died of a hemorrhage from the lungs," said Miranda. "She had been ill for five years, don't you remember?"

Cousin Eva was ready for that. "Ha, that was the story, indeed. The official account, you might say. Oh, yes, I heard that often enough. But did you ever hear about that fellow Raymond Somebody-or-other

from Calcasieu Parish, almost a stranger, who persuaded Amy to elope
with him from a dance one night, and she just ran out into the darkness without even stopping for her cloak, and your poor dear nice
father Harry—you weren't even thought of then—had to run him
down to earth and shoot him?"

Miranda leaned back from the advancing flood of speech. "Cousin
Eva, my father shot *at* him, don't you remember? He didn't hit
him. . . ."

"Well, that's a pity."

". . . and they had only gone out for a breath of air between dances.
It was Uncle Gabriel's jealousy. And my father shot at the man because he thought that was better than letting Uncle Gabriel fight a
duel about Aunt Amy. There was *nothing* in the whole affair except
Uncle Gabriel's jealousy."

"You poor baby," said Cousin Eva, and pity gave a light like daggers
to her eyes, "you dear innocent, you—do you believe that? How old
are you, anyway?"

"Just past eighteen," said Miranda.

"If you don't understand what I tell you," said Cousin Eva porten-
tously, "you will later. Knowledge can't hurt you. You mustn't live in
a romantic haze about life. You'll understand when you're married, at
any rate."

"I'm married now, Cousin Eva," said Miranda, feeling for almost the
first time that it might be an advantage, "nearly a year. I eloped from
school." It seemed very unreal even as she said it, and seemed to have
nothing at all to do with the future; still, it was important, it must be
declared, it was a situation in life which people seemed to be most ex-
acting about, and the only feeling she could rouse in herself about it
was an immense weariness as if it were an illness that she might one
day hope to recover from.

"Shameful, shameful," cried Cousin Eva, genuinely repelled. "If you
had been my child I should have brought you home and spanked you."

Miranda laughed out. Cousin Eva seemed to believed things could
be arranged like that. She was so solemn and fierce, so comic and
baffled.

"And you must know I should have just gone straight out again, through the nearest window," she taunted her. "If I went the first time, why not the second?"

"Yes, I suppose so," said Cousin Eva. "I hope you married rich."

"Not so very," said Miranda. "Enough." As if anyone could have stopped to think of such a thing!

Cousin Eva adjusted her spectacles and sized up Miranda's dress, her luggage, examined her engagement ring and wedding ring, with her nostrils fairly quivering as if she might smell out wealth on her.

"Well, that's better than nothing," said Cousin Eva. "I thank God every day of my life that I have a small income. It's a Rock of Ages. What would have become of me if I hadn't a cent of my own? Well, you'll be able now to do something for your family."

Miranda remembered what she had always heard about the Parringtons. They were money-hungry, they loved money and nothing else, and when they had got some they kept it. Blood was thinner than water between the Parringtons where money was concerned.

"We're pretty poor," said Miranda, stubbornly allying herself with her father's family instead of her husband's, "but a rich marriage is no way out," she said, with the snobbishness of poverty. She was thinking, "You don't know my branch of the family, dear Cousin Eva, if you think it is."

"Your branch of the family," said Cousin Eva, with that terrifying habit she had of lifting phrases out of one's mind, "has no more practical sense than so many children. Everything for love," she said, with a face of positive nausea, "that was it. Gabriel would have been rich if his grandfather had not disinherited him, but would Amy be sensible and marry him and make him settle down so the old man would have been pleased with him? No. And what could Gabriel do without money? I wish you could have seen the life he led Miss Honey, one day buying her Paris gowns and the next day pawning her earrings. It just depended on how the horses ran, and they ran worse and worse, and Gabriel drank more and more."

Miranda did not say, "I saw a little of it." She was trying to imagine Miss Honey in a Paris gown. She said, "But Uncle Gabriel was so mad about Aunt Amy, there was no question of her not marrying him at last, money or no money."

Cousin Eva strained her lips tightly over her teeth, let them fly again and leaned over, gripping Miranda's arm. "What I ask myself, what I ask myself over and over again," she whispered, "is, what connection did this man Raymond from Calcasieu have with Amy's sudden marriage to Gabriel, and *what* did Amy do to make away with herself so soon afterward? For mark my words, child, Amy wasn't so ill as all that. She'd been flying around for years after the doctors said her lungs were weak. Amy did away with herself to escape some disgrace, some exposure that she faced."

The beady black eyes glinted; Cousin Eva's face was quite frightening, so near and so intent. Miranda wanted to say, "Stop. Let her rest. What harm did she ever do you?" but she was timid and unnerved, and deep in her was a horrid fascination with the terrors and the darkness Cousin Eva had conjured up. What was the end of this story?

"She was a bad, wild girl, but I was fond of her to the last," said Cousin Eva, "she got into trouble somehow, and she couldn't get out again, and I have every reason to believe she killed herself with the drug they gave her to keep her quiet after a hemorrhage. If she didn't, what happened, what happened?"

"I don't know," said Miranda. "How should I know? She was very beautiful," she said, as if this explained everything. "Everybody said she was very beautiful."

"Not everybody," said Cousin Eva, firmly, shaking her head. "I for one never thought so. They made entirely too much fuss over her. She was good-looking enough, but why did they think she was beautiful? I cannot understand it. She was too thin when she was young, and later I always thought she was too fat, and again in her last year she was altogether too thin. She always got herself up to be looked at, and so people looked, of course. She rode too hard, and she danced too freely, and she talked too much, and you'd have to be blind, deaf and dumb not to notice her. I don't mean she was loud or vulgar, she wasn't, but she was *too free*," said Cousin Eva. She stopped for breath and put a peppermint in her mouth. Miranda could see Cousin Eva on the platform, making her speeches, stopping to take a peppermint. But why did she hate Aunt Amy so, when Aunt Amy was dead and she alive? Wasn't being alive enough?

"And her illness wasn't romantic, either," said Cousin Eva, "though to hear them tell it she faded like a lily. Well, she coughed blood, if that's romantic. If they had made her take proper care of herself, if she had been nursed sensibly, she might have been alive today. But no, nothing of the kind. She lay wrapped in beautiful shawls on a sofa with flowers around her, eating as she liked or not eating, getting up after a hemorrhage and going out to ride or dance, sleeping with the windows closed; with crowds coming in and out laughing and talking at all hours, and Amy sitting up so her hair wouldn't get out of curl. And why wouldn't that sort of thing kill a well person in time? I have almost died twice in my life," said Cousin Eva, "and both times I was sent to a hospital where I belonged and left there until I came out. And I came out," she said, her voice deepening to a bugle note, "and I went to work again."

"Beauty goes, character stays," said the small voice of axiomatic morality in Miranda's ear. It was a dreary prospect; why was a strong character so deforming? Miranda felt she truly wanted to be strong, but now could she face it, seeing what it did to one?

"She had a lovely complexion," said Cousin Eva, "perfectly transparent with a flush on each cheekbone. But it was tuberculosis, and is disease beautiful? And she brought it on herself by drinking lemon and salt to stop her periods when she wanted to go to dances. There was a superstition among young girls about that. They fancied that young men could tell what ailed them by touching their hands, or even by looking at them. As if it mattered! But they were terribly self-conscious and they had immense respect for man's worldly wisdom in those days. My own notion is that a man couldn't—but anyway, the whole thing was stupid."

"I should have thought they'd have stayed at home if they couldn't manage better than that," said Miranda, feeling very knowledgeable and modern.

"They didn't dare. Those parties and dances were their market, a girl couldn't afford to miss out, there were always rivals waiting to cut the ground from under her. The rivalry—" said Cousin Eva, and her head lifted, she arched like a cavalry horse getting a whiff of the battlefield —"you can't imagine what the rivalry was like. The way those girls treated each other—nothing was too mean, nothing too false—"

Cousin Eva wrung her hands. "It was just sex," she said in despair, "their minds dwelt on nothing else. They didn't call it that, it was all smothered under pretty names, but that's all it was, sex." She looked out of the window into the darkness, her sunken cheek near Miranda flushed deeply. She turned back. "I took to the soap box and the platform when I was called upon," she said proudly, "and I went to jail when it was necessary, and my condition didn't make any difference. I was booed and jeered and shoved around just as if I had been in perfect health. But it was part of our philosophy not to let our physical handicaps make any difference to our work. You know what I mean," she said, as if until now it was all mystery. "Well, Amy carried herself with more spirit than the others, and she didn't seem to be making any sort of fight, but she was simply sex-ridden, like the rest. She behaved as if she hadn't a rival on earth, and she pretended not to know what marriage was about, but I know better. None of them had, and they didn't want to have, anything else to think about, and they didn't really know anything about that, so they simply festered inside—they festered—"

Miranda found herself deliberately watching a long procession of living corpses, festering women stepping gaily towards the charnel house, their corruption concealed under laces and flowers, their dead faces lifted smiling, and thought quite coldly, "Of course it was not like that. This is no more true than what I was told before, it's every bit as romantic," and she realized that she was tired of her intense Cousin Eva, she wanted to go to sleep, she wanted to be at home, she wished it were tomorrow and she could see her father and her sister, who were so alive and solid; who would mention her freckles and ask her if she wanted something to eat.

"My mother was not like that," she said, childishly. "My mother was a perfectly natural woman who liked to cook. I have seen some of her sewing," she said. "I have read her diary."

"Your mother was a saint," said Cousin Eva, automatically.

Miranda sat silent, outraged. "My mother was nothing of the sort," she wanted to fling in Cousin Eva's big front teeth. But Cousin Eva had been gathering bitterness until more speech came of it.

" 'Hold your chin up, Eva,' Amy used to tell me," she began, doubling up both her fists and shaking them a little. "All my life the whole family bedeviled me about my chin. My entire girlhood was spoiled by it. Can you imagine," she asked, with a ferocity that seemed much too deep for this one cause, "people who call themselves civilized spoiling life for a young girl because she had one unlucky feature? Of course, you understand perfectly it was all in the very best humor, everybody was very amusing about it, no harm meant—oh no, no harm at all. That is the hellish thing about it. It is that I can't forgive," she cried out, and she twisted her hands together as if they were rags. "Ah, the family," she said, releasing her breath and sitting back quietly, "the whole hideous institution should be wiped from the face of the earth. It is the root of all human wrongs," she ended, and relaxed, and her face became calm. She was trembling. Miranda reached out and took Cousin Eva's hand and held it. The hand fluttered and lay still, and Cousin Eva said, "You've not the faintest idea what some of us went through, but I wanted you to hear the other side of the story. And I'm keeping you up when you need your beauty sleep," she said grimly, stirring herself with an immense rustle of petticoats.

Miranda pulled herself together, feeling limp, and stood up. Cousin Eva put out her hand again, and drew Miranda down to her. "Good night, you dear child," she said, "to think you're grown up." Miranda hesitated, then quite suddenly kissed her Cousin Eva on the cheek. The black eyes shone brightly through water for an instant, and Cousin Eva said with a warm note in her sharp clear orator's voice, "Tomorrow we'll be at home again. I'm looking forward to it, aren't you? Good night."

Miranda fell asleep while she was getting off her clothes. Instantly it was morning again. She was still trying to close her suitcase when the train pulled into the small station, and there on the platform she saw her father, looking tired and anxious, his hat pulled over his eyes. She rapped on the window to catch his attention, then ran out and threw herself upon him. He said, "Well, here's my big girl," as if she were still seven, but his hands on her arms held her off, the tone was forced. There was no welcome for her, and there had not been since she had run away. She could not persuade herself to remember how it would be; between one homecoming and the next her mind refused to accept its own knowledge. Her father looked over her head and said, without surprise, "Why, hello, Eva, I'm glad somebody sent you a telegram." Miranda, rebuffed again, let her arms fall away again, with the same painful dull jerk of the heart.

"No one in my family," said Eva, her face framed in the thin black veil she reserved, evidently, for family funerals, "ever sent me a telegram in my life. I had the news from young Keziah who had it from young Gabriel. I suppose Gabe is here?"

"Everybody seems to be here," said Father. "The house is getting full."

"I'll go to the hotel if you like," said Cousin Eva.

"Damnation, no," said Father. "I didn't mean that. You'll come with us where you belong."

Skid, the handy man, grabbed the suitcases and started down the rocky village street. "We've got the car," said Father. He took Miranda by the hand, then dropped it again, and reached for Cousin Eva's elbow.

"I'm perfectly able, thank you," said Cousin Eva, shying away.

"If you're so independent now," said Father, "God help us when you get that vote."

Cousin Eva pushed back her veil. She was smiling merrily. She liked Harry, she always had liked him, he could tease as much as he liked. She slipped her arm through his. "So it's all over with poor Gabriel, isn't it?"

"Oh, yes," said Father, "it's all over, all right. They're pegging out pretty regularly now. It will be our turn next, Eva?"

"I don't know, and I don't care," said Eva, recklessly. "It's good to be back now and then, Harry, even if it is only for funerals. I feel sinfully cheerful."

"Oh, Gabriel wouldn't mind, he'd like seeing you cheerful. Gabriel was the cheerfulest cuss I ever saw, when we were young. Life for Gabriel," said Father, "was just one perpetual picnic."

"Poor fellow," said Cousin Eva.

"Poor old Gabriel," said Father, heavily.

Miranda walked along beside her father, feeling homeless, but not sorry for it. He had not forgiven her, she knew that. When would he? She could not guess, but she felt it would come of itself, without words and without acknowledgment on either side, for by the time it arrived neither of them would need to remember what had caused their division, nor why it had seemed so important. Surely old people cannot hold their grudges forever because the young want to live, too, she thought, in her arrogance, her pride. I will make my own mistakes, not yours; I cannot depend upon you beyond a certain point, why depend at all? There was something more beyond, but this was a first step to take, and she took it, walking in silence beside her elders who were no longer Cousin Eva and Father, since they had forgotten her presence, but had become Eva and Harry, who knew each other well, who were comfortable with each other, being contemporaries on equal terms, who occupied by right their place in this world, at the time of life to which they had arrived by paths familiar to them both. They need not play their roles of daughter, of son, to aged persons who did not understand them; nor of father and elderly female cousin to young persons whom they did not understand. They were precisely themselves; their eyes cleared, their voices relaxed into perfect naturalness, they need not weigh their words or calculate the effect of their manner. "It is I who have no place," thought Miranda. "Where are my own people and my own time?" She resented, slowly and deeply and in profound silence, the presence of these aliens who lectured and admonished her, who loved her with bitterness and denied her the right to look at the world with her own eyes, who demanded that she accept their version of life and yet could not tell her the truth, not in the smallest thing. "I hate them both," her most inner and secret mind said plainly, *"I will be free of them, I shall not even remember them."*

She sat in the front seat with Skid, the Negro boy. "Come back with us, Miranda," said Cousin Eva, with the sharp little note of elderly command, "there is plenty of room."

"No, thank you," said Miranda, in a firm cold voice. "I'm quite comfortable. Don't disturb yourself."

Neither of them noticed her voice or her manner. They sat back and went on talking steadily in their friendly family voices, talking about their dead, their living, their affairs, their prospects, their common memories, interrupting each other, catching each other up on small points of dispute, laughing with a gaiety and freshness Miranda had not known they were capable of, going over old stories and finding new points of interest in them.

Miranda could not hear the stories above the noisy motor, but she felt she knew them well, or stories like them. She knew too many stories like them, she wanted something new of her own. The language was familiar to them, but not to her, not any more. The house, her father had said, was full. It would be full of cousins, many of them strangers. Would there be any young cousins there, to whom she could talk about things they both knew? She felt a vague distaste for seeing cousins. There were too many of them and her blood rebelled against the ties of blood. She was sick to death of cousins. She did not want any more ties with this house, she was going to leave it, and she was not going back to her husband's family either. She would have no more bonds that smothered her in love and hatred. She knew now why she had run away to marriage, and she knew that she was going to run away from marriage, and she was not going to stay in any place, with anyone, that threatened to forbid her making her own discoveries, that said "No" to her. She hoped no one had taken her old room, she would like to sleep there once more, she would say good-by there where she had loved sleeping once, sleeping and waking and waiting to be grown, to begin to live. Oh, what is life, she asked herself in desperate seriousness, in those childish unanswerable words, and what shall I do with it? It is something of my own, she thought in a fury of jealous possessiveness, what shall I make of it? She did not know that she asked herself this because all her earliest training had argued that life was a substance, a material to be used, it took shape and direction and meaning only as the possessor guided and worked it; living was a progress of continuous and varied acts of the will directed towards a definite end. She had been assured that there were good and evil ends, one must make a choice. But what was good, and what was evil? I hate love, she thought, as if this were the answer, I hate loving and being loved, I hate it. And her disturbed and seething mind received a shock of comfort from this sudden collapse of an old painful structure of distorted images and misconceptions. "You don't know anything about it," said Miranda to herself, with extraordinary clearness as if she were an elder admonishing some younger misguided creature. "You have to find out about it." But nothing in her prompted her to decide, "I will now do this, I will be that, I will go yonder, I will take a certain road to a certain end." There are questions to be asked first, she thought,

but who will answer them? No one, or there will be too many answers, none of them right. What is the truth, she asked herself as intently as if the question had never been asked, the truth, even about
the smallest, the least important of all the things I must find out? and
where shall I begin to look for it? Her mind closed stubbornly against
remembering, not the past but the legend of the past, other people's
memory of the past, at which she had spent her life peering in wonder like a child at a magic-lantern show. Ah, but there is my own life
to come yet, she thought, my own life now and beyond. I don't want
any promises, I won't have false hopes, I won't be romantic about myself. I can't live in their world any longer, she told herself, listening to
the voices back of her. Let them tell their stories to each other. Let
them go on explaining how things happened. I don't care. At least I
can know the truth about what happens to me, she assured herself
silently, making a promise to herself, in her hopefulness, her ignorance.*

INTERPRETATION

"Old Mortality" is much more complicated than any other story which
appears in this collection. It has, to begin with, many more characters
who definitely participate in the action—Miranda, Amy, Eva, Gabriel,
the father—and several others who are sketched in quite distinctly. It
has, in the first section particularly, a large number of incidents, some
of them seemingly casual and not closely connected with any line of
overt action—the anecdote about the aunt in Kentucky who was famous
for her heft, the anecdote about the assassination of Lincoln, and the
like. The time span of the story is quite long, covering many years and
involving the definite development of a character, that of Miranda.
These facts tend to give the impression of a novel, rather than of a
short story. And "Old Mortality" is a novelette rather than a short story.

There is no definition of a novelette which sets it off sharply from the
short story on the one hand and from the novel on the other. It is longer
than the story and shorter than the novel, but this description in terms
of length tells us nothing about any special aspect of its form. We have
said that "Old Mortality," because of its great number of characters,
its number of incidents, and its time span, gives the sense of the mass of
a novel, but "A Simple Heart," which is strongly centered on one character and has a very direct and uncomplicated method, is also called a

* From *Pale Horse, Pale Rider;* by permission of Harcourt, Brace & Company, Inc.

novelette by some critics. Perhaps there is no satisfactory definition to be made except that based on mere length. It is sometimes said that, because of its relative shortness, the novelette is more unified than the novel in its effect, but it is difficult to generalize even upon this point if by "unity" one means more than the mechanical fact that, other things being equal, a composition with few parts is more readily experienced as a whole by the reader than a composition with many parts. And, in fact, some novels have a high degree of unity, in terms of both theme and plot. The whole question of the *scale* (see Glossary and p. 596) of a piece of fiction is to be considered, not in the light of any fixed definition of a form—short story, novelette, or novel—but in the light of the material and intention of the particular composition.

Let us try to investigate "Old Mortality" in this light, in the hope that our investigation will help us to understand why the scale of this story is what it is.

It is divided, we see, into three parts. The first part involves a time span of seventeen years, and each of the other parts presents a single flash out of subsequent events. The method of treatment in Part I is very different from that in the other two sections. In Part I we are gradually introduced to the family of the little girl Miranda, her father, her sister, her grandmother, Cousin Eva, and others, all presented through the eyes of the child. But the central interest of the section lies in the story of the dead Amy, whose romantic history is given in flashes of anecdote, much as it would have come to the child from family reminiscences. There are, however, a number of other incidents which seem, at first glance, to be without relation to the story of Amy—the grandmother's weeping over the old trunks, the tale about Aunt Keziah, and the like. We have here the general atmosphere of Miranda's childhood presented with a kind of interweaving of past and present, a blurring of time distinctions, and with no obvious principle of unity except that provided by Miranda's curiosity about her family world and its stories. This is not to say, however, that no principle of unity is present— merely that the author has not yet fully defined the central issue of the story. In fact, the central issue is not fully defined until the very end of the story. The author follows, as it were, the line of Miranda's growing awareness from the time she is a child until the day when, as an adult, she is able to look back upon and try to interpret her own past and the past which she has heard about in the family stories.

The process of the definition of the central issue is, in one sense, the process of the story. After we have come to the end, we can look back and see that even the apparently unrelated anecdotes and episodes in Part I have a bearing on this central issue. The central issue, we have said, involves the attempt of one generation to understand its relation to a previous one, the question of the attitude toward the past, toward tradition. This issue is centered upon the story of Amy, which has become a romantic legend in the family. As Miranda first becomes aware of this story it is a thoroughly romantic one. To her father, and to most of the members of the family, there was never anyone so beautiful and captivating as Amy, or anyone who rode or danced as well. The photograph cannot do her justice, the father says. But Miranda, even when she is a child and is enchanted by the legend of Amy, wonders why all the grown-up people who look at the photograph say, "How lovely." So here we have the first contrast between the legend which makes Amy out to be a heroine of romance and the childish commonsense which sees only a faded photograph of a rather pretty girl. The photograph affords a kind of realistic criticism of the legend. And so it is with other things, apparently unrelated to the main issue of the story. When the father, thinking of Amy, says, "There were never any fat women in the family, thank God," Miranda remembers great-aunt Eliza and great-aunt Keziah, who was so fat that her husband would not permit her to ride his horses. This, too, works as a kind of criticism of the legend, for the father, with his romantic temperament, simply refuses to consider the fact of the fat great-aunts. When the grandmother sits by the old trunks and weeps over the keepsakes, the children inspect them and find them to be rather "dowdy little wreaths and necklaces." This is not to say that Miranda or her sister consciously criticize the legend; the legend to them, at this stage in their life, is something in the world of poetry, not subject to realistic, everyday judgments. But for the reader, the contrasts are working as preparation for the final issue.

In Part II, another sort of criticism of the legend appears. Before this, Amy, in the legend, has appeared as a beautiful, willful, charming creature, whom everybody loved, and even her death, in its mysterious circumstances, has a touch of tragedy and poetry about it. But now, we see something of the effect of Amy on other people. Gabriel has become a drunken follower of the races, gradually slipping down in the world, but still clinging to his old conception of Amy, the conception of the legend, the conception which, in a way, is the cause of his ruin. His second wife, Miss Honey, has suffered, we understand, by constant comparison with that legend; she seems to be filled with a "pallid, unquenchable hatred and bitterness," when the past is mentioned. In this scene we have, as has been suggested, another kind of criticism brought to bear upon the legend, not the merely realistic criticism, but a moral criticism—the effect of Amy's beauty and willfulness on other people who live after her.

In the first episode of Part III, the meeting of Miranda with Cousin Eva on the train, is introduced yet another criticism of the legend. After repeating the other types of criticism (Amy was not beautiful, just "good-looking enough," and her illness hadn't been romantic, for she "coughed blood, if that's romantic"—the realistic criticism; and Amy "went through life like a spoiled darling, doing as she pleased and letting other people suffer for it"—the moral criticism), Cousin Eva presents what may be called the scientific criticism of the legend. First, she interprets all the gaiety and beauty of the legend in economic terms: there hadn't been true gaiety and beauty, only bitter rivalry and vicious competition among the belles, and to miss out meant to risk one's whole future, for a good marriage was security. Second, she interprets the legend in biological terms: "Cousin Eva wrung her hands. 'It was just sex,' she said in despair; 'their minds dwelt on nothing else. They didn't call it that, it was all smothered under pretty names, but that's all it was, sex.'" Then Cousin Eva sums up her "debunking" interpretation of the legend. "They simply festered inside," she says of all the belles, "they festered."

But Miranda, catching a vision of "corruption concealed under laces and flowers," thinks quite coldly: "Of course it was not like that. This is no more true than what I was told before, it's every bit as romantic." She remembers her own mother's diary and thinks that her mother, who had liked to cook and sew, had been a perfectly natural woman, and not a creature of "corruption concealed under laces and flowers." Suddenly Miranda, in revulsion from Cousin Eva, wants to get home and see her father and sister, who are solid and alive—that is, who don't have to be defined, as the past has been defined, by any of the incomplete views. The father and sister represent the vital present, so Miranda thinks, as contrasted with the dead past, "dead" because it seems to be only a matter of abstract definitions, no one of which is completely "true."

In the next and final episode, however, the story takes another turn. Miranda finds herself cut off from her father. Her father, although his view of the past, of the legend, directly contradicts that of Cousin Eva, turns to Cousin Eva and not to his daughter. In other words, though the interpretations of the past held by the father and Cousin Eva contradict each other, yet they both belong to that past and understand each other and find more in common with each other than they can find with Miranda. The fact that they both belong to that past is more important than the fact that they interpret it differently. Miranda, hearing them talk about the past, suddenly feels herself cut off from it and from them. She will leave them, she thinks, to their sterile occupation of trying to make sense of their past, of trying to find out the "truth" about it. She says that she will at least know the truth about what happens to her.

Is this then simply a story about the revolt of the younger generation, which repudiates the past in order to "live its own life"? To accept that as the total reading would be to equate Miranda's view with the author's view. Let us look at the last sentence of the story: "At least I can know the truth about what happens to me, she assured herself silently, making a promise to herself, in her hopefulness, her ignorance." Miranda makes the promise to herself to know the "truth" about her own experience, about the present, but it is a promise which, the author implies, will never be kept fully; it is a promise made in "hopefulness" and in "ignorance." Just as her father had lived by one interpretation, by one "truth," and as Cousin Eva had lived by another, contradictory "truth," so Miranda will work out her own "truth," her own interpretation of her experience. But her "truth" may be no more complete than either of the competing views held by her father and by Cousin Eva. It may be a truth adequate for her own life, and she may live by it quite successfully, but it will not be communicable to the next generation, for each generation, each individual, has to work out "truth" anew. That is, truth is not a matter of abstractions and catchwords, for the abstractions and catchwords are meaningless unless tested by experience, unless lived out. Nobody can take another's definition for truth.

But does this mean that the past is to be totally repudiated? Miranda seems to think so. But we have said that Miranda's view and the view of the author are not to be equated. And in this connection, we can see that Miranda's approach to her own life will be conditioned by the past. The problem she has to work out is stated, as it were, in the terms given by her father and Cousin Eva. Her problem is to find a set of terms which will resolve the conflict between these two, just as their own sense of belonging to their past, their special world, overrides their disagreement about the basic interpretation of that past.

We began this attempt to interpret "Old Mortality" with the idea that an investigation of its intention might help us to understand why its scale is what it is. First, we may say that the full rendering of the life of Amy, if given in direct terms, if given in terms of Amy's own

experience, with psychological analysis of her motives at various stages
in her career, would have required a length approximating that of a
novel; and in addition to the problem of rendering Amy's experience,
there would have been the problem of the handling of the minor characters on an appropriate scale. But the author is finally concerned with
the effect of the legend of Amy on Miranda, not with the story of Amy
as such. Therefore, since only the aspects of Amy's story which are
pertinent to Miranda's problem of interpretation are needed, the story
can be given in terms of the flashes and fragments as they would appear
in the family anecdotes. And only such subsequent events as will directly illuminate the legend of Amy for Miranda are needed in the development of the composition—the meeting with Gabriel at the track
and the meeting with Cousin Eva on the train. The fact, then, that
the author is concerned with the problem of interpreting the legend
as it affects Miranda, and not with the realistic explanation and psychological documentation of the life of Amy, permits a scale much smaller
than that of a novel. Furthermore, because of the focus of the problem
of interpreting the legend, the facts of Miranda's life do not need a full
treatment; we learn about Miranda only in terms of her reaction to
the legend. At the same time, the reduction of scale cannot be carried
too far, for the author, wanting, apparently, to give the story of Amy
as it would come to Miranda over a period of time, cannot resort to the
method of summary. If such a method were used, we would miss the
sense of the dramatic impact of the story upon the child. Furthermore,
the characters like Gabriel and Eva have to be fairly well established
in order to make their function in the story clear. We must understand
a good deal about Gabriel's present condition to make the meaning
of Part II clear—to understand the implied criticism of the legend—
and we must know a good deal about Cousin Eva to understand the
meaning and scope of her interpretation. These factors, then, tend to
demand a fuller treatment than would be possible in a story of ordinary
length. But we can see that if the author had been interested in a different interpretation of the material the scale would have been affected.

1. How does the personal story of Cousin Eva give a kind of ironical
qualification to her criticism of the legend? That is, is she in a position
to give an unbiased view of the romantic legend? Likewise, how does
the fact of Gabriel's failure in life afford an ironical qualification of his
view of the legend?

2. How does the section about Cousin Eva's attempt to interest the

little girls in Latin and about the assassination of Lincoln tie into the main thematic line?

3. How does the attitude of the little girls toward the convent relate to the thematic line?

4. Read the novelette "Noon Wine," by Katherine Anne Porter, in the collection of her novelettes *Pale Horse, Pale Rider,* and prepare an interpretation of it.

A Simple Heart
GUSTAVE FLAUBERT
(*Translated by Frederick Whyte*)

I

FOR HALF A CENTURY past the good folk of Pont-l'Évêque had envied Mme. Aubain her servant, Félicité.

For a wage of a hundred francs a year she cooked and did all the work of the house, sewing, washing, ironing; she knew how to harness a horse, how to fatten up poultry, and how to make butter; moreover, she remained loyal to her mistress, and her mistress was not an amiable person.

Mme. Aubain had married a handsome fellow, without means, who had died at the beginning of the year 1809, leaving her with two very young children and a quantity of debts. She then sold what landed property she owned, with the exception of two farms, named Toucques and Geffosses, the rents of which brought her in at most five thousand francs a year; and she gave up her Saint-Melaine house, and moved into another which was less expensive—one which had belonged to her ancestors, and which was situated at the back of the market place.

This house, roofed with slate, stood between a narrow alley and a lane which ended down by the riverside. Within there were differences of level that made one stumble. A narrow vestibule separated the kitchen from the sitting room in which Mme. Aubain, seated near the window in a wicker armchair, spent the entire day. Eight mahogany chairs stood in line against the wainscoting, which was painted white. A pyramid of small wooden and pasteboard boxes was heaped up on an old piano, beneath a barometer. The yellow marble chimneypiece, style Louis XV, was flanked by two shepherdesses in tapestry. The clock in the center represented a temple of Vesta. An atmosphere of mustiness pervaded the room, which was on a lower level than the adjoining garden.

On the first floor you came at once upon Madame's bedroom, very large, a pale flower design on its wallpaper, and for its chief decoration a portrait of "Monsieur" in dandified costume. It communicated with a smaller room in which were to be seen two children's beds, without mattresses. Next came the drawing room, always kept closed, and filled with furniture covered over with a dust sheet. Beyond, a corridor led to a study; books and waste papers occupied the shelves of a bookcase, the three sides of which embraced, as it were, a wide desk made of black wood. The opposite walls were almost covered with pen drawings, water-colors, and l'Audran engravings—souvenirs of better times and vanished luxury. On the second floor was Félicité's room, lit by a dormer window which looked out over the fields.

Félicité rose at daybreak so as to be able to get to mass, and worked on till the evening without interruption; then, dinner over, the plates and dishes cleared, and the door closed and bolted, she would smother the burning log in the ashes and would drop off to sleep before the hearth, her rosary in her fingers. There was no better hand at a bargain than Félicité—nobody equaled her in determination. As for her trimness, the polish of her saucepans was the despair of other servants. Very economical, she ate her food slowly and gathered together the breadcrumbs on the table with her fingers—her loaf was baked specially for her, weighed twelve pounds, and lasted her twenty days.

At all times and all seasons she wore a cotton handkerchief over her shoulders, pinned at the back, a bonnet hiding her hair, gray stockings, red petticoat, and, over her bodice, an apron like those of hospital nurses.

Her face was thin and her voice sharp. At twenty-five, people had taken her for forty. After she had reached fifty, she had ceased to show any signs of increasing age; and, with her silent ways, her erect carriage and deliberate movements, she gave the impression of a woman made of wood, going through her work like an automaton.

II

Yet, like any other, Félicité had had her love story.

Her father, a stonemason, had been killed by a fall from a scaffolding. Then her mother died, her sisters dispersed, and a farmer took her into his service, setting her while still a tiny child to look after the cows in the pastures. She shivered with cold in her thin rags, quenched her thirst in pools—lying full length on the ground to drink—was beaten frequently for nothing, and finally was turned away for a theft of thirty sous, which she had not committed. Then she got into another farm, where she tended the poultry yard, and where she gave so much satisfaction to her employers that the other servants became jealous of her.

One evening in August (she was now eighteen) she was taken to the merrymaking at Colleville. She was bewildered, stupefied almost, by the din of the fiddlers, by the dazzling lights hung from the trees, the medley of costumes, the wealth of lace and gold crosses, the immense concourse of people. She was holding timidly aloof when a young man, well-to-do in appearance, who had been smoking his pipe with his two elbows resting upon the pole of a cart, came up and asked her to dance. He treated her to some cider and to coffee, and bought her cakes and a silk handkerchief, and, supposing that she guessed what he had in mind, offered to see her home. As they were passing by a field of oats he threw her backwards roughly. She was frightened and began to scream. He took himself off.

Another evening, on the Beaumont road, as she was trying to hurry past a great wagon of hay which was progressing slowly in the same direction as herself, she recognized Theodore as she rubbed against the wheels.

He addressed her calmly, saying that she must forgive him everything, as it was "the fault of the drink."

She did not know what reply to make, and her impulse was to take flight.

He went on, however, at once to talk about the crops and about the notable folk of the commune. It seemed that his father had quitted Colleville and had taken the farm at Écots, so that they were now neighbors. "Oh!" said Félicité. He added that he was anxious to settle down. He was in no hurry, though, and could wait till he found a wife to his taste. She lowered her head. Then he asked her whether she had thought of marriage. She replied, smiling, that he ought not make fun of her. "I'm not doing so, I swear I'm not!" he rejoined, and he put his left arm round her waist; thus supported, she walked along. They slackened their pace. There was a gentle breeze, the stars were shining; in front of them the huge wagon oscillated from side to side, the four horses moving slowly, raising a cloud of dust. Presently, of their own accord, they took a turning to the right. He kissed her once again, and she made off into the darkness.

Next week Theodore got her to meet him.

They met in yard corners, behind walls, under isolated trees. She had not the innocence of young ladies of her age—the ways of the animals had been an education to her; but common sense and the instinct of self-respect safeguarded her virtue. Her resistance so stimulated Theodore's desires that to compass them (perhaps, indeed, ingenuously) he asked her to marry him. She was distrustful at first, but he gave her his word.

Soon, however, he communicated a disturbing piece of news. His parents had bought him a substitute the year previously, but now at any moment he was liable to conscription, and the idea of having to serve in the army frightened him. This cowardice, in Félicité's eyes, was evidence of his devotion to her, and she became increasingly devoted to him. She began to meet him at night, and while they were together Theodore tortured her with his fears and his entreaties.

At last he declared one evening that he would go himself to the Prefecture to make definite inquiries, and that he would come back with his news on the following Sunday between eleven o'clock and midnight.

When the time came Félicité hastened to meet him.

In his place she found one of his friends.

He told her that she would not see Theodore again. In order to escape the conscription he had married a very rich old woman, Mme. Lehoussais, of Toucques.

A fit of passionate grief ensued. Félicité threw herself down on the ground, uttering cries of misery and appeals to God. She lay there all alone in the field, weeping and moaning, until sunrise. Then she returned to the farm and announced her intention of leaving it; and at the end of the month, having received her wages, she tied up all her belongings in a handkerchief and made her way to Pont-l'Évêque.

In front of the inn, she accosted a dame wearing widow's weeds, who happened at that very time to be on the lookout for a cook. The young girl clearly did not know much, but she seemed so willing and so easily pleased that Mme. Aubain ended by saying:

"Good. I engage you."

Half an hour later Félicité was installed in her new situation.

At first she lived there in a state of nervousness caused by the style of the house and the memories of "Monsieur" by which it seemed to be pervaded. Paul and Virginie, aged respectively seven and barely four, seemed to her beings of a finer clay; she would let them ride upon her back; Mme. Aubain mortified her by telling her not to keep kissing them every minute. She was happy, however. Her sorrow melted away in these pleasant surroundings.

Every Thursday certain friends of Mme. Aubain's came to play a game of "Boston." Félicité had to get ready the cards and the foot-warmers. The guests arrived always at exactly eight o'clock, and took their departure before the stroke of eleven.

Every Monday morning the curio-dealer who lived down the street spread out his wares on the ground in front. And on that day the whole town was filled with a babel of sounds, horses neighing, sheep bleating, pigs grunting—all these noises mingling with the sharp clattering of the carts in the streets. Towards midday, when the market was at its height, a tall old peasant with a hooked nose, his cap on the back of his head, would present himself at the hall door—this was Robelin, the tenant of the Geffosses farm. Shortly afterwards, Liébard, the Toucques farmer, would appear, short and fat and ruddy, wearing a gray coat and gaiters with spurs attached to them.

They both had fowls and cheeses to offer to Mme. Aubain. Félicité was always more than a match for them in guile, and they went off impressed by her astuteness.

At irregular intervals, Mme. Aubain received a visit from the Marquis de Gremanville, one of her uncles, a broken-down rake who lived now at Falaise on the last remnant of his estate. He always made his appearance at lunch time, accompanied by a hideous poodle whose paws left dirty tracks upon all the furniture. Despite his efforts to maintain the air of a gentleman of noble birth (he would, for instance, lift his hat every time he uttered the words, "my late father"), he had acquired the habit of filling himself glass after glass and giving forth questionable stories. Félicité would put him out of the house quite politely. "You have had enough, Monsieur de Gremanville! You must come again another time!" she would say, and shut the door on him.

To M. Bourais, a retired lawyer, Félicité would open the door with pleasure. His white *cravate,* his bald head, his shirt frills, his ample brown frock coat, his way of curving his arm when he took a pinch of snuff—in fact, his whole personality, produced in her that slight feeling of excitement which we experience at the sight of men of mark.

As he looked after Madame's property, he would be shut up in Monsieur's "sanctum" with her for hours at a time; he was cautious always not to commit himself, had a boundless reverence for the magistracy, and was by way of being something of a Latin scholar.

With a view to imparting a little instruction to the children in an agreeable fashion, he presented them with a series of geographical prints which included representations of scenes in different parts of the world—cannibals with headdresses of feathers, an ape carrying off a young lady, Bedouin Arabs in the desert, the harpooning of a whale, and the like.

Paul explained these pictures to Félicité. This, in fact, was her sole literary education.

That of the children was undertaken by Guyot, a poor wretch employed at the *Mairie,* famous for his beautiful penmanship and for the way he sharpened his penknife on his boot.

In fine weather all the household would go off at an early hour to the Geffosses farm.

The farmyard is on a slope, with the house in the middle; in the distance is the sea, looking like a spot of gray.

Félicité would take some slices of cold meat out of her basket, and they would all sit down to their *déjeuner* in a room forming part of the dairy. It was all that was left of a pleasure house now disappeared. The wallpaper, falling into shreds, shook as the wind blew through the room. Mme. Aubain leaned forward, a victim to sad memories;

the children did not dare to speak. "Why don't you go and play?" she would say to them, and they would run off.

Paul climbed up into the loft, caught birds, played ducks and drakes with flat stones upon the pond, or tapped with a stick the rows of big barrels which sounded like so many drums.

Virginie fed the rabbits, or went to pick cornflowers, her legs moving so quickly that you caught glimpses of her little embroidered drawers.

One evening in autumn they were going back by the cornfields.

The moon in its first quarter lit up a portion of the sky, and a mist hung like a cloud over the winding course of the Toucques. Oxen, lying in the meadows, gazed tranquilly at the four passers-by. In the third field, some got up and formed round them in a circle.

"Don't be afraid," said Félicité, and making a soothing kind of noise with her mouth she stroked the back of the animal nearest to her, on which it turned right round and went off followed by the others. But the little party had scarcely traversed the adjoining meadow when they heard a fierce bellowing. It was a bull, invisible till then by reason of the mist. He advanced towards the two women. Mme. Aubain began to run. "No! No! don't go so fast!" cried Félicité; they hurried none the less and heard loud snorts closer and closer behind them. His hoofs had begun to beat the ground like strokes of a hammer—he was coming down upon them full gallop! Félicité turned round, and snatching up handfuls of earth threw them into the animal's eyes. He lowered his head, shook his horns, and stood trembling with fury, bellowing terribly. Mme. Aubain had by now reached the end of the field with her children, and was making desperate efforts to climb up the high bank. Félicité backed away slowly from the bull, and continued to throw bits of earth into his eyes. She kept calling out to the others, "Be quick! Be quick!"

Mme. Aubain got down into the ditch, pushing Virginie and Paul before her, but fell several times while struggling to climb up the other side, which she pluckily achieved.

The bull had forced Félicité back against some palings. Flakes of foam from his mouth splashed her face, and in another second he would have ripped her up. She had just time to slip between two bars, and the huge animal pulled up short, quite astonished.

This event was a subject of conversation at Pont-l'Évêque for many years. Félicité herself, however, took no pride in it, having no notion that she had achieved anything heroic.

Virginie monopolized her attention, for, as a result of the shock, the child had contracted a nervous affection, and M. Poupart, the doctor, had recommended sea baths for her at Trouville.

Trouville was not a fashionable watering place in those days. Mme. Aubain made inquiries about it, and consulted Bourais, making preparations as though for a long journey.

Her luggage was sent on ahead, on the eve of her departure, in a cart of Liébard's. Next day he himself brought round two horses, one provided with a lady's saddle covered with velvet, the other with a cloak rolled up to form a seat. Mme. Aubain got up on one of them, behind Liébard, while Félicité mounted the other with Virginie under her charge, and Paul rode a donkey lent by M. Lechaptois on the express understanding that great care was to be taken of it.

The road was so bad that two hours were taken to compass its eight kilometers. The horses sank in the mud down to their pasterns, and had to make violent movements with their haunches to extricate themselves; now they had to struggle with deep ruts, now clamber over obstacles. Now and again Liébard's mare would come to a standstill. He waited patiently until she decided to go ahead again, and he held forth upon the people whose estates bordered the road and indulged in moral reflections upon their history. Thus, in the center of Toucques, while passing under windows full of geraniums, he began with a shrug of his shoulders, "There's a Mme. Lehoussais, who instead of taking a young man . . ." Félicité did not catch the rest of the remark; the horses broke into a trot, the ass into a gallop; they now went down a narrow path single file, a gateway was opened to them, two boys made their appearance, and all dismounted in front of a dungheap on the very threshold.

Old "Mère" Liébard on seeing her mistress indulged in warm expressions of delight. She served a *déjeuner* consisting of a sirloin, tripe, black pudding, a fricassee of fowl, sparkling cider, a jam tart, and prunes in brandy—all to a running accompaniment of compliments to Madame herself, who seemed "in the best of health," to Mademoiselle, who looked "magnificent," to M. Paul "grown so big and strong," and inquiries after their deceased grandparents whom the Liébards had known, having been in the service of the family for several generations. The farm, like its occupiers, bore the appearance of age. The beams across the ceiling were worm-eaten, the walls blackened with smoke, the tiles gray with dust. An oak cupboard was covered with all kinds of utensils, jugs, plates, tin porringers, wolf traps, sheep clippers; a huge squirt amused the children. In the three adjoining yards there was not a tree but had mushrooms growing at its base, and tufts of mistletoe sprouting among its branches. The wind had blown down some of them. They had sprouted again, and all were weighed down by their quantity of apples. The thatched roofs of the outhouses, looking like brown velvet and of unequal thickness, withstood the most violent gusts of wind, but the carthouse lay in ruins. Mme. Aubain declared she would have it seen to, and gave orders for the horses to be reharnessed.

Another half-hour elapsed before they reached Trouville. The little caravan dismounted to pass the Écores, a cliff beneath which boats were moored, and three minutes later, at the end of the quay, they made their way into the courtyard of the Golden Lamb, kept by "Mère" David.

Virginie began from the very first to feel less weak—the result of the change of air and the action of the baths. She went into the water in her chemise, having no bathing dress, and her nurse dressed her in a customs-house shed which was placed at the disposal of the bathers.

In the afternoon they went with the donkey beyond the Roches Noires, Hennequeville way. The path rose, at first, through a countryside undulating like the greensward of a park, then came to an upland in which meadows alternated with plowed fields. To either side of the road holly bushes stood up from among the tangle of briars; while here and there a great lifeless tree made a zigzag pattern against the blue sky with its bare branches.

They nearly always had a rest when they reached a certain meadow, whence they could see Deauville to the left, Havre to the right, and the open sea in front of them. The sea flashed in the sunlight, its surface smooth as a mirror, and so calm that you could scarcely hear its murmuring; sparrows twittered out of sight; the immense vault of the heavens was over all. Mme. Aubain, sitting on the ground, busied herself with her sewing; Virginie, beside her, plaited reeds; Félicité weeded out sprigs of lavender; Paul found it dull and was restless to be off.

On other occasions they would cross over the Toucques by boat and go looking for shells. At low tide they would find sea urchins, anemones, and jellyfish; and the children would run to catch the flakes of foam carried by the breeze. The tranquil waves, breaking upon the sands, unrolled themselves along the entire length of the beach; the beach stretched out as far as you could see, but to landward it ended in the dunes which divided it from the Marais—a wide extent of meadowland, shaped like a hippodrome. When they returned that way they saw Trouville at the foot of the hillside. At each step they took the town seemed to grow bigger and to spread itself out, with all its multiform dwellings, in gay disorder.

On days when the weather was too hot they did not leave their sitting room. The dazzling radiance outside formed golden bars of light between the shutters of the Venetian blinds. Not a sound was to be heard in the village. Not a soul stirred in the street below. This pervading silence intensified their sense of restfulness. In the distance the hammers of caulkers beat upon keels and the smell of tar was wafted upwards on the heavy air.

Their principal amusement was found in the return of the ships to port. As soon as the vessels had passed the buoys they began to tack. They came in, topsails down, their foresails swelling like balloons; they glided along through the chopping waves until they were in the middle of the harbor, when the anchor was suddenly dropped. Finally, the vessel came alongside the quay. The sailors threw out their harvest of fish still palpitating and alive; a long line of carts stood in readiness, and a crowd of women wearing cotton bonnets rushed forward to fill their baskets and give their men a welcome.

One day one of these women went up to Félicité, who a few minutes later re-entered the family sitting room with her face beaming. She had found a sister; and Nastasie Barette, by marriage Leroux, presented herself, carrying a baby at her breast, while at her right hand was another young child, and at her left a small cabin boy, with his fists doubled on his hips and his sailor's cap cocked over one ear.

At the end of a quarter of an hour Mme. Aubain signified to her that it was time to go.

They were to be met continually outside the kitchen or on their walks. The husband did not show himself.

Félicité grew fond of them. She bought them a blanket, some shirts, and a stove; it was evident that they were taking advantage of her. This weakness exasperated Mme. Aubain, who moreover resented the familiar way in which the boy addressed Paul; and as Virginie had begun to cough and the weather was no longer good, she decided on a return to Pont-l'Évêque.

M. Bourais helped her to choose a college for Paul. That of Caen was considered to be the best, and thither he was sent. He went bravely through with his leavetaking, content to go and live in a house where he was to have companions.

Mme. Aubain resigned herself to the parting from her son, because it was absolutely necessary. Virginie missed him less and less. Félicité felt the loss of his noisy ways. A new occupation, however, served to distract her thoughts. After Christmas it became one of her duties to take the little girl to have her catechism lesson every day.

III

Having made a genuflection at the door of the church, Félicité advanced along the lofty nave between two rows of chairs, opened Mme. Aubain's pew, sat down, and allowed her gaze to travel all round her.

Boys to the right, girls to the left, occupied the choir stalls; the *curé* remained standing by the lectern; a stained glass window in the apse represented the Holy Ghost overshadowing the Blessed Virgin; another showed her on her knees before the Infant Jesus and behind the tabernacle there was a woodcarving of St. Michael destroying the dragon.

The priest began with an outline of sacred history. Félicité formed pictures in her mind of Paradise, the Deluge, the Tower of Babel, cities in flames, throngs of people being annihilated, idols being shattered, and these bewildering visions filled her with awe of the Almighty and terror of His wrath. The story of the Passion moved her to tears. Why had Jesus been crucified—He who had cherished little children, who had given food to the multitude, who had cured the blind, and who had chosen, out of love and kindness, to be born in the midst of the poor, in a stable? The seed times, the harvest times, the pressing of the grapes, these and all the other familiar things spoken of in the Gospel belonged to her life; the coming of the Savior sanctified them; and she began to love lambs more tenderly for love of The Lamb, doves, because of the Holy Ghost.

She found it difficult to imagine His Person, for He was not only a bird but also a flame, and at other times a breath. Perhaps it was His light that flew hither and thither at night by the borders of the marshes, His breath that moved the clouds, His voice that lent harmony to the bells? She remained lost in these moods of adoration, taking pleasure also in the freshness of the walls of the church and in its atmosphere of peace.

As for dogmas, she understood nothing of them, made no effort to understand them. The *curé* discoursed, the children repeated what they had learnt; presently she fell asleep, waking suddenly when they all got up to go and their sabots began to clatter on the flagstones.

It was in this fashion that she learnt her catechism, hearing it repeated out loud, her religious education having been neglected in her youth, and henceforward she imitated all Virginie's practices, fasting like her and going to confession. On the festival of Corpus Christi they erected a small altar together.

Virginie's first communion was a matter of great concern to her for many days in advance. She busied herself over the necessary shoes, the rosary beads, the prayer book and gloves. How her hands trembled as she helped Mme. Aubain to dress her!

Throughout the mass she endured an agony of nervousness. M. Bourais prevented her from seeing one side of the choir, but immediately in front of her the little troop of maidens, adorned with white crowns above their drooping veils, looked to her like a field of snow; and she recognized her little dear one from afar by her peculiarly slender neck and her devout bearing. The bell rang, the heads bent forward; there was a silence. Then the organ pealed out, and the choristers and the whole congregation sang the Agnus Dei; after which the boys moved out of their seats in single file, the girls following. Slowly, with hands joined, they progressed towards the brilliantly lit altar, knelt down upon the first step, received the Sacrament one by one, and returned to their places in the same order. When Virginie's turn came Félicité leant forward to watch her, and in imagination, as happens in cases of such true devotion, she felt as though she herself were this child—Virginie's face had become her own, Virginie's clothes she herself wore, Virginie's heart was beating in her bosom—when the moment came to open the mouth, with eyelids lowered, she all but fainted.

Next day, early in the morning, Félicité presented herself at the Sacristy and asked M. le Curé to give her communion. She received it devoutly, but not with the same rapture.

Mme. Aubain was anxious to make an accomplished person of her daughter, and as Guyot could teach her neither English nor music, she determined to send her as a boarder to the Ursuline Convent at Honfleur.

Virginie raised no objection. Félicité sighed, and it seemed to her that Mme. Aubain was unfeeling. Afterwards she reflected that perhaps her mistress was well advised. These things were beyond the scope of her own judgment.

At last an old convent van stopped one day in front of the house and there stepped out of it one of the nuns who was come to fetch "Mademoiselle." Félicité placed Virginie's luggage on the roof of the conveyance, imparted some instructions to the driver, and put in the box under the driver's seat six pots of jam, a dozen pears, and a bouquet of violets.

At the last moment Virginie burst into tears; she embraced her mother who kissed her on the forehead, bidding her to be brave. The steps were raised and the vehicle started.

Then Mme. Aubain broke down; in the evening all her friends, the Lormeau household, Mme. Lechaptois, "those" Rochefeuille women, M. de Houppeville, and Bourais looked in to console her.

The loss of her daughter was a great grief to her at first. But three times a week she had a letter from her, and on the other days she wrote to her, walked about in the garden, or read, and in this way succeeded in passing the time.

From force of habit Félicité continued to enter Virginie's bedroom every morning and looked all around it. It saddened her that she no longer had her hair to comb, her boots to lace, herself to tuck up in bed—that she no longer had her pretty little face to gaze upon or her hand to hold, out walking. Feeling the want of occupation, she tried her hand at making lace, but her fingers were too clumsy and she broke the threads; she seemed to herself no good at anything, she became unable to sleep—as she put it herself, she was simply worn out.

To distract her mind she asked permission to have her nephew Victor to visit her.

He arrived on Sunday after mass, his cheeks glowing, his chest bare, odorous of the country which he had crossed. Félicité had a meal ready for him at once. They sat down to it face to face, and Félicité, eating as little as possible herself from motives of economy, so stuffed him up that at last he fell asleep. When the bells began to peal for vespers she woke him, brushed his trousers, tied his bow, and went off to church with him, leaning on his arm with a kind of maternal pride.

His parents made him bring something home always from these visits; it might be a packet of brown sugar or of soap, or some brandy —sometimes it would be money. And he would leave Félicité his clothes to mend—a task she enjoyed especially because it meant that he had to come back to get them again.

In August his father took him off on a cruise along the coast.

It was holiday time. The arrival of the children consoled Félicité. But Paul had become capricious, and Virginie had grown too old to be addressed in the accustomed familiar way, and this produced a feeling of awkwardness, raised a barrier between them.

Victor sailed first to Morlaix, then to Dunkerque, then to Brighton; on his return from each trip he brought Félicité a present. On the first occasion it was a box contrived of shells; next time it was a coffee cup; the time after, a great figure of a man made of gingerbread. The boy was improving in appearance, he was growing into quite a fine fellow; a mustache began to make its appearance, and there was a frank look in his eyes. He wore a little leather hat on the back of his head like a pilot. It amused Félicité to listen to him telling his yarns full of sailor's lingo.

On Monday, July 14, 1819 (she never forgot the date), Victor announced to her that he had signed on for a long voyage, and that on the night of the following day, he would have to go away on the Honfleur packet boat to rejoin his ship, which was shortly to put in at Havre. It was possible that he might be away two years.

The prospect of so long a separation went to Félicité's heart; and, to say good-by to him again, on the Wednesday evening, after Madame had dined, she put on her galoshes and trudged twelve miles between Pont-l'Évêque and Honfleur.

On arriving at the Calvary, instead of turning to the left she went to the right, and getting lost among the shipbuilders' yards she had to retrace her steps; some people of whom she asked the way warned her that she must hurry up. She made her way round the harbor, which was full of ships, stumbling against ropes as she hastened along; then the ground sloped down to the water's edge, there was a confusion of lights, and she thought she must have lost her senses, for she saw horses in the sky.

On the edge of the quay other horses were neighing, frightened at the sea. A crane was lifting them up and lowering them into a vessel, on the decks of which people were shoving their way between barrels of cider, hampers full of cheese, and sacks of grain; hens were to be heard clucking and the captain swearing; and a cabin boy was leaning over the cathead, regardless of all this. Félicité, who had not recognized him, called out "Victor." He raised his head; she rushed up, but they suddenly drew back the gangway.

The packet boat, towed at first by a number of women, cheering, moved out of port. Her timbers creaked, the heavy waves beat against her prow. Her sail had flapped round and nobody on board could now be seen. Soon nothing was visible upon the sea, silvered by the moon, but a black spot, which gradually grew less distinct, then sank and disappeared.

Félicité, passing close by the Calvary, wished to commend to God him whom she held nearest to her heart; and she stood there a long time praying, her face bathed in tears, her eyes turned towards the clouds. The town lay sleeping, the customs-house officials alone were moving about; there was the sound of water flowing unceasingly like a torrent through the holes in the lock-gates. Two o'clock struck.

The Convent would not be open until the morning. Mme. Aubain would be annoyed if she were delayed; and, in spite of her desire to see the other child, she went back. The girls at the inn were getting up when she reached Pont-l'Évêque.

For months and months to come that poor boy was to toss about on the waters of the deep. His cruises until then had given her no uneasiness. You might count on coming back safe from Brittany or from England; but America, the Colonies, the East Indies—these places were dubious regions, at the other end of the world.

Henceforth, all Félicité's thoughts were for her nephew. On sunny days she imagined him suffering from thirst; when it was stormy she dreaded the lightning for him. When she heard the wind shrieking down the chimney or blowing slates down from the roof, she saw him battered by this very tempest, on the top of a broken mast, drenched in foam. At another time—her imagination helped by those geographical pictures—she thought of him being eaten by savages, or in the grip of apes in a forest, or perishing on some desert shore. And she never spoke of these anxieties.

Mme. Aubain meanwhile experienced anxieties of another kind concerning her daughter. The good Sisters reported that she was an affectionate child, but delicate.

The least excitement upset her. They found it necessary to give up teaching her the piano.

Mme. Aubain expected the letters from the Convent to come to her with fixed regularity. One morning when there was no post, she became very impatient. She kept walking up and down the room from her armchair to the window. Really it was too extraordinary! Four whole days and no news!

To console her, Félicité remarked:

"It is six months, Madame, since I have heard any news."

"News from whom?"

"Why—from my nephew."

"Oh! Your nephew!" And Mme. Aubain, shrugging her shoulders, went on walking up and down, as much as to say, "You don't suppose I was thinking of him? He is nothing to me! A cabin boy, a little ragamuffin like that! The idea! It is my daughter I am talking about! Think a moment!"

Félicité, though hardened to rudeness by this time, took the affront to heart but presently forgot it.

It seemed to her natural enough to lose one's head over the little girl.

The two children were of equal importance in her eyes—they shared her heart, and their destinies were to be the same.

The chemist told her that Victor's ship had arrived at Havana. He had seen this item of news in a gazette.

On account of the cigars, Félicité imagined Havana to be a country in which people did nothing but smoke, and Victor went about among the Negroes in a cloud of tobacco. Would it be possible, "in case of need," to return from Havana by land? How far was it from Pont-l'Évêque? To find this out, she put the questions to M. Bourais.

He got out his atlas and entered upon explanations of longitudes and latitudes, and he smiled a very superior smile as he noted the dumfounded expression on her face. He ended by pointing out to her a small black spot, barely perceptible, somewhere in the irregular outline of an oval section in the map. "Here it is," he said. She leaned over the map, but the network of colored lines merely tried her eyes and told her nothing; and on Bourais' asking her to say what it was that puzzled her, she begged him to point out to her the house in which Victor was staying. Bourais lifted up his arms, roaring with laughter—such simplicity delighted him. Félicité didn't understand why he was laughing—how should she, inasmuch as she very likely expected to see even her nephew's portrait in the map, within such narrow limits did her intelligence work.

It was fifteen days after this that Liébard entered the kitchen, at market time as usual, and handed her a letter from her brother-in-law. As neither of them could read it, she had recourse to her mistress.

Mme. Aubain, who was counting the stitches of her knitting work, now put that aside, broke the seal of the letter, trembled, and said in a deep voice, a grave look in her eyes:

"This is to give you news of a calamity . . . your nephew——"

He was dead. That was all the letter told.

Félicité sank into a chair, and, leaning her head on the back of it, closed her eyes, which became suddenly red. Then bending forward, her eyes fixed, her hands drooping idly, she kept saying over and over again—

"Poor little fellow! Poor little fellow!"

Liébard, sighing, stood watching her. Mme. Aubain still trembled slightly.

She suggested to Félicité that she should go and visit her sister at Trouville.

Félicité signified by a gesture that she felt no need to do so.

There was a silence. Liébard thought it tactful for him to withdraw. Then Félicité exclaimed, "It means nothing to them."

Her head fell forward again; mechanically from time to time she lifted the long knitting needles upon the work table.

Some women passed into the yard with a cart from which odds and ends of linen kept falling out. Seeing them through the window, Félicité remembered her washing. Having soaked the things the day before, she had to wring them out today; she got up and left the room.

Her tub and her board were down by the Toucques. She threw a heap of underlinen down on the riverbank, rolled up her sleeves and took her bat in hand; the vigorous blows she dealt with it could be heard in the neighboring gardens. The meadows were empty, the wind ruffled the surface of the stream; lower down, tall grasses leaned over its sides, looking like the hair of corpses floating in water. Félicité restrained her feelings and was very brave until the evening; but in her own room she gave way to her sorrow and lay prostrate on her mattress, her face buried in the pillow, her hands clenched against her temples.

A good deal later she learned the particulars of Victor's death from the captain of the vessel. The boy had been bled to excess at the hospital for yellow fever. Four doctors had him in hand at the same time. He died immediately, and the principal doctor remarked:

"Good, one more!"

Victor's parents had always treated him brutally. Félicité preferred to see no more of them; and they for their part made no advance to her, either because they forgot all about her, or because of the callousness that comes from penury.

Virginie, meanwhile, was losing strength.

A weight on her chest, coughing, continued feverishness, and her flushed cheeks pointed to some deep-seated malady. M. Poupart had recommended a stay in Provence. Mme. Aubain decided upon this, and she would have fetched her daughter back again at once were it not for the climate of Pont-l'Évêque.

She made an arrangement with a man who let out carriages on hire, which enabled her to visit the Convent every Tuesday. There was in the garden a terrace from which a glimpse could be caught of the Seine. Virginie would walk up and down here over the vine leaves fallen on the ground, leaning on her mother's arm. Sometimes the sun, breaking through the clouds, forced her to lower her eyes, as she gazed upon the distant sails and along the entire horizon from the Château of Tancarville to the lighthouses at Havre. Afterwards they would have a rest in an arbor. Mme. Aubain had provided herself with a small cask of excellent Malaga; and, laughing at the idea of its possibly making her tipsy, Virginie would drink two thimblefuls, never more.

The girl's strength seemed to be coming back to her. The autumn passed smoothly. Félicité reassured Mme. Aubain. But one evening when she had been for a walk outside the town, she found M. Poupart's carriage outside the door on her return; and he himself was in the hall. Mme. Aubain was putting on her hat.

"Give me my foot-warmer, and my purse and gloves," she cried out. "Hurry up about it."

Virginie was suffering from inflammation of the lungs; perhaps it was already a hopeless case.

"Not yet," said the doctor; and he and Mme. Aubain stepped into the vehicle, beneath the whirling snowflakes. Night was approaching and the weather was very cold.

Félicité rushed off to the church to light a candle. Then she ran after the carriage, which she caught up with an hour later and jumped nimbly up behind, holding on to the hangings until suddenly the reflection came to her, "The yard was not closed. Supposing thieves found their way in!" And she got down.

First thing next day she presented herself at the doctor's. He had come back home, but had gone off again into the country. Then she stopped at the inn, thinking perhaps a letter might be brought thither by some stranger. Finally, towards dusk, she took the diligence for Lisieux.

The Convent was situated at the bottom of a steep lane. Half-way down it, she heard strange sounds—a death knell. "It must be for others," she thought; and she knocked vigorously at the Convent door.

After several minutes, she could hear the shuffling of shoes; the door was half opened and a nun appeared.

The good Sister, with a compassionate look, said that Virginie "had just passed away." At the same moment, the knell of Saint-Léonard was renewed.

Félicité made her way up to the second floor.

From the door she saw Virginie lying outstretched upon the bed, her arms clasped together, her mouth open, her head poised slightly backwards beneath a black cross leaning over her; between the motionless curtains, less white that her face, Mme. Aubain, clinging to the foot of the bed, gave out sobs of agony. The Mother Superior was standing to the right. Three candlesticks upon the chest of drawers made spots of red, and the fog spread a white mist over the windows. Some nuns led Mme. Aubain away.

For two nights Félicité did not leave the dead girl. She repeated the same prayers over and over again, throwing holy water over the sheets, and sitting down to gaze upon her. At the end of the first watch she noticed that the face had taken on a yellowish tint, the lips had become blue, the nose was thinner, the eyes were sinking in. She kissed them several times, and it would not have surprised her beyond measure had Virginie opened them again; for such souls the supernatural is quite simple. She dressed the body, wrapped it in the shroud, and laid it in the coffin, placed a wreath on her, and spread her hair. It was fair and extraordinarily long for her age. Félicité cut off a big lock of it and put half of it into her bosom, resolved never to part with it.

The corpse was taken back to Pont-l'Évêque, according to the wishes of Mme. Aubain, who followed the hearse in a closed carriage.

After the mass, it took the funeral *cortège* three-quarters of an hour to reach the cemetery. Paul walked at its head, sobbing. M. Bourais followed, and then the principal inhabitants of the village, the women wearing black cloaks, Félicité among them. Her thoughts went back to her nephew, and not having been able to render him these tokens of regard, she felt her sadness doubled—as if her nephew were also being taken to the grave.

Mme. Aubain's despair was boundless.

At first she revolted against God, accusing Him of injustice in robbing her of her child when she had never done any harm, and her conscience was so pure. . . . But no! She ought to have taken Virginie to the south! . . . Perhaps other doctors would have saved her life! She accused herself, wished to follow her child, and cried out distressfully in her dreams. One in particular obsessed her. Her husband, wearing the garb of a sailor, had returned from a long voyage and was saying to her, weeping the while, that he had been commanded to take Virginie away. Then he and she endeavored together to find a hiding place somewhere.

Once, she re-entered the house from the garden, quite overcome. A moment ago (she could point out the exact spot), father and child had appeared to her side by side. They were doing nothing; they were only looking at her.

For several months she remained in her room, listless. Félicité would lecture her gently—she must rouse herself for the sake of her son, and besides—in remembrance of "her."

"Of her," replied Mme. Aubain, as though coming back to consciousness. "Oh, of course! . . . You do not forget." She had been scrupulously forbidden any allusion to the cemetery.

Félicité went to it every day.

At four o'clock precisely she would walk past the houses, go up the hill, open the gate, and make her way to Virginie's grave. There was a little column of rose-colored marble, with a tablet at its base, and a chain all round enclosing a miniature garden plot. The borders were almost hidden by flowers. Félicité watered them and renewed the sand, going down on her knees the better to dress the ground. Mme. Aubain, when she was able to visit the grave, derived some relief and a kind of consolation from it.

After this, years passed by, all very much alike, and without other incidents than the return of the great festivals—Easter, the Assumption, All Saints. Domestic events constituted dates to serve as landmarks in years to come. Thus, in 1825, two glaziers whitewashed the hall; in 1827, a portion of the roof, falling down into the courtyard, nearly killed a man. In the summer of 1828 it fell to Madame to offer the Blessed Bread; Bourais, about this time, absented himself mysteriously; and gradually old acquaintances passed out of sight; Guyot, Liébard, Mme. Lechaptois, Robelin, the uncle Gremanville, paralyzed now for a considerable time past.

One night the mail-cart driver announced in Pont-l'Évêque the Revolution of July. A new subprefect was nominated some days later: the Baron de Larsonnière, who had been previously a consul in America, and who brought with him, in addition to his wife, his sister-in-law and her three daughters, almost grown up. They were all to be seen on their lawn, wearing loosely made blouses; they were the owners of a Negro and a parrot. Mme. Aubain received a visit from them and duly returned it. Félicité used always to run to her mistress to let her know whenever she saw any of them approaching, no matter how far off they might be. But the only things that could now arouse Mme. Aubain were her son's letters.

He could not follow any profession, spending all his time in drinking houses. She paid his debts, but he contracted new ones; and Mme. Aubain's sighs, as she sat knitting by the window, reached the ears of Félicité, turning her spinning wheel in the kitchen.

They used to walk together under the fruit wall; they talked always of Virginie, speculating as to whether such and such a thing would have pleased her, what she would have said on this occasion or on that.

All her little belongings were gathered together in a cupboard in the double-bedded room. Mme. Aubain abstained as much as possible from inspecting them. One summer's day she resigned herself to doing so, and moths flew out of the cupboard.

Her dresses lay folded under a shelf on which were three dolls, some hoops, a set of doll's-house furniture, and the basin she used. Mme. Aubain and Félicité also took out the petticoats, stockings, and handkerchiefs, and spread them out upon the two beds before folding them up again. The sun shining on these poor little treasures revealed spots and stains and the creases made by the movements of the body that had worn them. Outside, the atmosphere was warm and the sky blue; a thrush was warbling; the world seemed steeped in peace. Presently they came upon a small plush hat, with deep pile, chestnut colored; but it was all moth-eaten. Félicité took possession of it for herself. The eyes of the two women met and filled with tears. Then the mistress opened wide her arms and the servant threw herself into them; and they held each other fast, finding vent for their common grief in the kiss that annulled all difference of rank.

It was the first time in their lives that they had embraced, for Mme. Aubain was not demonstrative by nature. Félicité felt grateful to her as for some actual benefit, and henceforth tended her with as much devotion as a dumb animal, and with a religious veneration.

The benevolence of her heart developed.

When she heard in the street the drums of a regiment marching past, she would take up her position in front of the door with a jug of cider and invite the soldiers to drink. She helped to nurse those on the sick list. She took the Poles under her special protection, and one of them declared he wanted her to marry him. But she had a tiff with him; for, returning one morning from the angelus, she found him in her kitchen in which he had settled down comfortably to the consumption of a salad.

After the Poles came Père Comiche, an old man who was reputed to have been guilty of enormities in '93. He lived down by the riverside in what was left of a disguised pigsty. The street urchins spied at him through chinks in the wall, and chucked stones which fell down on the squalid bed upon which he lay, shaken continually by a cough, his hair worn long, his eyelids inflamed, and on one of his arms a tumor bigger than his head. She provided him with linen and made efforts to cleanse his hovel; she wanted, indeed, to establish him in the bakehouse, if only it could be managed without disturbance or annoyance to Madame. When the cancerous growth burst she doctored the sore every day, sometimes bringing him some cake which she would place in the sun in a box lined with straw. The poor old man, dribbling and trembling, thanked her in his faint voice, and, fearing always lest he should lose her, stretched out his arms as he watched her retreating figure. He died, and she had a mass said for the repose of his soul.

It was on that day that a piece of great good fortune befell her. Just as dinner was served, the Negro belonging to Mme. de Larsonnière made his appearance, carrying the parrot in its cage, with its perch, chain, and padlock. A note from the *baronne* informed Mme. Aubain that, her husband having been promoted to a prefecture, they were going away that evening, and begged her to accept the bird as a souvenir and a mark of her regard.

It had long excited Félicité's imagination, for it came from America, and the word recalled Victor—so much so that she had sometimes questioned the Negro on the subject. Once she had gone so far as to say, "How pleased Madame would be if she had it!"

The Negro had repeated the remark to his mistress, who, being unable to take it away with her, was glad to dispose of it in this manner.

IV

Its name was Loulou. Its body was green, the tips of its wings pink, its forehead blue, its throat golden.

But it had a tiresome habit of biting its perch, and it tore out its feathers, splashed about the water in its drinking trough, and made such a mess that Mme. Aubain found it a nuisance and handed it over altogether to Félicité.

She set about educating it; soon it learnt to say, "Charmant garçon." . . . "Serviteur, monsieur." . . . "Je vous salue, Marie." It was placed by the door, and people used to be surprised that it would not answer to the name of Jacquot, for all parrots are called Jacquot. It used to be likened sometimes to a turkey, sometimes even to a log of wood. These remarks stabbed Félicité to the heart. Certainly it was very perverse of Loulou to stop talking the moment anyone looked at it.

Yet it liked to have company, for on Sunday when "those" Rochefeuille women, Monsieur de Houppeville, and certain new members of Madame's social circle—the apothecary Onfroy, Monsieur Varin, and Captain Mathieu—were playing cards, it would beat against the window panes with its wings and conduct itself so violently that it was impossible to hear oneself speak.

No doubt old Bourais' countenance struck the bird as very droll. The moment it saw him it always began to laugh—to laugh with all the vigor at its command. Its clattering voice resounded through the courtyard; an echo repeated it, and the neighbors coming to their windows laughed too. M. Bourais, to avoid being seen by the parrot, used to slink along the wall, covering his face with his hat, and, getting down to the river, would enter the house from the garden; and the looks he would direct towards the bird were lacking in affection.

Loulou had been given a slap by the butcher's boy one morning, having taken the liberty of inserting its head into his basket; and ever since it had tried to pinch him through his shirt-sleeves. Fabu threatened to wring its neck for it, though in reality he was not cruel, despite his tattooed arms and heavy whiskers. Indeed, he had a liking for the parrot, and even insisted in his jovial way on teaching it how to curse. Félicité, horrified, removed it to the kitchen. It was now relieved of its chain and was allowed to wander about the house.

When coming downstairs it would first lean its beak upon each step, then raise its right claw, its left following. Félicité used to be afraid that these gymnastic exercises would make it dizzy. It became ill and could no more talk nor eat. There was a thickness under its tongue, such as poultry sometimes suffer from. She cured it by removing this growth with her fingernails. M. Paul one day was so imprudent as to puff the smoke of his cigar into the bird's nostrils. On another occasion Mme. Lormeau worried it with the end of her umbrella and it snatched at the ferrule. Finally, it got lost!

She had put it out on the grass to give it some fresh air and had gone away for a minute. When she returned there was no parrot to be seen. At first she looked about for it in the bushes, by the riverside, and on the roofs, paying no attention to her mistress, who was crying out to her, "Mind what you are doing. Have you taken leave of your senses?" Then she explored all the gardens of Pont-l'Évêque; and she inquired of everyone she met, "Do you happen by any chance to have seen my parrot?" To those who did not know the parrot she gave a description of its appearance. Suddenly she thought she descried something green flying behind the windmills at the bottom of the hill, but when she got near there was no sign of it. A peddler maintained that he had come across it shortly before at Saint-Melaine, in Mère Simon's shop. She ran thither. They knew nothing about it there. At last she returned home quite worn out, her shoes in rags, despair in her heart; and, sitting on the garden bench side by side with Madame, she had begun a recital of all her adventures, when suddenly a light weight fell upon her shoulder—it was Loulou! What in the world had it been up to? Perhaps it had gone for a turn in the neighborhood.

It took her a long time to recover from the effects of her overexertion—in fact, she never really recovered.

As a result of a cold, she had an attack of quinsy, followed soon afterwards by an affection of the ears. Three years later she was deaf and had got into the way of talking very loud even in church. Although her sins might have been made known in every corner of the diocese without shame to her or evil effect upon the world at large, the *curé* deemed it well to hear her confession henceforth only in the sacristy.

She suffered from buzzing in her ears. Often her mistress would cry out, "Mon Dieu! how stupid you are," and she would answer merely, "Yes, Madame," and go looking about for something close at hand.

The narrow field of her ideas became still further limited, and the pealing of bells and the lowing of cattle no longer existed for her. Living creatures of every description moved and acted with the noiselessness of phantoms. The only sound that penetrated to her ears was the voice of the parrot.

As though to amuse her, it would mimic the ticktock of the turnspit, the sharp cry of the fish vendor, the sound of the carpenter's saw from across the road, and, when the bell rang, Mme. Aubain's voice calling out "Félicité, the door! the door!"

They would talk together, the bird going incessantly through its three stock phrases, and Félicité replying in words which were no less inconsequent, yet in which her heart poured itself out. In her isolation Loulou was almost a son to her, or a lover. He walked up and down her fingers, nibbled at her lips, hung on to her kerchief, and when she leaned forward, shaking her head in the way nurses do, the great wings of her cap and the wings of the bird flapped in unison.

When the clouds gathered and the thunder rolled, Loulou would give forth cries, remembering perhaps the inundations of its native forests. The streaming down of the rain made it wild with excitement; it would dash about violently, flying up to the ceiling, knocking everything about, and escaping out of the window, would dabble about in the garden; but it would soon make its way in again to the fireplace, and, hopping about to dry its feathers, would display now its tail, now its beak.

One morning in the terrible winter of 1837, when Félicité had put the bird in front of the fire on account of the cold, she found it dead in the center of its cage, its head down, its claws grasping the iron bars. Doubtless it had died of a cold, but Félicité attributed its death to poisoning by eating parsley, and despite the lack of any kind of proof her suspicions fell upon Fabu.

She wept so much that her mistress said to her, "Well, well, have it stuffed."

She asked the advice of the chemist who had always been friendly to the parrot.

He wrote to Havre. A certain Fellacher volunteered to undertake the job. As parcels sometimes went astray when sent by diligence, Félicité preferred to take it to Honfleur herself.

Leafless apple trees lined both sides of the road. The water in the ditches was frozen. Dogs barked on the edges of farmyards. Félicité, her hands hidden under her cloak, trudged along briskly in the middle of the road, wearing her little black *sabots* and carrying her basket.

She crossed the forest, passed by the Haut-Chêne, and reached Saint-Gatien.

Behind her, in a cloud of dust, gathering momentum as it came, a mail cart at full gallop rushed down the incline like a waterspout. Catching sight of the woman, who turned neither to the right nor left, the driver jumped up from his seat and the postilion began to shout out warning, but the four horses clattered along ever faster. The two leaders grazed her; with a sudden jerk of the reins he contrived to swerve to one side of the road, but, furiously, he raised his arm and, as he passed, lashed Félicité with his great whip round stomach and neck so violently that she fell on her back.

Her first action when she regained consciousness was to open the basket. Loulou was all right, thank goodness! She felt a burning pain on her right cheek; putting her hands to it, she found them red. The blood was running.

She sat down on a heap of stones and stopped the bleeding of her face with a handkerchief; then she ate a crust of bread which she had had the forethought to put in her basket, and took consolation for her own wound in contemplating the bird.

When she had got to the summit of Ecquemanville, she saw the lights of Honfleur sparkling in the night like stars; beyond, the sea spread out indistinctly. Then a feeling of weakness overcame her, and her childhood's misery, the disillusionment of her first love, her nephew's departure, Virginie's death, came back all at once like a flood tide, rising to her neck and suffocating her.

Then the urge came upon her to speak to the captain of the vessel herself, and, without saying what it was she was consigning to his care, she gave him his instructions.

Fellacher kept the parrot a long time. He kept promising it for the following week; at the end of six months he announced its dispatch in a box, and then for a period there was no further news. It looked as though Loulou would never return to her. "They have stolen him from me," she thought.

But at last it arrived—and looking a magnificent sight, perched on the branch of a tree which was fixed on to a mahogany pedestal. One claw was in the air, the head was cocked on one side. Loulou was biting a nut to which the bird-stuffer, carried away by his love for the grandiose, had given a gilt coating!

Félicité put it away safely in her own room.

This spot, to which she admitted very few visitors, had the aspect at once of a chapel and a bazaar; it contained so many religious objects as well as other miscellaneous treasures.

A large cupboard was so placed as to make it difficult to open the door. Opposite the window which overlooked the garden there was a round one from which you could see the courtyard; on a table, standing near the folding bed, stood a jug of water, two combs, and a piece of blue soap on a notched plate. On the walls were hung rosaries, medals, several statues of the Blessed Virgin, and a holy-water font made of cocoanut wood; on the chest of drawers, covered with a cloth like an altar, stood the box made of shells which Victor had given her, together with a watering pot, a toy balloon, some copybooks, the series of geographical charts, and a pair of boots; Virginie's little plush hat was tied by its ribbons to the nail from which hung the looking glass. Félicité carried this form of respect so far as even to keep an old frock coat of Monsieur's. She took to this room of hers, in fact, all the old belongings for which Mme. Aubain had no use. This accounted for a case of artificial flowers on one side of the chest of drawers, and a portrait of the Comte d'Artois at the side of the window.

By means of a small bracket Loulou was set up on a portion of the chimney which projected into the room. Every morning, on waking, she caught sight of it in the clear light of the dawn, and without pain, full of peace, she recalled days that had gone and insignificant events in all their slightest details.

Cut off from communication with everybody, she continued to live on like a somnambulist, in a kind of trance. The Corpus Christi processions revived her. She applied to her neighbors for the loan of torches and colored mats in order to decorate the altar that was being erected in the street.

In church she would sit gazing at the Holy Ghost, and discovered in him some resemblance to the parrot. This resemblance came out in a more marked degree in an Épinal picture representing the Baptism of Our Lord. With the purple wings and emerald body, this really presented a portrait of Loulou.

She bought this picture, and hung it up in the place by the window where she had previously put the Comte d'Artois, so that she could see the parrot and it together in the same glance. They became associated together in her mind, the parrot becoming sanctified by this connection with the Holy Ghost, who thus became more real in her eyes and easier to understand. God the Father, to announce Himself, could not have chosen a dove, for these birds have no voice, but rather one of Loulou's ancestors. And Félicité prayed before the sacred picture, but would turn slightly from time to time in the direction of the bird.

She wanted to enroll herself in the confraternity of the *Demoiselles de la Vièrge,* but Mme. Aubain dissuaded her from doing so.

Presently an important event took place—Paul's marriage.

After having been first a clerk in a notary's office, and then in business, in the Customs and Revenue services, and after making an effort to get into the Rivers and Forests Department, at last in his thirty-sixth year he had discovered, as though by a heavenly inspiration, his natural calling, his *métier:* that of a registrar. He displayed such remarkable qualifications for this position that an inspector had offered him his daughter in marriage, promising at the same time to use his influence in his favor.

Paul, now sobered, brought her to visit his mother.

She sniffed at the ways of Pont-l'Évêque, played the princess, and hurt Félicité's feelings. Mme. Aubain felt relieved when she took her departure.

The following week news came of the death of M. Bourais, in Lower Brittany, in an inn. A rumor that he had committed suicide was confirmed, and doubts were raised as to his honesty. Mme. Aubain examined her books and was not long in learning the litany of his misdeeds: misappropriations, fictitious sales of timber, forged receipts, and the like. To add to this, he was the father of an illegitimate child, and had had "illicit relations with a creature from Dozule."

These iniquities afflicted her very much. In the month of March, 1853, she began to feel a pain in her chest; her tongue became clouded, and the application of leeches afforded her no relief. On the ninth evening she died, aged seventy-two precisely.

She had been believed to be less old on account of her brown hair, plaits of which framed her pallid face, marked by smallpox. Few friends regretted her, for her proud manners had kept people at a distance.

Félicité, however, mourned her in a way that masters are seldom mourned. It seemed to upset all her calculations that Madame should die before she did; it seemed out of keeping with the order of things, unallowable and uncanny.

Ten days later (it took ten days to rush up from Besançon) Paul and his wife appeared upon the scene. The latter turned out every drawer in the house, chose some furniture and sold the rest. The pair then returned home.

Mme. Aubain's armchair, her round table, her foot-warmer, the eight sitting-room chairs, disappeared. The wall space once occupied by the pictures was now a series of yellow squares. The children's beds with their mattresses had also been carried off, and the cupboard in which Virginie's belongings had been cherished was now empty. Félicité went upstairs, beside herself with misery.

Next day there was a notice posted up on the front door; the apothe-cary shouted in her ear that the house was for sale.

She tottered and had to sit down.

What chiefly troubled her was the idea of having to give up her own room—it suited poor Loulou so well. Gazing with anguish at the bird, she prayed fervently to the Holy Ghost. She contracted the idolatrous habit of kneeling in front of the parrot to say her prayers. Sometimes the sun coming through the window struck its glass eye, making it emit a great luminous ray, which threw her into an ecstasy.

She had an income of three hundred and eighty francs a year, be-queathed her by her mistress. The garden provided her with vegetables; as for clothes, she had enough to last her until the end of her days, while she saved lighting by going to bed at dusk.

She rarely went out, not liking to pass the second-hand shop in which some of the old furniture of the house was now displayed for sale. She had dragged one leg since her shock; and as she was losing her strength, Mère Simon, whose grocery business had come to grief, came now every morning to cut up wood and draw water for her.

Her eyes became weak. She gave up opening the window shutters. Many years passed. And the house remained unlet and unsold.

For fear lest they should get rid of her, Félicité refrained from ask-ing for repairs. The laths of the roof began to rot; for an entire winter the bolster on her bed was damp. After the following Easter she spat blood.

Then Mère Simon had recourse to a doctor. Félicité wanted to know what was the matter with her. But, too deaf to hear, she could only catch one word—"Pneumonia." It was familiar to her, and she said softly, "Ah! like Madame!" finding it natural to follow her mistress.

The time for the temporary altars now approached.

The first of them was erected always at the foot of the hill, the sec-ond in front of the post office, the third about half-way down the street. There was some contention as to the exact position of this one, and the parishioners had at last decided to place it in Mme Aubain's courtyard.

Félicité's sufferings increased, and she worried over her inability to do anything for the altar. If only she could have put something on it! Then the parrot occurred to her. The neighbors objected; it was not suitable, they maintained. But the *curé* granted her his permission, and this made her so happy that she begged him to accept Loulou, her only valuable, when she should die.

From the Tuesday until Saturday, the eve of Corpus Christi, she coughed more and more frequently. In the evening her face shriveled up, her lips clove to her gums, and she began to vomit; next day at early dawn, feeling herself to be very low, she had the priest call.

Three good women stood round her while she received extreme unction. Then she declared she wanted to speak to Fabu.

He arrived in his Sunday clothes, ill at ease in the dismal atmosphere.

"Forgive me," she said to him, trying to hold out her arms; "I believed it was you who killed him!"

What in the world was she talking about? The idea of her suspecting a man like him of murder! Fabu grew indignant, and began to get excited. "She is off her head! Anybody can see that!"

From time to time Félicité talked with shadows. The neighbors left her, Mère Simon ate her breakfast.

A little later she took Loulou and held him out towards Félicité.

"Come! Bid him good-by!"

Though it was not a corpse, the worms had begun to eat it; one of its wings was broken, and the stuffing had begun to escape from its stomach. But, quite blind now, she kissed it on the forehead, and pressed it against her cheek. Then Mère Simon took it away again to place it upon the altar.

V

The scent of summer came from the meadows; there was a buzzing of flies; the sunshine made the surface of the river sparkle, and warmed the slates upon the roof. Mère Simon had returned to the room, and was slumbering peacefully.

The striking of a bell woke her. People were coming away from vespers. Félicité's delirium left her, and, her thoughts intent on the procession, she saw it as though she were making part of it.

All the children from the schools, together with the choristers and the firemen, walked along the pavements, whilst in the middle of the road came first the Swiss with his halberd, the beadle with a great cross, the schoolmaster looking after his boys, the sister watching anxiously the little girls under her charge; three of the smallest of these, with curly hair like angels, threw rose petals into the air as they advanced; the deacon, his arms outstretched, beat time for the music; and two incense-bearers bowed at every step in front of the Blessed Sacrament, carried by M. le Curé, wearing his beautiful chasuble, beneath a daïs of red velvet, held up by four churchwardens. A mass of people followed, between the white cloths covering the walls of the houses. They arrived at the foot of the hill.

A cold sweat moistened Félicité's temples. Mère Simon wiped them with a piece of linen, saying to herself that some day her own time would come.

The murmur of the crowd grew in volume, for a moment waxed very loud, then faded away.

A fusillade shook the windows. It was the postilions firing a salute in front of the monstrance. Félicité, rolling her eyes, inquired in as low a tone as she could:

"Is he all right?"

She was worrying about the parrot.

Her death agony commenced. A rattle, more and more violent, shook her sides. Bubbles of foam rose to the corners of her mouth, and her whole body was in a tremble.

Now, the blare of the wind instruments made itself heard, the clear voices of children, the deep voices of men. There were intervals of silence, and the trampling of feet, muffled by the flowers strewn along the ground, sounded like the pattering of sheep upon the grass.

The priests appeared in the courtyard. Mère Simon climbed up on a chair so that she might look out of the circular window, and thus got a view of the altar.

Green garlands hung over the altar, which was decorated with a frill of English lace. In the center there was a small casket containing relics, two orange trees at either end, and all along it silver candlesticks and porcelain vases, from which rose sunflowers, lilies, peonies, foxgloves, and tufts of hydrangea. This mass of brilliant coloring sloped downwards, extending from above the altar down to the carpet which had been spread over the ground. A variety of rare objects caught the eye. A vermilion sugar basin had a wreath of violets; pendants of Alençon stone shone on tufts of moss; two Chinese screens depicted landscapes. Loulou, hidden beneath roses, displayed only his blue forehead, which looked like a slab of lapis lazuli.

The churchwardens, the choristers, and the children stood in a line along the three sides of the courtyard. The priest ascended slowly the steps of the altar and put down his great, shining, golden sun upon the lacework cloth. All knelt down. There was a deep silence. And the incense burners, swinging to and fro, grated upon their chains.

A cloud of blue smoke rose to Félicité's bedroom. She distended her nostrils, breathing it in with a mystical sensuousness; then closed her eyes. Her lips smiled. The movements of her heart became gradually more faint, more gentle, as a fountain runs out, as an echo fades away; and when she gave up her last breath, she believed she saw in the opening heavens a tremendous parrot hovering above her head.*

INTERPRETATION

One might approach a study of this story by asking why it is written on this particular scale (p. 596). But to answer this question one must first settle questions concerning other aspects of the story. For instance, what is the main idea of the story, the theme? And, how is this theme realized in the main character? In other words, in this relatively short account of a whole life, by what principle of selection has the author worked? Obviously, the principle of selection of incident has not involved complication of plot (p. 580) in the ordinary sense. Therefore, how is the story brought to focus? Where does one locate the "moment of revelation" (p. 577)? Write an account of the story with reference to these topics.

The following questions involving comparisons with previous stories in this volume may also help one to an understanding of the story:

1. How does the method of handling time in "A Simple Heart" compare with that in "Old Red"?

2. How can one compare the method of handling focus—the moment of revelation—in the two stories.

3. How can one compare the theme of this story with that of "The Lament"?

4. Why is the handling of character and time in the two stories different?

* From *Three Tales;* by permission of E. P. Dutton & Co.

Appendix: Technical Problems and Principles in the Composition of Fiction

IF ONE learns anything about fiction from reading even a limited number of short stories and novels, it is that there is no single, special technique or formula for writing good fiction. Rather, one learns that every good writer develops a method which, in so far as he is a good writer, is specially adapted to the kind of effect which he is trying to give. He has his own view of the world; certain kinds of persons interest him, and certain problems and issues; the experiences and observations from which his fiction is nourished differ from the experiences and observations of other writers. This does not mean that his fiction should be autobiographical, or semiautobiographical, or be limited in its scene to the world which he has been able to observe at first hand.* This interpretation would imply that fiction is nothing but a special kind of reporting, and would dismiss as unimportant the power of imagination by which a writer can create a scene which he has never observed, as in a historical novel—or can make comprehensible the character of, let us say, a murderer, when he has never known a murderer. But this exercise of imagination is very different from the dishonesty, the self-falsification, which, in its crudest form, may lead a writer to adopt certain attitudes or methods because they are fashionable. It is also very different from the mechanical manipulation of characters and scenes according to a set formula—the kind of manipulation which one can see in ordinary magazine fiction. In this kind of fiction one can detect certain stereotyped characters, scenes, and ideas which appear over and over again in different stories, with only a kind of superficial novelty such as would be gained, say, by transposing a typical "western" into a new setting, the jungles of Brazil, the slums of Chicago, or the bush of Australia, or by keeping accustomed settings and characters and working out new turns of plot. Such fiction depends on mechanical suspense, on surprise in event, on flattering the reader's prejudices and ideas, on appealing to *stock responses* (see Glossary). The writers of such fiction depend on the use of a bag of tricks. Their work is quickly exhausted

---

* It is a good general principle, however, that the relatively inexperienced writer should work in terms of life which he has been able to observe at first hand or about which he has some special knowledge.

because of this fact; it does not spring from any real perceptions about human experience.

A good writer knows that the technique of fiction involves not the mere exploiting of a bag of tricks, but the careful study of the possible relationships among the numerous elements which go to make up a piece of fiction. He knows that characterization, setting and atmosphere, plot, style, tone, symbolism, theme, and various other elements must be functionally related to each other to create a real unity—a unity in which every part bears an expressive relation to other parts. We can see, for example, that the very style of Anderson's "I Want to Know Why" contributes something to the total effect of the story; it is constantly telling us something about the boy himself (p. 344). We can see how a very different style in Joyce's "Araby," another story about an adolescent boy, is contributing to a very different effect (p. 423). We can see why elaborate analysis of the hero's past life is necessary in Caroline Gordon's "Old Red," but is not necessary in Pirandello's "War" (p. 571). We can see how, because of its underlying intellectual complication and irony, Kipling's "The Man Who Would Be King" differs from the ordinary thriller, in which violent action is scarcely meaningful.

The good writer knows that there is no single, ideal "form" for the short story—a fixed and sanctified way of handling things—or even a set of forms, already determined, into which he can fit his own story. He knows that, when he sets out to write a story, he is really engaged in a process of exploration and experiment: he is exploring the nature of his characters and the meaning of their acts, and, too, he is exploring his own feelings about them. He knows that any shift in the organization of his story, or any variation in style, will alter, however slightly, the total response of the reader. For instance, we have seen how the hard, crisp, factual style of Hemingway's "The Killers" and its sharp, cinematic flashes of scenes are to be associated in the process of conveying his general view of the world (p. 323); and we can contrast with these factors the highly wrought, complicated, meditative style of Joyce's "Araby," and the close analyses of the hero's feelings which fill out the scenes themselves. The whole "feel" of the two stories is different—and this difference, which may seem unimportant at first glance, is important, and central rather than accidental, because it is through such differences that the fundamental interpretations of an author may be registered.

But if there is not an ideal form for the short story—or set of forms—

the reader who is also interested in writing may well ask: *What is the use of studying stories if I cannot learn from them exactly how to write?* The answer might be put in this way: *There is no ideal form, or set of forms, for the short story, but there are certain principles to which one may become more sensitive by studying stories.* These principles involve the functional relationships existing among the elements of a story, the adjusting of means to ends, the organization of material to create an expressive unity.

It is the hope of the authors of this book that the more important principles have already been illustrated in the discussions and interpretations of the stories included here, but there may be some utility in presenting certain questions which arise in the composition of a story. It is not to be understood, however, that in the actual process of composition an author always encounters such questions in this order, for different writers have different ways of moving into their stories, different methods of exploring their material.

BEGINNING AND EXPOSITION

But let us assume that the writer has a pretty good general idea of his contemplated story: he has a grasp of the basic natures and motivations of his characters, he has decided on the general sequence of action, he knows, roughly at least, what his own attitude toward the material is. But where shall he begin? He is aware that his characters have histories reaching far back beyond the moment of his story. Some writers, we know, have had the method of preparing full biographies of their characters, even though they knew that most of the material in these imaginary biographies would not appear in the finished story; but any writer must have some notion of the history of his characters, enough at least to make him feel that he knows them. But, obviously, a story cannot begin at its absolute beginning. The writer wants to strike into his story at a point which will lead fairly quickly and logically to the crucial moment, the climax, the point of decision on which will hinge the fate of the characters. But in almost every case—or perhaps to some degree in every case—some explanation of the background is required to make the story intelligible. The characters must be introduced, the setting must be established, the basic situation defined. In other words, a certain amount of *exposition* must be presented.

But how much? The answer to this question is always to be determined by the demands of the particular case. In Pirandello's "War,"

Chekhov's "The Lament," or Hemingway's "The Killers," very little information about the past of the characters is required. In these stories the "ordinariness" of the characters contributes to the significance of the events. The parents in the railway compartment in "War" are primarily *parents,* ordinary parents, and the reactions they express show the various attitudes toward bereavement which one ordinarily encounters. Even the words of the main character, the man in the fawn-colored overcoat, are not remarkable, for we can well imagine how he has arrived at his view, from newspapers, funeral services, patriotic poems, and the like; it is simply an extreme expression of an ordinary form of consolation. And what makes the story a story is the sudden and dramatic discovery that the cliché of consolation is not working, that it has not conquered the sense of loss. But this sense of loss, too, is common—it is shared by all present. Thus, in this story, it is not the fact of special histories and backgrounds which is important, but the fact that the histories and backgrounds are *not* special. They do not have to be explained. So in "The Lament" the old man is just a poor and humble old man who has lost his son; his ordinariness, the fact that he does not have to be explained, is significant. The loneliness and pathos of the old man are more significant because he makes no special claim upon us; it is as though Chekhov were saying that it is particularly the poor and the outcast, the people without histories worth telling, who demand sympathy. So with Nick in "The Killers"; he is simply an ordinary boy in an ordinary American town. We sense his history without hearing it. And though the Nicks in real life undoubtedly do have definite personalities of their own, those personalities are not important for the purpose of this story.

But one can see how it is important for us to know much more about the history of the boy in "I Want to Know Why." This boy is more special. He is more reflective; he has begun to raise certain definite questions about the attitudes of society and about his own place in the world. His case is more extreme than that of Nick, and his sensitivity must be more fully realized by the reader. The same is true of Miss Emily, in Faulkner's story, or of Aleck Maury in Caroline Gordon's "Old Red." In fact, the past of the characters in these stories is so important that it is difficult to say exactly where preparatory exposition leaves off and immediate significance begins. One observes, for instance, how in these three stories the past is skillfully interwoven with the present. The element of time is important here; the crisis of each story sums up, as it were, a process which has been going on for years. An even more extreme case can be found in Flaubert's "A Simple Heart," in which a whole lifetime is narrated in a few pages.

DESCRIPTION AND SETTING

Just as, in managing the exposition in a story, the writer selects only what is significant for the final purpose of the story, so he must select the significant items in presenting his settings. Description of setting is not to be judged simply in terms of realistic accuracy; it is to be judged in terms of what it accomplishes for a story. But setting can be used for a number of purposes.

First, and most obviously, a setting which is recognizable, and which at the same time is rendered vividly and memorably, tends to increase the credibility of character and action; that is, if the reader accepts the setting as real, he tends more readily to accept, in a preliminary way at least, the inhabitants of the setting and their behavior. The most successfully rendered setting in the world will not make a reader accept characters and actions which are palpably improbable or preposterous; but the successfully rendered setting does increase, by a kind of transference, the general susceptibility of the reader. Many writers are inclined to bank too heavily on this susceptibility created by realism of setting, and to forget that such susceptibility is only preliminary and not final; the good reader is, after all, concerned with psychological and not physical realism, with internal and not external credibility.*

Second, the setting of a story can have a more direct relation to the general meaning of a story. It is easy to see how O. Henry, in "The Furnished Room," is trying to make the description of the room indicate to us the anonymity and isolation of the individual in a great city. And it is easy to see how Bret Harte in "Tennessee's Partner" is straining, by his use of natural setting, for emotional effects which are not validated in the story itself (p. 218). More successful instances can be found in "The Lament," in which, especially in the opening sentences, the setting is used to create the general atmosphere of loneliness (p. 247); or in Maupassant's "Two Little Soldiers," in which the description of the landscape is used to indicate the country life which the little soldiers miss (pp. 258–259). The greater degree of success in the use of setting found in the stories by Chekhov and Maupassant as compared with those by O. Henry and Bret Harte may depend, in part at least, on the fact that Chekhov and Maupassant do not insist on the significance of the setting

---

* Fiction which is overtly fantastic, such as "In the Penal Colony" and "Old Mr. Marble-hall," is a special case. See pp. 467–468, 479.

as such, do not strain for effect, but depend on the accumulation of details which are realistically valid in themselves, but which, at the same time, are suggestive of the main impulse. The reader tends to accept the setting at the straight realistic level, but the setting, because of the particular relevance of the details selected, is also creating an atmosphere appropriate to the general intention of the story.

Third, it may sometimes be the case that the setting may work for more definite purposes than that of creating an appropriate atmosphere. Let us look, for example, at "I Want to Know Why." A good deal of attention is given to the detailed rendering of the scene at the training track in the early morning: "At the track you sit on the fence with men, whites and niggers, and they chew tobacco and talk, and then the colts are brought out. It's early and the grass is covered with shiny dew and in another field a man is plowing and they are frying things in a shed where the track niggers sleep, and you know how a nigger can giggle and laugh and say things that make you laugh."

Or: "Well, out of the stables they come and the boys are on their backs and it is lovely to be there. You hunch down on top of the fence and itch inside you. Over in the sheds the niggers giggle and sing. Bacon is being fried and coffee made. Everything smells lovely. Nothing smells better than coffee and manure and horses and niggers and bacon frying and pipes being smoked out of doors on a morning like that. It just gets you, that's what it does."

One thing that is important about the setting here is the fact that the boy himself feels that he must dwell lovingly on each item. The way the setting is presented indicates the sensitivity of the boy, and his pleasure in the world of the senses; and we see how this is important in defining the boy's special character for us and in defining his belief in natural goodness which is altered by the experience at the "rummy farmhouse." In a like fashion, some of the descriptive material in "Old Red" serves as a kind of index to the character of the old man: his pleasure is not merely in catching fish for whatever value they may have, but in exercising his skill, his discipline, in enjoying the physical world in which fishing is possible. In other words, his attitude has a large aesthetic component, in that he enjoys the world by direct contact with it and not by what he can use it for. The nearest thing to a direct statement of this idea occurs at the pond, after the description, when he sees the Negro shack and thinks that Negroes always know how to pick out the good places. This remark comes to us charged, as it were, with the quiet beauty of the scene which has been described. But we can also re-member in this regard, how he refers to a stream he had fished in his youth as his "first love." And in the end we see him symbolically merged into the world of nature.

ATMOSPHERE

In discussing setting we have used the word *atmosphere*. This term is usually applied in connection with stories which have a considerable element of description, especially description which is obviously in-tended to evoke a certain mood, as in "The Fall of the House of Usher." In fact, some critics of the short story put such stories into a special category—"the atmosphere story"—just as they put other stories into categories called "the plot story," "the character story," and "the theme story." Now, as a matter of fact, all such categories may be misleading, for all stories involve plot, character, theme, and, likewise, atmosphere. But the category of "atmosphere story" is particularly misleading. What we call the atmosphere of a story—and the word is a loose metaphor for the total feel or mood of a story—is the product of all the other factors, of the nature of the plot, of setting, of character delineation, of style and symbolism, of the very rhythms of the prose. We may take atmosphere to be a result rather than a cause, and a result of the operation of many causes. Therefore description, and especially description of setting, can scarcely be taken as the fundamental cause of atmosphere in a story. Even in "The Fall of the House of Usher," which is frequently called an atmosphere story, the atmosphere is more dependent upon the partic-ular characters and actions than upon the preliminary description. As a matter of fact, it is not the description as such which is helpful in creating the particular atmosphere; it is the symbolic aspect of the de-scription—the crack across the face of the house, the dull tarn, and so on—which is important, for these symbolic items lead us to the central idea of the story. They are simply preliminary statements of the idea. People tend to use the word *atmosphere* in connection with stories like "The Fall of the House of Usher," stories in which the mysterious and poetic elements are played up, but such a story as "The Killers" has just as positively its own atmosphere. And in this case, it is easy to see that the atmosphere is not dependent upon set descriptions but upon the very style (pp. 323–324), the attitudes of the characters, the symbolic force of the scene with Mrs. Bell, and so on (pp. 318–319).

SELECTION AND SUGGESTION

After this digression concerning atmosphere, we may return to another aspect of the problem of setting and description. Just as a writer cannot give the total past in his exposition, so he cannot give the total present in his scene. His problem is to select the relevant details, the items which will suggest the whole scene, and in certain cases give clues to character, situation, and theme. Chekhov once told a writer to cut out his long passage describing the moonlight in a scene and give simply the glint of the moon on a piece of broken bottle. Such a perception might do more to give the sense of a scene than would a full rendering, because more vivid, more sharply focused, more stimulating to the imagination. The special items listed by the boy in "I Want to Know Why" in describing the early morning at the training track give us a sense of the place, but the boy tells us nothing, in any strict sense, about the landscape, the track itself, or the actual buildings. And we have already pointed out how the opening sentences of "The Lament" suggest the theme of the story (p. 247).

The description of persons in a story raises many of the same problems raised by description of setting. In the first place, a complete description is impossible, or if possible, awkward and unwieldy; since one cannot present the appearance fully and photographically, one must depend upon the sharpness of selection of detail, upon suggestiveness in regard to appearance, character, or idea. Inspect, for instance, the description of the main character in "War," or of the main character in Eudora Welty's "Old Mr. Marblehall," or of Miss Emily in Faulkner's story. Or observe the great economy in the description of the gangsters in "The Killers." The details given are few: they eat with their gloves on; the very anonymity and uniformity of their appearance is significant; in their tight-buttoned blue overcoats and derby hats, they look "like a vaudeville team." They have, as it were, no "faces," no personalities; in other words, they are dehumanized. A full description, personalizing each of them and distinguishing between them carefully, would have, in a sense, violated their very meaning in the story. We notice that the only real distinction made between them is on the point of their attitude toward the "job," their attitudes toward their code, and this distinction ties into the main idea of the story (p. 318).

In discussing the previous topics, we have several times referred to *selection*. But this principle applies not only to exposition and description; it applies with equal force to plot structure. The individual items in the chain of events in which presumably the character of a story would participate, in real life, during the span of time covered by the story, are not of equal significance; in fact, the writer does not try to follow, in most cases, an unbroken chronicle of events, but omits from the story itself many possible events, meals, casual meetings, routine occupations, and the like. He selects the events which have meaning, and meaning in terms of the basic impulse of the story, not simply in isolation or in relation to some idea not involved in the story. Even among the events which are actually to appear in the story, the writer exercises discriminations of emphasis and subordination. He selects a certain event to serve as the key to his whole plot sequence. Other events lead to, and sometimes lead away from, such a key event, but among these other events there is also operating a process of selection in terms of emphasis and subordination, for these other events are not all at the same level of importance.

KEY MOMENT

If a writer has not determined his key event, or if the key event is not truly a key, the structure of the story will be loose and vague, the effect will be one of diffuseness, and the reader will be puzzled rather than enlightened. We can examine any satisfactory story and locate the key event, or the key moment. In "The Man Who Would Be King," it occurs when Dravot, on the rope bridge, calls back to the tribesmen to cut. It is the moment when the man who would be king truly becomes king. In "The Lament" it is the moment when the old cabdriver, who has gone back to the stables to see about his horse, suddenly begins to tell the horse about the death of his son. In "War" it is the moment when the man in the fawn-colored overcoat bursts into unexpected sobs. Such a moment brings into focus all previous events and interprets all previous events. It is the moment of illumination for the whole story. It is the germ of the story, and contains in itself, by implication at least, the total meaning of the story.

CLIMAX

We have just said that the key moment, the moment of illumination, implies the total meaning of a story. The very use of the word *meaning* here suggests that the key event, or key moment, is not simply the decisive episode in any merely physical sense—not the moment when, for instance, the hero finally confronts the villain and grapples with him on the edge of the cliff. For instance, we can see that the moment, in

"The Man Who Would Be King," when the intended bride of Dravot bites him and blood flows to demonstrate that he is not god but man, is the decisive moment in the purely physical sense, in the strict plot sense. But that moment does not illuminate the meaning of the story; it merely tells us about the success or failure of the adventure at its practical level. In the same way, in "The Face," by Louis Moreau, the moment when the father tells the outlaw that he will not turn him in to the law is the decisive moment in the plot sense; but the moment of illumination, the key moment, comes almost at the very end of the story. Of course, in some stories, the decisive moment for the plot, as ordinarily conceived, may be identified with the moment of illumination. Such seems to be the case in "The Lament," "War," and "Old Red."

CONFLICT

How does the writer build toward the moment of illumination? He cannot move in an uncontested line to that moment, for if he does, he has no story. All of us tend to think of a story in terms of problem and solution, conflict and repose, tension and resolution, suspense and satisfaction, question and answer, mystery and revelation. A story is a movement through complexity to unity, through complication to simplicity, through confusion to order. The moment of illumination, then, is the moment when the underlying unity is perceived as inherent in the complexity, the simplicity in complication, order in confusion. It is the moment when the relationships among the elements become clear, the moment when the story is seen to have a form, a structure. But this sense of the unity, the form, the structure, the meaning, must be achieved by the movement through complexity, complication, confusion, meaninglessness. To sum up, we are generally told that story means conflict.

There are many types of conflict. There is conflict between man and man, man and society, one idea and another. There is conflict in the external world and conflict in a man's own mind. Now it might be argued that no narrative which presents a purely physical conflict, and nothing more, can be called fiction, a story in the proper sense of the word. For instance, we have said that the narrative of the attack on the fort by Jim Beckworth is not fiction (pp. 3-4). Our reason for refusing to call it fiction was that Jim Beckworth has no motive attributed to his action, that he has, in other words, no character. But now, as a corollary of that statement, we can say that the conflict as given is purely physical and therefore meaningless. If a writer were to try to make a story out of the incident, he would characterize Jim Beckworth, would investigate his motives; and as soon as he did that, he would imply sympathy or antipathy for the man; he would begin to imply evaluation, and, therefore, a conflict of ideas behind the physical events of the incident. In any story, however crude and simple, say the ordinary thriller or adventure story, as soon as even rudimentary characterization is established, as soon as sympathies and antipathies emerge, a conflict or contrast in ideas has become, by implication at least, a component in the story. "Hero" and "villain" mean good and bad, admirable and despicable; the words imply a conflict. In good fiction, however, distinctions are never so easy and crude as in the thriller, and the process of the story, at the level of ideas, may be the effort to make distinctions which are even provisionally tenable.

Let us look at a relatively simple story, "The Man Who Would Be King," with this general consideration in mind. There is an obvious external conflict, that between the adventurers and the tribesmen; then there is the internal conflict in Dravot's mind, that between his original motivation and the newly discovered motivation, a conflict between vanity and greed on the one hand and responsibility on the other. At the same time, in the story, there is a conflict or contrast between two ideas of kingship (p. 63). A story like "Old Red" is more complex. There is the conflict between family ties and personal inclination; the conflict between the individual and society; the conflict between the practical and the aesthetic views of life; the conflict between ambition and enjoyment; the conflict between the values of the modern world of efficiency and "getting on" and a past world, more easy-going. The conflicts in this story are more complex than in "The Man Who Would Be King," but they are not so positively resolved. Aleck Maury comes to a definition of himself, just as Dravot does, but in the case of Aleck Maury we cannot feel that the conflict of ideas behind the story is positively resolved in a "good," as in the case of Dravot. Dravot's final cry on the bridge sums up the view that true kingship is spiritual. But at the end of "Old Red," the background conflicts are still, in a sense, held in ironical suspension, and we are not totally committed to either side; we have simply become aware of the dramatic ramifications of the conflicts, and, perhaps, of the fact that the "good" can only be determined by a recognition of, or synthesis of, certain elements in the competing claims. The same is true in "Old Mortality" or "The Face."

COMPLICATION

We began this discussion of conflict in fiction by asking the question, how does the writer build toward his moment of illumination? He does this by establishing an ascending series of moments of *complication,* moments of tension. For instance, in "Two Little Soldiers," the first moment of complication occurs when the peasant girl meets the two little soldiers. Another, and more significant, occurs when one of the two discovers that his friend has asked for and received a leave without telling him, and has gone off alone. Or we can take as the moments of complication in "The Lament" the various attempts of the old cabdriver to speak of his bereavement.

We have said that such moments of complication form an ascending series. Usually this is true in a quite literal sense—the complications become greater in intensity as the plot moves toward the moment of decision, the climax. Such a direct scaling upward may be observed in "The Face," "Mediators to the Goatherd," or "I Want to Know Why." But sometimes this principle is not literally applied, for the increase in intensity may be simply the result of accumulation of complications, though the individual complications in themselves may be approximately equivalent. Such is the case in "The Lament," for it is difficult to see any great difference in intensity between the first and subsequent moments of complication; the increase in intensity is simply a result of the cumulative effect on the old man.* Furthermore, especially in long and complex stories, such as "Old Mortality," there may be a good deal of fluctuation in intensity among the moments of complication, although the general tendency is upward if one takes the process in the whole.

Earlier in this discussion, we mentioned the fact that a writer sometimes works from, as well as toward, the moment of decision and the moment of illumination. In "I Want to Know Why" it may be said that the moment of decision and the moment of illumination are identical —the moment when the boy looks into the window of the "rummy farmhouse." But the story does not end, as it might conceivably do, at that scene. The author returns to the scene of the training tracks, the place where the boy had known his innocent happiness, and sets up a

---

* There is, however, some difference in intensity, strictly speaking, between the last moment of complication and the preceding ones in "The Lament." In the last moment of complication, the old man is not appealing for attention to strangers, but to his own kind, who might be expected to have a readier sympathy for him.

contrast between the past attitude and the present attitude. Furthermore, we find introduced in this last paragraph, though introduced almost casually, a statement concerning the illumination, an explanation of it: "It's because a man like Jerry Tillford, *who knows what he does* . . ." This is implicit in the scene at the farmhouse, but the author feels the necessity of making explicit the idea which has been dramatized. Here the continuation of the story is not a winding up of the action, for the action has been completely ended; it is merely a rounding out of the basic contrast of ideas in the story, an additional clarification.

The situation is different in "The Killers." The moment of decision, the climax, may be said to come in Ole Andreson's room, and the moment of illumination at the very end of the story, in the last few words exchanged between George and Nick. In other words, after the scene in Ole Andreson's room the line of action directly concerned with the mission of the gangsters is decided, and at the same time Nick has confronted the crucial fact of the situation, the real horror, which is in Andreson's attitude. The story now moves toward the moment of illumination. There is a similar situation, although a situation much more complexly organized, in "Old Mortality." The meeting of Miranda with Cousin Eva on the train may be taken as the climax of the story, but after that, there is a series of incidents building to the moment of illumination which comes at the very end of the story. It might even be argued that the meeting with Gabriel and his second wife in their shabby apartment is the climax *in so far as the myth of Amy is concerned in itself;* that is, it is the moment when the myth of Amy is put to the final question. In that case, the meeting with Cousin Eva would be regarded as the moment of illumination *in regard to the myth of Amy*. But if we keep our eye on the larger thematic concern of the story, and specifically on the story of Miranda herself, the former interpretation seems more nearly just.

PATTERN OR DESIGN

Now after these comments upon plot, we are ready to turn to the question of plot as an aspect of *pattern* or *design* in fiction. The idea of pattern implies repetition. In terms of plot, an actual incident is not repeated; we have rather a variety of incidents in sequence. The repetition depends on the fact that each incident in the pattern of plot, no matter how different from the last, recalls us, directly or indirectly, to the central question, presents to us an aspect of the central conflict, affirms again the "line" of interest which makes us feel that the incidents have some significance. "The Lament" gives us a very simple example: each meeting of the old cabdriver repeats the fact of his isolation. Or each incident recounted by the poor relation in the story by Dickens gives us a statement of his special attitude toward the world. In the interpretation of "I Want to Know Why," it was pointed out how the references to Negroes and to Henry Rieback's father and the incident at the farmhouse all present aspects of the same question. In "Old Red," too, we can see how, no matter how casual each incident may seem to be at first glance, it always returns us to the main problem—the problem of the old man's relation to the world.

The nature of the connection of an incident with the rest of the pattern, with the "line" of interest, is not always simple and direct. For example, in "Old Mortality" the anecdote about the aunt in Kentucky who was "famous for her heft" and who was not permitted to ride her husband's horses, has a very indirect relation to the "line" of interest, to the central problem of myth and action (p. 531). But there is a clue in the romantic father's words, "Thank God, there were never any fat women in our family," and in Miranda's reflection that the aunt was, after all, in the family. Sometimes the connection may even be an ironical one, and work by contrast; that is, the meaning of a particular incident may seem to contradict the general meaning of other incidents. But in such cases, if the writer is successful, we see that, though the meanings may be in contrast, the incidents refer to the same question, tie to the same line of interest. The incident of the conversation between Nick and Mrs. Bell, in "The Killers," approximates such a situation.

It has been said above that plot provides one aspect of pattern. The total pattern of a story involves other aspects as well. For instance, in "Old Mortality" the characters may be conceived as embodying certain different views of the basic question. Details of setting, imagery, and description may also be an aspect, as in "The Lament" or "The Fall of the House of Usher." Furthermore, there may be, and usually are, subsidiary patterns involved in a piece of fiction, for instance, the pattern of presentation for an individual character. But in the actual experience of a piece of fiction, or in writing a piece of fiction, we are concerned, not with the individual aspects of the total pattern, but with the relationship among those aspects.

Though pattern involves repetition, it does not, in a fictional sense, mean mechanical repetition, as does the decorative pattern on a carpet or vase. In the first place, the items, taken in themselves, are different. The various incidents which obstruct the boy's effort to go to the bazaar, in "Araby," are different among themselves, but they have a similarity in function, in a plot sense—the function of obstruction—and have similar ties to the idea of the boy's relation to the world. So the writer of a story has to fulfill conflicting demands in creating his pattern, the demand for variety on the one hand and the demand for repetition on the other. If he fails to fulfill the first demand, his story will seem artificial and contrived; if he fails to fulfill the second, it will seem aimless and diffuse. In the second place, the repetition involved in a fictional pattern is not mechanical, because the individual items represent stages in a progression, because they are stages in a process. The items are all related to the line of interest, to the question, but each item introduces a modification, even if the modification is merely a modification of intensity through cumulative effect. In this sense, the pattern is a pattern of logical, and psychological, change, logical as it relates to the theme of the story, psychological as it relates to the motivation and development of character within the story. Sometimes the logical, and sometimes the psychological, aspect of the pattern may be the more obvious. For instance, in "The Little Dauphin," "The Birthmark," or "In the Penal Colony," the logical aspect of pattern is generally at the threshold of our attention; and in "Old Red" or "I Want to Know Why," the psychological aspect is at the threshold. But always both aspects are present in the total pattern. It is merely a matter of temporary exclusion or general emphasis.

DENOUEMENT

In terms of the aspects of pattern which we call plot, this progression of action leads to what is called the *denouement*—the point at which the fate of the character is clear, the moment of success or failure, or perhaps, the moment when the character comprehends his own final position, as in "Old Red," or when we finally comprehend the position, as in "Love and James K. Polk." In terms of theme, the pattern leads to the moment of illumination, which *may* or *may not* coincide with the denouement, just as it may or may not coincide with the climax of action (pp. 577–578).

CHARACTER AND ACTION

The general consideration of pattern involves a consideration of character; this is, of course, only a way of saying that character and plot imply each other, or that character and meaning imply each other. In other words, when the writer thinks of a character, he cannot think of him simply as a static portrait, or a psychological description, like the portrait of Hastings (p. 4). He must, rather, think of him as a complex of potentialities for action. Let us suppose that a writer wants to put this particular character, Hastings, into a story. He might well begin by considering what Hastings would do in this set of circumstances, or in that, if faced by this problem or by that. He would have to explore the character imaginatively to find a line of consistency, something which might explain apparent contradictions in behavior. That is, a character is a complex of potentialities for action, for many different kinds of action, but not for all kinds of action, only for certain kinds of action which can finally be rendered consistent with each other. A hero may become a villain, or a villain a hero, but the reader must not be permitted to feel that such changes are arbitrary, that they represent real contradictions; rather, he must be made to feel that both kinds of action, the good and the bad, were potential in the character and are consistent with each other. That is, there must be a psychological pattern, even in cases of apparent reversal of character, as in the case of "War" or "Love and James K. Polk."

How does the writer present this psychological pattern? There are many ways, and few, if any, stories can afford to confine themselves to a single way. Since action, movement, change is a central fact in fiction, the most significant way for presenting character is through action. The reader wants to see character realized concretely—through action. But action includes a number of things, violent physical action, the smallest gesture, a thought, a word, a decision. Analysis of motive, psychological portraiture, physical description are also important means of presenting character, but they are always subsidiary because their true function is to point to the moment when character and action are one, when we can realize that character *is* action. Therefore, in using these subsidiary means of presenting character, the writer must remain aware of his true intention; he is not merely trying to give the picture of a man but of a man who is capable of certain actions, certain particular actions. When the writer of a thriller says that the villain has "hard eyes" or a "cruel mouth like a scar," he is acting on a sound impulse. The trouble is simply that he is doing his job very crudely. The reader knows that all villains are not so easily advertised. But the reader, though he may reject the thriller's portraiture, also feels that there are siginficant relationships between appearance and character, even though he is prepared to admit that they are subtle and fleeting. The good writer sets out to detect such subtle and fleeting relationships when he uses description as a means for the presentation of character. The same principle holds good when a writer gives a small, apparently trivial detail. For instance, in "Two Little Soldiers" Maupassant says that on the holiday walks in the country one of the soldiers always carries a little switch while the other always carries the package of food and wine. At first glance, this seems meaningless, but it assumes meaning in relation to character when we realize that the soldier who merely carries the little switch and amuses himself with it is the dominant personality of the two—is the one who gets the girl.

FOCUS OF INTEREST

All the topics we have thus far discussed concern the organization of the material which goes to make up a story. But there are other topics concerning organization which have not yet been touched on, or have been touched on only by implication. These topics are closely related to each other. Let us call them (1) *focus of interest,* (2) *focus of character,* and (3) *focus of narration.* They represent certain questions which the writer confronts as he begins to put his story into shape.

When the writer begins his story he is up against the simple problem of catching the reader's attention. At the first moment, mere vividness of presentation may suffice, but it will not suffice for long. There must be some *focus of interest* to carry the reader along. The reader's curiosity is complex. He has many questions in mind, or in the back of his mind. He wants answers to a whole set of questions: *what? who? when? why? what does it mean?* The total answer is, of course, the total story, but it cannot render itself all at once, and different questions must come into focus at different times in the course of a story. And in different stories, the different questions have different degrees of importance. We can see, for example, that the *where* is intended to have great importance in "The Furnished Room" or "The Fall of the House of Usher," somewhat less importance in "The Face," and practically none in "The Necklace." And we can see that the *when* has immediate importance in "Christ in Flanders." We can see that the *who* is of immediate importance in "Old Red" or "Araby" or "I Want to Know Why" or "A Rose for Emily." Or we can see that the *what* is of immediate importance in "The Lament," and that the *what does it mean* has immediate importance in "War" or "Christ in Flanders" or "In the Penal Colony" or "Old Mortality."

By this it is not to be understood that every story does not involve all of these questions, but simply that certain questions are strongly focused in certain stories and less strongly focused in others. We said that the *what* is of great importance in "The Lament." This simply implies that the particular character of the old man is not played up; that the place might be any great city almost anywhere; that the situation with its loneliness and general defect of sympathy is at the threshold of attention. But this does not imply that the *what does it mean* is not fundamental; that question, however, is held in suspension without being specified. In "War," which, like "The Lament," does not bring the *who* or *where* or *when* into sharp focus, we find, however, that the *what,* the particular line of event, the situation, is not played up; instead, the *what does it mean* is put into sharp focus, for the characters debate in specific terms the question of the appropriate attitude of parents toward the giving of children to their country. In "I Want to Know Why" the *what does it mean* is kept in sharp focus (as the title indicates), but the *who* (the special character of the boy) is also played up, and the *where* (the special world of the racing town). But even in a story like "Two Little Soldiers" or "The Lament," in which the *what does it mean* is not sharply focused, the question is still fundamental. The whole matter is a matter of emphases in relationships among the questions; and it is often the case that a question which is not brought into sharp focus may be, for the whole story, more important than a question which is brought, temporarily perhaps, into sharp focus. In a good story, in which the underlying relationships among the elements are functionally established, the one question will always involve other questions; that is, the good story is unified. But for purposes of controlling the material, and directing the reader's interest, the writer must face the problem of focus. How it is to be solved in any given instance is determined by the nature of the particular story. Skill in handling the problem can best be achieved by the close analysis of other stories, by asking the question *why does the writer focus this and not the other?* and referring the question to the basic intention of the story for answer.

FOCUS OF CHARACTER

The problem of the *focus of character* may be stated thus: *whose story is it?* A story is not simply a series of events. The events are of importance to some special person, or some special group of persons. But even when it is a question of the importance of the events to a group of persons, the importance to some one person in the group is usually brought into the sharpest focus. For instance, in "War" the discussion in the railway compartment is of importance to all present, for all are parents who may be deprived of their children by war. But, first, the importance of the situation to the fat woman is emphasized, and finally, the importance to the man in the fawn-colored overcoat. There is, then, a scaling down of importance from the man in the fawn-colored overcoat, through the fat woman, to the nameless companions. Or in "The Killers" the final importance of the events is attached to Nick, and not to George, the cook, or even Ole Andreson. This does not mean that the events are necessarily seen through the eyes of the main character, but that the relation between the character and the events is a fundamental principle of organization in the story. For example, in "The Man Who Would Be King" the events are seen through the eyes of Peachey, but the relation between Dravot and the events is the fundamental principle of organization—the core of meaning.

In most short stories one character is clearly central. A story like "The Killers," in which the focus of character is not made until late in the development of the narrative, is relatively rare. One can see that in most of the stories in the present collection, some one character dominates the story from its early stages. Considerations of space—the fact that one does not have time to establish many characters—have something to do with this situation in the short story. In novels and novelettes, however, though the general principle of focus of character still holds good, subsidiary characters and their relation to the main situation and main idea may be more freely developed.

In this connection, let us glance at "Old Mortality." Whose story is it? We have several characters of some consequence, Amy, Gabriel, the father, Cousin Eva, and Miranda. In one sense the story of Amy is central. We have the account of her romance and the effect on various other people, Gabriel, Miss Honey, Cousin Eva, Miranda. In terms of action, then, Amy seems to be central. But what is the main line of interest in the story? In the early stages we get hints of the effect of Amy on other people, and become aware of their interpretations of her. But on whom is the effect most significant? On whose interpretation is the suspense finally centered? All the way through, it is Miranda who is trying to understand Amy. We gradually become aware that this is not merely curiosity about Amy, but that Miranda's whole conception of her own relation to the world depends on her interpretation of Amy's story. So it is finally Miranda's interpretation of Amy's story—Amy's effect on Miranda—which is central in the novelette. As in "The Killers," the focus of character does not become clear at the beginning. The focus of character gradually becomes clear as the basic question, or idea, of the story becomes clear, for the question, the idea, is dramatized in terms of the central character. The question here is not, *what does Amy do?* or *why did Amy do what she did?* but, *what does Miranda make of what Amy did?* And the basic conflict in terms of ideas—the conflict between past and present, between myth and fact— is dramatized in the form of Miranda's attempt to understand Amy's story.

When the writer approaches the rough materials of his story, he must always determine the focus of character, for this is one of the organizing principles of his narrative, one of the things which will give his narrative a form. He asks, *whose story is it?* And before he can answer that question he must answer another question, *whose fate is really at stake?* Out of the total context of the events which are, potentially at least, involved in the story, he then selects those items which, at one level or another, are pertinent to the fate of the character and pertinent to our understanding of that fate.

FOCUS OF NARRATION

We have said above that the events of a story are not necessarily seen through the eyes of the main character; and this consideration leads us to the problem of the *focus of narration*. Who sees the story? Or, who tells the story? There are many combinations of focus possible in extended pieces of fiction, such as novels, but for purposes of convenience we can distinguish certain basic types.

First, the main character may tell his own story. In such a case the focus of character and the focus of narration are identical. We have a clear case of this in "I Want to Know Why." Second, the story may be told by an observer who is, to a greater or lesser degree, a participant in the action. For instance, the narrator of "A Rose for Emily" is a citizen of the town in which the heroine lives, and serves as observer. The same situation prevails in "The Fall of the House of Usher." Both of these types of focus of narration involve a first-person account of the events of the story. When the account passes from the first person to the third person, we have a third type of focus, that of the observer-author. We have a case of this in "The Killers." In this story the author tells us everything that happens in the objective physical sense, and everything that is said, but he does not tell us what passes in the mind of any of the characters. Fourth, the story may be told by the omniscient author, or analytic author, the author who does undertake to present the working of the mind of one, or more, of the characters, and who may investigate and interpret motives and feelings. "The Lament" or "Old Red" presents a simple case of this method, a case in which the author confines himself to the penetration of one mind, that of the main character, with other persons presented objectively, that is, as through the method of the observer-author. This situation is the usual one in stories told by the omniscient author, for the scope of the short story can rarely permit the investigation of the consciousness of more than one character. In such cases, the focus of narration supports the focus of character, and tends to make for a unified effect. But in some stories, and in many novels, the omniscient author works in terms of more than one character.*

It is usually said that first-person narration, types one and two as given here, tends to make for greater credibility in that the mere affirmation, "I saw such-and-such," or "I did such-and-such," or "I felt such-and-such," is more readily acceptable to the reader than a rendering without the support of what pretends to be first-hand testimony. But the reader is not so innocent that he is actually taken in by the pretense of first-hand testimony. He is not deceived into thinking that the "I" of a story is a real person reporting actual events. He knows that this method represents a *convention* (see Glossary), just as the other methods do. And he knows from experience, if he has read much fiction, that the illusion of reality can be achieved in the other methods by sharpness of detail, emotional evocation and suggestion, and penetrating analysis. Furthermore, he knows that the mere fact of illusion in fiction is not crucial; the reader, again, is not deceived into taking the fictional illusion for reality, for the illusion is willingly assented to by the reader, and is itself a convention; that is, he knows that the illusion of fiction differs from the experience of actuality in that the illusion has a structure more closely wrought and meaningful than one ordinarily encounters in actuality, in that fiction represents an interpretation of

* If the student has difficulty in keeping these four types of focus straight, perhaps the following scheme may prove helpful:

	Internal analysis of events	Outside observation of events
Narrator as a character in the story	(1) MAIN CHARACTER TELLS HIS STORY.	(2) MINOR CHARACTER TELLS MAIN CHARACTER'S STORY.
Narrator not a character in the story	(4) ANALYTIC OR OMNISCIENT AUTHOR TELLS STORY.	(3) AUTHOR TELLS STORY AS OBSERVER.

experience. So granting that the first-person methods may increase the credibility of the story, that factor can never be taken as fundamental in the choice of the focus of narration.

But what factors do seem to be fundamental in the choice of one of the two types of focus of narration which involve the first person? It would be very hard to generalize on this point. One is forced, rather, to investigate particular instances, and to try to discern the logic of the method as applied in those instances. In "I Want to Know Why" the problem is complex. First, the use of the boy's own language and comment gives the author the advantage of being able to define the boy's basic character, his special sensitivity, without resorting to analysis. The author does not have to say that the boy is sensitive and perceptive; he simply lets the boy describe a morning at the training track or lets him try to tell about his feeling for horses. He does not have to say that the boy is unusually serious and reflective; he simply lets the boy tell how he wants to be O.K. and how he is puzzled about certain problems. The boy's sensitivity and reflective cast of mind enter into the whole texture of the story; we get them immediately and not in terms of analysis or description. Exposition here, preparation for the final situation, is accomplished directly and not indirectly. Second, the theme of the story, the distinction between "good" at the level of nature and "good" at the truly human level, though important and far-reaching in its consequences, is so commonplace that in real life it tends to be accepted as a platitude and then forgotten. By showing us the boy at the moment of discovery, at the moment when he is wrestling with the question, the author tries to revivify the issue. That is, the first-hand rendering of the boy's puzzlement and confusion of mind, as contrasted with, say, an analytical treatment which would imply that the narrator at least—the omniscient author, for example—had a clear conception of the nature of the problem, greatly increases the immediacy and freshness. The method implies some such statement as this: most adults in thinking that they have a clear conception of the moral issue (which is at the root of the story) really shelve the issue, forget it, or ignore it; therefore, to dramatize the significance of the issue, one must take it in terms of its first impact, before familiarity or the ready-made solutions of society have dulled the awareness. So the fact that the intelligence of the narrator, the boy, is not entirely adequate to the problem put before it and honestly admits its inadequacy (as the title indicates) is a kind of ironical rebuke to the complacency of those intelligences (of the readers, of society, and the like) which claim to have the ready answer; the rebuke exists because the complacent intelligences, though presumably having the answer, have ceased to regard the issue as important, and the irony exists because the young and inexperienced intelligence, in terms of its very inexperience, in terms of its fumbling, rebukes the old and wise.

What is the logic of the use of the first-person observer in "A Rose for Emily"? In our interpretation of the story it was said that the relation between Miss Emily and the town was important (p. 412). Therefore the use of one of the townspeople to tell the story enables the author to indicate constantly in a dozen small ways (metaphors, incidental comments, and the like) the attitude of the town toward Miss Emily and of Miss Emily toward the town. If a third-person focus were used, this relationship might be specified and analyzed, but it would scarcely be so pervasive—it would not enter fully into the very texture of the narrative. Furthermore, the very fact that the narrator is limited in his opportunities for observation, that he only sees Miss Emily in scattered flashes, provides a highly dramatic frame for the story—a device for suspense. The mounting curiosity in the town provides, as it were, the pattern which the reader will follow in his own effort to approach Miss Emily, to understand her and the significance of her act.

Or what is the logic behind the use of Peachey as observer-narrator for the main action of "The Man Who Would Be King"? Dravot's story could be told from the third person, and might still be quite effective. But one thing, now present, would be missing: Peachey's attempt to understand Dravot. It is the effect on Peachey which finally points up the full significance of Dravot's development—Peachey's vision of Dravot leading him through the mountains, Peachey's refusal to sell the crown, and so on. Therefore, Peachey's position is somewhat like the position of the narrator in "A Rose for Emily." His reactions provide a basis of reference by which the significance of the main action can be indicated.

In addition to such special functions of the first-person narrative in the above stories, it may be said that the use of the first person may provide a ready-made scheme for selection. That is, the opportunities for observation and experience by the character who tells the story are somewhat limited, whether the story is his own story or that of someone else. The boy in "I Want to Know Why," for instance, is limited in the commentary which he can make on his own situation—cannot fully understand it. Or the narrator in "A Rose for Emily" only sees Miss Emily and the foreman on the street; he cannot be a party to their

private conversations, and he cannot enter into her thoughts. Therefore, in the case of the first-person narrator, the writer has his field of
selection already narrowed; and in the further exercise of the principle
of selection, he must be governed by his consideration of the impact of
events upon the narrator. So the fact of the first person—his limited
opportunity for observation and interpretation, his special character—
gives a certain kind of unity to a story. But this kind of unity can only
be achieved in certain instances. The writer must ask himself: *Does the
narrator have the opportunity of observing or experiencing all that is
finally pertinent to the story?* And: *Is the narrator capable of serving,
directly or indirectly, as a means of interpreting the action?* Then, after
deciding these questions, he must ask another: *Is the style of the narration consistent with the character of the narrator?* (For instance, compare the style in "I Want to Know Why" with that of "Araby"—p. 335
and p. 414). And: *Is the style which is consistent with the character of
the narrator capable of rendering the effects I want?* (For example,
the style of "I Want to Know Why" could not consistently admit the
last paragraphs of "The Face" [pp. 180–181].

The focus of the observer-author obviously shares one basic limita-
tion with that of the first-person observer: it does not admit of any direct
account of mental process, states of feeling, or motives of persons under
observation, except in terms of surmise by the observer. At the same
time, unlike the focus of the first-person observer, it permits unlimited
opportunity for observation. The first-person observer is a *person,* and
he can see only what would be possible for a person to see, but the
observer-author can follow his character to a desert island or a locked
room. But this method must dispense with the advantage which the
method of the first-person observer may, as we have pointed out (pp. 589–
591), give: the use of the narrator as a kind of interpreter—a kind of
refractor for the action, a basis of reference by which the significance
of the main action may be indicated. In the method of observer-author,
all must depend directly on presentation of background, external action,
gesture, and speech. The method tends to reduce the story to a series
of objective scenes much after the manner of a play, as in "The Killers."
Therefore, the writer, in considering such a method for a story, must
ask himself: *Can I dispense with the advantage of the "refractor" and
still make my point?* For instance, suppose such a writer had in mind
the materials which we find in "A Rose for Emily," and wanted, like
Faulkner, to emphasize the town-Emily relationship. He might work
out the whole story of Emily scenically, and even give more of Emily's

career than Faulkner does. He might even put in two or three scenes between Emily and the townspeople. But he might find, in the end, that he had been unable by such a method to convey the constant sense of the eyes of the community upon her, and had been unable to define the strangely mixed reverential and condemnatory attitude of the community. So he might be forced to come back to the narrator who is, as it were, the eyes and voice of the community. But in "The Killers" the author is able to present his total meaning without a refractor, or interpreter; the material is such that it can be worked out in self-contained scenes, with no commentary beyond that implied in the special style (pp. 323–324).

But the observer-author method would be impossible in "Old Red," just as would be the method of observer-narrator. For in this case, the true stage of the action is inside the head of the old man; we are dealing with the psychological process by which he arrives at self-definition. The same thing is true of "Old Mortality" or "The Lament" or "The Kiss." We see that these stories share one characteristic: all of them depend, as stories, upon the analysis of states of feeling of the main character, upon subtle psychological changes. When this sort of "inwardness of character" is involved, obviously one cannot use the focus of first-person observer or of observer-author. Conceivably in such cases, the first-person hero might tell his own story, for he himself knows, presumably, what he thinks and feels. But does he always have the maturity and detachment and skill in psychological analysis necessary to understand himself? We have said that in "I Want to Know Why" the fact that the hero is fumbling with the question, that he has, presumably, less experience and psychological expertness than the reader, creates an irony which is functional in the story (p. 590). But in other stories we can understand how commentary, either direct or indirect, on the part of the omniscient author may be necessary. For instance, the last sentences of "Old Mortality" raise such a question: "At least I can know the truth about what happens to me, she assured herself silently, making a promise to herself, in her hopefulness, her ignorance." Miranda could have told her own story, but we would have missed the words *hopefulness* and *ignorance,* which represent a commentary from the author, and a commentary on which the story rests (p. 533). Or if the old man in "The Lament" should tell his own story, it would be almost impossible to avoid extreme sentimentality; the omniscient author can adopt an attitude of detachment, he can give us an account without overtly appealing to our feelings, he can summarize and analyze, he can keep his distance from the events, but if the old man himself were to tell the story, the mere fact of his telling it might imply a sort of self-pity, or at least an excessive self-consciousness which is not in keeping with the character.

DISTANCE

These last remarks on "The Lament" and the whole discussion of the focus of narration, suggest another problem with which the writer must deal, or rather, suggest two problems, that of *distance* and that of *tone*.

The word *distance* used in this sense is, of course, a metaphor, just as the word *atmosphere* is in criticism. But we do have the feeling that in some stories the writer is "closer" to his character than in others, that he wants the reader's feelings and attitudes to be more nearly equated with those of the character, that he wants the reader's sympathies to be more immediately implicated. We can see how the problem of the focus of narration may involve this problem of distance. First-person narration tends to shorten the distance between the reader and the fictional character; for instance, the character narrating his own story tends to give us the world strictly in his own terms, in his own feelings and attitudes, and he can scarcely see himself in a large context. He tends to reveal himself rather than to pass judgment upon himself, to give comments about himself, or to analyze himself. Such judgments, comments, and analyses exist in such a story, but they exist by implication, and the reader must formulate them for himself. Judgment and analysis depend upon detachment, upon a standard outside the character being judged and analyzed. Obviously such a method as that of the observer-author, which merely records objectively dialogue, setting, and action without ever going into the consciousness of characters, tends to imply a greater distance than either type which uses the first-person narrator; for even the first-person observer, though he may comment and pass judgment upon the main character, nevertheless, immediately involves the reader in the world in which the main character moves —as in "The Man Who Would Be King" or in "A Rose for Emily." But the fourth type of focus, that of the omniscient author, may involve very great or very little distance.

On this point, let us compare "Old Red" with "The Necklace." In the first story, we plunge immediately into the old man's view of the world about him, and as the story goes on, added details and events come to us primarily through him. When the past appears in the story, it is introduced in terms of the old man's recollection, in terms of his attempt to make his past make sense. By contrast, in "The Necklace," when the past is introduced in the very opening paragraphs, we have a bare, clipped summary given in terms of the writer's mind, and with his analyses and commentaries. He gives us the essential facts of the past, with a kind of brutal directness and economy, as though he were thinking, "Well, there's not a great deal in this woman's past worth recounting; so I'll only give you the essentials—the rest would probably bore you." The whole story is written from a considerable distance, a distance which permits the compact summaries, the sharp commentaries, the rigorous selection of incident. For instance, the passage of ten years is indicated in a sentence. It is not to be understood that such a degree of distance is always to be taken as implying a highly critical or unsympathetic attitude toward a character. At the very end of "The Necklace" we discover a sympathy for the heroine—as we understand the moral regeneration which the period of deprivation has brought about. And in "Two Little Soldiers" there is considerable distance from the characters, but here the attitude is definitely one of sympathy on the part of Maupassant; the distance works to give a kind of understatement. The writer does not try to make us sympathetic by means of a close treatment, by dwelling on the minute responses of the two little soldiers to their situation, by implicating us too closely. Such a treatment might eventuate in sentimentality, by insisting too much, as it were, on the pathos of the situation. It would seem, rather, that the author is thinking along these lines: "The pathos of the situation is such that I do not have to develop it in detail; all I have to do is to give an account which, because of the suggestiveness of the few details I select and because of the accuracy of the main line, will give its effect without any straining on my part." In "War," a similar line of argument might be surmised.

As has been said above, the problem of distance is closely related to that of *tone*. Again, as in the case of distance, one may come to an understanding of the term by considering it as a metaphor. When, in ordinary conversation, somebody says something, we depend on the tone of voice as well as on the actual words to tell us exactly what the speaker means. For example, the word *yes* may not mean yes at all. Because of an ironical inflection, it may mean quite the contrary, or it may mean a grudging and bitter assent. The tone of voice indicates the attitude of the speaker toward what is being said.

But obviously a writer cannot indicate his attitude by any such direct means. He must fall back on all sorts of devices to indicate his attitude. And usually, the underlying attitude of the writer is not given by statement, but by a complex of such devices. We have already indicated how in "The Necklace" and "Two Little Soldiers" the attitude of the writer is involved in the matter of distance. And we can see how, in such a story as "The Secret Life of Walter Mitty," the mixture of sympathy and amusement may be related to the particular degree of distance taken by the writer. He lets Mr. Mitty speak for himself, or rather, he give us in full detail certain sections of Mr. Mitty's thoughts. He comes very close to Mr. Mitty, but at the same time he renders Mr. Mitty preposterous and ridiculous. The style of Mr. Mitty's thoughts is the style of adventure stories in cheap magazines, or movie thrillers, and that style indicates the degree of seriousness which we are to attach to Mr. Mitty's meditations. But at the same time there is a certain sympathy for the henpecked little man whose only escape from the tyranny of his wife and the dullness of his routine is by means of these ridiculous daydreams. Here the style of Mr. Mitty's thoughts is the primary device used to indicate the writer's attitude. And, as we have already seen, the style of "The Killers" (p. 323) or that of "Araby" (p. 423) is important in indicating the underlying attitude. And it might be pointed out that the sudden shift of style from that of the main body of "The Face" to that of the last paragraph is important. The narrator, who in the main body of the story has been writing of his experience as a child, and who has used a rather simple reportorial style, suddenly shifts into a formal, highly wrought style as, from the vantage point of maturity, he looks back on the event of his childhood and tries to interpret it. We have already pointed out the special tone involved in "In the Penal Colony" and its relation to the questions of style and distance.

SCALE

In addition to all of the foregoing questions which the writer must confront, consciously or unconsciously, there are the problems of *scale* and *pace,* problems which involve a number of the preceding problems.

The problem of *scale* simply means this: *How long should the particular story be?* This question has two aspects, one mechanical and the other interpretive. The first aspect involves the degree of complication inherent in the story material. "The Man Who Would Be King" must, obviously, be longer than, say, "The Lament" or "Christ in Flanders." In "The Lament" nothing is necessary to the point of the action except a few immediate events: we need to know nothing of the son except the fact of his death, nothing about the old man except his overmastering impulse to tell of his bereavement (p. 250). In "The Man Who Would

Be King," however, we must have more than the events taken at the crisis: we need to know what Dravot was and what motives he had at the beginning of the adventure, if we are to appreciate the change which overtakes him, and we need to know the effect on Peachey. In other words, here the fact of change or development is important, and therefore must be documented. We must get a sense of the process, which involves time and the history of the character. Of course, there are ways to foreshorten the fictional "time"; that is, to give the impression of the passage of time, with consequent change, without the presentation of full documentation. In "Old Red" the sense of the past is rendered by a series of *cutbacks* (see Glossary) presented through the mind of the main character, and in "A Rose for Emily" the observer-narrator gives summaries which foreshorten the time. In "Araby," as has been previously stated (p. 423), the nature of the style implies a foreshortening of time; but this story and "The Face" really avoid the problem of development, for they take an incident from the past and simply interpret it as a single, inclusive symbol for a subsequent development, in no way specified, in the life of the character. But it is to be observed that in the actual body of the action, in both "The Face" and "Araby," no account of development *antecedent* to the action is required. The foreshortening is a foreshortening of future and not past time, in relation to the main body of the action. So the situation in these stories is, in so far as there is no need for exploration of a past which exists before the main action, similar to that in "The Lament," and different from that in "The Man Who Would Be King." In other words, the scale of these stories can be "short" and not "long"—relatively speaking.

It is not to be pretended that the consideration which we have called mechanical is to be distinguished too sharply from that which we have called interpretive, for in the above discussion it will be seen that, for instance in "The Man Who Would Be King," the necessity for rendering the past depends upon the point which the writer wishes to make concerning the action; that is, upon his interpretation. But the mechanical factors can be specified in such a case; we can see the amount of exposition required and the number of stages in complication required.

The distinction will perhaps become clearer if we examine "Old Mortality." We can see, for instance, that if the story of Amy were told completely we would have something which might be a full-length novel. The material for such a novel seems to be inherent in the story we now have; the implied situations are rich enough to stand a full analytic treatment if the author had chosen to give such a treatment—

the motives leading up to Amy's marriage, the desperation which caused her suicide, and so on. In such a treatment the author would have been compelled to make a rather close psychological study of Amy, and of some subordinate characters, Gabriel for example. We do have a fairly clear notion of Amy's character, but of her character as *it can be defined after her life, and summed up, and not as it would appear in terms of her day-by-day experience, that is, as she developed her character*. We do not have a rendering of Amy's character in the process of defining itself. There is no close psychological study. Nor is there any close psychological study of Miranda; we have, rather, a study of Miranda's attitude toward the myth of which Amy is the center, and finally, when we do fully enter into Miranda's mind at the end of the story, we find the question of the nature of the myth, the question of the past and the present, cast in fairly general terms—the terms of Miranda's decision to view herself and the world in a certain way. We have only hints of the steps which led Miranda up to this moment and which made it meaningful to her—her elopement and her estrangement from her father, for example. This does not mean that the author does not have a firm grasp on the psychology of the characters involved; it simply means that, for the special interpretation in which she is interested (p. 533), she can largely dispense with psychological documentation and analysis, and can rely on suggestion. Her basic interpretation concerns the impact of the past upon the present, and therefore she does not render the past (Amy's life) as a kind of "present" with a full body of event and analysis, but in terms of the flashes which come out of the past, in terms of hearsay and memories and family stories.

A similar situation is encountered in "A Rose for Emily." The author might have been compelled to give a much fuller account, perhaps a novelette, if he had attempted a direct psychological treatment of Emily. But for various reasons (p. 412), he is not concerned with the full psychological analysis of Emily. His observer-narrator, the citizen of the town, can give him all that is necessary for his interpretation, and by this means he can reduce the scale of the story. The story "A Simple Heart," which covers a whole lifetime in its span, offers another type of problem in scale. Here Flaubert, despite the great length of time covered, can select and summarize with great rigor, because he treats only incidents which have a direct bearing on the idea of the heroine's need to give affection. And yet we can also see that if he had carried the process of compression much farther, the story would have failed, for it depends on the cumulative effect of a series of simple incidents over a long period of time, and not on an immediate and dramatic situation, such as one finds in "The Lament" or in "War."

PACE

The problem of *pace* is closely associated with that of scale. In a short piece of fiction, the handling can more nearly move at the same rate of speed throughout without incurring the danger of monotony than in a longer piece. In regard to speed, we may think along these lines: summary is faster in rendering an action than is narrative; narrative tends to be faster than full rendering in terms of scene (for instance, we see how the narrative method rather than the scenic method in "A Rose for Emily" tends to reduce the scale); scene tends to be faster than analysis; and so on. Almost all stories involve a combination of these methods. For instance, "The Killers," which is almost purely scenic in method, does have of necessity a certain amount of narrative. But few stories, even quite short ones, are as single in method as "The Killers." Such a story as "Old Red" involves all of them, as does "The Kiss." Pace, then, we may take to be a term for indicating the relationships existing among these various methods in a given piece of fiction, the proportioning of analysis to action, of summary to scene, and the like. If the author relies on one method too exclusively the pace tends to become monotonous. The changes of pace, which really represent changes in emphasis and *may* represent changes in distance, tend to sharpen the reader's attention. But the changes in pace cannot be determined arbitrarily. As has been suggested above, the change of pace represents a change in emphasis. Obviously, the scenic method provides more emphasis than the method of summary, but even within any given method varying degrees of emphasis, and consequent changes of pace, are possible. And frequently a writer in rendering a single situation will mix the methods in an extremely complicated fashion, dialogue, narrative, flashbacks of memory, summary, and the like being used in building up the immediate effect. For example, we can turn to "Old Red" (p. 64).

We have tried to describe some of the problems which a writer encounters as he composes a piece of fiction, and have tried to indicate, in the interpretations of the individual stories in this volume and in this appendix, some of the solutions which have been arrived at in particular cases. But the solutions are always solutions for particular cases. All that one can do is to study the particular cases in the hope that such an effort will result in the sharpening of his own capacity for discrimination, that it will help him to see the relationships existing among the elements which go to make up a piece of fiction. Then, perhaps, he can, in his own writing, achieve a closer co-ordination of means and ends. But he must realize that no fictional problem can, finally, be solved in isolation from the other problems involved in the same composition, just as he must realize that the various elements as they appear in the particular work are not distinct but are organically unified. Henry James, in his essay on "The Art of Fiction," states this point very clearly. Speaking of the elements of fiction, he says:

"People often talk of these things as if they had a kind of internecine distinctness, instead of melting into each other at every breath, and being intimately associated parts of one general effort of expression. I cannot imagine composition existing in a series of blocks, nor conceive, in any novel worth discussing at all, of a passage of description that is not in its intention narrative, a passage of dialogue that is not in its intention descriptive, a touch of truth of any sort that does not partake of the nature of incident, or an incident that derives its interest from any other source than the general and only source of the success of a work of art—that of being illustrative. A novel is a living thing, all one and continuous, like any other organism, and in proportion as it lives will it be found, I think, that in each of the parts there is something of each of the other parts. The critic who over the close texture of a finished work shall pretend to trace a geography of items will mark some frontiers as artificial, I fear, as any that have been known to history."

In other words, a piece of fiction is a tissue of significances, some great and some small, but all of them aspects, finally, of the total significance of the piece. And one must remember that this total significance is not merely some idea which can be abstracted from the "story" and stated in general terms. It is the fact of the idea's living in action, in the "story," which makes the idea significant, for the underlying significance of all fiction may be the faith of the writer that experience itself is significant and is not a mere flux of unrelated items. That is, in other terms, he has a faith that man is a responsible being, and he tries to validate this faith by the responsible and vital organization of his art.

Glossary

ABSTRACT: Abstract statements deal with the general rather than the particular. Literature, however, deals with the concrete, with the particular. This is not to say that ideas, which are capable of being stated abstractly, are not involved in literature. But such ideas rarely emerge as abstractions; rather, they are incorporated in the concrete factors—in the case of fiction, in the particular characters and particular situations and events. The general observations which one may abstract from the particularities of a story—observations about human nature or about life—are not to be taken as the equivalent of the story. The generalization is something less than—merely a part of—the concrete particularity of the story itself. See pp. 6, 22–23, 286–287, 398.

ACTION STORY: A story in which the principal interest lies in plot suspense, such as adventure or detective fiction. See pp. 3–4, 61–63, 107–108.

ALLEGORY: An allegory is a kind of story in which the characters, objects, and events are not to be taken as real, but as standing for a system of ideas, item by item. See PARABLE, and pp. 103, 297–300, 467–468.

ALLITERATION: Repetition of consonants, particularly of initial consonants, as in *lullaby* or "*l*evels of the *l*ake."

ANTICLIMAX: A break in the climactic order of events or effects; a falling off from the expected intensification of effect. See CLIMAX and IRONY. See also pp. 215–216, 577–578.

ATMOSPHERE: The general pervasive feeling aroused by the various factors in a piece of fiction, such as setting, character, theme, and the like; the general effect of the handling of the total work. To be distinguished from SETTING and from TONE. Considerations of the metaphorical origin of the two terms, *atmosphere* and *tone*, may be helpful here. *Tone* is to be referred ultimately to the author's attitude (the tone of voice of a speaker as qualifying what he says) toward what is being presented, whereas *atmosphere* is to be referred to the general qualification provided by the materials themselves (an atmosphere of sunshine, of cheerfulness, an atmosphere of gloom, and the like). There is, however, a good deal of overlapping and vagueness about the use of these terms in ordinary discussion. The student, in referring to a particular case in fiction, should ask himself whether he wishes to emphasize the author's attitude or the mere effect of the materials as such. See p. 575.

CHRONICLE: An account of events arranged in the order of the time of happening; sometimes applied to a story which has relatively light emphasis on the central idea or situation, which has, in other words, an apparently loose organization. In this book, "A Simple Heart" will provide a good example of the chronicle method, as contrasted with other pieces in which a high degree of selectivity is practiced, and key events are sharply focused.

CLICHÉ: Usually used in reference to a phrase which has lost its force because of continual use; for example, "in the arms of Morpheus," or "a dull, sickening thud." But the term is also applied occasionally to fictional situations or events which have become hackneyed and stereotyped. The cliché represents one kind of appeal to a STOCK RESPONSE on the part of the reader. But, of course, clichés may be used justifiably by the author, for ironical effect, or because a certain kind of character would normally use clichés in his speech, or for other reasons. In general, it may be said that a cliché is bad when used with the intention of creating a vivid and memorable effect; it fails in such cases because it does not represent a fresh perception. See pp. 218, 256, 317, 576.

CLIMAX: The highest point in an ascending series; in fiction, for example, the point at which the forces in conflict reach the highest intensification. See pp. 215–216, 577–578.

COINCIDENCE: An accidental coming together of certain events. (See SURPRISE ENDING.) The use of coincidence, in one sense, is unavoidable in fiction, for the original situation in any story may be defined as a coincidence. But the use of coincidence is illegitimate when it functions to solve the fictional problem; that is, when the events which bring about the resolution of a plot have no logical connection with preceding events.

COMPLICATION: The interplay between character and event which builds up a tension in the character and develops a problem out of the original situation given in a story. See pp. 580–581.

CONCRETE: See ABSTRACT.

CONFLICT: All fiction involves, at one level or another, conflict. The characters struggle against environment or with each other (external conflict) or are engaged in struggles with themselves (internal conflict). One important approach to the understanding of any story is to determine the nature of the conflict involved and the pattern which the opposing forces assume. See pp. 578–579.

CONNOTATION: See DENOTATION.

CONVENTION: Any method, device, or rule which is accepted by explicit or tacit agreement. For example, the fact that the letter *t* shall have a certain consonantal value, or that a touchdown shall count for six points depends upon nothing intrinsic but is determined by convention. All the arts, including that of fiction, make use of *conventions*. For example, the omniscient author's ability to enter into the innermost thoughts of several of his characters depends upon a convention. The author continually makes use of traditional conventions handed down to him from the past. His work, however, is termed CONVENTIONAL in a bad sense only when it fails to justify the conventional items it employs by relating them freshly to the new problem.

CONVENTIONAL: See CONVENTION.

CUTBACK: A passage in a narrative which breaks the chronological sequence to deal with earlier events. (For example, the method of "Old Red" involves numerous cutbacks; see pp. 84, 572-573, 597.)

DENOTATION: The exact thing or idea indicated by a word. The denotation is not only the primary meaning, but it is the specific and abstract meaning. Scientific prose needs no more than the denotations of words, and the attempt to build up a scientific and technical language is in harmony with this situation. But the CONNOTATIONS of a word are the things suggested by or associated with the word. These connotations, though necessarily vague and inexact (as compared with denotations) are nevertheless powerful and important, and the skillful writer whose intention is literary rather than scientific makes full use of them. See pp. 421-422.

DENOUEMENT: The final resolution, or untying of the plot. See pp. 410, 583.

DRAMATIC: Strictly speaking, fictional method is said to be dramatic when the author gives a purely OBJECTIVE rendering of his material, without indulging either in editorial comment and generalization of his own or in analysis of the feelings and thoughts of his characters. The clearest case of such method in this book is "The Killers" (pp. 305-316). But in such a story as "The Lament" (pp. 240-249), though the method is less strictly dramatic, the old man's grief is not commented upon by the author until he has presented the grief in terms of action. In cases of dramatic method the reader must infer the inner situation from the external action. But the term is used more loosely to indicate merely the presence of strong tension and sharp conflict in a fictional situation; and it is used more loosely still to indicate concrete presentation as opposed to abstract statement.

EPISODE: A separate incident in a larger piece of action. In "The Lament" (pp. 242–247), for example, the visit to the stable to see the horse constitutes an episode.

EPISODIC: A piece of fiction is said to be *episodic* when there is not a strongly emphasized causal continuity between one episode and the next. Episodic structure is, logically, loose structure, in so far as the plot is concerned. "A Simple Heart" (pp. 535–568) is a good example of episodic structure. But the looseness of episodic structure does not mean that there is no principle of organization and continuity. For example, in "A Simple Heart," althought there is little causal connection among episodes, there is a strongly marked principle of organization found in the development and presentation of the character of the servant.

EXPOSITION: The process of giving the reader necessary information concerning characters and events existing before the action proper of a story begins. See pp. 571–573.

FICTION: See Section I, pp. 1–27, and p. 600.

FIRST-PERSON NARRATION: See FOCUS OF NARRATION, pp. 588–592.

FOCUS: The center around which the material of an imaginative work is concentrated. The focus may shift from moment to moment in a piece of fiction, or it may remain constant. For example, the focus may be primarily upon character, upon an idea, upon a setting, or the like. See pp. 585–594.

FOCUS OF CHARACTER: A piece of fiction is not merely a sequence of events. The events are of special concern to some person, or group of persons, involved in them, and the structure of the narrative depends, in one sense, upon the reference to the person, or persons, most fundamentally concerned. See pp. 586–588.

FOCUS OF NARRATION: This involves the question of who tells the story. We may make four basic distinctions: (1) a character may tell his own story in the first person; (2) a character may tell, in the first person, a story which he has observed; (3) the author may tell what happens in the purely objective sense—deeds, words, gestures—without going into the minds of the characters and without giving his own comment; (4) the author may tell what happens with full liberty to go into the minds of characters and to give his own comment. These four types of narration may be called: (1) first-person, (2) first-person observer, (3) author-observer, and (4) omniscient author. Combinations of these methods are, of course, possible. See pp. 588–594.

FORESHADOWING: The process of giving the reader an intimation of some event which is to follow later in the action.

FORM: The arrangement of various elements in a work of literature; the organization of various materials (ideas, images, characters, setting, and the like) to give a single effect. It may be said that a story is successful—that it has achieved form—when all of the elements are functionally related to each other, when each part contributes to the intended effect. Form is not to be thought of merely as a sort of container for the story; it is, rather, the total principle of organization and affects every aspect of the composition. (See pp. 1–27, 107, 570.) STRUCTURE and STYLE are also used to indicate the author's arrangement of his materials to give his effect. *Structure,* however, is usually used with more special reference to the ordering of the larger elements such as statements, episodes, scenes, and details of action, in contrast to the arrangement of words, for which the term *style* is ordinarily employed. In the fullest sense, both the terms become synonymous with form, but in this book *style* is used merely to refer to the selection and ordering of language. See pp. 323–324, 349, 423, 570, 590, 596.

FUNCTIONAL: Having to do with the development of the total effect of a piece of fiction. The term is used in this book to denote those elements of a story which actually play a part in building up the complex and rich unity of a story in contrast to those used merely because they are fashionable, or feed some external interest, or are merely sensational or decorative or engaging. See pp. 570–571 and p. 600.

IMAGERY: The representation of any sense experience. Imagery does not consist merely of "mental pictures," but may make an appeal to any of the senses. In keeping with its insistence upon the concrete and the particular, all literature, including fiction, makes much use of imagery, not only in obvious descriptive fashion but also in figurative language. The most common forms of figurative language are SIMILES and META-PHORS. A *simile* is a direct comparison between two things, and such a comparison is introduced by *like* or *as.* A *metaphor* does not announce the comparison and proceeds indirectly to indicate an identification of the two items involved. Although such details of style may seem trivial in fiction, their effects are subtle and important. Sometimes the fundamental attitude of an author, and hence the fundamental meaning of a piece of fiction, may be largely conveyed in terms of such details. See pp. 247, 323–324, 421–423, 591–596.

INEVITABILITY: The sense that the result presented is the only possible result of the situation previously given. It cannot be strictly maintained that inevitability in fiction is absolute, if one is to judge by realistic standards. The element of chance, or what appears as chance, in human affairs is too great to admit of such an interpretation. The term is simply used in most discussions to indicate a high degree of logic in the handling of the development of plot or character.

IRONY: Irony always involves contrast, a discrepancy between the expected and the actual, between the apparent and the real. Such contrast may appear in many forms. A speaker uses irony, for example, when he deliberately says something which he does not mean, but indicates by his tone what he does mean. UNDERSTATEMENT—the saying of less than one feels the occasion would warrant—and PARADOX—the saying of something which is apparently untrue but which on examination proves to be true, or partially true—both of these are forms of irony. In addition to such forms of IRONY OF STATEMENT, there are also various forms of IRONY OF SITUATION. The irony of situation involves a discrepancy between what we expect the outcome of an action to be, or what would seem to be the fitting outcome, and the actual outcome. In dealing with this term, the student should always remember that there are a thousand subtle shadings of irony, and must, therefore, not take it in too restricted a sense, for example, in the sense of obvious sarcasm. See Letter to the Teacher, and pp. 21–23, 63, 117–118, 127, 171, 250, 397–400.

MELODRAMATIC: An effect is said to be melodramatic when the violent or sensational seems to be used for its own sake without adequate reference to motivation of character or to other elements in the story. But it must be remembered that the mere fact of violence does not constitute melodrama. If the violence is logical and meaningful it is not melodramatic. See pp. 1–27, 61–64, 410–414.

METAPHOR: See IMAGERY.

MOTIVATION: The purpose, or mixture of purposes, that determines the behavior of a character.

OBJECTIVE: In relation to fiction, the pair of terms OBJECTIVE and SUBJECTIVE, is used in two connections. In the first, they are used with reference to the author, and in the second they are used with reference to a character, or characters, in the work of fiction. In the first connection, an *objective* treatment by the author implies an attitude of detachment toward the material which is being presented, a refusal to comment and interpret directly. (See DRAMATIC.) A *subjective* treatment, on the other hand, is one which is highly colored by the author's own feelings and beliefs. Of course, the amount of subjectivity or objectivity is always a matter of degree. Since all fiction involves, ultimately, the author's interpretations, feelings, judgments, and the like, there is strictly speaking no absolutely objective presentation; but we can say that, in terms of method the distinction can be made. In reference to the character, or characters, in a work of fiction, the terms can be applied more absolutely. When there is no direct presentation of the thoughts or feelings of a character, the treatment is said to be objective; when such presentation is made, the treatment is said to be subjective. But most pieces of fiction tend to mix the two methods, some events being rendered objectively, some being rendered subjectively, some characters being treated objectively and some subjectively. See pp. 588–594.

PARABLE: A story, usually simple, which makes an obvious point or has a rather obvious symbolic meaning. The method of parable is closely related to that of ALLEGORY, but the tendency is to use the term *allegory* to indicate a more systematic and complicated structure of equivalents. See pp. 103–106, 297–300, 400, 467–468.

PATHOS: The sense of pity. The author, however, must be on his guard to make sure that the pathos in a story emerges legitimately from the situation given. When there is no reasonable basis in character and situation for the pathos, one has an effect of SENTIMENTALITY. The quality of being *pathetic* is to be distinguished from that of being *tragic*. In a tragic situation the sense of pity is complicated by an effect of struggle and conflict. The pathetic effect may be given by the spectacle of a weak person suffering; the tragic effect requires that the sufferer have strength enough to struggle vigorously against his situation.

PERSONIFICATION: The attribution of the qualities of a person to an inanimate object or idea.

PLOT: The structure of action in fiction or drama. Plot, as PLOT PATTERN, is one aspect of the total design of a story. See pp. 1–27, 107–108, 577–583.

POINT OF VIEW: In discussions of fiction this term is used in two different connections. First, it is used in connection with the basic attitude or idea of the author, and second, it is used in connection with the method of narration. In the first meaning, one refers, for instance, to the author's ironical point of view, or his detached point of view, or his sympathetic point of view, or the like. Or one might say that a certain piece of fiction embodies a Christian point of view. In the second meaning, one refers to the mind through which the material of the story is presented—first person, first-person observer, author-observer, and omniscient author. Confusion will be avoided if the use of the term *point of view* be restricted to the first meaning, and if the term FOCUS OF NARRATION be used for the second meaning. See pp. 588–594.

PROPAGANDA: Propaganda literature is literature which tends to state its theme abstractly and tends to insist on its "message" at the expense of other elements in its structure. Usually it can be said that such literature tends to oversimplify its material in order to emphasize its meaning. (For a fuller discussion, in terms of irony and conflict, see Letter to the Teacher, pp. vii–xix.)

REALISTIC: Having a strong sense of fact or actuality. The term is used in this book to refer to the presentation of ordinary, easily observable details which give an impression of fidelity to experience. *Realistic* is to be contrasted with ROMANTIC, which implies the remote, the exotic, the exaggerated. (There is no attempt in this book to go into the distinction between *romantic* and *classic*.)

SCALE: The relative amount of detail of treatment allowed to the various elements in a story. See pp. 596–599.

SELECTION: See pp. 576–577.

SENTIMENTALITY: Emotional response in excess of the occasion; emotional response which has not been prepared for in the story in question. See pp. 219–220, 241, 247–250, 422–423.

SETTING: The physical background, the element of place, in a story. See pp. 573–575.

SIMILE: See IMAGERY.

STOCK RESPONSE: The automatic or conventional or generally uncritical response of a reader to some word, phrase, situation, character, or subject in literature.

STRUCTURE: See FORM.

STYLE: See FORM.

SUBJECTIVE: See OBJECTIVE.

SURPRISE ENDING: An ending in a story which comes with some sense of shock to the reader. (For the grounds for distinguishing between legitimate and illegitimate surprise, see pp. 117–118, 126–127, 146.)

SYMBOL: An object, character, or incident which stands for something else, or suggests something else, is a *symbol* of it. See pp. 23–25, 36, 86, 105.

THEME: The "point" or "meaning" of a story or novel. See pp. 286–287 and pp. xv–xvi.

TONE: See pp. 256, 470, 594–596. See also ATMOSPHERE.

TRAGEDY: See PATHOS. See also pp. 204, 414.

UNDERSTATEMENT: See IRONY.

UNITY: The sense of wholeness or oneness. See pp. 1–27, 370, 600.